READINGS IN NEUROPHYSIOLOGY

Readings in Neurophysiology

CHARLES D. BARNES

Department of Anatomy and Physiology
Indiana University

CHRISTOPHER KIRCHER

Department of Anatomy and Physiology
Center for Neural Sciences
Indiana University

JOHN WILEY & SONS, INC.　　　　　NEW YORK • LONDON • SYDNEY

Library of Congress Catalog Card Number: 68–15458
GB 471 05060X
Printed in the United States of America

Preface

The last seven decades of neurophysiological research have witnessed many outstanding advances, and it would be impossible to present in a volume such as ours all the papers that might be considered milestones in neurophysiology. Indeed, we did not even intend to select all the studies which could be considered classics in spinal-cord neurophysiology. Rather, this book presents a collection of papers which mark several related turning points in research—describing the simplest reflex in the spinal cord, the myotatic reflex, and assembling the material in a readily available single volume. Such an approach was elected because research on the myotatic reflex typifies the kind of thinking and experimentation that has been successfully employed: inasmuch as the monosynaptic reflex has been and continues to be used in so many investigations of spinal-cord activity, it has a representative role in the field.

Toward this end we have attempted to put the papers in perspective for the reader through the use of an introductory commentary preceding each section. Rather than presenting the papers chronologically, we have arranged them according to the anatomical components of the myotatic reflex, from the afferent side to the effector.

Most neurophysiologists should at least be aware of, if not familiar with, the papers we have selected. Thus this book is not directed to our colleagues, but rather to the student (graduate or undergraduate) who is beginning his study of the physiology of the nervous system. If the student thoroughly understands the papers we have chosen, our purpose will have been fulfilled—for he will have mastered concepts and terminology which will enable him to read other papers in this fascinating field.

We wish to acknowledge our thanks to the various journals for permission to reproduce the articles in this book. The fact that this material was photographed directly from the respective journals accounts for the different formats of the individual articles.

November 1967
Bloomington, Indiana

CHARLES D. BARNES
CHRISTOPHER KIRCHER

Contents

READINGS IN NEUROPHYSIOLOGY

INTRODUCTION

Sherrington wrote that in the simplest reflex we find "the co-ordination which a reflex action introduces when it makes an effector organ responsive to excitement of a receptor, all other parts of the organism being supposed indifferent to and indifferent for that reaction. A simple reflex is probably a purely abstract conception, because all parts of the nervous system are connected together and no part of it is probably ever capable of reaction without affecting and being affected by various other parts... The outcome of the normal reflex action of the organism is an orderly coadjustment and sequence of reactions. This is very patently expressed by the skeletal musculature..." (1) Glees' view of the reflex is typical: "The function of the whole nervous system, from the spinal cord up to the cerebral cortex, may rest on the principle of the reflex." Yet Glees echoes Sherrington when he cautions: "one must guard against the tendency of attributing too great an importance to the role of single reflexes in the total organization of nervous function; it is rather the *co-ordination* of these reflexes which is the basis of nervous function." (2)

The first paper, that of Liddell and Sherrington, is the first study of the myotatic reflex *per se.* Inasmuch as Sherrington formulated so many basic neurophysiological concepts, it is particularly fitting that one of his papers be presented first. The second section includes four papers that report studies of the afferent discharges from the sensory end organs in muscle. The next topic considered is the action potential in the "unmyelinated" nerve fiber. Although vertebrate axons have electrical characteristics different from those of the giant axons used in these experiments, many of the basic properties described are common to all nerve fibers. The next section consists of a paper which endeavors to explain the origin of the potentials recorded from the dorsal columns of the spinal cord as a result of afferent input. The fifth section presents evidence that the myotatic reflex is indeed a monosynaptic reflex. Thus a behavioral event is seen to be the result of the simplest reflex arc. The papers by Lloyd demonstrate the influences that various afferent inputs exert on the monosynaptic reflex. The seventh section presents a paper which demonstrates the negative feedback that alpha motoneuron activity exerts on itself in the form of recurrent inhibition. Next, the role of the gamma motoneuron activity on the muscle spindle is considered. The last section includes two papers which present studies of the events occurring at the myoneural junction.

1

Obvious omissions (with the exception of the paper on recurrent inhibition) are papers concerning the spinal-cord studies of the group headed by two of the most prolific and influential contemporary neurophysiologists, Sir John Eccles and Ragnar Granit. However, their findings are amply described in their books, which are readily available (3,4,5,6).

In 1949 Ling and Gerard reported a technique which allowed the insertion of a glass microelectrode through the membrane and into a living muscle cell without destroying the cell. The first papers reporting this technique as being successfully applied to spinal cord motoneurones appeared in 1952 (7,8). In 1955 a series of four papers appeared which heralded the beginning of a new era in the study of the synapse. As a section on the synapse has not been included in this volume, the student is referred to the articles by Coombs *et al.* *(Bibliography)* as well as several of the following References.

REFERENCES

1. Sherrington, C. *The Integrative Action of the Nervous System.* Yale University Press, New Haven 1906.

2. Glees, P. *Experimental Neurology.* Clarendon Press, Oxford 1961.

3. Eccles, J. C. *The Physiology of Nerve Cells.* Johns Hopkins Press, Baltimore 1957.

4. Eccles, J. C. *The Physiology of Synapses.* Academic Press, New York 1964.

5. Granit, R. *Receptors and Sensory Perception.* Yale University Press, New Haven, Connecticut 1955.

6. Granit, R. *Nobel Symposium I: Muscle Afferents and Motor Control.* John Wiley & Sons, New York 1966.

7. Brock, L. G., J. S. Coombs, and J. C. Eccles. The recording of potentials from motoneurones with an intracellular electrode. *J. Physiol.* **117:** 431–460 (1952).

8. Woodbury, J. W., and H. D. Patton. Electrical activity of single spinal cord elements. *Cold Spr. Harb. Symp. Quant. Biol.* **17:** 185–188 (1952).

BIBLIOGRAPHY

Coombs, J. S., J. C. Eccles, and P. Fatt. The electrical properties of the motoneurone membrane. *J. Physiol.* **130:** 291–325 (1955).

Coombs, J. S., J. C. Eccles, and P. Fatt. The specific ionic conductances and the ionic movements across the motoneuronal membrane that produce the inhibitory post-synaptic potential. *J. Physiol.* **130:** 326–73 (1955).

Coombs, J. S., J. C. Eccles, and P. Fatt. Excitatory synaptic action in motoneurones. *J. Physiol.* **130:** 374–95 (1955).

Coombs, J. S., J. C. Eccles, and P. Fatt. The inhibitory suppression of reflex discharges from motoneurones. *J. Physiol.* **130:** 396–413 (1955).

Eccles, J. C. *The Physiology of Nerve Cells.* Johns Hopkins Press, Baltimore, 1957.

Eccles, J. C. *The Physiology of Synapses.* Academic Press, New York, 1964.

McLennan, H. *Synaptic Transmission.* W. B. Saunders, Philadelphia, 1963.

deRobertis, E. *Histophysiology of Synapses and Neurosecretion.* Pergamon Press, New York, 1964.

SUGGESTED TEXTS

Ruch, T. C., H. D. Patton, J. W. Woodbury, and A. L. Towe. *Neurophysiology.* W. B. Saunders Co., Philadelphia, 1965.

Ochs, S. *Elements of Neurophysiology.* John Wiley & Sons, New York, 1965.

Mountcastle, V. *Medical Physiology.* Mosby, St. Louis, 1968.

To facilitate the reader's grasp of terminology used in the following sections a simplified diagram is presented.

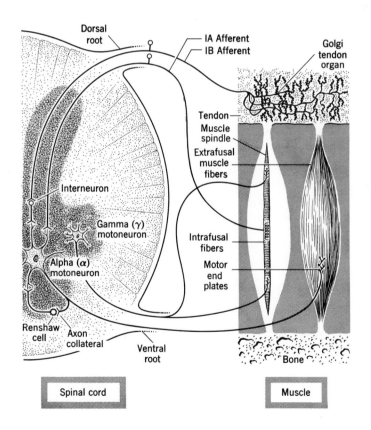

MYOTATIC REFLEX

In man, approximately 40 percent of the body mass is composed of skeletal muscle. To function effectively, man, as well as the lower animals, is dependent on co-ordinated muscular activity. The essential reflex for the mainenance of body posture is the stretch or extensor reflex, which Liddell and Sherrington termed the *myotatic reflex* (9). This mechanism was found to be responsible for the muscle contraction—called the tendon jerk—which occurred when the tendon of that muscle insertion was tapped.

Regulation of posture requires a tension or *tonus* of the skeletal musculature. The first demonstration that normal muscle tonus is dependent on the afferent influx to the spinal cord appeared more than a century ago (in 1860) when Brondgeest (10) showed that dorsal root section diminished the flexor tonus of the limbs. That the afferents involved came from muscle rather than skin was shown by Mommsen (11), who repeated Brondgeest's experiment on animals from which the skin had been stripped. Mommsen's finding was apparently not widely appreciated; until Sherrington's experiments (1894) it was generally believed that all nerve fibers seen entering a muscle were motor.

In 1898 Sherrington found that intercollicular sectioning of the brain stem produced a condition of increased tone in the muscles, particularly in the extensors (12). This phenomenon was termed *decerebrate rigidity,* and the rigidity was abolished by sectioning of the dorsal roots. The nature of the reflex involved in maintenance of extensor tone was not appreciated until Liddell and Sherrington published their 1925 paper that described the stretch reflex of the isolated quadriceps muscle of the cat. Until publication of this work it was stoutly held by many neurophysiologists that the tendon jerk was not a reflex action but rather resulted from direct mechanical stimulation of the muscle.

Pollock and Davis published a paper in 1930 describing a method for anemic decerebration (13). This less traumatic method produced decerebrate animals without the degree of hemorrhage and shock which accompanied the Sherrington technique for decerebration. The anemic method is based on the fact that once the carotid arteries have been ligated the brain receives its blood supply completely from the vertebral arteries which anastomose to form the basilar. Thus, by appropriately selecting the position of the basilar artery to be occluded, the blood supply to the anterior portion of the brain could be stopped. In describing the animals, the authors stated: "Without exception decerebrate rigidity similar to that described by Sherrington has resulted after ligation of the basilar and carotid arteries." A difference was observed, however, in that the dorsal roots of the anemic decerebrate cat could be sectioned without abolishing rigidity—a finding contrary to that reported by Sherrington. The reason for this apparent discrepancy was elaborated in 1955 in a paper by Granit *et al.* (14). They noted that the anemic decerebration technique infarcted not only the brain rostral to the inferior colliculus, but also the anterior portion of the cerebellum, thus confirming Pollock and Davis's findings. By coolong the anterior cerebellum in animals subjected to a Sherringtonian decerebration, they produced animals whose rigidity was similar to those prepared by the anemic decerebration. This work demonstrated that the involvement of the anterior cerebellum produces a different kind of rigidity: not gamma but rather alpha rigidity. That is, the reflex contractions of the limb extensors in the classical decerebrate cat are largely dependent on influences descending the spinal cord and setting up activity on the gamma efferents to the intrafusal muscle fibers. These in turn result in an intense inflow of excitatory impulses from the muscle spindles over the IA fibers ending on the alpha motoneurons. Thus, when the dorsal roots are cut, the input to the alpha motoneurons (the myotatic reflex) is interrupted. When the anterior part of the cerebellum is cooled, infarcted, or removed, paralysis of this gamma-activating mechanism results. Activity descending the cord then results in direct activation of the alpha motoneurons. Thus the rigidity does not depend upon the gamma loop and sectioning of the dorsal roots will not eliminate the rigidity. From this finding rose the concept of two routes of excitation: an alpha and a gamma—both able to produce muscle movements and the proportions of the two in use at any time, being in some way dependent on the cerebellum.

REFERENCES

9. Liddell, E. G. T., and C. S. Sherrington. Further observations on myotatic reflexes. *Proc. Roy. Soc.* **97B**: 267–283 (1925).

10. Brondgeest, P. Q. *De Tono Musculorum Voluntati Subditorum.* Utrect, X, 91 pp. 1860.

11. Mommsen, J. Beitrag zur Kenntniss des Muskeltonus. *Virchows Arch.* **101**: 22–36 (1885).

12. Sherrington, C. S. Decerebrate rigidity, and reflex coordination of movements. *J. Physiol.* **22**: 319–32 (1898).

13. Pollock, L. J., and L. Davis. The reflex activities of a decerebrate animal. *J. Comp. Neurol.* **50**: 377–411 (1930).

14. Granit, R., B. Holmgren, and P. A. Merton. The two routes for excitation of muscle and their subservience to the cerebellum. *J. Physiol.* **130**: 213–224 (1955).

BIBLIOGRAPHY

Sherrington, C. S. On the anatomical constitution of nerves of skeletal muscles; with remarks on recurrent fibres in the ventral spinal nerve-root. *J. Physiol.* **17:** 211–258 (1894).

Pollock, L. J., and L. Davis. Studies in decerebration: VI. The effect of deafferentation upon decerebrate rigidity. *Am. J. Physiol.* **98:** 47–49 (1931).

SUGGESTED TEXTS

Ruch et al. Chapter 7.

Ochs, S. Chapters 14 and 17.

Mountcastle, V. Chapters 72 and 75.

Reflexes in Response to Stretch (*Myotatic Reflexes*)

By E. G. T. LIDDELL and Sir CHARLES SHERRINGTON, Pres.R.S.

(Received March 1, 1924.)

Familiar to those who work with the decerebrate preparation must be the observation that passive flexion of the characteristically extended knee is felt to evoke some development of resistance of it against that passive movement. Examination by the myograph of this resistance formed the point of departure of the following observations.

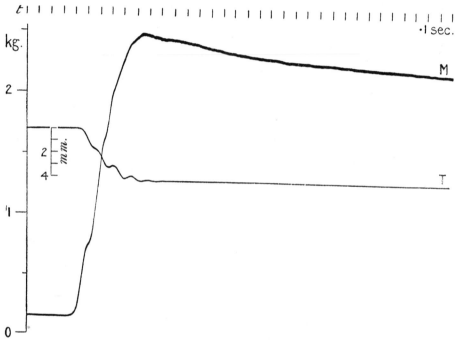

FIG. 1.—Whole quadriceps. Muscular response M to 4·5 mm. table-stretch T. Myograph multiplies tendon movement 42 times. Time in 0·1 sec. (For lettering see Explanation of Figures at end.)

In this same muscle the " knee jerk " is doubtless a reflex in response to a stretch ; but it is a reaction whose brevity makes it perhaps the most twitch-like of all reflexes, whereas the reflex under consideration here is tetanic and prolonged. Patellar-clonus, likewise a reaction to stretch, resembles a spaced series of knee jerks and, wanting tetanic character, likewise differs from the reflex under consideration here.

Liddell, E. G. T., and C. S. Sherrington. Reflexes in response to stretch (myotatic reflexes). *Proc. Roy. Soc.* **96B:** 212–242, 1924.

Method.—The fully freed tendon of the knee extensor has been attached unyieldingly to the lever of the isometric optical myograph used in our previous experiments. Femur and ilium carrying the proximal attachments of the muscle have been rigidly fixed to the table-top on which the preparation lay. The myograph screwed to a steel joist above the table was wholly separate from this latter except for the muscle bridging vertically between the two. The height of the table-top was adjustable by a screw fitted in the frame of the table-base. At outset of an experiment the table height was ordinarily so set as to keep the muscle just not slack. To stretch the muscle the table-top was lowered by the screw. For some of the experiments the lowering of the table was effected by the fall of a heavily weighted valved piston in an oil-

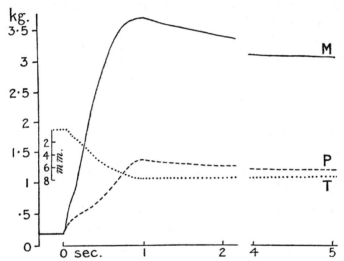

FIG. 2.—Whole quadriceps. Muscular response to 8 mm. table-stretch T before (M) and after (P) cutting nerve to muscle. Myograph multiplies tendon-movement 62 times. Time in secs.

filled cylinder, on the principle employed in the electrograph camera (Camb. Sci. Inst. Co.). A cam connected with the piston was arranged to catch in the course of the descent of the latter a gear attached to the table-top and to carry this last down with it for a distance which could be varied at will. The speed of descent was adjusted by varying the size of the valve-opening in the piston. This arrangement gave, for slower speeds of descent, a more equable movement than could be secured by the turning of the table-screw. The amplitude of the stretch given to the muscle was the distance the table-top sank less the movement of yield of the myograph-arm, this latter being about 0·3 mm. per kilogram of pull. The movement of the tendon attachment at the myograph-arm was multiplied usually sixty-two times in the record. The record registered the tension developed in the muscle under stretch, a tension compounded of (1) passive strain due to the stretch of the muscle by the lowering of the table-top, and (2) active tension developed by contraction (if such there were) of the muscle. The movement of rise or fall of the table-top was also optically recorded. The observations were made chiefly in the decerebrate preparation obtained as described in previous papers.

Results.—I. Fig. 1 gives an instance of the myograms obtained. Their form at once suggested the presence of some active contraction. To separate the active tension of contraction from the passive tension which must also be produced by the stretch, one procedure has been to compare the reaction to similar stretches obtained before and after severance of the muscle's nerve. A comparison of this kind is shown in fig. 2. The line recorded by the myogram after nerve-section can serve as a base-line for plotting the amount and time relations of the active contraction prior to nerve-section. Active contraction is answerable usually for the greater part of the muscle-tension developed in reaction to the stretch.

The augmenting effect on the contractile response of electrically excited muscle of a not excessive degree of initial stretch is well known and has recently been studied by several observers (5, 6, 9). In mammalian skeletal muscle our experience found it remarkably evident in the case of this muscle, the knee-extensor, both with peripheral and reflex contraction (13). A first point for examination in the stretch reaction dealt with here was therefore as to whether the active contraction observed might not possibly be peripheral in origin, a direct contractile response of the muscle fibres to the mechanical stretch imposed on them. To this the answer invariably given in our observations has been that on severance of the motor nerve of the muscle, the active-contraction component of the muscular tension developed under stretch has disappeared. We infer then that the contraction is reflex.

This being so it is useful to examine the tension curve of the paralytic muscle, *i.e.*, the muscle within an hour or so of total severance of its nerve-supply, under progressive stretch, in order to separate the passive element of tension from the rest of the strain when the muscle retains its nerve-supply intact. Fig. 3 illustrates such record of the tensile reaction of the paralytic vasto-crureus when subjected to a stretch by lowering the table 8 mm., the longest fleshy portion of the muscle measuring rather more than 90 mm. The tensions are ordinates and the steadily progressive stretch gives approximately equal

increments of extension for equal intervals of time.   The extension curves **of**
muscle usually given in works of reference exhibit the effect of equal increments

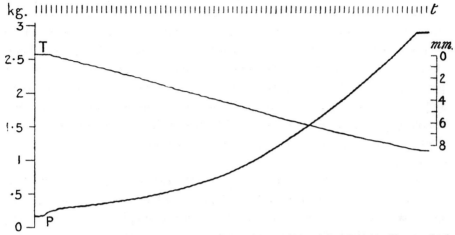

FIG. 3.—Vastocrureus.   P response of muscle after section of its nerve to T a gradual
8·5 mm. table-stretch : *t* in 1/10 sec.   Myograph multiplies tendon-movement 62 times.

of tension over equal intervals of time upon the elongation of the muscle.   For
our purpose it was preferable to have equal increments of elongation over equal
intervals of time and examine the tensions so resulting.   It has to be remembered that for measuring the extension of the muscle the amount of yield of
the myograph lever-arm has to be deducted from the table-fall ; the record of
the myograph magnifies the movement of its lever-arm 62 times, so that the
deduction even where the myograph line has risen 60 mm. is still less than
1 mm.   The curve shows, as would be expected, a gradual increasing resistance
to further extension.   It shows also a characteristic slightly steeper upgrade
of tensile resistance at commencement of the stretch than immediately following
that.   At end of the stretch the passive tension then reached gives a tension
plateau under continuance of the unrelieved static stress.   That plateau, however, is not horizontal, but slowly declines somewhat, and is evidence of a
viscosity after-action such as occurs in arteries, veins, and other passive
tissues, showing their residual plasticity.

II. Bearing in mind the general features of this elastic-plastic passive-
tension element in the muscular reaction to stretch, a next question was the
source of the reflex exciting the contraction.   On this information was obtainable
in several ways.

1. In preparing the muscle for observation all other muscles of both hind

limbs were put out of action, either by severance of their respective nerves or by resection of their attachments, and all skin nerves were severed where they enter the limb.

Thus, in both limbs the sciatic, pudic, internal saphenous, obturator, external cutaneous and the groin nerve of fourth lumbar root were cut, as well as the femoralis of the limb opposite to that used. Also in both limbs the psoas magnus and parvus, the glutæi, quadratus and gemelli, the obturator, pectineus, tensor fasciæ femoris muscles were severed from their insertions and the sartorius paralysed by nerve-section. Further, the sartorius and tensor fasciæ femoris of the ipsilateral limb were freely resected off to avoid their participating mechanically in the stretch applied to the underlying quadriceps.

These precautions left the quadriceps on the side required for observation the only hind-limb structure still retaining its afferent connection with the spinal cord and still retaining its afferent nerve supply. The skin of the hinder part of the back retained some afferent supply, but the drills and clamp fixing femur and pelvis were so arranged that the hinder part of the back was not in contact with the table ; this was done to obviate possible shift or change of pressure on the back, which might otherwise occur when the table-top was lowered or raised to produce or relieve the stretch. The tail retained afferent supply, but the tail was wholly free from the table, and was not disturbed in any way by lowering or raising the table-top for the few millimetres necessary. Moreover, mechanical stimuli applied to tail do not evoke quadriceps contraction such as here observed. We believe, therefore, that the mechanical effect on the preparation of lowering or raising the table-top was confined to the quadriceps muscle.

2. After severance of the afferent spinal roots supplying the limb from 4th to 7th post-thoracic segments inclusive, carried out from 10 days to 16 weeks prior to the myographic examination of the muscle, complete traumatic recovery having meanwhile ensued, we have uniformly failed to obtain any contraction of the muscle on stretching it, although ample reflex contractions were elicited as usual from it by stimulation of the afferent nerves of the contralateral limb ; also from the pinna and other usual reflex sources outside the ipsilateral limb itself. The reflex source of the stretch-reflex lies, therefore, in the ipsilateral limb itself. Further, after similar severance of the afferent roots of the ipsilateral 4th, 5th and 6th post-thoracic spinal nerves, the limb thus retaining still its afferent supply from the 7th and 8th spinal roots, the stretch reflex was found similarly abolished, although from

contralateral afferents ample reflex contractions were easily elicited from the muscle. These three afferent spinal roots are those which furnish the entire proprioceptive supply of the knee-extensor muscle. That from the muscle after its afferent nerve-supply has been cut off in the above way, no reflex contraction in response to stretch is obtainable was shown by the following evidence.

The myograms of stretching of the deafferented muscle revealed at a glance that reflex contraction if present was much less than normal. But to decide whether there is present any reflex contraction at all two tests can be employed :—

(1) The reaction to stretch can be compared with that to a similar stretch applied after the entire nerve-trunk to the muscle has been severed. This comparison has shown uniformly that the reaction of the deafferented muscle to stretch is so closely like that yielded by the muscle after severance of its nerve as to be in our experience practically indistinguishable from it (fig. 4).

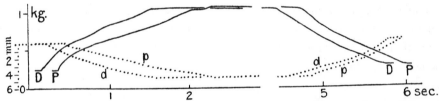

Fig. 4.—Whole quadriceps deafferented 112 days. Comparison of deafferented D and paralytic P (*i.e.*, after nerve-section) muscle to two comparable 5 mm. table-stretches, *d.* applied to deafferented, *p*, to paralysed muscle. Myograph multiplies tendon-movement 42 times. Time in secs.

(2) Search for any component of active reflex contraction in the reaction of the deafferented muscle to stretch can be made by provoking a reflex inhibition which would inhibit that contraction. If such contraction be present an intercurrent inhibition will cause a fall in the tension-height of the myogram of the muscle reacting to stretch. Uniformly in our experience no fall in the tension-height of the deafferented muscle's reaction to stretch is produced by the inhibition. We conclude, therefore, that after deafferentation of the muscle the reflex contraction of the muscle to stretch is absent wholly.

In one experiment where the ipsilateral post-thoracic afferent spinal roots severed were the 5th and 6th alone, the knee jerk repeatedly looked for had been unobtainable until after decerebration at the final examination before the myograph. Then a slight but indubitable trace of it became several times though not constantly detectable. The muscle, although yielding amply reflex contractions under stimulation of afferent nerves of the opposite limb, yet gave in response to stretch either no contraction or contraction so slight as to be of equivocal existence.   Since the 5th and 6th afferent roots are the two roots which in many individuals furnish practically the whole afferent supply of quadriceps muscle, this experiment in which all the other afferent roots of the limb remained intact and the stretch reflex nevertheless was reduced to a mere trace, if indeed retained at all, clinches the conclusion already drawn from the other evidence that the afferent nerves of the quadriceps are necessary for the elicitation of the stretch-reflex in that muscle.   The active contraction component of the tension developed by the muscle in response to stretch of the muscle appears, therefore, to be referable to mechanical stimulation, by stretch, of receptors in the muscle itself.

3. Stimulation of such ipsilateral afferent limb nerves as peroneal, popliteal and saphenous is well known to cause reflex inhibition of the proprioceptive arc of the knee-extensor muscle.   Stimulation of these nerves abolished the stretch-reflex of the muscle.   That this is so is shown in two ways.   (1) Such stimulation applied intercurrently during the reaction to stretch causes an immediate drop of the myogram line.   This drop even under quite moderate stimulation of the inhibitory afferent often carries the myogram line down to a horizontal (fig. 5), which, by comparing it with that given by the muscle

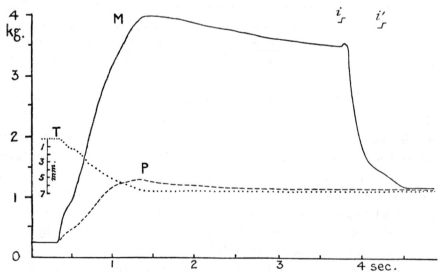

FIG. 5.—Whole quadriceps.   Effect of reflex inhibition, evoked between i and i' from ipsilateral afferent peroneo-popliteal nerve, on the muscular reaction M to 6·5 mm. table-stretch T compared with reaction P of the " paralysed " muscle to similar table-stretch.   Myograph multiplies tendon-movement 62 times.   Time in seconds.

under a similar stretch applied after the muscle's entire nerve-trunk has been severed, is found to correspond with the merely passive tension developed in the muscle by the stretch. The inhibition, therefore, readily annuls completely all reflex contraction elicited by the stretch. (2) Under reflex inhibition induced before and continued during the stretch, the reaction to the stretch does not differ from that given by the muscle after paralysis by severance of its motor nerve (figs. 14, 15). The reflex inhibition readily precludes the muscle from all reflex contraction in response to stretch.

From these results in (1), (2) and (3) taken together we conclude that the contraction evoked in the quadriceps by the pull applied is excited not extraneously to it, but from receptors thus mechanically stimulated in the muscle itself, in short that it is a proprioceptive reflex excited by the stretch of the muscle.

Germane to this conclusion is the interesting observation by J. de Meyer (17) (*further see* W. A. Jolly (10)) that mechanical extension of the gastrocnemius muscle in the frog produces in the peripheral stump of the cut sciatic nerve supplying it galvanometric evidence of " petits courants nerveux très faibles," which are extinguished by warming the nerve to 43° C. Galvanometric changes have also been observed in muscle itself when subjected to mechanical strain (Buytendijk (4), J. de Meyer (17), A. Forbes, Ray and Hopkins (7)) ; Forbes, Ray and Hopkins (7) have, however, pointed out the difficulties in the interpretation of such currents.

As to the situation in the muscle of the proprioceptive receptors which passive stretch evoking the stretch-reflex excites, removal of the tendo-patellæ makes no observable difference to the reaction. Neither does tight ligation of the insertion of the muscle into the patella, nor removal of the patella itself, nor, indeed, free resection of the muscle from the patella. Liberal application of 2 per cent. novocain in normal saline on and into the tendon close above and around the patella also caused no obvious impairment of the stretch reflex.

III. *Contraction-curve.*—Our means of applying a stretch to the muscle was in several ways difficult of fine adjustment. But closely comparable stretches have been numerously obtained, and with these from one and the same experiment, the passive stretch curve from the " paralytic " muscle has been used as a base line from which to set off the active contraction curve from the reflex muscle.

The reflex curves thus obtained, though their latency of commencement is quite short, show often an ascent of long duration. This might suggest that what in a previous paper we termed " recruitment " was in process in this reflex as in the extensor reflexes then studied. But in those reflexes an essential condition was that the stimulus exciting the reflex remained unaltered in strength throughout its application. In the reflex evoked by the stretch-movement the ascent of contraction, *i.e.*, the period of increasing contraction usually continues for so long as the stretch-movement continues. The build of the quadriceps, especially of its vastocrureus portion, suggests that as the pull of the patellar tendon on the muscle increases, namely as the stretch increases, the mechanical stretch involves progressively increasing numbers of the muscle-bands composing the muscle. The increase of the reflex contraction as the stretch proceeds would therefore be explicable by corresponding increase of the number of receptors in the muscle coming under the influence of the mechanical stimulus.   This is supported by several features of the reflex contraction. Thus, the increase of contraction goes on fairly equably so long as the stretch continues being equably increased, and all irregularities in the process of the stretch are closely reflected in the contraction ascent.   This is also indicated by the rapid rise of contractile tension after an earlier inhibition in fig. 15.

One thing that the ascent portion of the reflex contraction shows is the extreme delicacy of the grading of the contraction in accordance with grading of amplitude of the passive stretch imposed. Increase of the stretch is accompanied by increase in the number of its proprioceptors stimulated and of the motoneurones excited which supply it. This proprioceptive reflex tends, therefore, constantly to bring about equilibrium between the extending force and the contractile reaction which the former induces in the extended muscle.

The climax of height (tension) of the contraction occurs sometimes before but usually with, or very little later than, the completion of the stretch-movement, The contraction then commonly declines, the amount to which it does so varying (*i*) in different experiments. Of usual and typical occurrence is the ensuance after the climax of a long slowly descending plateau of contraction. This ensuent contraction might from its appearance be a reflex after-discharge due to after-action of the stretch-movement reflex, like the after-discharge which is so characteristic of the reflex-contractions of this muscle evoked contralaterally in, as here, the decerebrate preparation. On the other hand, it might be contraction reflexly excited by the stretched posture (static stretch) brought about by, and left after completion of, the stretch-movement. This latter supposition is confirmed by the result observed on raising the table-top back to its previous height and so unstretching the muscle. All trace of the contraction then disappears, even within a tenth of a second after completion of the unstretching (fig. 6). This is so whether the unstretching is performed

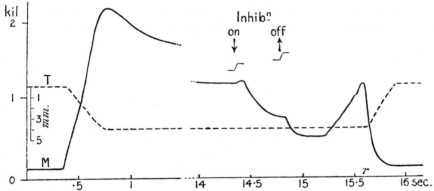

FIG. 6.—Whole quadriceps. Reaction M to 4 mm. table-stretch T. Inhibition applied in later course of response showing post-stimulatory reduction to state of passive tension, followed by return of the contraction under continuance of the stretched-posture, and final immediate subsidence of the contraction on removing at r the passive stretch. Time in secs. Myograph multiplying tendon-movement 62 times.

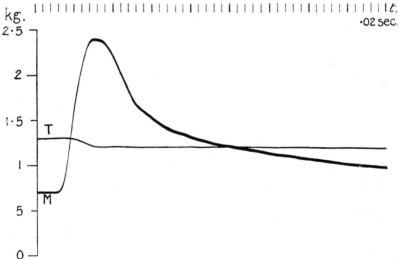

FIG. 7.—Whole quadriceps: "rigidity" slight. Reaction M to table-stretch T of less than 1 mm. applied in 1/25 sec. Myograph multiplying tendon-movement 62 times. Time in 0·02 sec.

late on in the plateau contraction or quite soon, e.g., 3/10 sec. after the climax contraction.

If the stretch-movement reflex brought in its train a long central after-discharge, such as do the ordinary contralateral reflexes of the muscle, the undoing of the stretch which excited the reflex, being simply equivalent to withdrawal of the stimulus in a contralateral reflex, would, as there, still be followed by the after-discharge contraction. The myogram height (tension) would fall owing to subtraction of the passive tension from the summed

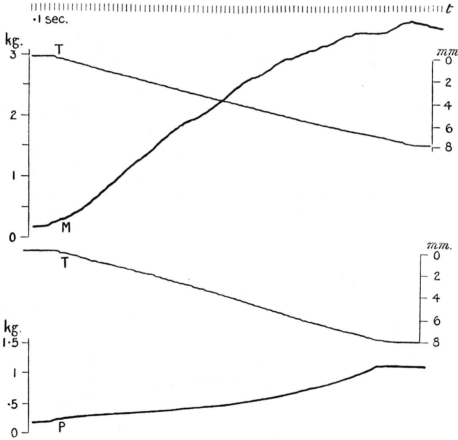

FIG. 8.—**Vastocrureus.** Reactions to 8 mm. table-stretch T performed slowly, *i.e.*, 8 secs.; M before and P after severance of the muscle's nerve. Initial tension low. Myograph multiplying tendon-movement 62 times. Time in 0·1 sec.

passive and active (contraction) tension, and owing to the effect of lowering the favourable influence of stretch in the contracting muscle ; but after the fall the after-discharge would be expected to show itself again by a rebuilding up of tension. The result indicates (1) that the reflex evoked by the stretch-movement brings in its train little or no after-discharge from the reflex centres ;

(2) that the stretch-movement reflex is followed by a stretched-posture reflex due to the passive stretched posture brought about by and left after completion of the stretch-movement ; (3) that the stretched posture reflex like the stretch-movement reflex brings in its train little or no after-discharge from the reflex centres involved in it.

Evidence that the stretch considered as a stimulus has to be regarded in two separate specific forms, *i.e.*, a kinetic, a stretch-movement, and a static, a stretched posture, seems inconclusive. The reflex mechanism, so far as ascertained, does not apparently make distinction between them. On the other hand, in whichever of these two forms the stretch is applied the reflex

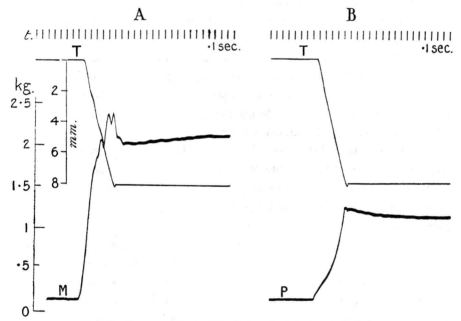

FIG. 9.—Same as 8 but with quicker stretch, *i.e.*, in 0·4 sec.

response itself tends to consist of two modes (figs. 1 and 7) of reaction—(1) " phasic," or short-lasting but relatively intense reaction ; (2) " postural," or tonic, often less powerful but much longer lasting. These may be distinguished as the phasic contraction and the postural contraction. The relative development of these two seems to depend on central neural conditions of the preparation (fig. 7), difficult sometimes to trace and to control. But the second or postural seems especially to be accentuated in decerebrate rigidity, and to be greatly impaired by spinal transection. Quickness of the stretch has often seemed to favour the phasic element in the reaction (figs. 8, 9).

The duration of the stretched-posture reflex under persistence of the passively imposed stretched-posture can be ascertained by employing reflex inhibition at various times subsequent to the induction of the stretched-posture. Examined in this way, the reflex contraction under the stretched-posture was found still persisting six minutes and more after its first induction, by a stretch-movement itself lasting but a fraction of a second. The stretched-posture reflex is therefore a postural reflex, an active reflex posture evoked and maintained in response to a passively imposed posture.

IV. To examine the stretched-posture reflex in further isolation from that due to the stretch-movement, we used an expedient as follows. Under inhibition the stretch-movement evokes no reflex in the muscle. We therefore carried out the stretch-movement during complete reflex inhibition of the muscle's proprioceptive arc, and then, while the muscle remained under the simple unaltering passive tension imposed by the already completed stretch-movement, withdrew the inhibitory stimulus, and set free the proprioceptive arc from inhibition. In this way, the proprioceptive arc which had been, as it were, put to sleep for the duration of the stretch-movement and for somewhat longer, awoke, uncomplicated by previous reaction to the stretch-movement, to find its muscle's mechanical state one of steady static strain, *i.e.*, stretched posture, transition to which from the previous slack posture had happened, so to say, unawares. The observations show (fig. 10) that the proprioceptive arc then at once enters into action, replying by postural contraction to the imposed passive posture. The myogram makes a smooth ascent to a steady plateau. To resolve whether active reflex contraction were really answerable for the new plateau reflex inhibition was again evoked (fig. 10, i'' to i'''). The result was that the myogram tension again fell at once under the renewed inhibition to the old level of purely passive tension, the reflex inhibition annulling the whole of the increase of tension to which the myogram had risen in its tonic reaction. That ascent had therefore been due wholly to active contraction.

There remained the question whether the contraction thus developed when the muscle after withdrawal of inhibition finds itself under static strain is not merely a post-inhibitory rebound contraction, such as often ensues after strong inhibitory stimuli. In regard to this (1) the stretched-posture contraction occurs after inhibitory stimuli which are quite weak, *e.g.*, 16·5 cm. secondary coil distance, coreless primary, fed by 0·23 amp. Such weak inhibitory stimuli are not usually followed by rebound. (2) The inhibitory stimuli did not give post-inhibitory rebound when applied in absence of the passive stretch. Passive stretch does, however, greatly increase post-inhibitory rebound contraction :

the contraction might therefore still be possibly a post-inhibitory rebound evoked by or rendered visible by the favouring circumstance of passive stretched-posture. The latent period of rebound, *i.e.*, the interval between it and the removal of the inhibitory stimulus, is, however, commonly very long, and longer than that of the stretched-posture reflex after inhibition. Though here again

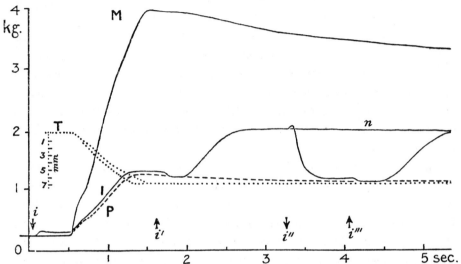

Fig. 10.—Whole quadriceps. Successive reactions M of normal, I of reflexly inhibited, and P of paralysed (*i.e.*, after nerve section) muscle to table-stretch T of 7 mm. The inhibition (by ipsilateral afferent peroneo-popliteal nerve) was on first occasion from *i* to *i'*, on second occasion from *i'* to *i''* and again from *i''* to *i'''*, giving therefore on second occasion the fall from and reascent to the plateau line *n* of the first occasion. The inhibitory nerve gave slight concomitant contraction (see text) so that full inhibitory effect is seen only close subsequent to cessation of the inhibitory stimulation. The less steep dotted line T gives the table-stretch for observation M ; the other for observations I and P. Myograph multiplying tendon-movement 62 times. Time in seconds.

passive stretch shortens the latency of rebound. Decision of the question seems settled, fortunately, by cases where the reflex contraction to stretched-posture after inhibition is separated from rebound contraction by the different post-inhibitory latencies of the two, the stretched-posture reflex commencing and reaching its plateau before any supervention of the rebound contraction itself.

The long duration of the reflex contraction responsive to a stretched posture raised the question whether even in the slightly stretched initial condition of the muscle—initial in the sense that it was the condition from which each stretch observation was started and in which the muscle was to all appearance quiescent —there might not be present some degree of active contraction. Reflex inhibition offered a convenient test for this, and showed that though often no reflex contraction was detectable under the slight residuum of stretch used as the zero from which the stretch to be applied for the stretch-reflex was to start, yet often even then there was present a slight amount of reflex contraction. Considering that the muscle had in these cases often remained for ten minutes or more under the same light unaltered tension, of perhaps 100-150 gm. only, the postural character of this reflex action seems assured.

V. The speed with which the passive stretch of the muscle is performed influences the form of the tension-myogram. A 6-mm. stretch performed in 6 seconds may give a contraction of no less height (tension) than is evoked by a stretch of similar amplitude just previously performed in 0·4 second. Usually, however (figs. 8, 9), a quite quick stretch provokes a contraction of which the climax lies higher above the ensuent plateau than does the climax given by a quite slow stretch.

As to the minimal extent of stretch which serves to evoke the reflex contraction, our records show reflexes from stretches of less than 0·5 mm. amplitude. A stretch of less than 1 mm. may give a contraction developing more than 2 kg. tension (fig. 7). The percentage elongation of the muscle which 1 mm. of stretch applied by the patellar tendon represents is difficult to assess when the whole quadriceps is used for the experiment, because some parts of the muscle passing between the femur and patella are much shorter than others. A given amplitude of pull on the freed patellar tendon will presumably produce a much greater percentage elongation in the former than the latter. A stretch confined to vastocrureus portion of quadriceps evokes (v.i.) a reflex contraction in it without evoking a contraction in the rectus femoris portion, and conversely. Rectus femoris, however, is a long band of muscle reaching from patella to ilium without any intermediate attachments. With vastocrureus wholly detached from patella and furthermore paralysed by nerve section, the rectus fully freed from it gives the stretch reflex in response to stretches, applied to its distal end by patellar tendon, of certainly less than 1 mm. amplitude. And this has been so when the length of the fleshy part of rectus has measured 116 mm. Hence an elongation considerably less than 0·9 per cent. of the muscle length suffices as a stretch stimulus for the stretch-reflex.

VI. *Reflex Inhibition.*—Stimulation of such afferent nerves as ipsilateral, peroneal or popliteal readily (figs. 5, 14, 15) inhibits the stretch reflex. Weak faradisation amply suffices. In this inhibition, however, it is not infrequently found that even under comparatively strong stimuli the inhibitory relaxation of the muscle is not quite complete during the stimulus, although immediately on cessation of the stimulus it becomes so.   Explanation of this is supplied by observations as follow.

When application of the inhibitory stimulus is made at a time when the muscle is quiescent and unexcited either by stretch or by other reflex excitation, the inhibitory stimulus during its application usually causes no visible effect whatever, although, if it has been strong, the well-known after-effect, rebound contraction, may follow its withdrawal.   But in not infrequent instances, the inhibitory stimulus applied when the muscle is at rest, evokes during its application some, though never ample, contraction.   This reflex effect is the ipsilateral knee-extensor contraction reflex referred to in a previous paper (14). But in cases where this reflex is thus evoked,the same ipsilateral stimulus applied when the muscle is not at rest, but actively contracting from stimulation of, e.g., a contralateral limb-nerve, causes a result which at first sight might appear a complete reversal of that just mentioned.   The reflex contraction due to the contralateral afferent relaxes so that an inhibitory effect might seem to have replaced the previous excitatory effect of the ipsilateral nerve.   But the records in fact show that the inhibition, even with strong stimuli, does not relax the contractile tension fully to the base line given by the muscle when at rest.   The relaxation stops short abruptly above that base line, remaining there during the ipsilateral nerve stimulation, and only on withdrawal of this latter stimulation, does it proceed downward to the original base line of the quiescent muscle.   On comparing in successive observations (fig. 11) from the same experiment the level at which the inhibitory fall during the stimulation was checked above the base line with the height of the contraction evoked by similar stimulation from the quiescent muscle, the heights of the two are found to correspond.   Moreover, the inhibitory relaxation is usually preceded by a brief augmentation of the pre-existent contraction.   It is, therefore, evident that whether reflex contraction of the muscle be in process or not at the time when the ipsilateral afferent is stimulated, this nerve regularly, in certain experiments, unfolds concurrently a two-fold effect on the muscle, namely a large inhibitory effect (which requires a contraction background to make it evident) and a smaller excitatory effect.   This latter documents itself independently and in spite of the inhibitory.   It sets in quicker than and, on cessation of the stimulus, subsides earlier than the inhibitory.   Hence, where this excitatory effect is present, the inhibitory relaxation is precluded from full completeness by it, but on withdrawal of the ipsilateral nerve-stimulation, the inhibition, owing to its outlasting the excitatory contraction, produces the full relaxation of its pure inhibitory component.   Such myograms therefore as fig. 12 gives conclusive evidence that the deafferented muscle yields **no** stretch-reflex, because the inhibitory stimulus produces no relaxation.

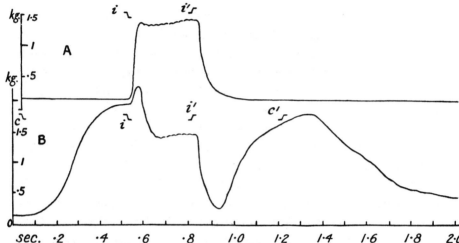

Fig. 11.—Vastus internus and crureus. A. Reflex evoked by stimulation from *i* to *i′* of ipsilateral afferent peroneo-popliteal nerve. B. Similar to A but evoked during reflex excited by stimulation from C to C′ of contralateral afferent peroneo-popliteal nerve. Stimulation of ipsilateral afferent nerve from *i* to *i′*, as in A. The rhythm of the stimulus is in the originals very evident in the ipsilateral reflex but is absent from the contralateral. Myograph multiplying tendon-movement 62 times. Time in 0·1 sec.

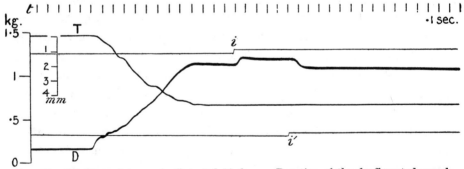

Fig. 12.—Whole quadriceps, deafferented 10 days. Reaction of the deafferented muscle D to 5 mm. table-stretch T. From *i* to *i′* stimulation of ipsilateral afferent peroneo-popliteal nerve ; this exhibits its own slight contraction (see text) but develops **no** inhibitory effect, proving that the stretch has evoked no reflex contraction in the deafferented muscle. That the reaction to the stretch is one of passive tension only is indicated further by the character of the ascent curve, *cf.* figs. 2, 3, 5, etc. Myograph multiplying tendon-movement 62 times. Time in 0·1 sec.

Interesting in regard to the two effects, inhibitory and excitatory, unfolded by stimulation of the ipsilateral nerve is that the former effect, potent as it is against the excitatory effects of other nerves and of the stretch-reflex, remains impotent against the excitatory effects of some of the fibres of its own nerve. The result of concurrent stimulation of VII and VIII afferent spinal roots of the frog obtained by Vesci (23) would seem to carry a similar interpretation.

When the reflex contraction which is being maintained by a stretched-posture is subjected to temporary inhibition, that inhibition often outlasts considerably the duration of the intercurrent inhibitory stimulation. The latency of commencement of the inhibition is short, but often a long interval after withdrawal of the inhibitory stimulus succeeds before the stretch-reflex again becomes operative, although its stimulus, the stretched-posture, is uninterruptedly and, owing to the greater length of the muscle when relaxed, augmentedly present. This long interval indicates that the inhibitory reflex exhibits an inhibitory after-action, seemingly analogous to the excitatory after-action of an excitatory reflex. Evidence of such inhibitory after-action is not confined to reflex-inhibitions of the stretch-reflex, but in this latter the steady nature of the stretch-posture stimulus renders the evidence of the inhibitory after-action operative against it particularly clear.

VII. The effect of executing a stretching movement on the muscle during the latter's contraction under activation from some other reflex source has interest because that conjunction of circumstances must occur in certain natural reflex acts (*v. infra*). Trial of this was, therefore, made by us on the isolated vasto-crureus during its contraction in the reflex evoked from contralateral peroneo-popliteal nerve. Our previous experiments had shown that the contractile tension developed by this reflex is greater when the initial stretch of the quiescent muscle at the time of excitation of the reflex is somewhat greater than when it is less. But the effect of producing a stretch of the muscle actually during the course of the reflex had not been examined. The result (fig. 13) obtained by this second procedure is, as might be expected, an augmentation by the stretch of the tension already developed by the reflex in operation at the time when the stretch is given. The augmentation is far in excess of the passive tension produced by the stretch in the quiescent phase. (Fig. 13, *n.*) Change undergone by the co-efficient of extension in the active state is difficult to evaluate. Almost the whole of the augmentation is due to increase in the active contractile tension. How far it is a peripheral contraction and how far of central origin is difficult at present to decide, but reflex inhibition (fig. 13) practically annuls it, making no distinction between it and the original reflex already present before the stretch is performed.

VIII. As has been shown the tensile reaction to stretch of the muscle with proprioceptive arc inhibited differs greatly from that of the muscle with its proprioceptive arc uninhibited. So also from this latter differ the tensile reactions given by the deafferented muscle and the muscle made paralytic by severance of its motor nerve and examined within an hour or so of that severance. The tensile reaction of the muscle to stretch contrasts, therefore, in (1) the inhibited, (2) the deafferented, and (3) the paralytic states on the one hand with that of what on the other hand may be called (4) the " normal "

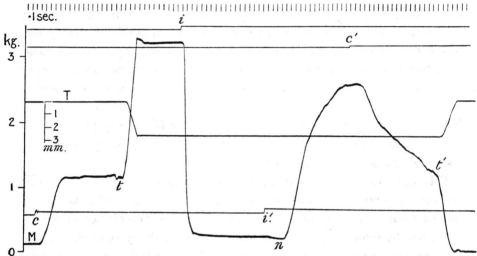

Fig. 13.—Vasto-crureus. From C to C' stimulation of contralateral afferent peroneopopliteal nerve (break-shocks at 40 per sec., coreless primary fed by 0·2 amp., secondary coil 16·3 cm. from primary) evoking reflex contraction. At t a 2·5 mm. table-stretch ; at t' table raised to initial height relieving the residual stretched-posture. From i to i' stimulation of ipsilateral (i.e., inhibitory) afferent nerve ; this nerve as frequently (see text) evoked besides inhibition of the contralateral nerve's reflex contraction slight reflex contraction on its own part, so that full inhibition revealing the passive tension component in the reaction to this stretch is fully evident only at n, where on cessation of the ipsilateral stimulus the slight ipsilateral contraction passed off though the inhibition temporarily remained. Myograph multiplying tendon-movement 62 times. Time in 0·1 sec.

state, i.e., in the decerebrate preparation. A decisive factor in this difference is that in (4) the proprioceptive reflex arc is operative, whereas in (1), (2) and (3) it is not. Whether this factor is merely a predominant one, or whether it is the sole one involved can be examined by comparing the tensile reaction in states (1), (2) and (3) one with another. Figs. 14, 15 show such a comparison between (1) and (3) ; the reaction in (4) is also given, but in the case of (4) the stretch given is less comparable than between (1) and (3) because in (4) the active contraction element by shortening the muscle, although only slightly since the myograph multiplies by 62, detracts more from the course of elongation of the muscle than in the other two stretches.   The reactions in (1) and (2) are closely similar, and have been constantly found so.   So also have been the reactions in the deafferented and the paralytic (fig. 4).   We infer that the putting out of action of the proprioceptive arc by severance of its peripheral neurones, or by inhibition of its central part, reduces the tensile reaction of the muscle to stretch to the condition obtaining when the muscle is wholly para-lysed.   The cutting off of the muscle altogether from connection with the central nervous system seems to add nothing further to this change in its tensile reaction effected by reflex inhibition or by section of its afferent nerve. The whole change would, therefore, be referable to the non-reaction of the proprioceptive arc ; and conversely the whole difference between the stretch-reaction of the " normal " muscle and of the muscle inhibited, deafferented or paralytic is due to action in the former case of the proprioceptive arc.

In the tension curve of the paralytic, inhibited, and deafferented muscle tensions (due to progressive passive increase of length as ordinates above abscissæ of time) a feature both with the parallel-fibred rectus (fig. 14) and the more complex vasto-crureus (figs. 3, 15) is a brief-lasting

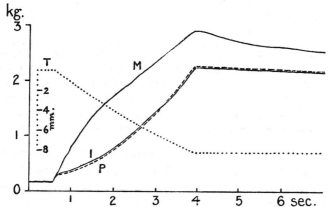

Fɪɢ. 14.—Rectus femoris. 8 mm. table-stretch T.   Reaction of uninhibited muscle M, of reflexly inhibited muscle I, and of paralysed (by nerve-section) muscle P (broken line).   For the inhibited muscle the stimulation of the inhibitory nerve was begun before and continued until after the course of the reaction I included in the figure was run through, so that the inhibition was operative throughout the course of I. Myograph multiplying tendon-movement 62 times.   Time in seconds.

initial gradient of tension steeper than that then following for a time.   In the reflex preparation this rise is accentuated, but at the same time its passive component is masked by the accompanying active contraction.   Taken broadly, the difference between the tension curve of the muscle with proprioceptive arc intact and uninhibited as compared with that during inhibition, or after deafferentation or motor paralysis, is that in the former the curve is convex to the abscissa, especially in its lower part, whereas in the latter it is concave.

The studies by Langelaan (11, 12) of the reaction of muscle to extension by weights applied slowly and quickly and for various times have shown how intimately commingled are its elasticity and its plasticity, a result in harmony with the complexity of its structure as analysed by the microscope.   Of its

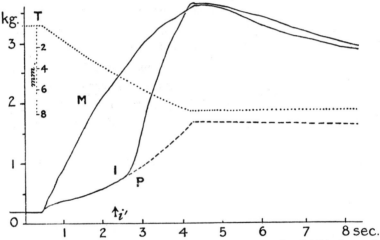

FIG. 15.—Vasto-crureus. 8 mm. table-stretch T. Reaction of uninhibited muscle M, of muscle reflexly inhibited for earlier half of the reaction I and of paralysed (by nerve-section) muscle P (broken line). The stimulation of the inhibitory afferent was begun before the course of the reaction shown in the figure but was discontinued at i' in the figure. Myograph multiplying tendon-movement 62 times. Time in seconds.

histological components the connective tissue and the sarcolemma of the muscle-fibres may be presumed to remain unaffected by reflex inhibition or in the few hours after severance of the motor nerve. That the tensile reaction to stretch—the coefficients of elasticity and plasticity, if in view of Langelaan's papers we may use such terms—should in the reflexly inhibited muscle be practically indistinguishable from that of the wholly paralysed muscle is therefore interesting, as indicating that the state of the contractile element of the muscle is practically identical in the two.

IX. The knee-jerk and patellar-clonus have doubtless for their excitant, like the reflexes here described, mechanical stretch of the muscle. The question rises whether they, together with these latter, are not related though distinguishable forms of one comprehensive proprioceptive reflex. The knee-jerk would seem to be an example of it reduced and simplified by the extreme brevity and slightness of the mechanical stretch employed. In some of our records a stretch of less than $\frac{1}{20}$ mm., and lasting less than $\frac{1}{20}$ sec., seems to suffice for eliciting a knee-jerk. The well-known favouring of the knee-jerk by an inactive, semiflexed posture of the knee-joint conforms with the conditions for reflex here described. Contributory to the brevity of the jerk-contraction may be that the shortening of the muscle by the relatively unhindered contraction tends of itself, as shown above, by undoing the stretch of the muscle, to cut short the reflex contraction. Patellar-clonus in its myogram records resembles a rhythmic series of knee-jerks, sometimes partly fused. The stretch eliciting it can be regarded as one temporarily relieved by each contraction of the clonus itself, the stretch becoming operative again as each contraction subsides. The view that patellar-clonus reveals the rate of the natural intrinsic rhythm of discharge from the central nervous system is untenable in view of facts well ascertained ; and the somewhat wide variations in frequency of the clonus accord with each contraction of the clonus being due to self-excitation of the muscle as the imposed stretch, after being broken by the shortening due to the last precedent contraction, returns once more into play. Viets (24) found a certain initial posture optimal for the clonus. We have noticed the clonus-frequency increase as the pull on the freed tendon increased. The clonus is suppressed by the myograph spring when that is above a certain degree of stiffness which yet allows the tetanic stretch-reflexes, the subject of this paper. With intermediate resistances of the spring our observations show transitions between clonus of ordinary rates and clonus rates up to 40 per second, amounting in effect to coarsely tremulent tetani (fig. 16). Knee-jerk and patellar-clonus seem, in fact, to be fractional examples of the more comprehensive stretch-reflex, which in its full entirety comprises much more than those fractional manifestations.

The stretch reflex of the knee-extensor is much impaired by severance of the spinal cord. The impairment seems to fall unequally on those two components of the reflex contraction which, as exhibited in the decerebrate preparation, we have considered distinguishable and termed respectively the phasic and the postural. The latter in the spinal preparation as compared with decerebrate seems in our experience practically abolished. The former is, though weakened, still obtainable. The reaction of the quadriceps to stretch five and six days after spinal transection between second and third lumbar roots is greatly wanting in power, and under the progress of the increasing stretch exhibits a tremulent character which may be attributed to brief phasic contractions successively excited by the stretch and unsupported by tonic contraction. The character of the knee-jerk contraction in the spinal preparation as compared with the decerebrate (22) conforms with this difference observed in the stretch-reflex. The knee-jerk contraction in the spinal preparation consists practically wholly of a phasic reaction, and is lacking in the tonic or postural component it possesses in the decerebrate. And this agrees with our argument that the knee-jerk is a fractional manifestation of the stretch-reflex itself.

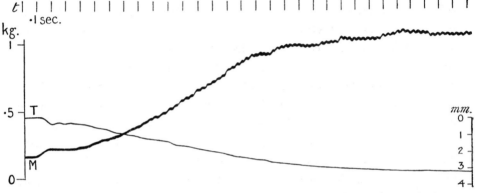

FIG. 16.—Whole quadriceps. Rapid clonic contraction, showing frequency of about 36 per sec., developing under a slight slow table-stretch T of 3 mm. Myograph multiplying tendon-movement 40 times. Time in 0·1 sec.

X. (i) Reflex tetanic contraction of a muscle in response to mechanical stretch suggests itself as important for the performance of natural muscular acts. Reflex standing is a large and composite postural reflex (20, 21), and in its execution a fundamental element is the contraction of the " antigravity muscles " counteracting the superincumbent weight that would otherwise flex the joints and cause the body to sink to the ground. Among these muscles are in the limbs (quadruped) the extensors of hip, knee, ankle, shoulder, and elbow. A typical example of them is that muscle with which our observations deal—the knee-extensor, quadriceps femoris. In that muscle tensile stretch such as gravity in the animal's erect position produces is shown in our observations to excite proprioceptively a reflex contraction of the passively tautened muscle, and that contraction produces an equilibrium between the imposed stretch and itself. It would thus appear that the tendency for the limb-joints to fold up under the weight superincumbent on them in the erect posture is counteracted by the proprioceptive stretch-reflex of the antigravity muscles themselves. In other words, the stretch-reflex of the antigravity muscles is a fundamental element in the reflex posture of standing.   Evidencing this rôle played by the postural stretch-reflex of the antigravity muscles in reflex standing is the similarity of influence of transcollicular decerebration and of spinal transection respectively upon reflex standing and upon the postural stretch-reflex of the knee-extensor.   After transcollicular decerebration, reflex standing, in the above-mentioned sense, and the knee-extensor's postural stretch-reflex are markedly evident.   On the other hand, spinal transection at once, for the time being, practically annuls both.

Reflex standing as a stretch-reflex affecting the body as a whole is, of course, a *composite* stretch-reflex ; in it are compounded the stretch-reflexes individual to the individual antigravity muscles.   That fact provides it with latitude of modifiability in detail.   And further, as our observations in quadriceps femoris show, the stretch-reflex, unlike the reflexes provoked from skin-nerves and other sources outside the muscle itself, remains confined not only to the particular muscle stretched, but to that portion of it which the stretch affects. In the decerebrate preparation without labyrinths and set on its feet, a foot may then be passively put further forward or backward and yet the standing be maintained in the new posture.   Local modifications are possible to the posture.   Each such shift, altering somewhat the degree and incidence of the stretch, *e.g.*, of knee extensor, shifts somewhat the play of the proprio-ceptive reflex action in it conformably with the shift.   And consequential shift of the incidence of gravity upon the other limbs will in their antigravity muscles induce likewise shift of their stretch-reflexes and readjust the contrac-tion in conformity with that.   Moreover, there is at least one important exception to the limitation of the stretch-reflex contraction to the stretched muscle itself : stretch of the knee-extensor, as shown above, does clearly excite reflex contraction of its fellow muscle of the contralateral limb.

The stretch-reflexes exhibited in reflex standing are of relatively weak intensity as compared with some obtained in the experimental observations given here.   They are slight because the stretch imposed by gravity is slight, further yield which would carry the stretch further being successfully counter-acted by the reflex contraction already evoked.   The stretch is therefore slight, and because the stretch is slight the reflex contraction is for its part slight. That an essential element in reflex standing is the stretch reflex of the anti-gravity muscles makes evident why the reflex standing posture in decerebrate rigidity is an exaggerated one—a caricature, as has rightly been said of it, of standing.   In decerebrate rigidity the extensor tonic contraction is accen-tuated by loss of higher centres which control it ; this accentuation is recognized as a " release " phenomenon. In that circumstance the stretch-reflex as regards its tonic postural component shares in the effect of the release, and consequently is abnormally accentuated.   The knee-jerk was mentioned above as a fractional elicitation of the stretch-reflex of the knee-extensor.   The knee-jerk can serve, therefore, as a test of the condition of the stretch-reflex, though sampling better the latter's phasic component than its tonic or postural component (v. sup.).

That in disease where the knee-jerk is impaired there should also be impairment of standing conforms with the argument that the stretch-reflex of the antigravity muscles is a factor in reflex standing.   The stretch reflex, as explaining the counteracting of gravity in reflex standing, accords with the seeming absence of reflex contraction in the flexor muscles in standing ; not only does gravity not tend directly to stretch them, but in our experience the postural stretch-reflex is far less readily elicitable from a flexor ; our search so far has been a limited one, but we are in doubt whether in semi-tendinosus, the typical knee-flexor, we have elicited such a reflex at all.   Such indirect stretch as gravity in the erect posture exerts on the flexor by the slight contraction of the extensor may well, therefore, excite no postural stretch-reflex from the former.

In allotting to the postural stretch-reflex this rôle in reflex standing we would not be understood to mean that it plays more than a contributory, though an elemental and important, part in that great reflex.   The admirable experiments of Magnus (15) and his co-workers, de Kleijn (16), Dusser de Barenne (15), and others, have made clear reflex adjuvants and adjustments of it, due to neck postures, labyrinth positions, &c.   The stretch-reflex as a " gravity " reflex in standing thus dovetails in with other gravity reflexes, the otolith reflexes, elucidated by Magnus and de Kleijn (16) in a series of researches which contribute a fascinating chapter to experimental physiology.   The extreme ease with which, in our experience, the postural stretch-reflex of the knee extensor is affected by reflex inhibition from its own limb and other sources conforms with the stretch reflexes of the antigravity muscles being delicately susceptible to modification in the ways and from the relatively distant sources demonstrated by researches of the Utrecht School.

(ii) Again, in the execution of the step, the knee-extensor is subjected to stretch by the muscles bending the knee in the flexion-phase of that act. Analysis by Philippson (18) of cinematograph records of the dog taken by Marey shows that in the trot the femoro-tibial joint passes from an angle of 130 deg. to one of 80 deg., in the gallop from an angle of 140 deg. to one of 60 deg. In the cat these transitions would correspond with amplitudes of stretch of the quadriceps extensor much above the threshold observed by us for the stretch-reflex of that muscle. In six small cats the lengthenings of rectus femoris produced by altering the pose of the knee-joint from full extension to full flexion are shown in the accompanying table.

Length of rectus femoris from acetabulum to upper border of patella, hip being at right angles to trunk :—

Weight of animal in grammes.	Knee fully flexed. mm.	Knee fully extended. mm.
2,370	107	89
2,080	98	78
1,680	88	70
1,665	103	84
1,865	100	79
2,470	108	88

The percentage of lengthening in terms of the muscle's length is even greater in the case of the vasto-crureus. If the ordinary flexion reflex evoked by stimulation of an afferent nerve of the limb be taken as in its measure a paradigm for the flexion phase of the reflex step, there has to be remembered that the reflex contraction of the flexors is accompanied by reflex inhibition of their antagonists, the extensors (reciprocal innervation). Such inhibition, as shown above, can readily and completely preclude and annul for the time being the extensor's stretch-reflex. Reciprocal inhibition may have its *raison d'être* in preventing the stretch-reflex of the antagonist extensor and thus avoiding unnecessary work spent against opposed muscular contractions. But on diminution and subsidence of the reflex flexion the reciprocal inhibition of the extensor likewise diminishes and subsides ; there then remains the stretched posture imposed on the extensor by the flexed position given to the knee. This stretched posture of the extensor excites, as the inhibition of the extensor muscle's proprioceptive arc subsides, a reflex contraction, as shown above, in the stretched muscle. This reflex contraction will in its turn, by opening the knee-angle and relieving the muscle of its stretch, diminish or abrogate the reflex extensor's contraction, lessening the stimulus which excites it, undermining its contraction as shown above, and undoing the peripheral augmentation of contraction which lengthened condition of the muscle carries with it, especially markedly in the case of this muscle.

The knee-extensor is composed of a single-joint portion, *vasto-crureus*, and a double-joint portion, *rectus femoris*. This latter, since it crosses the flexor aspect of the hip joint, will, when the hip-extensors contract, be stretched unless a fully compensatory extension of the knee concurrently occurs.   Reflex contraction of the hip-extensors is, in the ordinary extension reflex of the limb, not accompanied by reciprocal inhibition of the knee-extensor.   In this instance the hip-extensors' contraction stretches a muscle synergic with themselves.   If the synergy of the ordinary extension reflex be taken as paradigm for the extension phase of the step the stretch-reflex will be a factor in that phase. In the flexion phase of the step the knee and hip are both undergoing flexion, and whether stretch of rectus femoris results will depend on the ratio of those two movements one to another ; the rectus will, however, be under reciprocal inhibition greater or less throughout the flexion phase.   In the first quarter of the extension phase of the step, the knee is extending while the hip is still slightly flexing, so that stretch of rectus will hardly occur then.   In the second period of the extension phase a longer lasting period, the ilio-femoral angle opens by about 40 deg., while the femoro-tibial changes little—it flexes through some 15 deg. in the earlier half of the period and extends through some 15 deg. in the latter half.   During this period the rectus is, therefore, undergoing a stretch movement.   Not only can at beginning of this phase the stretched posture then obtaining in vasto-crureus evoke its reflex contraction of that muscle, but a stretch movement setting in in rectus femoris will develop reflex contraction in that muscle.   These reflex contractions will in due turn, as the knee straightens and eases off the stretch, be diminished and cut short by lessening and removal of their stimulus and subsidence of augmenting peripheral conditions, and by the supervention of reciprocal extensor inhibition with recommencement of the ensuing flexion-phase.

It is, however, rather as an adjuvant to and accessorily adjusting the fundamental phasic movements of the step than as actually producing them, that the stretch-reflex must be regarded.   In light of it we see that in the various amplitudes and tempos of the step a restricted and brief flexion-phase will induce a restricted and brief extension-phase.   But the fact that the deafferented knee-extensor when isolated and attached to the myograph not infrequently shows rhythmic contractions resembling those of its " stepping " warns against the supposition that the stretch-reflex or indeed the entirety of the proprioceptive arc itself is absolutely necessary for fundamental exhibition of " stepping."   Graham Brown (3) has advanced the view, and adduced considerable evidence in favour of it, that the essential nature of " stepping " is entirely central in origin, an autochthonous rhythmic activity proper to the spinal cord.   Taking the view that the stretch-reflex is nevertheless an element in the normal adjusting taxis of the step, and remembering that in the locomotor ataxy of tabes dorsalis the knee-jerk is commonly lost or impaired, which in light of our observations must mean loss or impairment of the extensor's stretch-reflex, the inference seems that loss or impairment of the stretch-reflex is a factor of dominant importance in locomotor and other tabetic forms of ataxy. In our observations the deafferented knee-extensor behaves to stretch not otherwise than does the muscle wholly paralysed by severance of its motor nerve.

XI. Though the knee-extensor when subjected to a stretch responds by a proprioceptive reflex contraction, faradisation of the central end of cut branches of its own nerve produces reflex inhibitory relaxation (19) of the muscle. This is so in our experience whether the faradic stimulation be strong or weak. We have seen full inhibitory relaxation given by faradisation at 30 cm. distance of secondary coil from primary. The inhibitory relaxation is evident in several ways : (1) by inhibiting a tonic postural contraction, *e.g.*, in decerebrate rigidity ; (2) by inhibiting a reflex contraction produced by stimulation of an afferent nerve of the contralateral fellow limb ; (3) by inhibiting a post-inhibitory rebound contraction ensuent after inhibition that has been produced by just previous stimulation of the cut branch of the extensor's own nerve ; (4) by post-stimulatory rebound contraction following on stimulation of the cut branch of the extensor's own nerve. The inhibition can also be excited by mechanical stimulation, *i.e.*, ligation of the cut branch of the extensor's nerve. The stimulation, whether faradic or mechanical, causes along with inhibition of the ipsilateral extensor itself, reflex contraction of the fellow muscle of the contralateral limb.

The afferent nerve-fibres of an extensor muscle appear to be of two functional kinds. " One kind produces reflex inhibition of its own muscle and of other allied extensor muscles, and reflex contraction of flexor muscles antagonistic to the muscles it inhibits. The other kind produces reflex contraction of its own muscle " (22). That in experiments such as the above stimulation of the central end of the cut branch of the extensor muscle's own nerve is not found to produce any contraction of the muscle may be due to the circumstance that, as mentioned above, those of the afferent fibres of the muscle which produce reflex contraction of it produce that contraction seemingly only in that part of the muscle from which they themselves proceed, and the motor nerve-fibres to that part of the muscle have perforce in such experiments as the above been severed. The absence of reflex contraction in other parts of the muscle on stimulating the central end of the nerve supplying some even large fraction of the muscle obtains even when this latter includes the whole vasto-crureus ; we have not seen the rectus then evince the least contraction.   Apart from the stretch-reflex itself, including knee-jerk under that term, the only evidence we have met with in the quadriceps of proprioceptives in it evoking reflex contraction of it, has been that in dissecting rectus femoris from vastus externus reflex contraction of the proximal parts of this latter is sometimes evoked by even light touches of a delicate fibrous tissue sheet lying between the adjacent surfaces of the distal portions of rectus and vastus externus.   Other-wise apart from the stretch-reflex there has been no evidence of the " pressor " proprioceptives in the muscle.   Also the mitigation or cessation, whether gradual or abrupt, of the imposed stretch, seems wholly to fail to excite them.

XII. In the extensor, the stretch-reflexes differ markedly from the ordinary contralateral reflexes of that muscle.   The former being proprioceptive are, of course, ipsilateral.   Their latency is much shorter, they exhibit little or no " recruitment " and little or no after-discharge, nor is there, in our experience, " terminal rebound."   The absence of terminal rebound may be due to the stimulus employed being a natural and " adequate " one, exciting, therefore, a functionally homogeneous set of receptors and afferents, so that admixture of afferents of opposed, e.g., inhibitory effect does not occur.   The spatial distribution of the ipsilateral motor discharge remains limited to the stimu-lated muscle itself, and seemingly even to that portion of the muscle to which the stimulus is actually applied, and also does not involve other muscles or even a part of the same muscle other than that stimulated by stretch.   Deafferentation of the muscle instead of, as in the contralateral reflexes, merely modifying the reflex contraction renders it wholly un-obtainable.   From the reflex of the knee-extensor commonly obtainable by faradisation of afferent nerves of the ipsilateral limb itself the stretch-reflex differs less.   There is, however, the marked difference that the former is not inhibited by those ipsilateral afferents, whereas the stretch-reflex is readily so.

XIII. The term stretch-reflex, although simple and descriptive, is awkward for use in adjectival form.   Gowers, in 1881, proposed for the "tendon-phenomena," then not commonly accepted as reflex, the term "myotatic contractions," from τακτικός, extended.   His suggested adjective would suitably apply to the reflexes brought forward in this paper and would conveniently avoid the periphrases that this paper has had to employ. Myotatic reflexes could embrace stretch-reflexes in general, including " jerk " and " clonus," which we regard as fractional forms of the complete and fully functional myotatic reflex.

Summary of Conclusions.

In the knee-extensor (decerebrate preparation) a stretch applied to the muscle evokes contraction in it. This is reflex and purely proprioceptive, its receptors lying in the fleshy region of the muscle. A stretch less in extent than ·8 per cent. of the total muscle-length suffices to evoke the reflex. Slow stretches, e.g., of 5 mm., performed in 6 sec., evoke the reflex as well as do quick. The latency of the reflex is short, e.g., less than 20σ, but the lower limit of latency we have not determined.

Within limits, so long as the stretch increases, the reflex continues to increase. When augmentation of the stretch ceases, augmentation of the reflex contraction also ceases and the reflex usually declines, merging into long-lasting plateau-like contraction, which is maintained by the stretched-posture, consequent from the precurrent stretch-movement. Withdrawal of the stretch causes immediate cessation of this postural stretch contraction. The stretch-reflex, unlike the ordinary contralateral extensor reflexes, therefore, exhibits little or no after-discharge, i.e., the reflex is relatively dead-beat.

When the application of the stretch is confined to a portion only of the muscle, the reflex contraction is also confined to that portion.

The reflex is readily diminished and annulled by reflex inhibition provoked from the sources recognized as regularly inhibitory for the knee-extensor. Under this inhibition, the muscle's reaction to stretch resembles indistinguishably in our records that yielded by the muscle after complete paralysis from severance of its motor nerve. Similarly, after severance of the afferent nerve-fibres of the muscle the reaction of the muscle to stretch becomes indistinguishable from that of the inhibited or paralysed muscle, and no trace of reflex contraction in response to the stretch has been discoverable. Direct stimulation, electrical or mechanical, of the afferent nerve of a part of the muscle produces inhibitory relaxation of the stretch contraction in the other parts of the muscle, i.e., among receptors in the muscle, there are in addition to those excitable by stretch and provoking reflex contraction in the muscle, others which provoke reflex inhibition of the muscle.

Post-inhibitory rebound is facilitated and augmented by stretch of the muscle; this is so even when the stretched-posture has been maintained for many minutes at the time when the post-inhibitory period occurs. Knee-jerk and patellar clonus seem to be fractional examples of the stretch-reflex.

Some application of the experimental results to the reflex co-ordination of standing and of locomotor acts is attempted.

LETTERING APPLICABLE TO ALL THE FIGURES.

T, Record of table-height : there is a lag in the record of the table-movement as compared with that of the myograph.

mm, Scale of table-movement in millimetres.

kg, Scale of muscle-tensions in kilograms.

For figs. 1, 4, 6, and 16 the originals run 30 mm. vertical per 1 kilog. tension, in the remaining figures 24 mm. per 1 kilog. tension ; to these *original* sizes the magnification by the myograph mentioned under each figure applies.

REFERENCES.

(1) E. D. Adrian, ' Journ. of Physiol.,' vol. 57 (1923) ; ' Proc. Physiol. Soc.,' p. 11.

(2) M. Blix, ' Skand. Arch. f. Physiol.,' vol. 3, p. 295 (1892) ; *ibid.*, vol. 4, p. 321 (1893).

(3) T. Graham Brown, ' Journ. of Physiol.,' vol. 48, p. 18 (1914).

(4) F. J. Buytendijk, ' Zeits. f. Biol.,' vol. 59, p. 42 (1912).

(5) Y. Doi, ' Journ. of Physiol.,' vol. 54, pp. 213 and 335 (1920–21).

(6) C. L. Evans and A. V. Hill, ' Journ. of Physiol.,' vol. 49, p. 10 (1914).

(7) A. Forbes, L. H. Ray and A. M. Hopkins, ' Amer. Journ. of Physiol.,' vol. 65, p. 300 (1923).

(8) W. R. Gowers, ' Diagnosis of Diseases of the Spinal Cord,' London : 2nd edit., p. 29 (1881).

(9) W. Hartree and A. V. Hill, ' Journ. of Physiol.,' vol. 55, p. 389 (1921).

(10) W. A. Jolly, ' Quart. Journ. of Expt. Physiol.,' vol. 4, p. 67 (1911).

(11) J. W. Langelaan, ' Brain,' vol. 38, p. 325 (1915).

(12) J. W. Langelaan, ' Proc. Roy. Acad. Sci., Amsterdam,' vol. 5 B, p. 57 (1902).

(13) E. G. T. Liddell and C. S. Sherrington, these ' Proceedings,' Ser. B., vol. 95, p. 299 (1923).

(14) E. G. T. Liddell and C. S. Sherrington, these ' Proceedings,' Ser. B., vol. 95, p. 150 (1923).

(15) R. Magnus and J. G. Dusser de Barenne, ' Arch. f. d. ges. Physiol.,' 180 (1920).

(16) R. Magnus and de Kleijn, 23 papers in ' Arch. f. d. ges. Physiol.' (1912–1923).

(17) J. de Meyer, ' Arch. internat. de Physiol.,' vol. 16, p. 64–99 (1921).

(18) M. Philippson, ' Trav. d. Lab. d. Physiol. Instit., Solvay,' Bruxelles, vol. 5 (1905).

(19) C. S. Sherrington, these ' Proceedings,' B., vol. 77, p. 478, 1906, *ibid*, vol. 79, p. 337 (1907).

(20) C. S. Sherrington, ' Brain,' vol. 29, p. 467 (1906).

(21) C. S. Sherrington, ' Journ. of Physiol.,' vol. 40, p. 28 (1910).

(22) C. S. Sherrington, ' Brain,' vol. 38, p. 211, 1915.

(23) J. Vesci, ' Zeits. f. allg. Physiol.,' vol. 11, p. 173 (1910).

(24) H. Viets, ' Brain,' vol. 43, p. 269 (1920).

MUSCLE RECEPTORS

Recent anatomical descriptions of the muscle spindle fully confirm Ruffini's belief that the spindles should be classified among the most highly developed sense organs in the body, being second only to the eye and the ear in complexity. The muscle spindle was named by Kühne in 1863 (15); in 1894 Sherrington proved it to be sensory (16). The first adequate description of the muscle spindle appears to be that of Ruffini (17,18). In 1928 Fulton and Pi-Suñer (19) proposed that the muscle spindle must be arranged in parallel with the extrafusal muscle fibers to account for the myotatic reflex and, furthermore, that the Golgi tendon organ served an inhibitory function; both assumptions were later to be verified.

Although several laboratories had studied muscle receptors during the 1920's, a classic experiment on unitary activity was reported in 1931 by Matthews from Adrian's laboratory. The experiment utilized frog toe-muscle preparations, in which the experimentor isolated single muscle spindles. This permitted a quantitative analysis of the activity of the spindle and provided data for the formulation of the first working hypothesis for the nature of adaptation. When the muscle was stretched, the spindle initially increased its discharge and then gradually adapted to a constant but slower frequency. When the muscle was made to contract by stimulation of the motor nerve, the spindle response stopped—thus supporting the Fulton-Pi-Suñer hypothesis (if the muscle spindle fibers are in parallel with the extrafusal fibers, contraction of the extrafusal fibers would remove the stimulus of stretch to the spindles). The quantitative studies of adaptation to a constant stimulus demonstrated that impulse frequency is linearly related to the logarithm of the load at any given time after onset of the stretch.

In a 1933 paper in which he studied the muscle spindle afferents in the cat, Matthews formulated a classification of fiber types which was to serve as the basis for later nomenclature (20). Research continued along the lines of anatomical investigation of the location of muscle receptors and the response in adaptation of these receptors to stretching the muscle. A notable contribution was the 1948 study of Barker (21), concerning the histologic characteristics of the muscle spindle of the rabbit. Questions concerning the mechanism of initiation of impulses at nerve endings and their propagation along the axon were not answered until 1950, when they were approached in the studies of Katz. Katz was the first successfully to attack the question of the transducer properties of muscle receptors and also that of how mechanical stretch of a muscle is translated into a propagated electrical potential in the afferent nerve.

The 1933 Matthews paper described response patterns of several types of receptors in cat muscle to passive stretch and contraction. However, the definitive work in describing the different kinds of muscle afferents arising from different types of receptors, the muscle spindle, and the Golgi tendon organ, was that of Hunt and Kuffler in 1951. Their paper sets forth the now common nomenclature of two types of Group I (largest afferent) size fibers, IA's and the IB's. The IA's were described as having a low threshold to stretch and discharging to passive stretch of the muscle while being silenced during active contraction. They were therefore presumed to arise from the muscle spindles—a presumption which has proved correct. The IB's were found to have a much higher threshold to stretch and a discharge rate which accelerated during active contraction of the muscle. Here again Hunt and Kuffler correctly assumed that the IB's originated from the tendon organ.

REFERENCES

15. Kühne, W. Die Muskelspindeln: Ein Beitrag zur Lehre von der entwickelung der Muskeln und Nervenfasern. *Virchows Arch.* **28**: 528–538 (1863).

16. Sherrington, C. S. On the anatomical constitution of nerves of skeletal muscles; with remarks on recurrent fibres in the ventral spinal nerve-root. *J. Physiol.* **17**: 211–258 (1894).

17. Ruffini, A. Observations on sensory nerve-endings in voluntary muscles. *Brain* **20**: 368–374 (1897).

18 Ruffini, A. On the minute anatomy of the neuromuscular spindles of the cat, and on their physiological significance. *J. Physiol.* **23**: 190–208 (1898).

19. Fulton, J. F., and J. Pi-Suñer. A note concerning the probable function of various afferent end-organs in skeletal muscle. *Am. J. Physiol.* **83**: 554–562 (1928).

20. Matthews, B. H. C. Nerve endings in mammalian muscle. *J. Physiol.* **78**: 1–33 (1933).

21. Barker, D. The innervation of the muscle spindles. *Quart. J. Micr. Sci.* **89**: 143–186 (1948).

BIBLIOGRAPHY

Hunt, C. C. Relation of function to diameter in afferent fibers of muscle nerves. *J. Gen. Physiol.* **38**: 117–131 (1954).

Granit, R. *Receptors and Sensory Perception.* Yale University Press, New Haven, Connecticut 1955.

Diamond, J., J. A. B. Gray, and M. Sato. The site of initiation of impulses in Pacinian corpuscles. *J. Physiol.* **133**: 54–67 (1956).

Barker, D., Ed. *Symposium on Muscle Receptors.* Hong Kong University Press, Hong Kong 1962.

Granit, R., Ed. *Nobel Symposium I: Muscle Afferents and Motor Control.* John Wiley & Sons, New York, 1966.

SUGGESTED TEXTS

Ruch *et al.* Chapters 4 and 7.

Ochs, S. Chapters 12 and 17.

Mountcastle, V. Chapters 61 and 73.

THE RESPONSE OF A SINGLE END ORGAN

By BRYAN H. C. MATTHEWS (*Beit Memorial Fellow*),
Fellow of King's College, Cambridge.

(*From the Physiological Laboratory, Cambridge.*)

INTRODUCTION.

THIS paper describes a series of experiments that have been made to investigate the general properties of the sensory end organ which is stimulated by the stretching of a muscle, and is especially concerned with the phenomena of adaptation, *i.e.* the gradual fall in the frequency of the discharge under a constant stimulus.

The muscle receptors were used by Adrian and Zotterman [1926 *a*] in their original study of the response of the end organ, and by Bronk [1929] in the study of fatigue, but in the present work a much more detailed survey has been made possible by the use of a preparation which can be relied upon to contain one and only one end organ. This preparation has given such constant results that the effect of a number of factors which influence the response has been analysed in a quantitative way, and with the aid of these data it has been possible to formulate a working hypothesis as to the nature of adaptation.

PART I.

METHOD OF INVESTIGATION AND GENERAL FEATURES OF THE RESPONSE.

Adrian and Zotterman [1926 *b*] have shown that all the types of end organ which they examined reacted qualitatively in much the same way, giving a rhythmic discharge, so that a study of any one type will give results which probably have a general application. The end organs chosen for the present investigation were muscle proprioceptors, as their responses could be evoked repeatedly without difficulty, and their stimulus, stretching, could be easily measured, controlled and graded. The oscillograph described in a previous paper [Matthews, 1929 *a*] was used to record the action currents from the nerves, and with this instrument frequencies as high as 2000 per sec. can be detected and measured.

Matthews, B. H. C. The response of a single end organ. *J. Physiol.* **71**: 64–110, 1931.

In the early experiments the muscle part of the double preparation described in a previous paper [Matthews, 1929 *b*] was used. This muscle contained a small number of end organs, and sometimes rhythmic discharges could be picked out from the records. But it soon became clear that little could be learnt without studying the response of a single end organ.

Adrian and Zotterman investigated the response of a single end organ in the sterno-cutaneous muscle by cutting the muscle down until only one end organ was left, and Bronk [1929] has succeeded in recording action currents from a single end organ by the method devised by Adrian and Bronk [1929] to lead off the response of a single motor

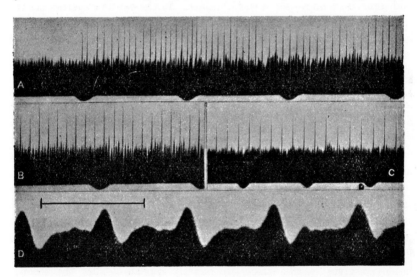

Fig. 1. Rhythmic response in nerve evoked by stretching preparation from the frog's toe. Temperature 17° C. [90·11.] A. On loading with 5 g. B. 2 sec. later. C. 5 sec. later. D. Similar response recorded at high speed to show extreme regularity of the discharge. Time marker 1/5 sec. in A, B and C. Line in D represents 0·01 sec. All figures read left to right. The numbers in brackets are the reference numbers of the experiment from which the figures are taken.

neurone, viz. transecting the nerve distal to the electrodes until only one active fibre remains. Either of these methods might have been used. However, the experiments on the skin-nerve-muscle preparation suggested that a suitable preparation might be found intact in one of the tiny muscles in the frog's toe, and after some search a preparation was found which yielded responses showing a single rhythm (see Fig. 1). This preparation avoided the uncertainty of cutting nerve or muscle and when set up on the electrodes would remain in good condition for some hours.

The preparation.

The preparation consists of the small muscle on the upper outer side of the middle toe of the frog (M. ext. br. prof. dig. III): the contraction of this muscle causes extension of the toe with some flexion to the side. The nerve which supplies it is the peroneal, of which the lateral branch only is required for this preparation. The dissection presents no special difficulties, and some 500 preparations have been made. It was found that about two out of three preparations gave a single rhythmic response; of the others, sometimes more than one rhythm appeared, and sometimes no response was obtained. In the earlier experiments the tendon of the muscle was cut and a silk thread attached to it, but in the later experiments the whole muscle was freed from its neighbours and only the top end was left attached to the bone; as the nerve entered high up in the muscle this could be done without damage to it.

The evidence that a regular rhythm from a muscle receptor is the response of a single end organ has been fully gone into by Adrian and Zotterman [1926 a]. Although there is no absolute proof of this, the regularity of the discharge and the fact that it can be evoked many times successively from the same muscle preparation, leave little doubt that it is produced by a physiological unit of some sort.

There are obvious advantages in using such a single end organ preparation when investigating the discharge of impulses, rather than a preparation containing several end organs, for all the difficulties that arise in analysing a composite discharge are avoided and the smallest changes in rhythm can be followed with great accuracy. The preparation employed gives results which are exactly repeatable, for the records obtained from two similar loadings with an interval of rest between have the same rhythm at any instant after loading.

Nature of the end organ responding to stretch.

The muscles from the preparations were usually stained and examined under the microscope at the conclusion of an experiment. Various stains were used, methylene blue, gold chloride, gold chloride and osmic acid. It was usually possible to find one end organ of the type described by Cajal [1904] and classed as muscle spindles; once two were found, but never more. They have a much simpler structure in the frog than the mammal, and were never found to be supplied by more than one nerve fibre.

As it has been suggested [Denny Brown, 1928] that the mammalian muscle spindle is an organ responding to active contraction of the muscle but not to passive stretch, tests were made in two experiments to see if the end organ responding to stretch was indeed the muscle spindle. Fine threads of silk were placed round the muscle at intervals of 1–2 mm. and drawn tight successively, starting at the tendon end; the response to stretch was investigated with a pair of telephones connected to the amplifier. Tightening the first three or four threads had no effect on the response, but, as the next was drawn tight, a burst of impulses was set up and the preparation ceased to yield any response to stretch. The muscles were then stained with methylene blue and examined under the microscope. In one a muscle spindle was seen between the last thread which did not abolish the response and the one which did, and in the other a muscle spindle was found under the thread which abolished the response. No other end organs could be found in either muscle. There seems little doubt that the structure which responds to stretch and tension is the muscle spindle. In all the preparations examined it was found about the middle of the muscle.

Method.

The preparation was set up with the nerve passing into a moist chamber and over electrodes of thread dipping into U-tubes of Ringer's fluid (see Fig. 2); from these leads were taken to the amplifier by silver wires coated with silver chloride. The muscle itself was supported through the bone by a pin which stuck into the floor of a small ebonite chamber, containing about 5 c.c. of Ringer so that the muscle was completely immersed, and the thread from the tendon was led out through a slot. This thread was led over a pulley and arranged so that it could be loaded with weights or springs; for gradual loading these could be controlled by a dashpot or loading machine (see p. 96). In some experiments the preparation was enclosed in a double-walled brass box. The thread to the tendon was led out through a slot, and water could be circulated between the double walls, so that the preparation could be brought to any desired temperature. The temperature was measured by a small copper-constantan couple coated with celluloid, placed in the fluid close to the muscle, and connected to a mirror galvanometer; this enabled the temperature to be read to 0·05° C. The cold junction was immersed in water in a thermos flask.

A slow-speed camera driving Ciné Bromide paper (Kodak) at 9 or 18 cm. per sec. was used to record the oscillograph deflections, with a clock time marker showing 1/5 second. In the later experiments (115 onwards) a double camera was used, which had the advantage of being able to give simultaneous records at 4 metres and at 18 cm. per sec.

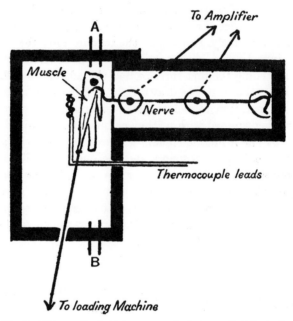

Fig. 2. Diagram to show arrangement of preparation electrodes, etc., in the moist chambers.

In this camera part of the beam of light from the oscillograph falls on a moving mirror camera such as has been described in a previous paper [Matthews, 1929 *b*], and part is diverted by prisms into a slow-speed moving paper camera. The two parts of the camera are driven by one motor through magnetic clutches and can be engaged independently.

In the earlier experiments the apparatus was not effectively shielded from a 93 cycle A.C. power main which induced currents in the leads, etc., causing regular waves at 93 per sec. to appear in some of the records. Fortunately the action currents stand out clearly from this artefact, especially when they are recorded diphasically. Further shielding has now eliminated it.

Results.

In the initial experiments a weight of 2 g. was used and the load was put on in about 1/5 sec. When the muscle is tetanized the maximum tension it develops is of the order of 10 g., so that a tension of 2 g. is such as might be expected to occur during life. The discharge reaches a maximum rate of about 120 per sec. as the load reaches its full value, and declines in the way shown in Fig. 3. Examples of typical records are shown in Fig. 1.

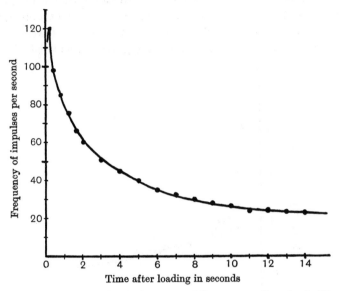

Fig. 3. Graph to show the decline in frequency of the response after a load of 2 g. is hung on the thread from the tendon. Temperature 15° C. [81·3.]

Regularity.

The regularity of the discharge is very striking. If each successive interval is measured and plotted against the number of impulses set up, and a smooth curve drawn among the points, the mean fluctuations of the points on either side of the curve are never more than 3 p.c. when the mean rate is 70 per sec. (see Fig. 4); the irregularity increases at lower frequencies and the series becomes quite irregular when the frequency has fallen below about 20 per sec.

It will be seen from Fig. 3 that the frequency reaches a maximum rate at about the same time as the stimulus and then declines steadily, the fall becoming slower towards the right, and tending to reach a steady value. Often the frequency here becomes steady for 20–30 sec., and when the frequency falls further the discharge loses its regularity and becomes a random series of impulses, though occasionally there is a tendency for impulses to drop out of an otherwise regular series, as has been noticed by Bronk [1929]. With small loads the slow random discharge goes on for some minutes, but with heavier loads the discharge stops entirely much earlier, and with very heavy loads the discharge is often completely over in a few seconds, but the latter seem to inflict permanent damage on the end organ and, after a few such loadings, there is no response. With heavy loads the irregularity sets in at a much higher frequency. A rate of about 20 per sec. seems to be the lowest at which these end organs can set up impulses in a regular series (at 15° C.). When

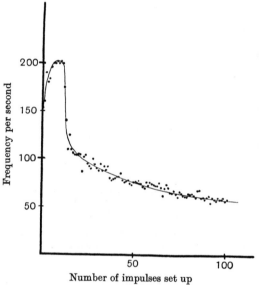

Fig. 4. Graph showing the regularity of the discharge. Each point is determined by measuring the interval between one impulse and its successor. Temperature 15° C. Sudden loading 10 g. [113·42.]

rates of less than 20 per sec. occur the impulses are irregularly spaced, but often groups of four or five impulses appear at a spacing corresponding to 20 per sec. when the mean rate has fallen to 12–14 impulses in the second.

Constancy of results.

The close agreement of successive discharges is very remarkable. If the muscle is loaded at 5-minute intervals, the discharges of impulses are so closely alike that the number of impulses set up in any fixed period, e.g. 5 sec., rarely varies from the mean by 1 p.c. The 5-minute interval between the loadings is necessary, for, as Bronk [1929] has shown, if a muscle is loaded repeatedly at very short intervals, the discharge is much reduced, which reduction he ascribed to fatigue. Loadings are, therefore, always carried out at an interval of 5 minutes or more, and after each the fluid in the muscle chamber is changed. Under these conditions records can always be repeated on any given preparation with discrepancies of only 1 or 2 p.c. For the first hour after the preparation is set up the rhythms tend to rise slightly: this may be due to the removal of harmful substances set free in the dissection, or recovery from minor injuries. After this the rhythms remain steady for a period of 3–4 hours, and then begin to vary again. Occasionally the end organ ceases to set

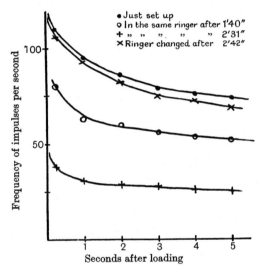

Fig. 5. Graphs showing the effect on the end organ response of keeping the preparation in the same 5 c.c. of Ringer. Temperature 15° C. [138.]

up impulses abruptly without any previous signs of failure, but whether this is due to cessation of conduction by the fibre concerned or to some sudden change in the end organ or its neighbourhood is uncertain. In these cases the muscle still responds to electrical stimulation of the nerve through the recording electrodes.

It is found that if the preparation is not irrigated frequently but kept in the same 5 c.c. of Ringer the frequency of impulses set up by a given load rises slightly in the first hour, but falls steadily throughout the next, the preparation giving no response after about 2½ hours. If the inexcitable preparation is then washed with fresh Ringer the response returns in a few minutes to its initial value. This is illustrated in Fig. 5. Bubbling air through the Ringer does not delay this onset of inexcitability; so that it seems probable that the inexcitability is the result of some product of the tissues themselves. It is interesting to compare this loss of excitability in the end organ and recovery in fresh Ringer with the reversible inexcitability of muscle studied by Dulière and Horton [1929]. Here, too, there is a rapid recovery in fresh Ringer, and the explanation suggested by them, namely, a raised potassium content in the interspace of the tissue, may account equally for the failure of the sensory end organ.

The composition of the Ringer used throughout these experiments was as follows: NaCl 0·65 p.c., NaHCO₃ 0·015 p.c., KCl 0·02 p.c., CaCl₂ 0·025 p.c.

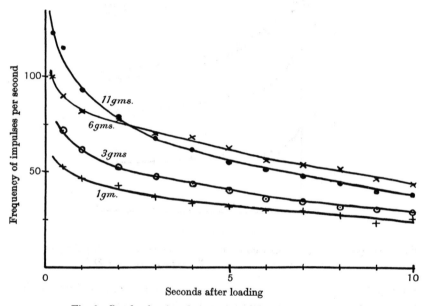

Fig. 6. Graphs showing the response evoked by various loads.
Temperature 16·5° C. [135.]

Relation of load to discharge.

Adrian and Zotterman [1926 b] have shown that, for all end organs so far investigated, the frequency of impulses set up increases with the stimulus. With this single end organ preparation it has been possible to investigate this relationship with considerable accuracy.

The discharges obtained with different loads are shown graphically in Fig. 6, and it will be seen that the curves are of the same general shape, but with the heaviest load the fall in frequency is more rapid.

If the frequency at any instant in the first 2 seconds after loading be plotted against the logarithm of the load, the points lie very nearly on a straight line; this is illustrated from two experiments in Fig. 7. It has long been held that, as a stimulus increases in geometric progression, the sensation increases in arithmetic progression (Fechner's Law). These experiments suggest that this is due in part, at least, to properties of the end organs rather than to the central interpretation of the sensory message by the brain. For a group of end organs the relation of the stimulus to the total frequency will be somewhat modified, because the stronger stimuli will affect end organs which do not respond to weak

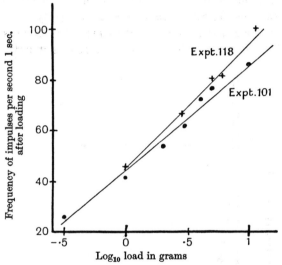

Fig. 7. Graphs showing the relationship of the frequency 1 sec. after loading to the logarithm of the load. Temperature 15° C.

stimuli. This can be seen in a muscle containing several end organs; only one end organ may respond to the small load, but as the load is increased the response of other organs appear severally. Such end organs would thus appear to have a definite threshold, and this is confirmed by the response of some single end organ preparations to small loads. A load of $\frac{1}{2}$ g. may produce a considerable response starting at 25–30 per sec. and soon becoming irregular; but a load of $\frac{1}{4}$ g. often produces no response at all, although controls show that the tension reaches the tendon. But this is only found to occur in preparations from which there is no resting discharge; when a resting discharge is present it is increased by the slightest stimulus.

Resting discharge.

Adrian and Zotterman [1926 *a*] found that the end organs in frog's muscles set up a slight discharge of impulses (3–5 per sec.) in the absence of any external tension. In the single end organs studied in this work the rate of discharge was much less, rarely above 2 per sec., and often completely absent. When present it was quite irregular. It was found to cease for 10–30 sec. after the preparation had been stimulated, thus confirming Adrian's findings. In some preparations the end organ appears to be in a no-threshold state (evidenced by the response in absence of stimulation), and in others cited above to have a definite threshold. This might be due to the way in which the end organ is situated in the muscle, rather than to some property of the organ; in some cases it being under slight deformation when there is no tension on the tendon, in others the tension not reaching it until the muscle

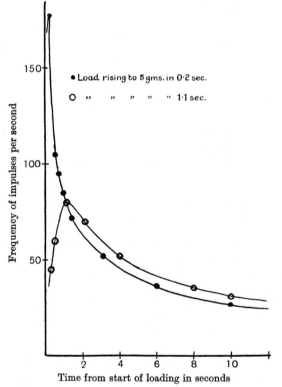

Fig. 8 A. Response evoked by loading the muscle with 5 g. in 0·2 and 1·1 sec. Temperature 19° C. [98, 12, 13, 14.]

has been slightly deformed. There is little doubt that the resting discharge originates in the same nerve fibre as the response to tension, as
it never appears superimposed on this, as might be expected were it in
an independent fibre, and moreover its absence after stimulation makes
it highly probable that it arises in the same physiological unit.

Rate of loading.

In Fig. 8 A are shown the responses recorded when a single end
organ is loaded at various rates. As might be expected, with slower
loading the frequency falls less rapidly than when the load has reached
its full value in a very short time. The degree of adaptation at any
moment after the start is therefore less with the slower loading. These
results are replotted in Fig. 8 B. Here abscissæ represent the number

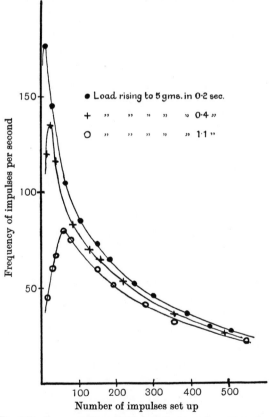

Fig. 8 B. Same results replotted against number of impulses
set up, also for loading in 0·4 sec.

of impulses set up, and it is clear that the fall in frequency of the response is not conditioned only by the number of impulses which have been discharged; after *e.g.* 200 impulses have been set up the frequency after rapid loading is greater than that with slow loading. In the first case the load is at its full value throughout the discharge, but in the second it is smaller at the beginning. It appears, therefore, that in setting up a given number of impulses the larger load produces less change in state of the end organ, and less adaptation per impulse set up. More direct evidence on this point will be presented in Part III of this paper.

It is clear from the curve of the rapid loading (Fig. 8 A) that, at the beginning of the discharge, the adaptation to the stimulus takes place very fast, so that considerable adaptation will already have taken place when the load reached its full value. Now, however great the stimulus, there must be some limit to the frequency of impulses which can be set up even before any adaptation has occurred, and in order to determine this absolute maximum frequency the loading would have to be instantaneous and very excessive, so as to constitute an invariable and maximal stimulus. If this were done the end organ should discharge at its maximum rate, and this rate should depend on its internal conditions rather than on the stimulus.

Rapid loading.

An attempt was made to load the muscle in this way by dropping a weight through about 1 cm. before letting the thread to the tendon take the load. A record of the results is shown in Pl. I, A. The decline in frequency during the first second after loading is shown graphically in Fig. 9. The initial frequency is about 240 per sec., and the fall is very rapid during the first 0·2 sec. and then slows up and becomes more and more gradual.

In these experiments the loading still took a finite time, probably about 0·01 sec., and owing to the momentum of the falling load the initial tension must have been much more than the weight of the load. This raised a doubt as to whether the initial rapid fall in frequency was caused by internal factors of the end organ, or was merely due to the fall in the stimulus after the momentum had been absorbed. For these reasons a spring-loading device was made. It consisted of a light spiral spring, which could be set to any desired tension by moving the anchorage at one end, the other being attached to a light wire hook to which the thread from the tendon was tied. The hook was held by a trigger so

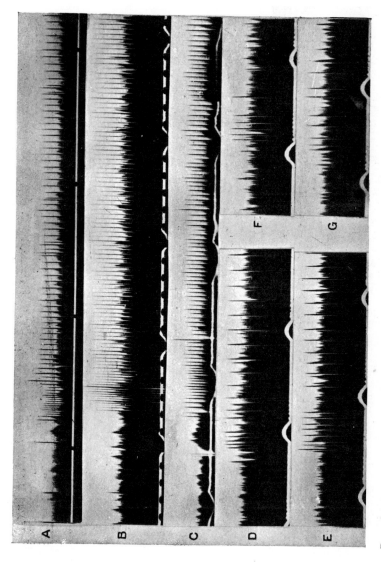

Records of responses evoked by sudden loading. A. 20 g. wt. Temperature 15° C. [82.] B. 20 g. spring. Temperature 15·4° C. [113.] C. 20 g. spring. Temperature 14·5° C. [136.] D, E. 2 g. Temperature 16° C. [105.] F, G. Response to stretch only, 2 g. 15·5° C. [190.] (D, F, rapid loading. E, G, less rapid loading.)

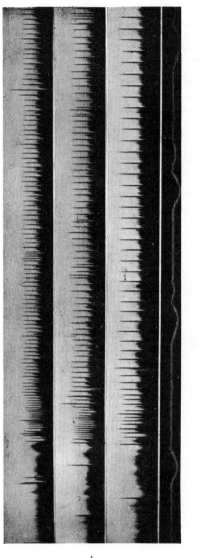

Fig. 1.

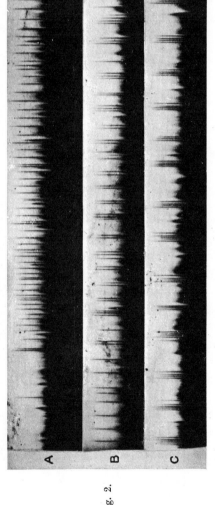

Fig. 2.

Fig. 1. Response of the same preparation at various temperatures to a tension of 20 g. applied rapidly. A. Temperature 19·8° C. [132, 6.] B. Temperature 15·0° C. [132, 7.] C. Temperature 11·0° C. [132, 8.] Time marker 1/5 sec.

Fig. 2. Response of preparation that has been kept at 24° C. in sodium chloride alone for 30 minutes. Temperature 20° C. [143.]
A. On loading. B. 2 sec. later. C. 5 sec. later. Time marker 1/5 sec.

that the thread was just taut, and on releasing the trigger the spring tension was communicated to the thread almost instantaneously. The moving parts of this apparatus weighed about 0·2 g., and tests with a tension of 20 g. showed no detectable overloading.

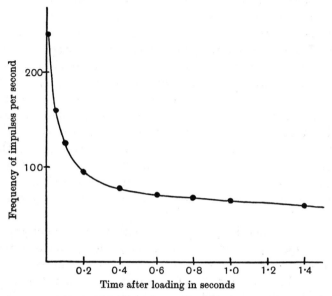

Fig. 9. Graph of response during first second after sudden loading with a large load. 100 g. Temperature 14° C. [82·2.]

With this method of loading the time-frequency curves were much the same as those previously recorded. The maximum frequency often reached 260 per sec. (at 14° C.). We must, therefore, conclude that the rapid initial fall of frequency is due to the properties of the end organ, and not to a fall in the external stimulus.

Extension and tension.

Close examination of records such as those of Pl. I, A, B and C, reveals that, with large loads, the frequency falls throughout the discharge and there is no sharp discontinuity, so that there is little doubt that the rapid initial discharge is produced by the same physiological unit as the later part of the discharge. But with small loads applied rapidly the frequency falls very abruptly after about 0·05 sec., and there is often even a slight pause in the discharge (see Pl. I, D, E). This still occurred when all possible precautions were taken to avoid initial overloading; the pulley was eliminated, and the thread made to slide over a smooth brass ring, a thread loop was substituted for the wire hook so that the moving parts of the system were reduced to a mass of 70 mg. In four preparations a brief response appeared during extension, and there was no response to continued tension (see Pl. I, F, G). The brief response in Pl. I, F, G is not unlike the initial part of the response in Pl. I, D, E, and suggests that the initial rapid response is connected with extension. Another possibility is that, owing to differences in viscosity, the initial elongation of the various elements in the muscle differs from the equilibrium attained later. Thus, if the terminal parts of the structure upon which the nerve endings are distributed were more viscous than the middle region, there would be an initial over extension of this region followed by a certain amount of contraction as the more viscous portions elongate. Or if the end organ were relatively more viscous than the surrounding muscle fibres, just after rapid loading, it would support more than its share of the load, and as it yielded the muscle fibres would take up more of the tension.

When the stimulus is large, small variations in it do not appreciably affect the frequency of impulses set up (see paragraph on load-frequency relationship), and so any effect of viscosity in causing initial overloading will be much less apparent. The fall in frequency must then depend on the internal state of the end organ, the stimulus being in effect very great throughout. It seems possible that the abrupt initial fall with small loads and the smooth fall with large loads may be accounted for in this way. In the former case the initial stimulus to the nerve ending is large, and would fall as viscous yielding occurred, leading to an abrupt fall in the frequency of response; in the latter the stimulus is very great all the time, and the smooth fall of frequency results from changes in the state of the end organ occurring progressively.

Refractory period.

Adrian [1921] gives the duration of the absolute and relative refractory periods for frog's motor nerve as 0·0025 and 0·01 sec. respectively at 16° C., and it has been shown in a previous paper [Matthews, 1929 b] that, in the frog, the fibres carrying motor impulses have similar characteristics to those carrying proprioceptor impulses, so that these values will apply to the fibre supplying the end organ. The highest frequency recorded at 16° C. is 290 per sec. In this case each impulse is set up 0·0035 sec. after its predecessor, so it is evident that, before much adaptation has occurred, a second impulse is set up in the nerve fibre very soon after the end of the absolute refractory period, and throughout the early part of the discharge with sudden loading the impulses will be travelling in incompletely recovered nerve. Gotch [1910] and Gasser and Erlanger [1925], working with electrical stimulation, have shown that impulses travelling in incompletely recovered nerve are conducted more slowly than in rested nerve, and that the absolute magnitude of the second action potential from the whole trunk is smaller than the

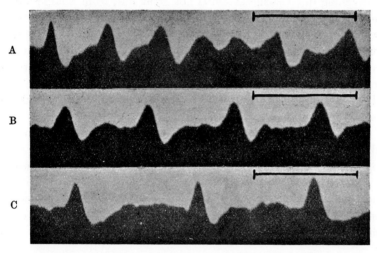

Fig. 10. High-speed records of the discharge produced by sudden application of a 20 g. spring load. A, B and C are records of the response to the same load. Temperature 14·5° C. [136.] A was taken coincident with loading; the left-hand deflection being that of the first impulse of the series. B. 2 sec. later. C. 5 sec. later. The line in each represents 0·01 sec.

first. These effects should be detectable in the early part of discharge from the end organ, although conditions are not entirely comparable, for these effects were found for the second of two impulses set up by electrical stimulation, and here a series of more than two impulses is being considered and, as Brücke [1926], Forbes [1929] and others have shown, when a nerve trunk is stimulated repeatedly there are signs of a progressive change in time relations.

High-speed records of the response to sudden application of large loads were taken (see Fig. 10). With diphasic recording there is clear evidence that the early impulses of the series are conducted more slowly than the later impulses which are not following each other at so short an interval, and all seem to be conducted more slowly than the first impulse which is travelling in fresh nerve. The rising potential gradient also appears to be less steep.

Monophasic records have also been taken after the nerve was damaged at the distal electrode by application of a drop of boiling Ringer. This always led to a reduction in the absolute magnitude of the potentials necessitating the use of more amplification, which caused a rather unsteady base line. The reduction in the potential when the impulses are travelling in close succession is not great but, from a large number of measurements, amounts to as much as 15–20 p.c. when the interval between the responses is 4σ. There is also some slowing of the rising potential gradient, but it is difficult to assess its magnitude accurately. This result is in general agreement with that obtained recently by Adrian [1930] in mammalian sensory fibres.

That the impulses are modified when travelling close behind each other shows that they are all carried by one and the same nerve fibre. And it is interesting that the diphasic records show that the impulse is conducted more slowly, and differs markedly from the first of the series, even when it occurs at an interval of 0·012 sec. after the previous one (see Fig. 10 A, C). This supports the view that recovery from each impulse of a long series may be rather different from that occurring when only two isolated impulses are considered, as in most of the published data on recovery.

Recovery curve of the nerve ending.

Adrian and Zotterman [1926 a] have fully discussed the rhythmic activity of nerve endings, and have pointed out that a regular discharge is to be expected from the general properties of excitable tissues, which after activity are at first completely inexcitable and then recover their excitability gradually. Thus, as the nerve ending recovers from the first impulse, at a certain stage in its recovery it becomes sufficiently excitable for the stimulus to re-excite it, and this leads to a rhythmic discharge of impulses. The greater the stimulus the earlier in its recovery will the nerve be excited, and so the frequency will increase with the stimulus. These authors have shown that adaptation might be the result of a fall of the excitability of the end organ leading to a decline in the effectiveness of the stimulus or to a slowing of the recovery or to both. By plotting the interval between responses against the load, they obtained a representation of the recovery curve of the end organ at a certain time after loading and, on the assumption that adaptation occurred at the same rate throughout the discharge, they deduced the recovery curve for the unadapted ending and found it very much slower than that of a nerve fibre. But they were not able to record the discharge during the first second after rapid loading owing to their base line being upset by a large deflection at the moment of loading, which they attributed to a mechanical movement of the nerve on the electrodes. In the present research this disturbance was eliminated by passing the nerve through a slot into a chamber separate from that containing the muscle (see Fig. 2), and by having the electrode nearest to the muscle connected to earth. Under these conditions it has always been possible to see every impulse right from the start without any serious disturbance (see Pl. I).

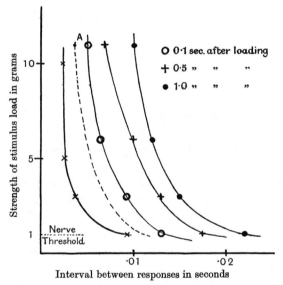

Fig. 11. Recovery curves of end organ at various intervals after loading (15° C.). The left-hand curve is the recovery curve of a nerve fibre at 15° C. plotted to the same time scale determined by the method of muscular summation.

The experimental findings failed to confirm Adrian and Zotterman's assumption, for, as has been shown in a previous section, just after loading adaptation occurs very rapidly and, before it has occurred to any extent, the interval between the impulses is only slightly longer than the absolute refractory period of the nerve fibre.

In Fig. 11 are plotted the strength of stimulus and interval between response for a single end organ 1·0, 0·5 and 0·1 sec. after loading; one point is also given for the interval 0·05 sec. after loading. It has been pointed out above that, with small loads, it is possible that viscous overloading occurs, so that the points for the small loads just after loading are uncertain, as the end organ may be sustaining a greater fraction of the load at the start. With the large loads, however, this has little effect on the response, and so the values are reliable and the recovery curve 0·05 sec. after loading must pass through the point A. If the curve obtained 1 sec. after loading is reconstructed through this point, we shall probably obtain a tolerably accurate representation of the recovery curve of the end organ that has been loaded for 0·05 sec. The recovery curve of the motor fibres of the frog's sciatic is shown on the same time scale. This suggests that the nerve fibre and ending have very similar characteristics, and that before adaptation occurs the recovery of the two may even have identical time relations.

DISCUSSION.

The most surprising of the above observations is that the end organ is able to respond at such a high rate initially. The rhythmic responses that have been recorded range from 260 down to about 20 per sec. (at 15° C.). If these rhythms are due to the return of excitability in one and the same structure in the way discussed above, we must conclude that the return of full excitability takes at least thirteen times as long as the first return of excitability. In the nerve fibre it takes about 10 times as long; but there is another possibility that must be considered in this connection. It will be seen from Fig. 9 that, with rapid loading, the response starts at such a rate that the impulses are separated by little more than the refractory period of the nerve fibre, and that the frequency falls rapidly until the impulses are separated by about the interval necessary for complete recovery of the nerve fibre, and thereafter falls slowly. These facts suggest that, with very intense stimuli applied suddenly, a continuous instead of a rhythmic state of excitation may be produced in the end organ, and that this sets up an impulse in the proximal part of the nerve fibre whenever the latter has recovered sufficiently and that, at a later stage, the response of the end organ becomes rhythmic and gives the lower frequencies which appear.

If the higher initial rates are, in fact, produced by continuous instead of intermittent activity in the end organ, it is clear that this can have no absolute refractory period at all. The chief argument against this view is the absence of any discontinuity in the curve with large stimuli, but an injured region in a sensory nerve fibre can certainly act as a continuous stimulus to the neighbouring intact fibre [Adrian, 1930], and the initial disorganization produced by the rapid extension of the end organ may cause it to behave temporarily as a region of continuous activity. This disorganization caused by rapid stretch might be comparable to that which Gasser and Hill [1924] found to occur in muscle fibres if they were rapidly stretched while contracting.

That some sort of continuous activity can occur in the end organs will be shown in Part II of this paper, where experiments are cited in

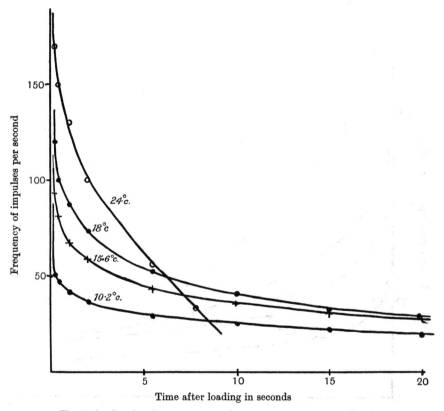

Fig. 12 A. Graphs of response at various temperatures to a load of 2 g.

which an end organ under abnormal conditions is found to set up groups of impulses following each other at a high frequency, the groups occurring at rates of 20–50 per sec. and strongly suggesting the presence of two rhythmic structures having different time relations, one presumably being the nerve fibre and the other some modified part of it in the end organ.

PART II.

FACTORS AFFECTING THE RESPONSE TO STIMULATION.

Temperature.

When the temperature of the preparation was altered the response changed very markedly; records from a typical experiment are shown in Pl. II, fig. 1, and discharges are shown graphically in Fig. 12 A.

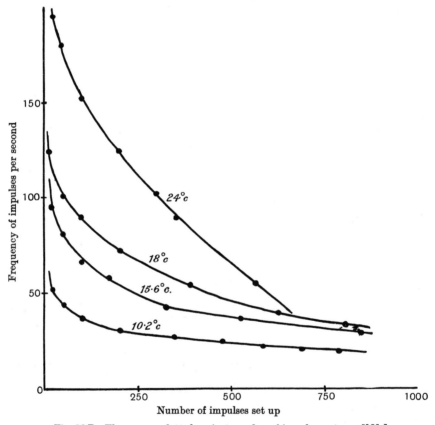

Fig. 12 B. The same replotted against number of impulses set up. [131.]

A rise in temperature caused a large increase in the initial frequency of impulses set up for a given stimulus, but the response declines much more rapidly, and at the higher temperatures became more and more brief, but for the same stimulus the number of impulses set up since the start at any instant is much greater than at lower temperatures, and the whole change in the response might be due to a more rapid recovery after each impulse, and not to any change in the process which constitutes adaptation, for if this was partly the result of the setting up of impulses the more rapidly they were set up the faster would adaptation occur. The results shown in Fig. 12 A are therefore replotted in Fig. 12 B with the number of impulses set up, as ordinates. The fall of frequency is still greatest at the higher temperatures, and so evidently adaptation is accelerated by the rise of temperature; but clearly by these methods it is impossible to dissociate the effect of temperature on the recovery after each impulse, and on the process of adaptation, and so no numerical measure of the effect of temperature on adaptation can be obtained.

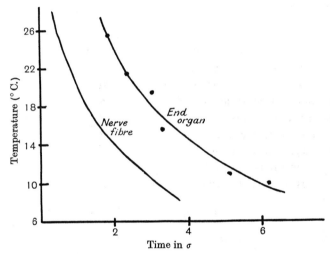

Fig. 13. Graph showing the effect of temperature on the least interval between impulses recorded from the end organ and also on the absolute refractory period of a nerve trunk.

Temperature and refractory period.

Experiments were made to see if the maximum frequency of impulses which the ending set up varied with temperature in the same way as does the refractory period of a nerve fibre. The results of such an experiment are shown in Fig. 13, in which the temperature is plotted against the interval between the responses 0·05 sec., after sudden application of a large spring load. The left-hand curve shows the effect of temperature on the absolute refractory period of a frog's sciatic nerve. The data are those of Amberson [1930] which he has shown are in general agreement with the results of other researches on this point. His method, that of measuring the least separation between two stimuli that gives rise to a greater total action current than the first alone, will give the refractory period of the fibres which recover most rapidly, but Erlanger, Gasser and Bishop [1927] have shown that the fibres of a mixed nerve trunk differ little in their absolute refractory periods, so that for the fibres with which we are concerned here the temperature-refractory period curve will be approximately that shown.

From these considerations it is evident that, throughout this range of temperature, tension on the muscle can re-excite the nerve fibre soon after its absolute refractory period is over. It was suggested in Part I that the initial rapid part of the discharge might result from the end organ being in a continuous state of excitation, and the rhythm then depending on the recovery of the nerve fibre. The similarity of the effect of temperature on the refractory period of the nerve and the least interval between the responses to tension certainly fits in with this view; if continuous excitation can take place, the highest frequencies will always be determined by the fibre rather than the end organ. On the other hand, if continuous excitation does not occur, we must conclude that the absolute refractory period of the end organ is of the same order as that of the nerve fibre, and is affected by temperature in much the same way. Owing to the probable change in adaptation rate with the temperature it is impossible to say whether the temperature coefficient of recovery remains the same for low as for high frequencies of discharge.

The effects of ions.

It was found that the nerve ending was very sensitive to changes in the ions present in the Ringer in which it was immersed. Experiments were made to investigate the effects of the common ions separately, and together.

The following solutions were used:

			p.c.		p.c.
(1)	Ringer	NaCl	0·65	NaHCO$_3$	0·015
		KCl	0·02	CaCl$_2$	0·025
(2)	Na ion	NaCl	0·75	—	—
(3)	Na and K ions	NaCl	0·75	KCl	0·037
(4)	Na and Ca ions	NaCl	0·75	CaCl$_2$	0·025

There is no great difference in the anion content of these solutions, so that differences in their effects must be attributed to the metallic ions. It was found that slight variations occurred, using solutions more or less concentrated, but these were quite insignificant in comparison with the differences that occurred when any of the cations was present or absent. The effect of changes in the latter are very striking, and begin to appear 2 or 3 minutes after the change has been made in the fluid bathing the muscle.

In all the experiments records were first taken from the preparation in Ringer, then the irrigating fluid was changed and records were taken

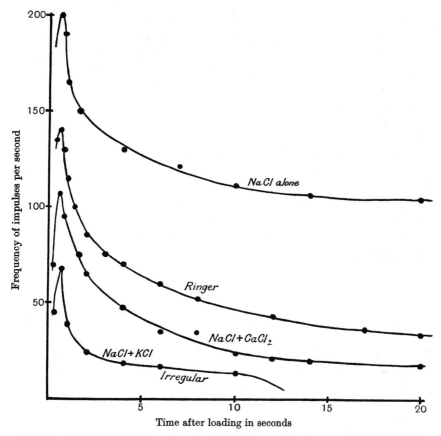

Fig. 14. Graphs showing the response of an end organ when the muscle is loaded with 5 g. in fluids of various ionic compositions. Temperature 17° C. [92.]

every 5 minutes to follow any change that occurred in the response. After each record the preparation was irrigated with the solution which was being examined. At the conclusion the preparation was again irrigated with Ringer, and records were taken for a further half-hour to see if the response would return to its original value or whether irreversible changes had taken place.

The results of a typical experiment are shown graphically in Fig. 14. The results of experiments on nine preparations were in complete agreement with each other and may be summarized as follows:

1. When Ringer is replaced by a solution containing only sodium chloride and potassium chloride.

(a) The discharge soon becomes small.

(b) A considerable resting discharge appears (15–16 per sec.).

(c) The discharge becomes irregular at a higher frequency than usual.

(d) The depression rapidly proceeds to extinction of the discharge, after about 40 minutes the preparation becomes inexcitable and unless transferred to Ringer at once fails to recover at all; in any case recovery is never complete.

2. When Ringer is replaced by a solution containing only sodium chloride and calcium chloride.

(a) The discharge is slowly depressed.

(b) A considerable resting discharge is present (4–12 per sec.).

(c) The discharge is very regular even at low frequencies (10 per sec.).

(d) Complete inexcitability is not reached in 2 hours, and preparation has never failed to recover in Ringer.

3. When Ringer is replaced with a solution containing sodium chloride only.

(a) The discharge increases rapidly, and reaches a steady state in about $1\frac{1}{2}$ hours.

(b) A resting discharge of 2–6 per sec. appears.

(c) After loading the discharge falls in about 10 sec. to a steady very rapid discharge which continues for some minutes. It only falls very slowly and becomes irregular when the frequency has fallen to about 85 per sec. This irregular discharge continues at a rate of about 60 per sec. for 10–30 minutes, the frequency falling very slightly.

(d) The preparation returns to normal in a few minutes when replaced in Ringer.

It will be seen that potassium and calcium are apparently antagonistic, for if either is absent from the Ringer the discharge is much depressed, but if both are absent the discharge is enormously increased. Thus, if we start with the end organ in sodium alone and add either sodium or potassium the response is rapidly suppressed, but if both are added the resulting depression is very much less and the preparation soon comes to a steady state. We must, therefore, conclude that potassium and calcium each partially neutralize the depression caused by the other. This is further supported by the observation that the resting discharge which is small in sodium alone becomes large if either potassium or calcium are added, but disappears if both are added.

Calcium unopposed by potassium merely has a depressing action, but potassium unopposed by calcium has a further toxic effect; for if the preparation is left without calcium for some time, it fails to recover when calcium is replaced, but after potassium has been absent for some time recovery occurs when it is replaced. So that it seems that the action of calcium is depressant only, while potassium has in addition a toxic action. The increased resting discharge in NaCl + CaCl or NaCl + KCl suggests that the excitability is above normal, and if this is so the depression of the response to loading by calcium or potassium, when added to sodium chloride, cannot be attributed to lowered excitability, but must rather be due to alterations in the adaptation and rhythmicity.

It will be seen in Fig. 14 that when only sodium is present the discharge maintains a very high rate. This cannot be due to increased excitability alone, for however great the stimulus given to an end organ in Ringer, a discharge of this type does not occur. It is possible to produce a high initial frequency with large loads, but the frequency falls in a few seconds to far less than that which is maintained for minutes by the same end organ in sodium alone. There must, therefore, be in addition a large change in the course of adaptation. Further information on this can be obtained from the records of the response of the same end organ to various loads in Ringer and in sodium alone (see Fig. 15 A, B). It will be seen that the earlier parts of the discharges evoked by a load of 1 g. do not differ materially, but that the frequency is maintained at a higher level in sodium alone. There does not here appear to be much alteration in excitability. But with heavier loads applied slowly the whole response is of higher frequency when the end organ is in sodium alone, but if the load is applied rapidly the differences in the early part of the discharge are not very great. It seems that in sodium alone the course of adaptation is delayed, and this delay is most marked when the end organ is being "worked hard." In Part III more direct evidence will be brought forward that the increased response in sodium is due partly, if not entirely, to an increase in the rate of a process which antagonizes adaptation.

In a preceding section it has been noted that a strong stimulus is able to re-excite the nerve fibre soon after its absolute refractory period is over. The great increase in the discharge in sodium suggested that the maximum rate of discharge might also be greater, and experiments were made to investigate this point. It was found that the maximum frequencies produced by sudden loading with large spring loads were only slightly greater in sodium alone than in Ringer throughout the range of temperature investigated. That the greatest initial frequency

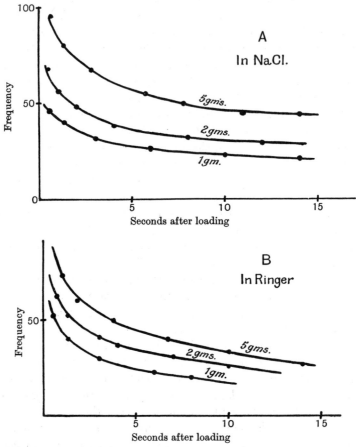

Fig. 15. Response of an end organ to various loads. Temperature 15·7° C. [101.]
A. In sodium chloride alone. B. In Ringer.

is little higher in sodium makes it very probable that the limit is set by a structure, the absolute refractory period of which is little affected by the absence of potassium and sodium.

Grouped impulses.

It is found that if the end organ preparation is kept at about 25° C. in sodium chloride alone for some time a discharge of a most striking type develops, and once it has developed remains until the temperature is lowered below 18° C. This is illustrated in Pl. II, fig. 2. When the preparation is loaded the discharge starts rhythmically in the normal manner, but when the frequency has fallen to 50 per sec. the impulses begin to occur in pairs instead of singly, and as the rhythm slows further the impulses appear in groups of three, four and five, separated from one another by time intervals of 2–5σ. This discharge continues for about a minute, the rhythm becomes slower, and the groups a little longer. The regular evolution of this type of discharge and the high rate at which the groups appear rule out the possibility of their being due to twitching of the muscle fibres. This muscle only gave occasional twitches in NaCl.

These grouped discharges show a remarkable resemblance to those Adrian [1930] has found to occur in mammalian sensory nerves, and suggest that the two have a common origin in fundamental properties of end organs and nerve fibres.

This type of discharge has only been met with under somewhat abnormal conditions, and probably never occurs in the living frog; but nevertheless it is extremely interesting in the light it throws on the end organ. The rhythm of the groups' response is quite normal, and is presumably determined by the recovery of the end organ. To what then are the groups due? The short interval between the impulses in the groups suggests that this rapid rate is connected with the return of excitability in the nerve fibre. It is suggested that, under the conditions existing here, the end organ is rhythmically producing a state of excitation, but that this state of excitation lasts abnormally long so that the nerve responds again to the state of excitation as soon as it has recovered sufficient excitability. At the beginning of the discharge only one impulse is set up at each excitation, so we must conclude that, as adaptation takes place, the duration of the excitatory state increases as the discharge of the end organ becomes slower. It has been suggested in Part I of this paper that the rapid rate of the first part of the response to rapid loading may be due to the rhythmic properties of the nerve fibre rather than the nerve ending, and these dual discharges increase the probability of this being the true explanation. Spontaneous rhythmic discharges of groups of impulses have also been observed at temperatures of 22° C. and over in Ringer, but it has not been possible to obtain them with certainty; for the present their discussion has been omitted.

Effects of an electric current.

Since the end organ is very sensitive to the ionic composition of the fluid round it, it seemed worth while to see how it would be affected by the passage of an electric current through it. We know so little of the site of the structures where the rhythm of the end organ originates that it is impossible to orientate a flow of current with respect to their arrangement, but it is possible to send a current through the muscle and see whether the response is affected by it and depends on its direction. The non-polarizable electrodes A, B (Fig. 2) were connected through a reversing switch in series with a battery, rheostat and milliameter,

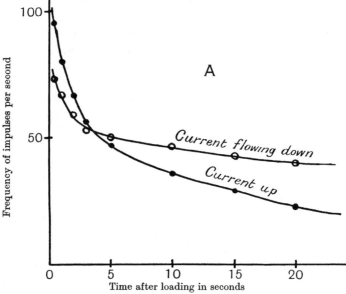

Fig. 16 A, B, C. Effect of current flow through the muscle on the response of the end organ to a load of 5 g. Current 7 m.a. Temperature 15·4° C. [140.] A. The current was turned on 5 sec. before loading.

so that currents could be sent through the tissue in either direction. The currents used were only a few milliamps and, as the cross-section of the chamber was some ten times that of the muscle, the currents in the muscle itself were very small, and were not sufficient to make the muscle twitch when they were started or stopped. There was some current escape into the recording electrodes but only at the moment of make or break, and this did not seriously interfere with the record of the sensory impulses.

The effect of a current flowing up or down the muscle is shown in Fig. 16 A; the current was switched on 5 sec. before loading and left on throughout the discharge. The flow is said to be up when the tendon end of the muscle is connected to the positive pole of the battery, and down when it is connected to the negative pole. The first part of the discharge is affected very little by a flow of current, but afterwards,

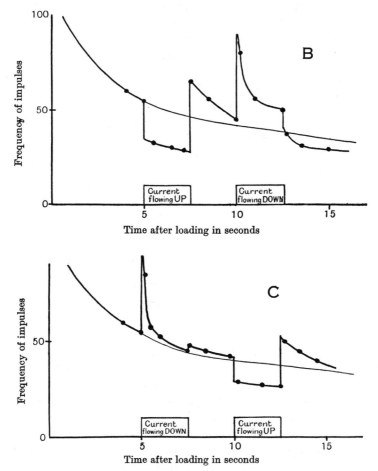

Fig. 16 B, C. Muscle was first loaded and the current turned on at the points indicated. Temperature 16·5° C. [139.]

when the current is flowing up, the frequency falls more rapidly than when it is flowing down. This occurred in all of five preparations on which it was tried. With the current flowing down the muscle the response continued regularly for 3 minutes, but with the current reversed the discharge fell much more rapidly and became irregular after 30 sec., and ceased entirely about 1 minute after loading. With the current flowing up adaptation is more rapid than with no current, when flowing down it is less rapid.

The effects of current flow through the muscle are more striking if the current is turned on after the muscle has been loaded. The results of experiments in which this was done are shown in Fig. 16 B, C. Again, it will be seen that an upward flowing current reduced the response whilst it is increased when the current flows down.

Hydrogen-ion concentration.

Experiments made to discover if the end organ response was influenced by the pH of the Ringer bathing it. Buffered solutions were made up in the way described by Mines [1913], using borate and acetate mixtures, and their approximate pH determined with indicators. The discharges from the end organ were recorded when it was irrigated with Ringer of pH 8·7, 7·3 and 6·0, but it was found that any of the solutions produced a gradual reduction of the response, which seemed to occur at about the same rate with all these H-ion concentrations. This depressing action of the buffer solutions made it impossible to determine the effect of the pH with certainty. There did not seem to be any great difference in the action of the solutions of different pH, but clearly further experiments are required to determine this, using buffers that do not themselves influence the response. These have not yet been undertaken.

Hydrocyanic acid.

The effect of irrigating the single end organ preparation with 0·05 p.c. hydrocyanic acid was to cause a slight increase in the discharge, which was rapidly followed by depression of the response and complete extinction in about 30 minutes. The results of a typical experiment are shown in Fig. 17. It will be seen that the discharge becomes more and more brief. The response never returned even if the preparation was irrigated with Ringer alone before the response had completely disappeared, but under these circumstances it continued to respond to loading with a very brief discharge of moderate frequency for an hour or more. It is interesting to compare these results with those of Bronk [1929], who found that if a muscle was placed in nitrogen the response from its receptors to tension was depressed in much the same way; the discharge became more and more brief, but complete recovery took place when the oxygen was re-admitted to the muscle. The general action of hydrocyanic acid on living cells is to destroy some link in the oxygen utilizing mechanism, and so these results confirm those of Bronk in showing that the continued action of the end organ is dependent on some oxidative process.

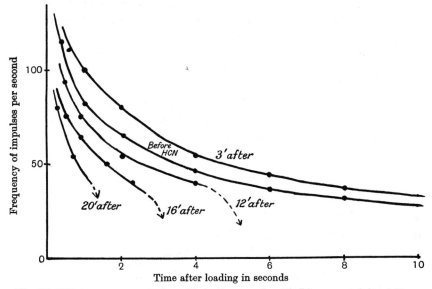

Fig. 17. Effect on response to 2 g. of irrigating muscle with Ringer containing 0·05 p.c. hydrocyanic acid. Temperature 19° C. [98.]

PART III.

THE MECHANISM OF ADAPTATION.

The records obtained by Adrian and Zotterman [1926 *b*] on the cat's pressure receptors and by Bronk [1929] on the tension receptors of the frog's muscle seem to indicate that the adapted state passes off very rapidly when the stimulus is withdrawn, for after a rest of 1 sec. a renewal of the stimulus gives nearly the same maximum frequency as in the fresh preparation, and the frequency after 5 sec. stimulation is also not greatly reduced. But an analysis of the response of the single ending to repeated loading shows that there is a considerable after effect which appears after a few seconds of loading and disappears in a few seconds after unloading, and is therefore quite distinct from the fatigue process studied by Bronk, which took a minute or more to appear and many minutes to disappear completely. This transient depression of the response after loading is thus an adaptation remainder rather than a true fatigue. The evidence of this adaptation remainder is that, when the preparation is reloaded after a few seconds' rest, the initial high frequency falls off much more rapidly, reaching the low value (which Bronk speaks of as the plateau) in a shorter time (see Fig. 18). So although the capacity to respond initially at a high rate returns very rapidly on cessation of the stimulus, the capacity to maintain the discharge at a high rate does not return so rapidly. The total number of impulses set up by a given period of stimulation will be smaller than in the fresh preparation, and in this sense the adaptation passes off relatively slowly.

So clearly in investigating the state of the end organ, we must consider not only the frequency of impulses set up at the beginning but also the maintenance of this frequency. If we judge the state of the end

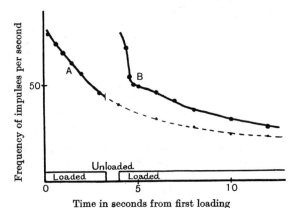

Fig. 18. Response of fresh end organ *A* compared with that from the same end organ after 3·3 sec. of loading and 0·7 sec. of rest *B*. Temperature 16° C. Load 2 g. [104.]

organ by the number of impulses it sets up in a given time of fairly long duration, we obtain a measure of adaptation which takes into account not only frequency at any instant, but also its maintenance and the "adaptation remainder" referred to above. It has been possible in this way to map out the course of the development of the adapted state, and of the recovery from it.

Disappearance of adaptation.

The preparation was loaded with a small weight (2–5 g.), and after 5 sec. the weight was raised and then lowered again after varying intervals. These were determined to 0·02 sec. by an automatic loading machine.

The thread from the tendon was led over a small pulley and tied to one end of a light aluminium lever to which the loading weight was also attached. As long as the other end of the lever was depressed the weight was supported by the lever, but when this was released the thread supported the load. This end of the lever was depressed by a cam, and when the latter was rotated half a turn the lever was free to rise, and the other end fell until the thread from the tendon supported the load. Thus rotation of the cam caused loading and unloading to occur alternately every half revolution. The cam was driven from a gramophone motor through a magnetic clutch, and the current to the latter was controlled by a timing plate, consisting of a large metal disc rotated by the gramophone motor every 5 sec. In the rim were sixty equidistant holes in which pins could be inserted to make contact with a brush which closed the circuit of the magnetic clutch for just long enough for the cam to make one half revolution. Thus if the cam was placed to depress the lever and lift the load, and three pins were inserted in the timing disc, the first caused the cam to make half a revolution, thus loading the muscle, the second caused unloading, and the third reloading. By varying the positions of the pins these operations could be carried out at any predetermined instants.

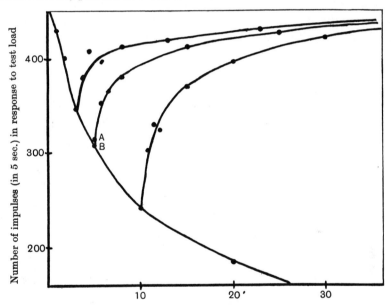

Time in seconds from start of first loading to start of test load

Fig. 19. Number of impulses set up in 5 sec. when a test load is applied after various periods of loading and rest. Temperature 15·2. Load 5 g. throughout. [141.]
    The falling curve shows the fall in response to the test load when it is applied immediately on unloading after various durations of initial load.
    The rising curves show how this response rises again when the muscle is unloaded for varying rest intervals after 2·9, 5, and 10 seconds' loading.

The number of impulses set up in the first 5 sec. after reloading was counted in the photographic record of the discharge, and compared with the number set up when the same load is applied to the resting end organ. By this method the comparison is between the effect of extension and 5 sec. tension on resting end organ and adapted end organ, differences in the responses can only be due to differences in the state of the end organ when the second (test) loading was carried out. By measuring the response to a test load it is possible to obtain a quantity which represents the end organ's capacity to set up and maintain a discharge of impulses in response to a fixed load, and it is assumed that the smaller the response to the test load the greater the adaptation of the end organ, and that the response to the test load and the adaptation are related quantitatively.

In Fig. 19 the falling curve shows the number of impulses set up by the end organ in response to the test load when it is applied later and later after the first loading (the first load is raised just before the test load is applied). The capacity of the end organ to respond becomes progressively less as the first loading is prolonged, but the fall is most rapid at first and becomes slower as the fall progresses.

If now the end organ is given longer periods of rest before the test load is applied, the return of the end organ to the resting state can be mapped out in the same way. An illustrative protocol of a typical experiment is given in Table I: the results are those shown graphically in

TABLE I. Exp. 141. Temp. 16·5° C. Load 5 g. throughout.

Number	Time	Interval in sec. between first loading and unloading	Interval in sec. between first loading and reloading	No. of impulses set up by first loading in 5 sec. Mean 450	No. of impulses set up by test (2nd) loading in 5 sec.
1	3.11	10·0	10·8	457	302
2	3.16	2·9	3·7	—	380
4	3.26	5·0	5·8	448	352
5	3.31	10·0	15·0	453	370
7	3.40	2·9	7·9	—	413
9	3.55	10·0	20·0	453	396
10	4.3	2·9	12·9	—	420
12	4.13	5·0	15·0	455	414
13	4.19	10·0	10·2	452	242
14	4.24	2·9	3·1	—	346
15	4.32	5·0	5·2	454	307
16	4.37	10·0	12·1	451	325
17	4.43	2·9	5·9	—	396
18	4.54	5·0	7·9	448	380
19	5.0	10·0	30·0	447	422
20	5.6	2·9	22·9	—	430
21	5.12	5·0	25·0	448	428
22	5.20	10·0	11·65	446	330
23	5.25	2·9	4·5	—	408
24	5.32	5·0	6·65	445	365
25	5.39	0·9	1·1	—	429
26	5.46	20·0	20·2	447	184
28	5.56	5·0	5·2	446	311
29	6.2	1·75	1·95	—	400

Fig. 19, the falling curve shows the fall in the response to the test load; the rising curves show how the response returns towards normal when the preparation is left unloaded after three durations of first load (complete recovery after 5 sec. loading takes about 1 minute). The general reliability of the determinations shown in Fig. 19 is well illustrated by the points *A* and *B*, which are readings of the same point taken near the beginning and end of the experiment. Between them some $1\frac{1}{2}$ hours and fourteen loadings intervened.

Thus activity on the part of the end organ leads to a state of depressed rhythmicity, which gradually passes off during rest. The organ is, however, still able to set up impulses at nearly as high a rate as the resting organ if the stimulus is increased or renewed.

It was mentioned in a previous section that when a muscle was loaded, unloaded, and immediately reloaded, the frequency rose to almost its initial value. In some preparations the rise on reloading was much less marked than in others, and in these when reloading was carried out immediately after unloading the frequency did not rise at all except for one or two irregular impulses at the start. If reloading was carried out very rapidly there was a much more definite rise. The results of a typical experiment in which little rise occurred on immediate reloading are shown graphically in Fig. 20. The left-hand curve represents the response to the initial loading, the other curves represent the discharges produced by reloading later and later after unloading. The first is a smooth curve, but the later curves are obviously not smooth. A large number of points were taken from the records to construct these curves, so that the irregularities of the records might be fully represented. It is clear that the irregularities in the curves are due to physiological variations and are far outside the experimental error, moreover the trough in the curve shows a certain regularity in the different records if the curves are placed below each other with the instants of reloading superimposed as in Fig. 20 B. The trough in the curve shows that about 1 sec. after reloading there is a pause in the adaptation of the end organ; its possible significance will be discussed later. This phenomenon was found in many (sixteen) preparations, though seldom as clearly marked as in the experiment cited. The slight inflexion in Fig. 18, curve *B*, is typical of a number of experiments.

In the experiment illustrated in Fig. 20 there was very little rise in frequency just after reloading if this was effected soon after unloading; this was not always the case. The discharges shown in Fig. 18 are typical of a larger number of experiments. In most preparations the capacity to respond initially at a high rate returned on unloading much more rapidly than the capacity to maintain the discharge at a high rate.

In Part II it was pointed out what an enormous change occurs in the discharge of an end organ when it is irrigated with sodium chloride alone.

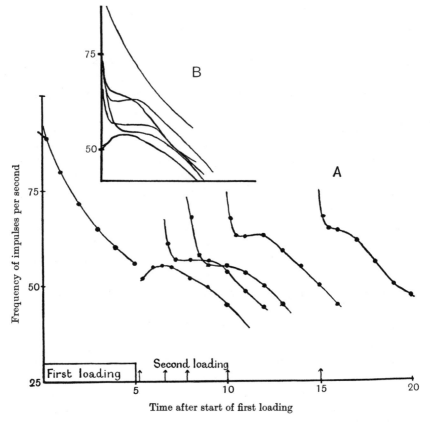

Fig. 20. Response of end organ to test load when applied later and later after the end of 5 sec. loading. Inset: same curves with the moment of loading superimposed. Load 5 g. Temperature 15° C. [135.]

The recovery of an end organ from the adapted state in Ringer and sodium chloride has been mapped out on several preparations, and it is found that the end organ returns to the resting state very much more rapidly in sodium chloride. The results of a typical experiment are shown in Fig. 21: ordinates represent the number of impulses set up in response to the test load in the 5 sec. following reloading. It will be seen that in sodium chloride the end organ has returned nearly to the resting condition after 4 sec., whereas in Ringer about 10 sec. is necessary for a comparable recovery.

The great increase of the response in sodium chloride, and the cessation of the fall of frequency after about 10 sec., is therefore due in part if not wholly to an acceleration of the process which causes the organ to recover from adaptation. The response of the same organ to different loads in Ringer and sodium chloride is illustrated in Fig. 15. It will be seen that the response to the small loads is not very different in

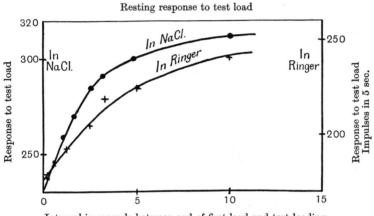

Fig. 21. Disappearance of adaptation in Ringer and sodium chloride solutions.
Load 2 g. Temperature 16° C. [111.]

the two fluids, but that with the heavier loads the discharge is maintained at a much higher level in sodium chloride. Thus the recovery from the adapted state is nearly as fast in Ringer when the adaptation and recovery are small, but when they are large (with the heavier loads) the recovery from adaptation is less rapid in Ringer than in sodium chloride.

Rate of recovery.

It has been shown above that, as adaptation progresses, the rate of recovery from the adapted state increases (see Fig. 19). Experiments were made to determine the course of the change in the recovery rate. This can be done by finding the difference between the responses to reloading immediately after unloading and also after a rest of 1 sec. The difference gives a measure of the recovery that has occurred in the 1 sec. rest, and by placing the unloading and reloading later and later after the initial loading, a series of values can be obtained representing the recovery rate when more and more adaptation has occurred. The results from such an experiment are shown in Fig. 22. It will be seen that after about 10 sec. loading the recovery in Ringer tends to reach a steady maximum rate. It has already been shown that, after irrigation with sodium chloride alone, recovery takes place more rapidly. It was found that after the preparation had been irrigated with sodium chloride for 1½ hours the initial recovery rate throughout the discharge was much

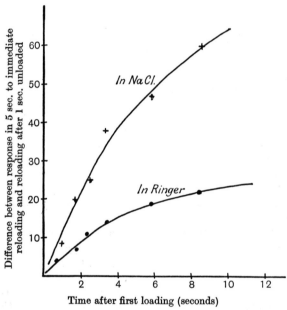

Fig. 22. Rate of recovery in Ringer and sodium chloride. Abscissæ difference between the number of impulses set up in 5 sec. if preparation is reloaded immediately or after 1 sec. of rest. Ordinates time after start of the first load when the test is made. Load 4 g. Temperature 16° C. [112, 113.]

increased (see Fig. 22), and this supports the view expressed above that the increased discharge in sodium chloride is largely a result of an increased recovery rate preventing the nerve ending from becoming as much adapted as it does in Ringer.

Adaptation and load.

By these methods it is possible to map out the course of adaptation when varying loads are applied to the muscle. A weight is applied to the thread from the tendon, and after an interval is lifted and immediately

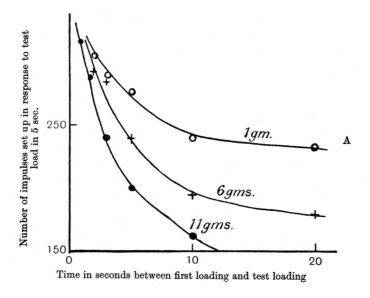

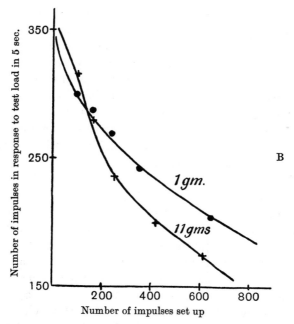

Fig. 23. Adaptation to various loads measured by the response to a test load of 11 g. A. Response to test load plotted against duration of first loading. B. Ditto against number of impulses set up during first loading. Temperature 16·5° C. [135.]

replaced by the test load; the resulting response will depend on the state of the end organ at the instant of reloading. In this way a measure of the adaptation is obtained; by altering the first load, and the time when it is replaced by the test load, the course of adaptation to various loads is determined. The results of such determinations are shown in Fig. 23 A. As might be expected, adaptation occurs much more rapidly with large loads; the larger load sets up a much greater number of impulses in a given instant of time. For this reason the figures are replotted in Fig. 23 B against the number of impulses that have been set up by the first load. It will be seen that at first the curves for small loads fall most rapidly, but are later overtaken by those of the larger loads. Thus, at the beginning, the large loads set up more impulses for the same change in state of the end organ than do the small loads, so that there is less adaptation per impulse, and this has always been found to occur in a number of experiments in which this point has been investigated.

Test load.

In all the above experiments the test load was equal to or greater than the largest initial load used. The reason for this was that if a small test load was applied after a large initial load the small load produced very little or no response in the first 5 sec. after its application, and only later did impulses appear, so the method cannot be used in these cases.

It is evident from this that a definite threshold which is absent from the resting end organ (evidenced by the resting discharge in the absence of any stimulus) appears and increases with adaptation, so that loads which produce a discharge from the resting end organ are sub-threshold when applied to the adapted end organ. Thus with adaptation the excitability of the end organ falls.

DISCUSSION.

It has been shown that the end organ has a maximum power of setting up impulses when resting and that, during stimulation, in proportion to the stimulus and time it has been acting, this power is reduced and returns when the stimulus ceases or is reduced. Bronk [1929] has shown that these end organs undergo fatigue which is greatly increased in the absence of oxygen, and we must here consider why the processes which are investigated in this paper are classed as adaptation rather than fatigue. The fall of response which Bronk investigated, and which was affected by the presence or absence of oxygen, only appeared after some minutes of activity, and took many minutes to disappear, whereas the process considered in this paper began to appear in the first second of activity and the end organ returned to very nearly its resting state in a few seconds. From his experiments on the response in oxygen and nitrogen Bronk concluded that the initial fall of frequency must be ascribed to causes other than fatigue. He says: "It has been pointed out that the rapid decline in impulse frequency described as adaptation may be due to different causes from those producing the decease in activity which results from prolonged stimulation. The experiments described show that the later, or fatigue effect, is greatly increased by lack of oxygen, whereas the former seems to be little modified thereby— all of the experiments show that an unfatigued muscle adapts about as rapidly in pure oxygen as in nitrogen." So that it is probable that the initial fall of frequency and development of the adaptation remainder is not influenced by the presence or absence of oxygen, and is quite distinct from fatigue. It has been shown that the development and disappearance of the adaptation remainder are greatly influenced by the ionic composition of the fluid in which the preparation is immersed. It is difficult to see why this should occur if the adaptation remainder was the result of fatigue.

The end organ has a potential store of impulses which is used up during stimulation and replaced during rest, and it is probable that this restoration is not immediately dependent on oxygen, though Bronk's [1929] work and the observations on hydrocyanic acid quoted above show that the whole process is ultimately dependent on changes of an oxidative character. What then are the changes underlying adaptation which are responsible for the fall in the end organ's power to respond? It is generally supposed that the occurrence of an impulse in a nerve (or muscle) fibre is due to the breakdown of a polarized surface, and the resulting passage of ions from the interior of the fibre. During the period immediately following the impulse the surface reverts to the polarized, impermeable state. An electric stimulus acts because it can depolarize the fibre, and a mechanical stimulus presumably has the same effect because it causes a momentary (or permanent) disintegration of the surface layers. Since there is no reason to suppose that the end organ differs essentially from any other excitable structure, we may assume that tension on the end organ stimulates it by deforming the surface membrane sufficiently to produce complete instability. The breakdown is followed by a refractory phase and a gradual return of the membrane to its normal polarized condition, but the continued action of the stimulus causes a renewed breakdown as soon as recovery has advanced far enough for the stimulus to become effective. Various explanations of the refractory phase and its gradual disappearance have been put forward, but it is probably safe to assume that the recovery depends on the gradual restoration of some component, *e.g.* a replenishing of the store of ions which maintain the surface polarization. It seems possible to account for most, if not all, of the facts on the assumption that the rate of recovery depends on the concentration of this substance in the immediate neighbourhood of the surface membrane, that the concentration is reduced by the stimulus and whenever an impulse is set up, and that it is restored from two sources: (*a*) by diffusion from neighbouring regions, (*b*) by a process of replacement, probably involving a chemical breakdown.

The depletion of the store would be caused in the first instance by the stimulus, and an inadequate stimulus might cause some loss without ever setting up an impulse. Whether the loss would be greater when an impulse is set up is an open question. Up to the present it has been impossible to stimulate these end organs in such a way that they become adapted without setting up any impulses, but Adrian's experiments with gradually increasing stimuli show that it is the stimulus rather than the setting up of impulses that is the important factor in producing adaptation, though the stimulus always results in the setting up of impulses the two factors causing adaptation cannot be completely dissociated.

The above hypothesis agrees with all the existing data on end organs, but several points need amplification. It is assumed that the substance which is removed during adaptation is replaced rapidly at the membrane (by the (*b*) process) and that it is also drawn from a "reservoir" by diffusion ((*a*) process) and similarly replaced during rest. It is necessary to assume this diffusion from a reservoir to explain the observation that, on cessation of the stimulus, there is a rapid return of the power to respond initially at a high rate but a slower return of the power to maintain a high rate of response. Most of the data on adaptation might perhaps have agreed with a simpler hypothesis, *e.g.* one involving restoration by coupled chemical reactions, but one set of observations, namely, the inflexion in the curves of Fig. 20, can only be accounted for if it is assumed that diffusion from neighbouring regions is an important factor in the restoration of the substance removed during adaptation, and it is very difficult to account for these observations in any other way. The hypothesis offers an elegant explanation of this which is most easily shown with the aid of diagrams.

In Fig. 24 A is shown the resting concentration of the substance up to the membrane; on stimulation the concentration near the membrane will fall as in B and will be restored by the (b) process occurring at the membrane, and also by diffusion. Consequently as the stimulus is prolonged the concentration gradient up to the membrane will change as in B, C and D. If now the stimulus is removed the concentration close to the membrane rises rapidly (Fig. 20 E) owing to process (b), and the

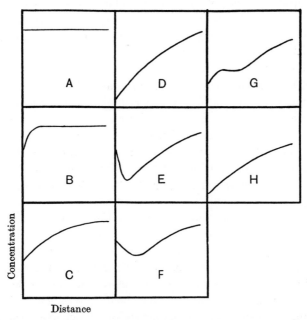

Fig. 24. Diagrams to show concentration of a substance diffusing from a region of fixed concentration up to a point where it is being utilized. The different figures show the concentration gradient at different times.

concentration farther from the membrane will rise slowly owing to diffusion as in F; so on reloading the conditions at the membrane are nearly the same as in the resting end organ, and at first it will respond at nearly the same initial rate, but the concentration at the membrane and therefore the rate of response will fall much more rapidly than on first loading (see Fig. 20 G). Moreover, a hump will occur in the concentration gradient, and until this has smoothed out there will be a pause in the fall in concentration at the membrane. It seems possible that this might account for the pause in the fall of frequency of response of the end organ which occurs soon after reloading.

The mechanism which has been ascribed to the nerve ending differs very little from that of the nerve fibre, and if adaptation is due to removal of the ions along a polarized membrane we should expect it to occur to some extent in the nerve fibre. Brücke [1926] has shown that, during the prolonged activity of a nerve fibre, the refractory period lengthens. This slowing of recovery might be due to the causes that have been suggested to produce adaptation of the nerve ending, but it is very slight compared to that of the ending, and so it is suggested that in the fibre the removal of ions is much less owing to the permeability never being increased by deformation, and so the fibre is not much affected by the slight loss of ions.

It is clear from the profound effect an electric current has on the decline of the end organ response, that adaptation is closely bound up with membrane polarization. The mechanism suggested for the end organ might certainly be influenced by an electric current in the way observed, a current flow in one direction tending to delay the diffusion (a) process and cause an earlier fall of the concentration of the substance at the membrane, reversed current flow aiding diffusion and maintaining the concentration at the membrane, and thus the response, at a higher level.

Cylindrical diffusion from the centre to the membrane surface of the fibre would be too rapid to account for the behaviour of the end organ in the way suggested, so that it must be assumed either that diffusion occurs from some reservoir, e.g. from the myelinated part of the fibre to the adjacent non-myelinated part at the termination of the medullary sheath, or else that adaptation is due to substances which escape from the membrane into the surrounding regions "clogging" the action of the membrane. The above hypothesis holds equally in the latter case.

SUMMARY.

1. A method is described of making a muscle preparation containing a single nerve ending responding to stretch.

2. This nerve ending is found to lie in the centre of the muscle, where histological preparations reveal a single muscle spindle.

3. The response in the nerve when the muscle is stretched is recorded with a moving iron oscillograph. It is found to be extremely constant for any given tension.

4. If the muscle is kept in a small quantity of Ringer for some time the response in the nerve is first depressed and then disappears, but returns to its initial magnitude when the Ringer is changed.

5. The frequency of response is found to be roughly proportional to the logarithm of the load.

6. When the muscle is loaded rapidly the interval between the impulses set up is only a little greater than the absolute refractory period of the nerve fibres concerned, and also the time relations of the action currents of these impulses are modified, showing that they are travelling in an incompletely recovered nerve fibre. It seems possible that these rapid discharges may be due to continuous rather than intermittent excitation of the nerve fibre.

7. The viscosity of the end organ may account for the discontinuities in the response when small loads are applied rapidly.

8. The interval between the impulses at the highest frequency recorded varies with temperature in much the same way as does the absolute refractory period of a nerve trunk.

9. The behaviour of the end organ is greatly modified by the ionic composition of the surrounding fluid. In sodium chloride the frequency of discharge remains high for some minutes; addition of either calcium or potassium alone reduces the response below that obtained in Ringer. Moreover, calcium and potassium appear to have an antagonistic action.

10. Rhythmic discharge of grouped impulses occurs when the preparation is kept at 25° in sodium chloride; the significance of these is discussed.

11. The response can be modified by passing a steady current through the muscle. The change in the response depends on the direction of current flow.

12. Hydrocyanic acid is found to cause a transient increase in the response later followed by extinction of the discharge.

13. Adaptation is examined, and it is found that there is an after effect lasting several seconds after the stimulus is removed.

14. This adaptation remainder has been measured quantitatively and is found to develop as stimulation is prolonged and vanish in a few seconds after the stimulus is removed.

15. The adaptation remainder is found to be a function of the total stimulation, *i.e.* the magnitude of the load and the time it has been acting.

16. A hypothesis is suggested to account for the observed behaviour of these end organs.

I wish to express my gratitude to Professor Adrian for his very valuable encouragement and criticism throughout this work.

The expenses of this research were in part defrayed by a grant from the Government Grants Committee of the Royal Society.

REFERENCES.

Adrian (1921). *J. Physiol.* **55,** 193.
Adrian (1930). *Proc. Roy. Soc.* B, **106,** 596.
Adrian and Bronk (1929). *J. Physiol.* **67,** 181.
Adrian and Zotterman (1926 *a*). *J. Physiol.* **61,** 151.
Adrian and Zotterman (1926 *b*). *J. Physiol.* **61,** 465.
Amberson (1930). *J. Physiol.* **69,** 60.
Bronk (1929). *J. Physiol.* **67,** 270.
Field and Brücke (1926). *Pfluegers Arch.* **214,** 103.
Cajal (1904). *Textura del sistema nervioso,* **1,** 404.
Denny Brown (1928). *Proc. Roy. Soc.* B, **103,** 321.
Dulière and Horton (1929). *J. Physiol.* **67,** 152.
Erlanger, Gasser and Bishop (1927). *Amer. J. Physiol.* **81,** 473.
Forbes and Rice (1929). *Amer. J. Physiol.* **90,** 119.
Gasser and Erlanger (1925). *Amer. J. Physiol.* **73,** 613.
Gasser and Hill (1924). *Proc. Roy. Soc.* B, **96,** 398.
Gotch (1910). *J. Physiol.* **40,** 250.
Matthews (1929 *a*). *J. Sci. Inst.* **6,** 220.
Matthews (1929 *b*). *J. Physiol.* **67,** 169.
Mines (1913). *J. Physiol.* **46,** 217.

ACTION POTENTIALS FROM A SENSORY NERVE ENDING

BY BERNHARD KATZ

From the Biophysics Research Unit, University College, London

(*Received* 10 *November* 1949)

The initiation of sensory impulses presents a series of problems: (*a*) the transmission of the stimulus from its external source to the receptor cell; (*b*) the mechanism whereby the stimulus is transformed into an electrical membrane change capable of exciting nerve terminals; (*c*) the initiation of impulses at the nerve ending and their propagation into the afferent axon trunk. An attempt has been made here to throw further light on these problems by studying the electrical changes in a sensory nerve fibre at a point close to its peripheral terminals. It is clear that only the last aspect of the problem (*c*) is directly amenable to electrical investigation, but such a study may also provide important clues to the preceding links of the process (*a* and *b*).

A suitable preparation was obtained from the muscle spindle of the frog. The electric response in the sensory axon close to the spindle differs in certain respects from a simple nerve spike, and some of these features can be related to the local events which take place in the sense organ. In the present paper the action potential in the terminal portions of the fibre will be described. It will also be shown that the initiation of an impulse at a sensory nerve ending does not invariably lead to a propagated message in the main axon. In the following paper, stretching of the muscle will be shown to depolarize the sensory nerve endings and thereby give rise to a repetitive discharge of impulses.

METHOD

Preparation. The experiments in this and the following paper were made on stretch receptors of the M. extensor longus dig. IV of the frog, the results being obtained from seventy-nine preparations at temperatures of 15–24° C. The muscle is supplied by a branch of N. peroneus. Before entering the muscle the nerve divides into a few twigs of which the proximal one often contains a motor and two sensory axons. Occasionally, one or two sensory fibres leave the N. peron. lat. several millimetres above the point of departure of the main branch to the muscle and, surrounded by a separate connective tissue sheath, run to the proximal part of the muscle. After the muscle with its nerve had been isolated, one of the proximal axons was selected, and all other nerve fibres were cut. The remaining axon could often be seen to end within a millimetre of its point of entry into the muscle, and many of these preparations were mounted without further dissection. Some muscles were divided until the intramuscular part of the sensory fibre had been cleared and the

Katz, B. Action potentials from a sensory nerve ending. *J. Physiol.* **111:** 248–260, 1950.

spindle with a portion of the intrafusal muscle bundle freed from adjacent tissue (cf. Fig. 1). In such cases the recording electrode could be placed a little closer to the nerve endings, but the results were substantially the same with either type of preparation.

The intramuscular course of the nerve and the position of the sensory endings was checked after many experiments by staining the preparation with osmic acid. The histological pattern of the sensory terminations varies a good deal. In some cases the axon is connected to a single end organ and

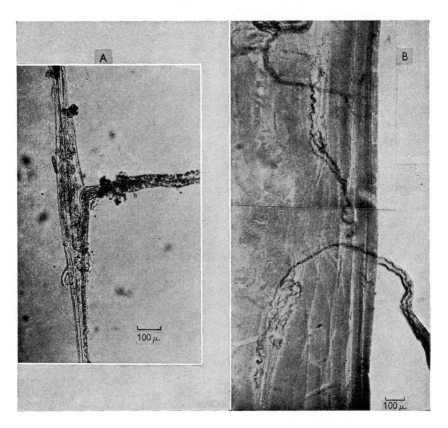

Fig. 1. Photomicrographs of frog muscle spindles. A, isolated living spindle, immersed in Ringer solution, showing capsule, intrafusal muscle fibres and nerve supply. The nerve contained a sensory and a motor axon which was cut. B, stained preparation (osmic acid). Muscle with two sensory axons one of which was cut. The muscle was flattened between slides before fixation.

does not divide into branches until it has reached, or entered, the spindle capsule. In other cases, the sensory nerve fibre enters the muscle and then divides into two branches which supply separate spindles (cf. Young, 1950). These end organs are located either on the same or on different intrafusal muscle bundles. Finally, the axon may divide before entering the muscle. The results described in this paper were obtained in preparations in which the fibre divided *distal to*, and not *between*, the recording leads. This is important because complications arise if a bifurcation of the axon occurs between the recording electrodes; in this case an afferent impulse starting from one of the spindles passes the distal lead and returns to it by 'axon reflex', and this alters the shape of the spike potential.

Apparatus. The recording system has been described elsewhere (Katz, 1949). The recording electrodes consisted of chlorided silver wires connected to the preparation through capillary tubes filled with Agar-Ringer. The amplifier was either direct coupled or had coupling condensers causing its response to decline to one-half in about 0·25 sec. In several experiments a condenser and grid leak were placed into the input lead to check whether the grid current of the first valve (about 10^{-10} A.) affected the nerve fibre. For antidromic stimulation, platinum electrodes were applied to the sciatic nerve, and brief thyratron shocks were used, isolated from earth by means of an air-cored transformer.

The tendons of the muscle were clamped by ruling pens and the whole preparation lifted into oil. Two recording electrodes were applied, usually one to nerve and one to muscle (Fig. 2). There are obvious advantages in placing the electrodes on relatively robust and immobile parts of the preparation, and therefore, when the whole muscle was used, the recording leads were applied preferably to the end of the muscle and to the peroneal nerve, rather than to the isolated portion of the axon. The muscle and nerve tissues on either side of the isolated stretch merely acted as low-resistance connectors without contributing any noticeable electric response themselves. This was verified by short-circuiting the sensory axon (letting it lie along the muscle) which made the afferent response invisible, and by moving the recording electrodes along muscle or nerve trunk, there being no noticeable change in the shape of the afferent spike until the electrodes were moved on to the isolated axon itself. However, the present method could not be used for recording *antidromic* impulses in the sensory fibre: in this case the central electrode had to be applied to the isolated axon itself, to avoid recording responses of cut fibres of the peroneal nerve.

The isolated axon, together with its sheath, was usually 30–60 μ. thick and a few millimetres long. The resistance of this stretch was very high, and in some experiments con-

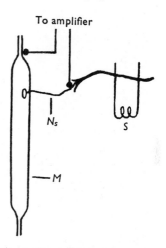

Fig. 2. Electrode arrangement showing stimulating (S) and recording leads. M, M. extensor longus dig. IV; N_s, isolated sensory fibre.

siderably magnified the time constant of the input circuit. Hence, the spike potential was sometimes appreciably slowed and attenuated. Square pulse calibrations indicated that the time constant of the delay of the recording system varied in different preparations between less than 40 and 250 μsec. In the former case, the distortion of the action potential was slight, but in the latter case the peak of the spike may have been reduced by as much as 50 %. The size of the spike (usually 2–3 mV.) was, however, of little interest, and the interpretation of the records was not seriously affected by this amplifier lag.

To summarize the present technique, electric responses are led off from a sensory axon at two points, a few millimetres apart. The distal lead is close to the sensory terminals of the spindle, but not in direct contact with them. Even when the spindle had been isolated (Fig. 1) the terminal structures remained enclosed inside the spindle capsule, and any localized potential changes could only be recorded at a distance determined by the length of the intra-capsular nerve branches. The electrotonic spread along the fine terminal branches is bound to involve an appreciable decrement, and the residual signal recorded on the outside of the capsule must be a reduced and distorted image of the local events at the sensory endings. It is important to keep this reservation in mind when interpreting the potential changes recorded with the present method.

RESULTS

When the tension of the resting muscle is low, afferent impulses are discharged occasionally, at apparently irregular intervals. If these impulses are recorded in the neighbourhood of the spindle, two characteristic phenomena are observed which differ from the properties of the ordinary conducted axon spike:

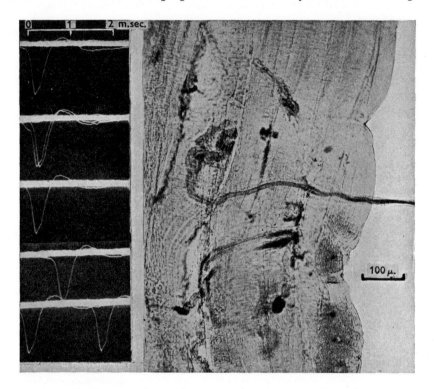

Fig. 3. (Left): Afferent impulse from a muscle spindle. Note: All records, in this and the subsequent paper, read from left to right. Downward deflexion means 'spindle negative' (i.e. a positive potential difference between the proximal and distal recording electrode). The spikes were recorded on a fast repetitive time-base, without synchronization. (Right): Photomicrograph of same muscle with single sensory axon and spindle. The preparation was treated as in Fig. 1B.

(i) instead of a diphasic wave, a triphasic potential change is seen the third phase of which will be shown to be a residual depolarization of the nerve endings; (ii) the afferent impulses are initiated by discrete local action potentials which either remain abortive or lead to a propagated spike after a small but visible delay. The first observation suggests that the terminal portions of the nerve fibre differ in certain respects from the axon trunk; the second phenomenon indicates that there are discrete regions of low safety margin, or 'partial block' in the initial path of the afferent impulse.

A localized 'negative after-potential'

Figs. 3–5 illustrate the shape of typical afferent spikes recorded with the distal lead close to, i.e. within less than 1 mm. of, the spindle capsule. The triphasic potential change was observed in every fresh preparation, provided the sensory axon was not injured nearby or partly depolarized by preceding stimuli (cf. Katz, 1950). The third phase lasts several milliseconds at 20° C. and may reach 40–50 % of the initial spike deflexion.

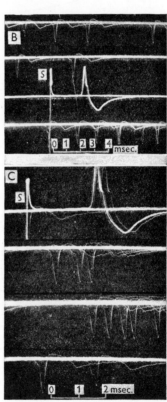

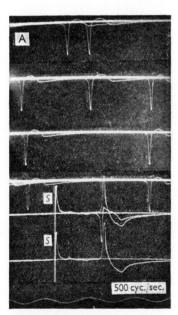

Fig. 4. Afferent (first deflexion downward) and antidromic (first deflexion upward) impulses in single sensory axons. In experiment A, the second record from below shows a superposition, by chance, of an antidromic and afferent impulse. *S*, stimulus artifact preceding the antidromic impulse.

When the proximal lead was applied to an injured region, the afferent impulse became monophasic and showed a prolonged tail portion which corresponded to the third phase previously observed. It appears that the electric response at the terminal portions of the axon is more prolonged than along the rest of the fibre and thereby gives rise to a third phase. Such an effect may be described as a 'terminal negative after-potential'.

A corollary to this phenomenon was observed when afferent and antidromic spikes were compared (Figs. 4, 5). This was done by stimulating the sciatic nerve with a short shock, without moving the recording electrodes. There are

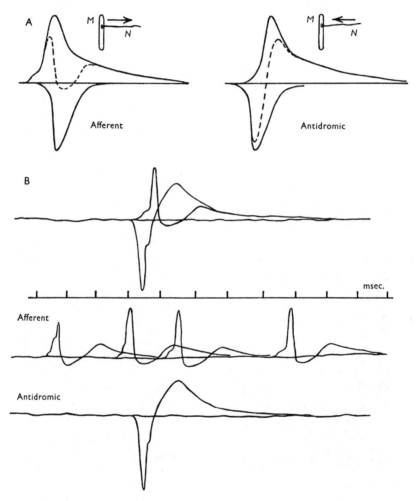

Fig. 5. A, diagram illustrating the assumed composite nature of the afferent and antidromic spike record. In this figure 'spindle negativity' (first deflexion of afferent spike) is shown upward. *M*, muscle; *N*, nerve. B, tracings of afferent and antidromic spikes. Same experiment as in Fig. 4, B and C.

obvious differences in the shapes of the two action potentials, the afferent spike being triphasic, with a brief and small second phase, while the antidromic impulse is diphasic with a large and prolonged second phase. When the two action potentials are superimposed, as in Figs. 4 and 5, their final phases are seen to be identical in time course and electrical sign, although the initial spikes have opposite polarity. These observations can be explained in the following way. If there is a prolonged depolarization at the terminal portions of the fibre, this would add its effect to the second phase of the descending anti-dromic impulse, while it would oppose the second, and give rise to the third phase of the afferent impulse (see diagram in Fig. 5).

The mechanism of this localized after-potential is not clear, but it may be pointed out that an effect of this kind would arise if the terminal parts of the nerve fibre were more strongly polarized than the rest of the axon (see Discussion).

In the course of a prolonged experiment, the third phase of the afferent action potential tended to diminish and eventually to vanish before the main spike was noticeably affected, a feature which seems to be characteristic of negative after-potentials generally (Lorente de Nó, 1947).

Sensory 'pre-potentials'

When the muscle was under little tension, the frequency of the afferent impulses was low and irregular, and in many preparations propagated impulses alternated at random with small monophasic action potentials which did not spread to the proximal recording electrode (Figs. 6–8). When the propagated impulses were examined on a fast time base, it was found that there were discrete 'steps' in the foot and rising phase of the action potentials (Figs. 3–5 and 7). These initial steps were clearly preliminary potential changes ('pre-potentials', Arvanitaki, 1939) which, only after a perceptible delay, led to a conducted sensory impulse.

The step-like rise was shown by the afferent, but not by the antidromic, spike. If a series of antidromic impulses was produced by repetitive stimula-tion of the sciatic nerve, the successive action potentials were all of identical shape; on the other hand, the shape of afferent spikes from the spindle was not constant, but exhibited a definite 'play' in the step-like composition of their wave front (Figs. 3–5 and 7). It was clear that successive impulses in the same axon conformed to two or three discrete patterns characterized by a different shape of foot and rising phase. Similarly, in those preparations where abortive impulses were seen, they appeared in two or three recurrent sizes. In the experiment of Fig. 6B, for instance, random responses from an almost slack spindle were recorded during a period of approximately 5 sec. Out of 74 detectable action potentials, 30 were propagated (relative size: 100), while the rest were abortive impulses of two, or possibly three discrete amplitudes (relative sizes: 25, 12 and 8–10; frequencies: 14, 1 and 29, respectively). In another experiment, during a period of 8·5 sec., 112 action potentials were recorded of which 70 were propagated (size: 100), while the others were local responses (sizes: 32, 10 and 5; frequencies: 7, 18 and 17, respec-tively).

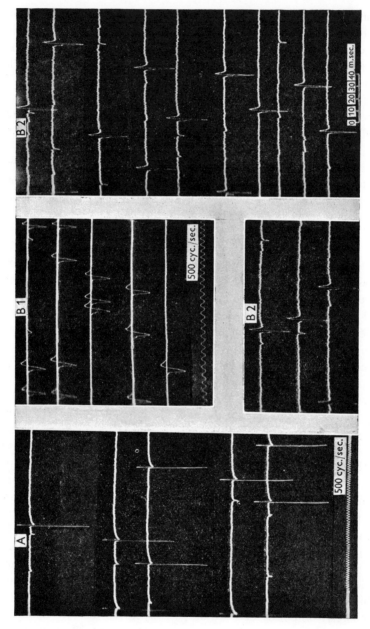

Fig. 6. Afferent discharges in single axons, showing occasional abortive spikes (small and monophasic). A and B2, single sweep records; B1, multiple sweeps superimposed. 'Spindle-negativity' downward.

98

It should be noted that the propagated spikes are likely to have been attenuated more severely by the present recording technique than the local action potentials (see Method), and that the relative size of the local responses given by the above figures may be somewhat too high.

Another significant fact was found when the intervals between successive afferent potential changes were measured. In the almost slack preparation, these intervals varied over a wide range, but it was clear that after a *propagated* impulse the preparation became silent for at least $\frac{1}{20}$ sec., that is no spike, full-size or abortive, could be observed during this time. It was equally clear that after an *abortive* impulse no such silent period occurred. For example, in the second experiment quoted above, the least observed interval between a propagated spike and the next, local or propagated, action potential was 50 msec. (the maximum being 290 msec.), but the shortest interval between an abortive impulse and the next potential change, local or propagated, was about 1 msec.

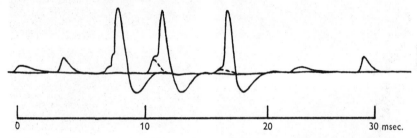

Fig. 7. Tracings of propagated and abortive spikes in a sensory axon. 'Spindle negativity' upward. Same experiment as in Fig. 6B.

Abortive impulses were observed when the muscle was almost slack and its afferent discharge infrequent and irregular, but they disappeared on stretching and gave way to a regular series of propagated spikes (Fig. 8). They also disappeared, together with all afferent response, when the spindle was subjected to a bombardment by antidromic impulses at a rate of about 100 per sec. The interval between the antidromic spikes at this frequency was longer than the refractory period of the nerve, but shorter than the repetition period of the afferent discharges in the almost slack muscle. The stoppage of all afferent potentials indicates that the antidromic impulses must have reached the active terminals of the spindle and made them temporarily irresponsive (see also Matthews, 1931). Thus, while the afferent potentials were not all propagated, the antidromic impulses never seemed to fail in reaching the terminal structures.

The properties of the 'pre-potentials' here described differ in important respects from the local responses found in nerve during subthreshold stimulation, or at the end-plate region during neuromuscular block. The sensory pre-potentials occur in discrete quantal sizes and are not subject to continuous gradation which is quite different from the end-plate potential or the local cathodic response in nerve. This observation provides an interesting clue, and it suggests that we are dealing with discrete sensory spikes which have started in one of the terminal branches, but for some reason encounter an obstacle before propagating into the axon trunk. It appears that the spindle contains a number of terminal units which—at least under a condition of low tension—are capable of firing separately and producing miniature spikes. Such

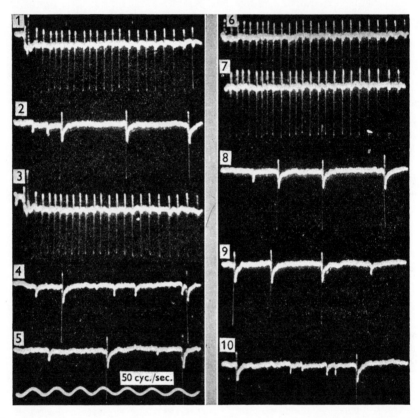

Fig. 8. Effect of moderate stretching on propagated and abortive spikes. In records 2, 4, 5 and 8–10, the muscle was under little tension, 14–15 mm. long. Note occasional abortive spikes. In records 1, 3, 6 and 7 the muscle was stretched to a 1·2 mm. greater length. Note burst of propagated discharges, but no sign of abortive spikes.

a miniature spike might raise the excitability of other near-by terminals by means of its electrotonic spread, and it apparently can sum with other 'steps' and build up to a propagated impulse (see Fig. 7). Once a full-size spike, whether afferent or antidromic, has arisen, it apparently invades all the terminal branches and so produces a period of complete silence (p. 256). A miniature spike which fails to propagate cannot render the other terminal units refractory, and this probably explains the absence of a silent period in these instances.

DISCUSSION

The 'negative after-potential' at the nerve endings

It has been pointed out that this effect might be caused by a gradient of membrane polarization along the terminal branches, the endings being at a higher resting potential than the trunk of the axon. It is well known (Schaefer, 1934) that the action potential becomes longer and is followed by a 'negative after-potential' when it travels through an anelectrotonic, i.e. more strongly polarized, region. The characteristic difference between afferent and antidromic spike could, therefore, be explained if the peripheral end of the fibre were more strongly polarized and thus normally in an 'anelectrotonic' state. Unfortunately, the present preparation does not lend itself to a direct test of this matter, for with a spike amplitude of 2–3 mV., a resting potential difference of less than 1 mV. would have to be looked for, and a steady potential difference of this size is impossible to measure in the presence of cut nerve branches.

It might be argued that a steady potential difference and, therefore, the triphasic action potential may arise, not because of some special property of the nerve endings, but perhaps because the region of the fibre near the *central* recording electrode might have been depolarized by injury currents from the cut peroneal nerve (cf. Fig. 2). This suggestion, however, can be dismissed because the presence of the third phase depended upon the proximity of a spindle to the peripheral lead. The local after-potential was not seen in fibres which did not terminate near-by, although they must have been equally affected by any injury currents from the cut peroneal branches.

The propagation of 'new-born' impulses from the spindle

It might be suggested that an anelectrotonic gradient along terminal branches would also account for the apparent obstacle which bars the propagation of newborn afferent impulses and for the 'notches' and 'steps' in Figs. 3–5 and 8, which resemble those described by Erlanger & Blair (1934) during partial anodal block. But there is another and perhaps simpler way of explaining these effects. Before the sensory axon terminates it divides into several small branches (cf. Fig. 1B). It is conceivable that the transmission of an impulse from a fine terminal, or pre-terminal, branch into the main axon occurs with a lower safety margin than in the reverse direction. A sudden increase of diameter, at some points of bifurcation, would cause the afferent action currents to be reduced in density, and the geometrical disparity between a fine and coarse adjoining portion of the axon cylinder may account for different facility of propagation in the two directions, and, in extreme cases, even for a one-way block. This is speculative, but of some general interest because similar events would be likely to occur at the dendrites of central neurones. Whatever the correct explanation, the quantal size and the brief time course of the observed 'step-potentials' distinguish them sharply from any graded local potential such as that described in the following paper. There is little doubt that the two or three local 'steps' shown above are true spikes which have started independently at terminal points of the spindle, and have yet to overcome some physiological obstacle before a sensory message is originated.

The 'random discharge' at low tension

An interesting question is posed by the large and apparently random variations in the frequency of the afferent discharges when the tension of the muscle is very low. There is no evidence of a regular rhythm in either propagated or local action potentials (Figs. 6, 8). Apparently, there are considerable fluctuations in the excitatory state of the stretch receptor, but their cause is at present unknown. It is pertinent that the local abortive spikes form part of this 'random discharge' at low tension, and are replaced by a regular pattern of propagated impulses when the tension is raised. It has been argued that abortive impulses arise from fractional activity within the spindle, that is from a separate excitation of individual groups of receptor terminals. If that argument is accepted, it would follow that the irregular disturbances which become so evident at low tension are due to highly localized events which take place at individual endings within the spindle. It is not inconceivable that molecular agitation in the mechanical receptor substance, or ionic noise in the terminal nerve membrane is ultimately responsible for the observed fluctuations in the local excitatory level.

SUMMARY

1. Sensory impulses from frog muscle were recorded at a point close to the spindle. The shape of these impulses differs in two respects from the ordinary axon spike: (a) there is a localized 'negative after-potential' at the nerve endings; (b) afferent spikes are initiated by brief step-like 'pre-potentials' which at times remain abortive.

2. The negative after-potential at the nerve endings follows the afferent as well as the antidromic spike and persists for several milliseconds, at 20° C.

3. At low levels of tension, successive spikes in the same axon show characteristic differences in shape. Two or three discrete patterns of 'pre-potentials' can be distinguished which recur consistently throughout the experiment. In many preparations, 'pre-potentials' are observed which occasionally fail to propagate and then form small monophasic spikes of discrete 'quantal' sizes. Such abortive spikes are wiped out by antidromic bombardment of the spindle at a rate of about 100 per sec., and by moderate stretch which gives rise to a regular series of full-size afferent impulses.

4. The presence of step-like pre-potentials and of abortive spikes indicates that there are local obstacles which delay and sometimes block the propagation of 'new-born' impulses after they have arisen at the receptor terminals. It is suggested that transmission from a fine terminal branch into the axon trunk

has a lower safety margin than transmission in the reverse direction, and that a delay or partial block might occur at some points of bifurcation of the sensory nerve fibre.

I wish to thank Prof. A. V. Hill for the facilities provided in his laboratory and Mr J. L. Parkinson for his invaluable assistance. I am indebted to Prof. J. Z. Young and the staff of his department, in particular to Mr F. J. Pittock and Mr J. Armstrong, for frequent help.

REFERENCES

Arvanitaki, A. (1939). *Arch. int. Physiol.* **49**, 209.

Erlanger, J. & Blair, E. A. (1934). *Amer. J. Physiol.* **110**, 287.

Katz, B. (1949). *J. exp. Biol.* **26**, 201.

Katz, B. (1950). *J. Physiol.* **111**, 261.

Lorente de Nó, R. (1947). *A Study of Nerve Physiology*, **1** and **2**. In *Stud. Rockefeller Inst. med. Res.* **131** and **132**. New York.

Matthews, B. H. C. (1931). *J. Physiol.* **72**, 153.

Schaefer, H. (1934). *Ergebn. Physiol.* **36**, 151.

Young, J. Z. (1950). In preparation.

DEPOLARIZATION OF SENSORY TERMINALS AND THE INITIATION OF IMPULSES IN THE MUSCLE SPINDLE

By BERNHARD KATZ

From the Biophysics Research Unit, University College, London

(*Received* 10 *November* 1949)

It has been shown by several authors (Adrian & Gelfan, 1933; Fessard, 1936; Arvanitaki, 1938; Hodgkin, 1948) that the rhythmic response of a muscle or nerve fibre to an electrical or chemical stimulus is initiated by a local preliminary depolarization which re-develops after each discharge and which varies with the strength of the stimulus. It has been suggested that similar local potential changes intervene between the various forms of sensory stimuli and the initiation of afferent impulses (Pantin (1937, p. 418); Granit's 'generator potential' (1947); Stevens & Davis's 'transducer effect' (1938)). The existence of local potential changes in sense organs, e.g. the electro-retinogram, or the cochlear microphonic effect, has been known for many years, but their exact significance and relation to the discharge of impulses has not been established with certainty. Recently, important evidence was obtained by Hartline & Graham (1932), by Granit (1947) and by Bernhard (1942), who showed that visual stimulation of the eye gives rise to electrotonic potentials in the optic nerve (see also Parry, 1947). In the present paper, further evidence is presented using the muscle spindle of the frog. It will be shown that stretching of the muscle produces a depolarization of the sensory nerve endings which spreads electrotonically along the axon and varies directly with the rate and amplitude of the mechanical stimulus. By a suitable dose of a local anaesthetic the sensory nerve impulses can be abolished and the spindle potential obtained separately. The local spindle potential appears to be an essential link between input and output of the sense organ, and the mechanism whereby a mechanical deformation is converted into this electrical membrane change will be discussed.

METHOD

Preparation and method of recording have been described in preceding papers (Katz, 1949 a; 1950 b). The electrode arrangement is shown in Fig. 1. To apply a synchronized stretch to the muscle, two procedures were used. In some experiments where only qualitative information was required the preparation was stretched by stimulating another frog muscle which had been placed in series with the preparation. Usually, however, one tendon was connected via a lever to a magnetic relay. The

Katz, B. Depolarization of sensory terminals and the initiation of impulses in the muscle spindle. *J. Physiol.* **111**: 261–282, 1950.

velocity of stretching was adjusted by varying the energizing current or a viscous resistance which opposed the motion of the lever. The mechanical excursion could be registered together with the electric response of the sensory axon on a double-beam oscilloscope. The movement of the lever was recorded without noticeable delay by using a photocell with cathode follower output.

Several checks were made to discriminate against electrical artifacts which might accompany stretching of the muscle. Such artifacts could arise from resistance changes in the presence of grid current, but tests with a blocking condenser at the input (Katz, 1950 b) showed that this effect was quite negligible.

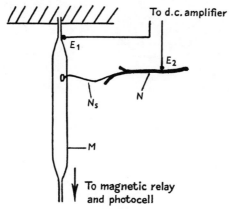

Fig. 1. Electrode arrangement. *M.* M. extensor longus dig. IV.;
N_s, isolated sensory axon; N, peroneal nerve.

A more serious possibility of error arose from the fact that a portion of the muscle was included between the recording electrodes (Fig. 1), and any potential change occurring in the muscle would vitiate the experiment. Artifacts of this kind were checked by short-circuiting the sensory axon (letting it lie along the muscle) or by crushing it at the point of entry into the muscle (see, for example, Figs. 7 (3); 9 (7)). In this way, electric potential differences in the sensory nerve were eliminated, and artifacts due to the muscle were recorded alone. In many preparations, the potential changes were abolished by this procedure, and this showed that the electric response to stretching originated wholly in the spindle. In some instances, however, small residual potential changes in the muscle were observed, and it was then safest to discard the experiment altogether. Artifacts of this kind appeared to be due to local injury or to tissue debris which had been left on the muscle. The best way of avoiding this difficulty was clean and careful dissection.

It is worth mentioning that in a few experiments an intact motor axon was isolated instead of a sensory fibre. In these cases, no potential change could be recorded while the muscle was stretched, and this provided a satisfactory additional check.

RESULTS

Qualitative observations

Fig. 2 shows the electric response in the peripheral end of a sensory axon during a transient lengthening of the muscle. The stretching was produced by the contraction of a sartorius muscle to which single shocks of varying strength were applied. Records 2–4 were obtained with increasing shock intensity, 'diphasic' as well as 'monophasic' records being shown. During 'rest' there were occasional discharges of either propagated impulses showing the usual

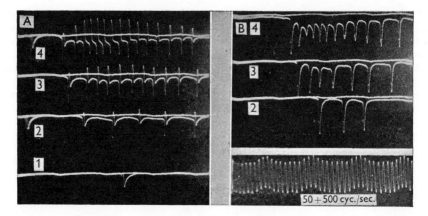

Fig. 2. Potential changes in a sensory axon when the muscle is subjected to a transient stretch. The stretch was applied by a sartorius muscle contracting against the M. extensor dig. IV. All records in this paper read from left to right and show 'spindle negativity' (i.e. a positive potential difference between electrodes E_2 and E_1) as a downward deflexion. A: usual recording from uninjured axon. 1, at 'rest'; 2–4, with increasing intensity of stretching. B: the records have been made monophasic by crushing the central portion of the axon. *Note.* In this preparation, the axon divided into two branches before entering the muscle. Occasional alternations in spike size (e.g. record A, 2) are probably to be attributed to impulses starting along alternate branches of the axon.

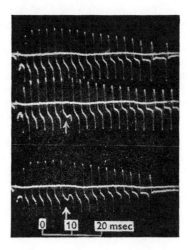

Fig. 3. Occasional 'block' during intense depolarization. Same experiment as in Fig. 2. The places where an impulse has dropped out are marked by arrows.

106

triphasic pattern or of small abortive impulses (Katz, 1950 b). During the stretching, a burst of propagated spikes occurred, superimposed on a slow depolarization which was localized at the peripheral lead. The amplitude of this depolarization and the frequency of the spike discharge increased with the intensity of the mechanical stimulus.

It is interesting to note that during the intense depolarization in Fig. 2, record 4, the size of the spike diminished. This cannot be attributed simply to the refractory state left behind by preceding impulses, for the *diphasic* record indicates that, after conduction to the proximal lead a few millimetres away, the spikes have reached their normal amplitude. The reduction in spike height must be the result of the local depolarization—an effect which has previously been described as a cathodic depression (e.g. Hodgkin, 1948; Lorente de Nó, 1947). This depressing action can become so intense that spikes fail to propagate (see Fig. 3), so that during a vigorous stretch impulses may appear to drop out of an otherwise regular series.

A curious fact, invariably observed, was the marked difference in size between the small initial depolarization which precedes the first impulse and the conspicuous potential change leading up to the second and later impulses of a series. In fact, in some experiments (e.g. Fig. 4B), no distinct step could be seen preliminary to the first discharge, while there was always a large depolarization preceding the later impulses. The significance of this observation will be discussed at a later stage (pp. 273–4), but it is necessary to dispose at once of an important objection. It might be argued that the local depolarization in Fig. 2 is not the direct result of stretching, but a cumulative effect of after-potentials left by a train of nerve impulses. It has previously been shown that the spike is followed by a local negative after-potential at the nerve endings (Katz, 1950 b), but it can now be shown that the depolarization during stretching is a separate phenomenon: (a) in many experiments (e.g. Figs. 2, 3 and 4A), there is no doubt that a small initial depolarization occurs *before* the first spike arises; (b) the depolarization builds up gradually during the interval between spikes *after* the negative after-potential has declined (Figs. 2, 4–6 and 12); (c) spikes and after-potential can be eliminated by a local anaesthetic without affecting the depolarizing effect of stretching (p. 269); (d) when an intense depolarization has been produced by stretching (Figs. 4 and 5), the negative after-potential becomes reduced or even disappears. Evidently we are dealing with a direct action of the mechanical stimulus on the nerve membrane, without the intervention of a nerve impulse.

Dynamic and static stretch effects

The time relations between stimulus and response were examined by using a double-beam oscilloscope and recording the change of length of the muscle simultaneously with the electric changes in the sensory nerve.

In Fig. 4B, an experiment is illustrated in which a small test stretch, of 1·3 mm. amplitude, was applied at various speeds to a muscle of 17·5 mm. initial length. There is a discharge of nerve impulses superimposed on a slow depolarization. The most striking phenomenon, however, is the apparent separation of the electrical changes into two phases: (*a*) a relatively intense dynamic effect which coincides with the period of initial lengthening, and (*b*) a final static effect during which the local depolarization and the rate of discharge are maintained at a lower level (see also Figs. 6, 7 and 9, and Katz, 1949*b*).

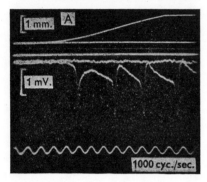
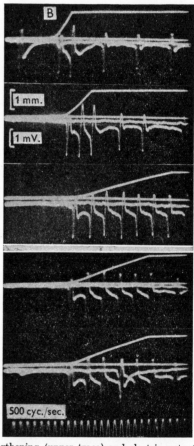

Fig. 4. Double-beam recording of mechanical lengthening (upper trace) and electric potential changes (lower trace). A, fast time base. Monophasic recording. Initial muscle length 16 mm. B, another preparation. Slower time base, Diphasic recording. Initial length 17·5 mm. Occasionally an impulse from the 'resting spindle' is superimposed on the record of the stretch response. Each record consists of two exposures, (i) a 'base-line' (with an occasional impulse appearing on it) and (ii) the stretch response.

It is noteworthy that the discharge of impulses begins as soon as stretching commences; in fact, the first impulse is often discharged when the mechanical record has barely risen from its base-line. It should be remembered, however, that the 'resting' spindle is on the verge of firing and that, therefore, the initiation of the first impulse may require only a minute stimulus.

The intensity of local depolarization can be measured during the interval between impulses. This measurement is somewhat arbitrary because the potential does not remain at a steady level. In practice, the 'flattest' portion

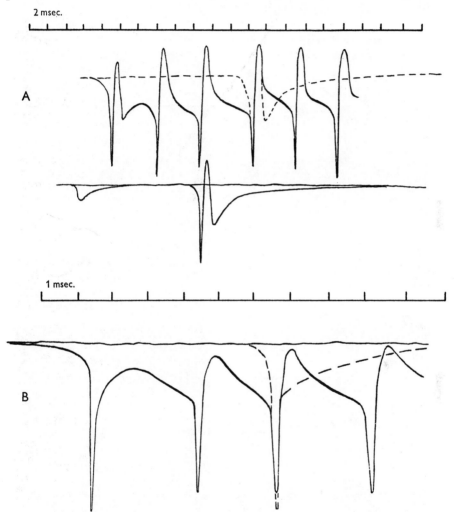

Fig. 5. Stretch response and resting discharge in a sensory axon. Note the reduction of the negative after-potential during stretching. A, upper record: continuous tracing shows the response to stretching. Broken line tracing shows an impulse from the 'resting' spindle. Lower record shows an abortive and a propagated spike from the 'resting' spindle. B, stretch response (continuous tracing) and 'resting' discharge (broken line) in another preparation. Records were monophasic in this instance.

of the curve between successive spikes was chosen for measurement and mean values were determined in each record (a) for the 'dynamic' and (b) for the 'static' depolarization (see also Katz, 1950a). The 'dynamic' effect with various rates of stretching is plotted in Fig. 8. These results were taken from a single preparation; in seven other experiments similar results were obtained. The

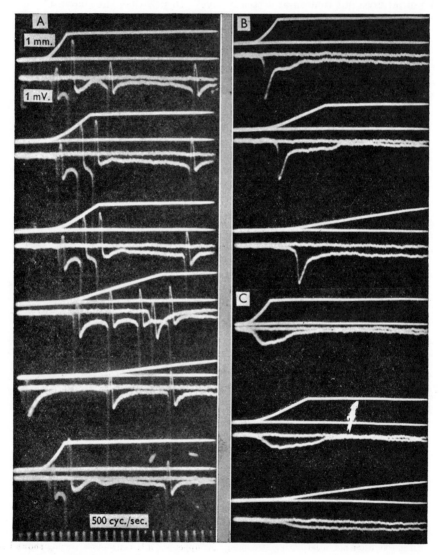

Fig. 6. Effect of procaine on the stretch response. A, normal preparation. Various rates of stretching. B, after application of 0·25% procaine. C, after application of 0·5% procaine. Note the initial non-propagated spike in B.

depolarization increases with the velocity of stretching up to a maximum which, in the case of Fig. 8, was 0·75 mV., or about 20% of the recorded spike height. When the muscle was stretched at a rate greater than 1–1·5% per msec.

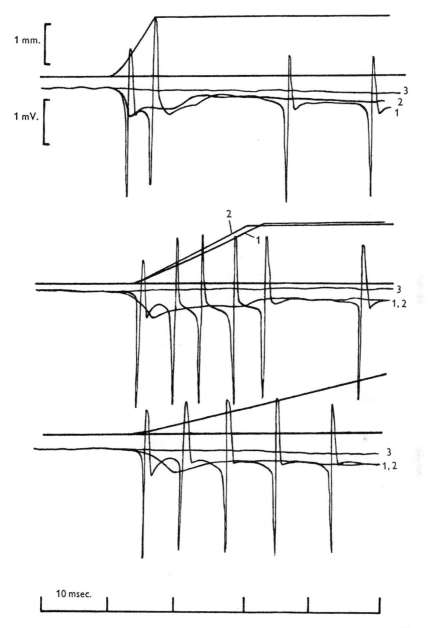

Fig. 7. Superimposed tracings of stretch responses before and during local anaesthesia. Three different rates of stretch shown approximately in the upper drawings. The electrical potential changes were recorded (1) in the normal preparation, showing repetitive spikes and local depolarization; (2) after application of 0·35 % procaine showing only local depolarization (with a trace of an initial local spike); (3) after crushing the axon at its point of entry into the muscle, the record becoming now indistinguishable from a base-line.

no further increase in the local depolarization occurred. A half-maximal effect was produced by stretching at a rate of 0·28 % per msec. (mean of eight experiments, at 16–20° C.: 0·23 % per msec., s.e. of mean ±0·034 % per msec.). The 'static' effect of a 1·3 mm. extension (about 8 % of muscle length) amounted to 0·26 mV.: an equivalent 'dynamic effect' was produced by stretching the muscle at a rate of 23 μ. (0·15 % of its length) per msec.

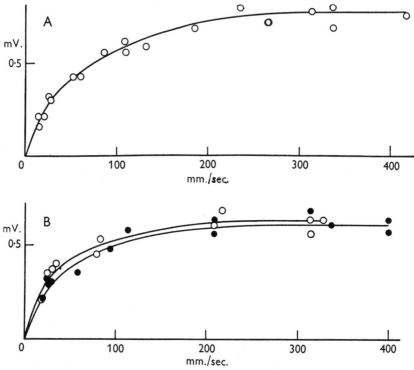

Fig. 8. 'Dynamic' effect of stretching. Initial length of muscle 15·5 mm. Abscissae: rate of stretching of muscle. Ordinates: local depolarization. A, normal preparation. B, anaesthetized preparation. Hollow circles, 0·25 % procaine. Full circles, 0·5 % procaine.

The effect of local anaesthetics

When the preparation was soaked for several minutes in a buffered solution of procaine/Ringer, the impulse discharge was curtailed or abolished, according to the concentration of the anaesthetic. With 0·1 % procaine, a single propagated impulse usually remained: with 0·2 % there was evidence of a residual non-propagated spike: with higher concentrations all signs of excitatory activity usually became extinguished while the prolonged depolarization during stretch was either unaffected (with concentrations up to 0·3 %) or somewhat reduced (0·4–0·5 %). Similar effects were seen when the preparation was treated with a sodium-free solution (0·12 m/l. choline chloride plus the usual

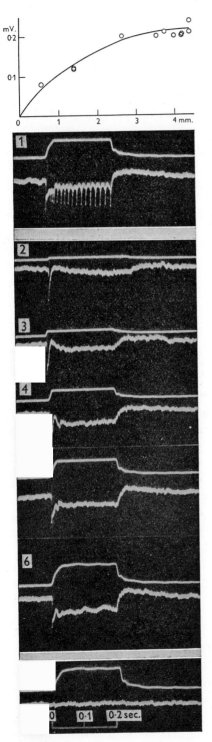

Fig. 9. 'Static' effect of stretching. The diagram shows the relation between extension (initial length 16 mm.) and local depolarization in the anaesthetized preparation (cf. records 2–6). In records 1–7, the upper trace indicates change of length of the muscle, the lower trace shows potential changes in the sensory axon. Record 1, normal. Records 2–6, after 0·1% procaine. (An initial spike remains.) In record 6, the slight mechanical oscillations are accompanied by more pronounced (dynamic) potential changes. Record 7, same conditions as in record 6 except that the axon has been crushed at the point of entry into the muscle.

amounts of KCl and $CaCl_2$). After soaking for 10 min. in this medium, a single impulse was seen instead of a burst of discharges; after a further 30 min. immersion, all traces of spikes, local and propagated had vanished while the prolonged depolarization was still obtained.

In Figs. 6 and 7 the effect of procaine is illustrated, and in Fig. 8A and B, the 'dynamic stretch potentials' are plotted before and after paralysis. The two curves are practically the same. When a large dose of procaine (more than 0·4 %) was applied, the local stretch potentials diminished in size, and it was often noticed that the 'static' depolarization diminished more than the 'dynamic'.

A number of tests were made (see also Method) to ascertain that the stretch potentials were, in fact, a depolarization of the sensory axon and could not be attributed to artifacts. In many preparations, when the sensory axon was short-circuited, or crushed at the point of entry into the muscle, all electric changes were abolished. This was a satisfactory test and confirmed the view that the stretch potentials were electrotonically conducted into, and recorded from, the sensory nerve. In some preparations electrical artifacts were seen which could be traced to potential differences in the muscle tissue; they varied in sign and were usually not large enough to mask the genuine depolarization of the nerve, but it was considered best to discard such experiments.

Relation between local depolarization and impulse discharge

The stretch potential is closely related, in its time course and amplitude, to the mechanical stimulus: it is presumably the direct result of the deformation of nerve endings and their receptor membranes. The potential change persists even when the excitatory mechanism of the nerve membrane has been paralysed: this suggests that, whatever the mechanism of the electro-mechanical conversion, it does not involve an 'active response' of the nerve endings, at least not of the kind which is associated with the action potential. The discharge of nerve impulses appears to be a secondary phenomenon, initiated by the stretch potential in a manner analogous to electric excitation in nerve or muscle.

This view is supported by the close relation which exists between the intensity of the local depolarization and the frequency of impulses. The relation is obvious from the records, and was tested statistically in one experiment, illustrated in Fig. 10. The intervals between successive impulses were measured as well as the level of depolarization during the intervals. There was a highly significant correlation with a coefficient of 0·97 (ninety-one pairs of observations). The regression line in Fig. 10 was fitted by the usual statistical method and shown to have a highly significant slope.

There is an interesting analogy between the discharge from a muscle spindle and the repetitive response to constant current in a crustacean nerve fibre (Fessard, 1936; Hodgkin, 1948; see also Fig. 11). In both instances, a continuous stimulus gives rise to rhythmic impulses whose frequency depends upon the stimulus strength. Furthermore, both types of response are mediated by a local depolarization. There are, however, noticeable differences. In the crustacean axon, the level of the depolarization from which successive spikes

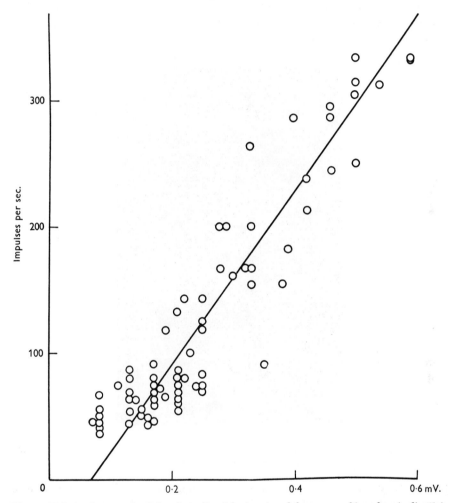

Fig. 10. Relation between local depolarization (abscissae) and frequency of impulses (ordinates). A regression line has been drawn through the results which were obtained from ninety-one pairs of observations. For further explanation see text.

take off remains almost constant: it is practically the same for the first as for the following spikes of a series of impulses, and does not vary much with the frequency of the discharge. In the spindle axon, however, the local depolarization which precedes the first of a series of impulses is always small, and the 'firing level' increases markedly with the frequency of the impulses. An explanation of this difference may be found along the following lines. The recovery from a nerve impulse involves two changes: (i) a restoration of the membrane resistance, and (ii) a gradual return of 'excitability'. The existence of two different processes is indicated by the fact (Hodgkin, 1938) that (1) a stronger current is required during the refractory period to build up a given potential change across the membrane, and (2) a larger potential change is required to evoke a membrane response. How these two factors are coupled is not yet

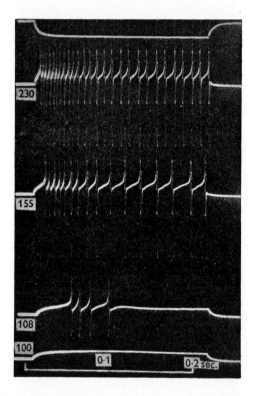

Fig. 11. Response of *Carcinus* nerve fibre to electric currents, recorded at the cathode (cf. Hodgkin, 1948). The numbers indicate relative current strength.

known; they may depend upon different mechanisms, and there is no reason to suppose that they proceed at identical rates or even at the same relative rates in different tissues. If the repair of the membrane leakage were considerably quicker than the return of excitability, a behaviour as seen in the spindle axon would be obtained, for a larger local depolarization would be required before the second, third, etc. impulse of a series could be initiated. If, on the other hand, both recovery processes occurred at approximately the same rate, or the second one were faster, then all the impulses would take off at practically the same level as is found in the *Carcinus* axon.

In this way it seems possible to explain the differences between the electrotonic stretch effects at the spindle and the cathodic potentials in isolated crustacean axons. The depolarization, which precedes the first of a series of sensory impulses, is small, probably because the threshold of the normal 'rested' nerve terminals is low. It should be remembered that the normal 'resting' spindle is on the verge of firing (it does, in fact, discharge impulses at a low irregular rate), and that therefore the initial impulse during stretch may be set up by a very weak stimulus and a very small local depolarization, just enough to trigger the most excitable nerve terminal. The next impulses are initiated at a time when all the nerve endings are relatively refractory, and a much larger depolarization is then required to give rise to a spike. Similarly, a large local stretch potential is obtained when the threshold has been raised by other means, e.g. by the application of an anaesthetic. Thus, the observed relation between local and propagated changes can be explained in simple terms, and there is no reason to suppose that the sensory impulses arise from any agent other than the local stretch potential.

Sensory potential changes accompanying the release of a stretched muscle

It has been shown by Matthews (1931 b) that during the release of a stretched muscle the discharge of impulses from a spindle drops below its final steady rate immediately after the tension is reduced. It was of interest to investigate the

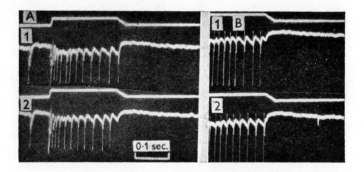

Fig. 12. 'Off-effect' at the end of a period of stretching. Note the appearance of a miniature spike in A 2 and B 1.

local potential changes which accompany this phenomenon. When a normal muscle is released, the depolarization in the sensory axon suddenly falls and the discharge of impulses stops (Fig. 12). This 'cut-off' occurs without noticeable lag; the depolarization falls, in fact, so quickly that a local 'miniature spike' is formed when the mechanical release happens to coincide with the preliminary rise which precedes the firing of an action potential (Fig. 12). There is evidence for a transient *positive* potential change, i.e. a dynamic 'off-effect'. Examples are shown in Fig. 13. The positive spindle potential is usually smaller and more prolonged than the 'on-effect', but this is to be expected, for the mechanical conditions during release are not the exact converse of those during forcible extension. The speed at which the sense organ returns to its initial shape depends upon its own elastic restoring forces and viscous resistances rather than upon the speed of the applied lever and, therefore, the effects of stretch and release can be compared only qualitatively.

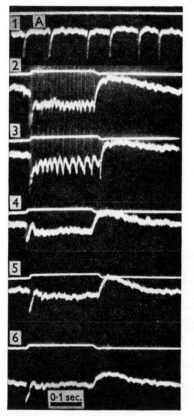
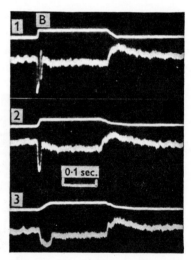

Fig. 13. 'Off-effect' at the end of a period of stretching. A, initial length 15–16 mm. In records 2–6 a 1·8 mm. stretch was applied. Records 1–3, normal preparation, initial length being slightly less in 3 than in 1 and 2. Record 1 shows 'resting' discharge. Records 4 and 5, after application of 0·15% procaine; record 6, after 0·3% procaine. (In records 4 and 5 an initial spike was present, but is not visible in the reproduction.) B, another preparation, treated with 0·3% procaine. Initial length 15 mm. Three stretches of 1·3 mm. amplitude, applied at different rates. (In B1 an initial spike was set up in the region between the recording leads.)

The 'off-effect', in Fig. 13, might be interpreted in various ways: (a) it might be an after-potential left behind by the preceding train of impulses; (b) there is 'adaptation' during the static period of stretch shown by the gradual fall in the discharge rate: if 'adaptation' were due to some process opposing the local depolarization, a positive 'off-effect' could appear as a consequence; (c) it might be the counterpart of the dynamic 'on-effect' as suggested above, associated with a relatively slow return of the sensory structure to its initial length.

It is possible to decide between these suggestions by the use of procaine (Fig. 13). In the absence of sensory impulses, the positive potential change is still obtained; hence it cannot be an after-effect of nerve activity. Nor can it be ascribed to 'adaptation', for this would require a slow decline of the depolarization during the static period of stretch, and no such decline is observed. It is, therefore, more likely that the positive potential change is a dynamic 'off-effect', similar to the dynamic depolarization described above (p. 265).

DISCUSSION

The spindle potentials described in this paper can be satisfactorily explained as a local link between stimulus and response, arising in the terminal receptor membrane and giving rise, in turn, to discrete messages in the attached nerve fibre. The problem remains how the energy of the mechanical stretch is converted into a local depolarization. The present experiments provide no direct evidence on this matter, but it may be of interest to consider some simple hypotheses.

If we compare the time courses of the stimulus and the resulting depolarization, it is clear that a certain degree of 'differentiation' has taken place, a large component of the spindle potential depending upon rate rather than magnitude of stretch. This might be accomplished in different ways and two factors will be discussed both of which may be involved.

The 'differentiation' could occur during the mechanical transmission of the stimulus from the tendon to the receptor membrane (see Matthews, 1931a). For example, if the sensory portion of the spindle were less viscous than the muscular portion in series with it, the sense organ would suffer greater deformation during the dynamic than during the static phase of stretching. While this possibility cannot be dismissed, there is another way of explaining the differentiation of the time course as well as the origin of the spindle potential.

When the polarized surface membrane of a nerve or muscle fibre is stretched, electrical changes may arise in several ways: first, there may be a transient fall in the membrane potential while the membrane is being stretched and its capacity increased (cf. Ramsey, 1947). This action would be similar to that of a 'condenser microphone'. If we knew the time constant of the membrane, its resting potential and rate of stretching, the resulting depolarization could be calculated as shown in the Appendix. Secondly, the membrane permeability may be altered by stretching, ionic pores, for instance, might be enlarged and consequently the resting potential may fall. Thirdly, chemical changes may take place in the interior of the cell as a result of stretching (cf. Feng, 1932), and these may subsequently affect the distribution of ions and the potential across the surface membrane. The capacitative effect seems almost inevitable, provided that the membrane is initially in an expanded state. If it were not, stretching would merely straighten out some folds without altering the electrical properties. But the surface area of an expanded membrane would increase and its thickness diminish when it is stretched, and one would therefore expect that the capacity (C) of the membrane becomes greater, and its transverse resistance (R) less, as the fibre is lengthened. The increase of capacity must be accompanied by an immediate fall of the membrane potential; but this would be a transient effect and the membrane would be recharged, at a rate depending upon its time constant RC, to its resting potential at the new length.

Thus, it is conceivable that the dynamic component of the spindle potential is simply the result of a change in membrane capacity. The ensuing static component may be due to a different mechanism, namely a change in membrane permeability. It is not intended to pursue these speculations seriously until more evidence is available to support them, but a method of calculating the 'dynamic component' of this receptor model is shown in the Appendix. As a point of interest, the observed depolarization is too great to be explained without some mechanical amplification of the applied stretch. Unless the deformation of the receptors were larger than that of other parts of the muscle, the present hypothesis would be untenable, but this difficulty would be removed, if the sensory structure of the spindle were more 'compliant' than the rest of the intrafusal bundle.

It may be objected that this hypothesis unnecessarily invokes two different mechanisms for the dynamic and static response. This assumption, however, is not entirely unfounded. There were indications in several experiments that the two components are affected differently by large doses of procaine, the static potential change being reduced more drastically than the dynamic change. Furthermore, the discharge of impulses frequently occurs in two discrete groups, corresponding to the dynamic and static phases of stretch (cf. Matthews, 1931 a). This is seen in Fig. 7 and further illustrated in Fig. 14. There is a gap between the two groups of impulses, and this gap corresponds to a 'dip' in the stretch potential observed in the procaine-treated preparation (Fig. 7). This would agree with the suggestion of two separate components of the potential change, the 'static' effect developing more slowly and at times rising after the quick 'dynamic' effect has already begun to decline. These observations are not conclusive but they would fall into line with the idea of two separate components of the stretch potential, and would be more difficult to explain on the idea of a simple mechanical differentiation (p. 276).

The mechanism of the stretch receptor suggested here does not invoke any specific properties other than those found in nerve or muscle fibres. The factors which distinguish mechanical receptor endings from ordinary nerve or muscle membranes may be of a rather simple nature: first, as suggested above, the nerve endings may be subject to greater deformation than the adjacent tissue. Secondly, the surface membranes of muscle fibres, and of nerve axons *in situ*, may not be in the fully extended state without which the theoretical mechanism could not work (cf. Katz 1950a). Finally, the threshold at the nerve endings might be lower than elsewhere so that a relatively small amount of depolarization would be sufficient to start an impulse. While such factors would suffice

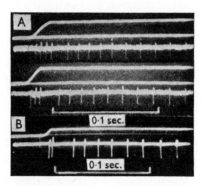

Fig. 14. The 'gap' between the dynamic and static discharge of impulses. A and B, two different preparations. Amplitude of stretching: A, 17%; B, 8% of the initial length.

to explain the differentiation of the spindle receptors, one cannot dismiss the possibility of a specially adapted molecular mechanism, for example some piezo-electric substance, being responsible for the conversion of stretch into a spindle potential. The problem thus remains whether muscle spindles and mechanical receptors generally work on a specific molecular basis, like most photo- and chemo-receptors, depending upon specific chemical reactions, or, as suggested here, like an ordinary electro-mechanical converter system, as condenser microphones or resistance strain gauges.

SUMMARY

1. When a frog muscle is stretched, its sensory nerve endings become depolarized, and a local potential change can be recorded from the sensory axon at a point close to the spindle.

2. This potential change varies with the rate and amplitude of stretching, and gives rise to repetitive impulses in the sensory nerve.

3. By applying a local anaesthetic it is possible to abolish the nerve impulses without affecting the local electric reactions to stretch. There is evidence for two distinct components of the potential change associated with the dynamic process of stretching and with static extension respectively.

4. When a stretched muscle is released, a transient potential change in the opposite direction (i.e. a positive variation at the nerve endings) is observed.

5. The local potential change appears to arise from a direct action of the mechanical stimulus on the sensory nerve endings and to be a link between the mechanical input and the rhythmic output of impulses from the sense organ. The mechanism whereby the mechanical deformation is converted into an electrical membrane change is discussed.

APPENDIX

The immediate effect of stretching on an electrically charged membrane may be represented by a simple model (Figs. 15, 16). A membrane element of capacity C_0 and conductance G_0 ($=1/R_0$) is normally charged to the resting potential E.

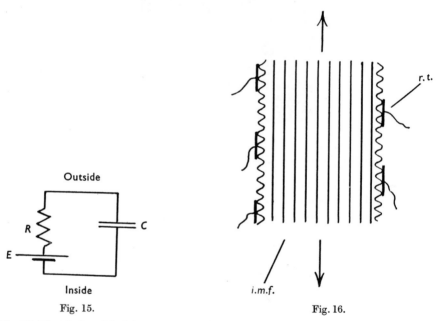

Fig. 15.   Fig. 16.

Fig. 15. Electrical model of the receptor membrane.
Fig. 16. Schematic diagram of intrafusal muscle fibre (*i.m.f.*) with several receptor terminals (*r.t.*) on its surface. Arrows indicate direction of stretching.

When the tissue is stretched, the volume of the stretched elements remains constant but their surface area increases and thickness diminishes (provided that these elements are fully extended and their surface membrane is in an unfolded state). The terminal membrane of the sensory nerve is assumed to change in this manner when the muscle is stretched.

If it be assumed further that the dielectric constant and specific conductivity of the membrane material remain unaltered, then the total capacity and conductance of the membrane must become greater as its surface area increases and its thickness diminishes. In a cylindrical structure, area and reciprocal thickness vary as the square root of length, hence the membrane capacity and conductance, being proportional to both variables, would change in direct proportion to the length.

If the muscle is subjected to a constant rate of stretching ('dynamic' phase), the length of the muscle varies according to

$$l = l_0 (1 + kt), \tag{1}$$

where l is varying length, l_0 the initial length of the muscle, t is time and k a velocity constant determining the rate of stretching. The changes in capacity and conductance of the membrane are then described by equations (2) and (3):

$$C = C_0 (1 + kt), \tag{2}$$

$$1/R = G = G_0 (1 + kt), \tag{3}$$

where R and C are the varying values of membrane resistance and capacity. It is seen that the membrane time constant RC remains constant during the stretch ($= R_0 C_0$; cf. Ramsey, 1947). Current will flow from the source E into the capacity tending to keep it charged to the resting potential. The flow of charge dQ/dt is described by equation (4):

$$\frac{dQ}{dt} = p \frac{dC}{dt} + C \frac{dp}{dt} = \frac{E - p}{R}, \tag{4}$$

where p is the varying potential across the membrane. From equation (2)

$$\frac{dC}{dt} = kC_0; \tag{5}$$

hence
$$\frac{dp}{dt} = \frac{E - p}{RC} - \frac{pk}{1 + kt}. \tag{6}$$

The solution of equation (6), for which I am indebted to Dr E. J. Harris, is given by

$$p = E \left[1 - \frac{kRC}{1 + kt} (1 - e^{-t/RC}) \right] \tag{7}$$

for $p = E$, at $t = 0$. The 'dynamic depolarization' is given by $E - p$, and its relative value by $(E - p)/E$:

$$\frac{E - p}{E} = \frac{kRC}{1 + kt} (1 - e^{-t/RC}). \tag{8}$$

To find this value we must know the time constant RC and the rate of stretching k. When k is made very small compared with $1/RC$, the depolarization, i.e. $(E - p)/E$, develops exponentially with time constant RC to a value given approximately by kRC, and with continued stretching it slowly declines. Tentatively, one may, therefore, derive an approximate value of RC from the initial development of the depolarization with low rates of stretch (p. 267, Fig. 6C), the result being of the order of 3 msec.

With a rate of stretching of 20 mm. per sec. and an initial length of 16 mm., k is 1·25 sec.$^{-1}$. The maximum depolarization in this case should be only 0·4 % of the resting potential. Experimentally, a depolarization was observed which amounted to about 10 % of the recorded spike, and the value at the terminal membrane must have been even greater on account of the inevitable attenuation in the terminal axon branches.

It is clear that with a total extension of 10 % of the muscle length the membrane capacity, according to equation (2), could not increase more than 10 % and, therefore, the depolarization could not exceed this value, no matter at what rate the muscle was being extended.

For very fast 'instantaneous' stretches at which k becomes very large, and t very small compared with RC, equation (8) reduces to

$$\frac{E-p}{E} = \frac{kt}{1+kt};$$

hence a 10 % stretch (i.e. $kt = 0\cdot1$) could reduce the resting potential of the membrane, at the most, by 9 %.

In the experiments, however, depolarizations of up to 30–50 % of the spike potential were found. Although there are uncertainties in comparing the amplitudes of local, and propagated, potential changes (see Katz, 1950b, Method), the observed stretch effect must involve a large reduction of the resting potential at the sensory terminals. The fact that the depolarization reaches a maximum level with rates of 0·2 m. per sec. indicates that at this and higher rates of stretching the local depolarization may be complete. All these observations suggest that the electrical effect of stretching is much greater than that calculated on the simple condenser hypothesis. This hypothesis, therefore, must either be discarded or coupled with a further assumption, namely that the mechanical deformation of the nerve endings is greater than that of the adjoining muscle tissue (see p. 277).

My thanks are due to Prof. A. V. Hill for the facilities provided in his laboratory and to Mr J. L. Parkinson for his invaluable assistance. I am also indebted to Dr E. J. Harris and Mr D. A. Scholl for frequent discussion and advice.

REFERENCES

Adrian, E. D. & Gelfan, S. (1933). *J. Physiol.* **78**, 271.
Arvanitaki, A. (1938). *Les Variations Graduées de la Polarisation des Systèmes Excitables.* Paris.
Bernhard, C. G. (1942). *J. Neurophysiol.* **5**, 32.
Feng, T. P. (1932). *J. Physiol.* **74**, 441.
Fessard, A. (1936). *Recherches sur l'Activité Rythmique des Nerfs Isolés.* Paris.
Granit, R. (1947). *Sensory Mechanisms of the Retina.* London.
Hartline, H. K. & Graham, C. H. (1932). *J. cell. comp. Physiol.* **1**, 277.
Hodgkin, A. L. (1938). *Proc. Roy. Soc.* B, **126**, 87.
Hodgkin, A. L. (1948). *J. Physiol.* **107**, 165.
Katz, B. (1949a). *J. exp. Biol.* **26**, 201.
Katz, B. (1949b). *J. Physiol.* **109**, 9 P.
Katz, B. (1950a). *Colloques Internat. C.N.R.S.* Paris.

Katz, B. (1950b). *J. Physiol.* **111**, 248.

Lorente de Nó, R. (1947). *A Study of Nerve Physiology*, **1** and **2**. In *Stud. Rockefeller Inst. med. Res.* **131** and **132**. New York.

Matthews, B. H. C. (1931a). *J. Physiol.* **71**, 64.

Matthews, B. H. C. (1931b). *J. Physiol.* **72**, 153.

Pantin, C. F. A. (1937). *Proc. Roy. Soc.* B, **123**, 397.

Parry, D. A. (1947). *J. exp. Biol.* **24**, 211.

Ramsey, R. W. (1947). *Ann. New York Acad. Sci.* **47**, 675.

Stevens, S. S. & Davis, H. (1938). *Hearing.* New York.

STRETCH RECEPTOR DISCHARGES DURING MUSCLE CONTRACTION

By CARLTON C. HUNT* AND STEPHEN W. KUFFLER

From the Wilmer Institute, The Johns Hopkins Hospital and University, Baltimore, Maryland

(*Received* 4 *July* 1950)

The analysis of the behaviour of individual sensory fibres was begun by Adrian over twenty years ago and was extended by Bronk, Zotterman, Matthews, and others. A requisite to such analysis was the recording from single fibre preparations. By this technique, Matthews made a detailed study of stretch receptors in muscles of the frog (1931 *a*, *b*) and of the cat (1933). In the latter paper he described the response patterns of different types of receptors to external stretch and to contraction of the muscle. This classical paper provides the background for the present study. Matthews (1933) found that the individual stretch receptors in the cat fell into two principal categories: (1) the A fibres (A_1 and A_2) which under most conditions showed a slowing or cessation of their discharge rate during contraction; and (2) the B fibres which exhibited an acceleration of their discharge rate during contraction. He concluded that A fibres come from endings located in the muscle spindles, their decreased response during contraction being due to a lessened stretch on the spindle when the surrounding muscle fibres contracted. The B fibres he regarded as originating in the tendon organs, their behaviour indicating that they were further stretched during contraction. Fulton and Pi-Suñer (1928) had predicted such an 'in series' and 'in parallel' behaviour of receptors from tendon organs and from muscle spindles on the basis of the 'silent period' of the muscle during the stretch reflex.

In a recent study (Kuffler, Hunt & Quilliam, 1951) of the function of small diameter efferent fibres in the lumbosacral ventral roots of cats, it was found that stimulation of these fibres increased the afferent discharge from A-type receptors in muscle, and it was concluded that these efferent fibres excited contractile elements within the muscle spindle, the intrafusal muscle fibres. Accordingly, the muscle spindle discharge is influenced by external stretch and the various modifications of stretch during contraction, as well as by the nervous mechanism of the efferent small-nerve fibres.

* Senior Fellow of the National Research Council.

Hunt, C. C., and S. W. Kuffler. Stretch receptor discharges during muscle contraction. *J. Physiol.* **113**: 298–315, 1951.

It has been the main purpose of the present study to differentiate between the responses from sensory endings in the muscle spindles which are solely a consequence of contraction of the extrafusal muscle fibres, and those in which nervous excitation of muscle elements within the spindle is also involved. The responses of over 500 stretch receptors from the soleus and several hundred from other leg muscles, principally the flexor digitorum longus, have been investigated during contraction. An attempt has been made to correlate the discharges with the dynamic events occurring in the different components of the muscle.

Matthews's classification of A and B receptor types has been used. However, in the present study the A group includes all receptors which show a decrease in discharge rate during contraction, although under various conditions responses may appear during the development of tension.

METHOD

The experimental procedure has been fully described in the previous papers (Kuffler *et al.* 1951; Hunt & Kuffler, 1951). Cats were usually anaesthetized with Dial-Urethane (Ciba) and, when required, with supplementary pentobarbitone sodium. Several experiments were performed on cats decerebrated under preliminary ether anaesthesia without any appreciable difference in results. In most experiments a rigid isometric arrangement was used, but occasionally responses were observed during isotonic contractions. Sensory discharges in single afferent fibres from the muscle were recorded in dorsal root filaments. The speed of conduction in sensory fibres was derived from the stimulus-response intervals following excitation of the nerve to the muscle. The conduction distance was carefully measured at the end of the experiment and the average velocities calculated.

RESULTS

(1) *The A-discharge type*

When appreciable muscle shortening was permitted, or during isometric contractions at low initial tensions, the discharge in A fibres, set up by steady external stretch, abruptly ceased during a submaximal or maximal twitch. The discharge was resumed at times during relaxation which varied in different receptors. This could be seen especially well in the simultaneous recording of impulses from two A receptors (Fig. 1). The unit giving the smaller potential showed no baseline discharge with this initial tension but exhibited a group of discharges during relaxation which began earlier than those of the 'larger' unit. In the latter the discharge during relaxation was at a higher rate than the baseline, as was frequently seen. When the initial tension was sufficiently great, the baseline discharge rate was generally high and some units showed merely a slowing of this rate rather than a complete 'silence' during contraction, as already observed by Matthews (1933). All the findings support the view that A receptors are located in the muscle spindles (Matthews, 1933). The diversity in the discharge pattern of different A-type receptors during contraction can probably be explained by the varied position of these spindles within the muscles (see discussion).

In general, the endings giving A-type discharges had a lower threshold to external stretch than the B group, and many exhibited spontaneous activity when no external tension was applied to the tendon (cf. also Matthews, 1933). However, A units were occasionally encountered which required a steady stretch of 100–200 g. to evoke a continuous discharge.

Increased discharge rates in A units during contraction were observed under a variety of conditions. Most of these could probably be classed as A_2 types according to Matthews (see below). As shown in the previous papers, the afferent discharge during contraction could be increased by small-nerve stimulation. However, in addition, exclusive excitation of the large diameter motor fibre group sometimes caused the endings in spindles to discharge during contraction. A differentiation between afferent discharges set up by nerve fibres

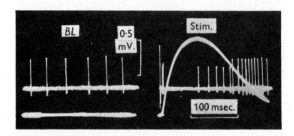

Fig. 1. Recording of two individual A-unit responses from soleus in a dorsal root filament. Initial tension 40 g. *BL*: baseline discharge. Stim.: maximal single stimulus to motor nerve. Note unit giving larger potential ceased discharging during contraction and resumed at a high rate during relaxation. Unit giving smaller potential had no baseline discharge at this initial tension. It discharged during relaxation much earlier than the larger unit. Second beam represents strain gauge record, maximal twitch tension is 340 g.

in the distinct large or small diameter groups was not difficult. The latter were activated by stimuli to the muscle nerve which were two to four times the strength required to excite the larger fibres. Furthermore, small-nerve excitation was not effective with single stimuli during comparable degrees of muscle contraction. It was therefore of particular interest, after exclusion of small-nerve effects, to decide whether discharges of certain A units during contraction were: (1) due to excitation of the intrafusal muscle fibres in the spindle by efferent fibres of the larger diameter group; or (2) the result of tension changes set up solely by the extrafusal muscle elements, the muscle spindle reacting passively to stretch.

Afferent discharges from spindles caused by large diameter motor nerve stimulation. In the present study a number of A units were found which showed responses during twitch contraction, in most cases only when there was a high initial tension (100–300 g.) on the tendon and only when external shortening was minimal. These responses were rare in receptors from the soleus, but were seen fairly frequently in such muscles as the peroneus longus and brevis, and flexor digitorum longus. A number of examples of these response types are given below, but it should be emphasized that there are no rigid categories, and numerous intermediate responses were observed.

Certain receptors gave a pause or slowing of discharge during an isometric twitch at low initial tensions (0–50 g.), but at higher tensions showed discharges during contraction. In some cases the response appeared at a strength of stimulus to the muscle nerve near maximal for contraction. This showed the

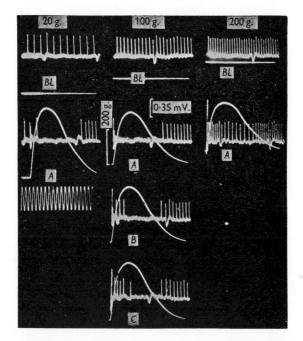

Fig. 2. Recording of single A-unit discharge from soleus. *BL*: baseline discharges at 20, 100 and 200 g. *A*, 20 g.: maximal single stimulus to nerve. Cessation of discharge during contraction. *A*, 100 g.: submaximal stimulus to nerve causes contraction of 295 g. with pause. *B*: slightly stronger stimulus, contraction of 315 g. with discharge during tension rise. *C*: just maximal stimulus. Contraction of 325 g. with more discharge during rise of tension. *A*, 200 g.: maximal stimulus. Note increased discharge rate during tension rise, no pause. Time base 50 c.p.s.

closest similarity to Matthews's A_2 response (see later). An example is seen in Fig. 2. The receptor ceased to discharge during an isometric twitch at an initial tension of 20 g. with submaximal or maximal (*A*, 20 g.) stimulation of the nerve to the muscle. When the initial tension was raised to 100 g., a contraction 90 % of maximal (*A*, 100 g.) produced only a pause, but with a contraction 97 % of maximal (*B*, 100 g.) or maximal (*C*, 100 g.), a group of discharges appeared during the rising phase of the twitch response. This was followed by a pause before the discharges during relaxation began. At a higher initial tension of 200 g. a single maximal nerve stimulus (A, 200 g.) increased the discharge rate during the rising phase of contraction and no pause was observed.

In a number of units this type of response could also be elicited at higher initial tensions with submaximal stimulation of the muscle nerve. An example is provided by Fig. 3, which illustrates a unit with a pause during a maximal twitch at an initial tension of 10 g. and a discharge during a maximal, or 46 % of maximal, twitch at an initial tension of 100 g.

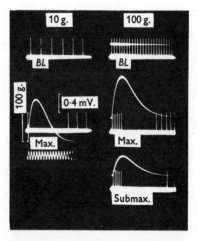

Fig. 3. Recording of single A-discharge unit from a small soleus muscle in a kitten. Left: initial tension 10 g. *BL*: baseline discharge. Max.: maximal stimulus to muscle nerve with cessation of discharge during contraction. Time base 50 c.p.s. Right: initial tension 100 g. Max.: maximal stimulus to nerve; contraction 148 g. Submax.: submaximal stimulus to nerve; contraction 68 g. Note similar discharges during contraction.

The large nerve fibres which set up discharges during contraction could sometimes be isolated in ventral root subdivisions, as illustrated in Fig. 4. There a discharge was set up during the rising phase of a twitch when the whole nerve to the flexor digitorum longus was maximally stimulated (C). When the ventral root was subdivided, it was found that only one efferent fibre produced a similar effect (A), while all the remaining nerve fibres caused only a pause during contraction. With tetanic stimulation (B) to the single fibre, a series of discharges resulted during the tension rise. This large motor fibre was easily identified when recording from the nerve before its entry into the muscle. It conducted at 104 m./sec. (D). It is also of interest that this single motor unit produced a maximum tetanic tension of 42·5 g., and 15 g. following a single stimulus at an optimal initial tension of 10 g. This is considerably in excess of previous estimates of the tension developed by individual motor units as deduced from motor fibre counts (Eccles & Sherrington, 1930; Clark, 1931).

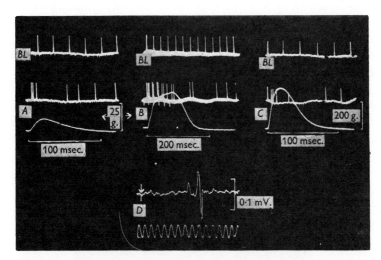

Fig. 4. Recording of single A-unit response from flexor digitorum longus. Initial tension 25 g. *BL*: baseline discharges. Note differences in sweep speeds. *A*: single stimulus to single large efferent fibre in ventral root filament. *B*: train of 6 stimuli at 68/sec. to the same efferent fibre (artefacts, small downward deflexions). *C*: maximal single stimulus to whole muscle nerve. Note similar discharges during tension rise as in *A*. *D*: stimulation of the single efferent fibre in ventral root filament, recording from nerve to muscle. Time base 5000 c.p.s. Conduction distance 16·2 cm. Average conduction velocity 104 m./sec. Potentials: *A* to *C*, 0·5 mV. Note different strain gauge sensitivities.

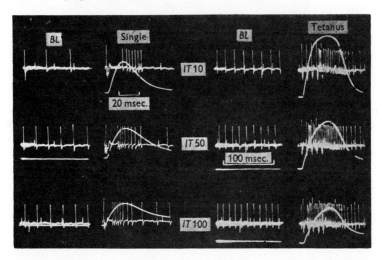

Fig. 5. Recording of single A unit from flexor digitorum longus. Left: baseline discharge (*BL*) and response to single maximal nerve stimulus (Single) at initial tensions (*IT*) of 10, 50, and 100 g. Note that discharge during twitch is resumed progressively earlier as tension is raised. Right: slower sweep speed. Baseline discharge (*BL*), and tetanus of 5 stimuli at 10 msec. intervals, strength just maximal for contraction. Note artifacts. The discharges again occur earlier as initial tension is raised. Potentials 0·4 mV. At *IT* 10 g. twitch tension 260 g.; strain gauge sensitivity reduced for tetanus.

Multiple innervation of individual muscle fibres mainly accounts for the higher tensions recorded. This will be reported at a later date.

In many receptors in which the discharges ceased during contraction, they were resumed progressively earlier as the initial tension was raised. An example is seen in Fig. 5. At an initial tension of 10 g. a single stimulus to the muscle nerve gave a pause during the rising phase of contraction, followed by a group of discharges beginning at about the peak of tension. Increasing the initial tension to 50 g. caused this group of discharges to begin earlier, actually during

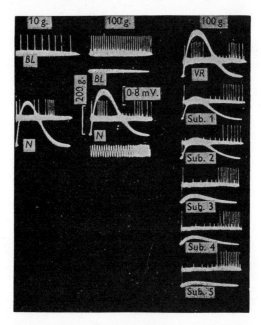

Fig. 6. Recording of single A unit from soleus. Initial tension, 10 and 100 g. *BL*: baseline discharge. *N*, 10 g. and *N*, 100 g.: stimulus to nerve just maximal for contraction. Note discharges during twitch at 100 g. *VR*: single stimulus to V.R. S2. Subdivisions 1–5: single stimulus to five subdivisions comprising V.R. S2. Note discharges during twitch on stimulation of *VR* (or nerve), but not of subdivisions 1–5. Time base 50 c.p.s.

the rising phase of the twitch, and at a tension of 100 g. the onset was still earlier. During a tetanus (5 stimuli at 10 msec. intervals) discharges were elicited during contraction even at initial tension 10 g. At higher initial tensions (50 and 100 g.) discharges started much sooner.

Absence of specific spindle innervation by large efferent twitch-producing nerve fibres. The diverse discharge types during contraction, as illustrated in Figs. 2–4, were analysed by stimulation of various components of the motor innervation, particularly by subdividing the ventral root outflow. The following results indicate that this type of response during contraction may not be due to specific motor innervation of the muscle spindle.

(1) Fig. 6 shows an example of a unit which gave discharges during a twitch set up by stimulation of either the muscle nerve (N, 100 g.) or of the second sacral ventral root (VR), at an initial tension of 100 g. At a lower tension of 10 g. only a pause occurred during maximal nerve stimulation (N, 10 g.). When this ventral root was divided into five parts and these were stimulated separately at an initial tension of 100 g. (subdivisions 1–5), only a pause occurred during contraction. When these five subdivisions were subsequently stimulated together, they again gave the discharge during contraction. If the responses during contraction were a consequence of excitation of muscle elements within

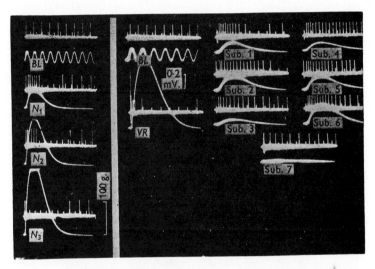

Fig. 7. Recording of single A unit from soleus.   Left column—BL: baseline, initial tension 11 g. Time base 20 c.p.s. N_1 and N_2, submaximal single stimulus to muscle nerve. N_3, maximal stimulus. Note discharges during submaximal contraction and pause during maximal contraction. Right—initial tension 20 g. BL: baseline. Time base 20 c.p.s. VR: maximal single shock to V.R. S2. Note the pause. Subdivisions 1–7: single stimulus to seven subdivisions of V.R. S2. Each of these causes an increased discharge rate during contraction.

the spindle, they should have occurred on stimulation of at least one of the VR subdivisions. In fact, due to the contraction of fewer of the extrafusal muscle fibres when only a portion of the motor outflow was stimulated, excitation of the subdivisions separately would provide conditions more favourable for demonstration of the effect of intrafusal muscle fibre contraction (see previous paper).

(2) Conversely, in some A units discharges during contraction could be obtained by stimulation of a number of subdivisions of the ventral root outflow. Fig. 7 illustrates an A unit which gave discharges during a submaximal twitch (N_1 and N_2). However, on maximal stimulation of the nerve (N_3), or of the entire ventral root outflow (VR) to the muscle, there occurred a cessation of the

discharge during contraction. When the ventral root outflow was then divided into seven parts, stimulation of each of these produced an increased discharge rate during contraction (subdivisions 1–7). The seven subdivisions, collected and stimulated together, again gave only a pause in the discharge during contraction. If the discharges resulting from stimulation of subdivisions 1–7 were due to specific efferent innervation to the spindle, one would have to assume that each subdivision contained at least one large diameter nerve fibre to that spindle. However, histological data do not support such an assumption.

From such experiments, it is concluded that the discharges during contraction in certain A units, resulting from stimulation of large efferent fibres, are not due to activation of the intrafusal muscle elements. An explanation must rather be sought in the contractile events outside the muscle spindle.

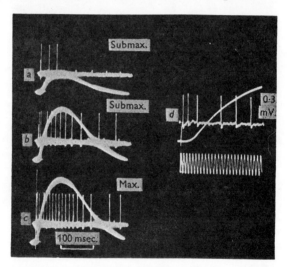

Fig. 8. Recording of single B-unit response from soleus. *a*, *b*, and *c*: single stimuli to muscle nerve at increasing strengths. Note gradation of afferent discharge rate with increasing tension. There was no baseline discharge at this initial tension of 20 g. *d*: same as *c* but faster sweep. Single maximal nerve shock. Time 500 c.p.s. Note 'early discharge' is followed by a pause before 'usual' B response begins (see section 4). Maximal twitch tension 340 g.

(2) *B-type receptors*

The responses of these endings during contraction were found to be identical with those described by Matthews (1933). Their discharge rate was always increased during contraction in relation to the tension developed, as illustrated in Fig. 8, *a-c*. About one-quarter of the endings which Matthews examined were of this type. We have the impression, from the examination of about 500 fibres in the soleus alone, that they may occur somewhat more frequently, perhaps up to 40% (Fig. 9). In general, the B units had a high threshold to stretch, and many gave no steady discharge with a maintained external tension

of 100–200 g. However, occasional B fibres were found to discharge continu-
ously even at 5–10 g. tension.

No effect of small-nerve innervation on B receptors has been observed. The
discharge rate in these units appeared to depend only on the tension developed.
The lack of any physiological evidence of a specific efferent innervation to these
units is in accord with their identification as tendon organ receptors.

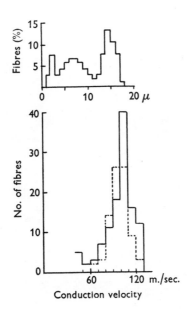

Fig. 9. Above: histological fibre diameter spectrum of nerve to soleus (cat) taken from Lloyd &
Chang (1948). Below: conduction velocities of individual fibres from stretch receptors in soleus
plotted against number of fibres. Solid line: *A* units; broken line: *B* units. Scale of conduction
velocity has been made comparable to scale of diameters in upper figure. Note lack of difference in velocities in *A* and *B* fibres. Both fall into the larger group (I) of the histological
spectrum.

(3) *Conduction Velocities of A and B Fibres*

Conduction velocities of over 200 individual fibres from stretch receptors in the
soleus were determined by stimulation of the muscle nerve and recording from
dorsal root filaments. From the stimulus-response interval 0·1 msec. was
deducted for 'setting-up' time at the stimulating cathode (Blair & Erlanger,
1936). Fig. 9 illustrates graphically the results and the histological afferent fibre
diameter spectrum obtained from this same muscle nerve by Lloyd & Chang
(1948). Since the conduction velocity and diameter are directly related, the
scale of the abscissa has been made comparable, a factor of 6 being used for
conversion (Hursh, 1939; Gasser & Grundfest, 1939). It is striking that there is
no consistent difference in conduction velocity between A and B fibres. Also,
the majority of the stretch afferent fibres fall into group I of the histological

spectrum, i.e. the group of largest diameters. The whole conduction velocity distribution is slightly shifted in the direction of faster conduction from what is expected from the histological data. Some small consistent error in measurement may be responsible for this discrepancy.

The group of fibres conducting below 60 m./sec. has not yet been investigated, although such fibres have been detected in filaments of the dorsal roots. Many of these slow-conducting fibres do not show responses to contractions or to stretch of the muscle.

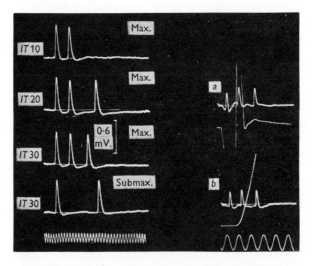

Fig. 10. Left: recording from single A unit from soleus at indicated initial tensions and strength of single stimulus to muscle nerve. Time base 2000 c.p.s. In each record the first impulse is set up by direct stimulation of the afferent fibre within the muscle nerve; the subsequent impulses arise from the sensory ending. Note that with maximal stimulation the early discharge varies with the initial tension. Also, submaximal stimulation changes number and latency of discharge. Right: recording from single unit from flexor digitorum longus at initial tension of 10 g. *a*: early discharge recorded together with earliest onset of muscle action potential. *b*: early discharge recorded together with tension. Strain gauge sensitivity high. Time base 500 c.p.s. (see text).

(4) *The Early Discharge*

A response not previously described has been detected in many stretch afferents following stimulation of the ventral roots or of the whole nerve to muscles. This response, termed the 'early discharge', consists of several impulses at high frequency occurring with a brief latency after stimulation. It was found in a large proportion of both A and B units from all muscles which have been examined and was seen in decerebrate preparations as well as those anaesthetized with 'Dial'. Fig. 10 illustrates such an early discharge in an A unit from the soleus. As a result of maximal stimulation of the whole nerve near its entry into the muscle, the afferent fibre is directly excited, resulting in an antidromic impulse passing down towards the nerve terminal, and an impulse conducted centrally to the dorsal root filament where it is recorded. Thus, the first impulse in each sweep of Fig. 10 is the result of direct stimulation of the afferent fibre, and its latency provides a measure of its conduction velocity. The subsequent impulses conducted in the same nerve fibre can be shown to result from excitation of a stretch receptor in the muscle. The fact that the 'directly' excited impulse is identical with those from the receptor, proves that only one afferent from this muscle is recorded in the dorsal rootlet. Whenever other fibres were present an additional potential was readily seen. Similar early discharges, as in Fig. 10, were elicited when the ventral root outflow to the muscle was stimulated. The number of impulses in the early discharge, and their latencies, could be varied by changing the initial tension of the muscle. Thus, maximal stimulation at a tension of 30 g. (Fig. 10) caused an early discharge of two impulses with latencies of 3·8 and 6·7 msec. When the initial tension was reduced to 10 g., only one impulse was set up by the same stimulation with a latency of 3·7 msec. The relationship between stretch and the process that causes the early discharge has been regularly observed. At a constant initial tension the early discharge also showed variation with the strength of stimulation of the motor nerve. In Fig. 10, for instance, at an initial tension of 30 g., when the stimulus was made submaximal the early discharge was reduced to one impulse with a greater latency of 8·7 msec.

The number of impulses in the early discharge varied from one afferent fibre to another. Most frequently it consisted of one to three impulses, and more than five impulses were not seen. The frequency of the discharge could be as high as 600 to 700/sec. In fact, the intervals were sometimes so short that successive impulses travelled in the relative refractory periods produced by the previous ones and showed, therefore, a decreased amplitude.

Estimates of the time course of the processes involved in setting up the early discharge are best obtained by simultaneous recording of the earliest onset of the muscle action potential. From the interval between the latter and the first afferent impulse from the stretch receptor must be deducted the conduction time from the sensory ending to the dorsal root filament. After such calculations it was found that the first impulse in the early discharge may be set up as little as 1·0 msec. after the earliest propagated muscle impulse (Fig. 10 a). The latencies between the muscle potential and early discharge were similar when the muscle nerve or ventral roots were stimulated.

When the early discharge was recorded together with the tension changes, it often preceded slightly the earliest tension rise at the tendon (0·7 msec. in Fig. 10 b). In comparing these two events the conduction time in the sensory fibre was again deducted.

There appears to be no indication that the early discharge is due to the effect of any specific efferent innervation to the spindles. In the first place it occurs in both A and B receptors. Secondly, stimulation of the ventral root outflow indicates that this discharge depends essentially on tension development. Thus, in a representative experiment an early discharge was elicited on stimulation of one portion of the ventral root, but when this was further subdivided into several parts, each of these, stimulated separately, gave none. The subdivisions when collected again and stimulated together, set up the discharge. In some experiments, on the other hand, an early discharge was obtained on stimulation of a whole ventral root and of several of its subdivisions.

Since the above experiments show that the early discharge is not caused by a specific efferent innervation acting on stretch receptors, one has to look for some other excitatory mechanism. An excitation of the stretch receptor by 'direct' action of the muscle action potential is quite unlikely, since the phenomenon (i) depends on muscle tension, (ii) can be caused by excitation of motor units (cf. above), *each* of which would not be expected to cause potential changes sufficient for excitation in the immediate receptor surround, and (iii) the latency prolongation with lowered muscle tension may be up to 6 msec., a delay too long for a strong excitatory effect of the muscle action potential to persist. One therefore has to assume that the early discharge is caused by tension changes which arise within the muscle before they are recorded myographically. This is not unreasonable, since it is known from Hill's work (1949) that even under the most favourable conditions for recording, a considerable delay is present between the actual tension rise within the muscle and its detection at the tendon.

The early discharge cannot be the result of 'simple' stretch on elements in series with the receptor. Otherwise it would be expected quite regularly in B receptors, and not in A units. Furthermore, there is always a distinct interval between the early discharge and the onset of the 'regular' B response (Fig. 8d). One may perhaps think that the initial shortening in different contractile elements proceeds at slightly different rates, resulting in a short transient rise of tension in some receptors.

DISCUSSION

Matthews (1933) found that some 25 % of the units from cat muscles showed a pause in the baseline discharge during submaximal contraction, but with near-maximal stimulus strength (80–130 % of maximal) an increased discharge rate resulted during contraction. This effect (A_2) consisted of a group of discharges during the rising phase of a twitch response and frequently depended on the presence of considerable initial muscle tension. Many afferent units examined in the present study showed similar responses. Whenever discharges with maximal single stimuli appeared, they became more pronounced during a tetanus. As far as can be determined from stimulus strengths, the efferent fibres producing these effects belong to the large fibre group. In a few units afferent discharges have been evoked during a twitch, only when the stimulus strength was increased to about 25 % above that necessary to cause apparently maximal contraction. However, on ventral root subdivision the efferent fibres producing this effect were still shown to be twitch-producing fibres of the large group. Some units also gave discharges during contraction with half 'maximal' or even weaker stimulation. Thus it appears that stimulation of large efferent fibres of diverse threshold and size can evoke discharges in A units during contraction.

In the preceding study (Hunt & Kuffler, 1951) evidence was presented that all afferents which arise in muscle spindles can be excited by small-nerve fibres through their action on the intrafusal muscle fibres. Since the same muscle afferents may also be caused to discharge by stimulation of the larger ventral root fibres, an attempt was made to decide whether the latter also innervate the spindle intrafusal elements. It is known from histological studies (for references see Barker, 1948) that the mammalian muscle spindle can receive one or perhaps two efferent fibres of 6–7 μ. in diameter, in addition to a larger number of smaller fibres of 3–4 μ., as measured within or near the spindle. However, the average diameter of these fibres during their course between the ventral roots and the muscle is not known.

The diameters of the efferent fibres in the muscle nerves are distributed in two distinct groups, the larger having a peak of around 10–14 μ., the smaller about 4 to 5 μ. The efferent fibres of 3–4 μ. at the spindle certainly belong to the latter group which has been the subject of the present 'small-nerve' studies. The 6–7 μ. fibres may also belong to the small-nerve group but might possibly be derived from the large ventral root fibres, their diameter reduced by tapering. In the latter case they would not innervate the spindles exclusively because it has been shown that all the large fibres set up motor unit twitch responses in the extrafusal muscle fibres (Kuffler *et al.* 1951). In the frog, Katz (1949) has clearly shown that large efferent fibres innervating extrafusal elements may also send branches to the intrafusal muscle fibres of the spindle.

Although it could not be excluded with certainty that large nerve fibres in the cat may sometimes innervate both intrafusal (spindle) and extrafusal muscle fibres, it was never found to be so in all instances examined in this study. This was clearly shown whenever the ventral root contribution to muscles was scrutinized by stimulating its components separately (section 1). One may therefore conclude that the largest efferent fibres to the spindles which were studied do not arise from the large diameter group of ventral root fibres. It would also be difficult to assume that the responses during a twitch, set up by large nerve fibres, are the result of intrafusal muscle fibre contraction, since similar responses are not seen when these same muscle spindle elements are excited by small-nerve fibres. Since the 3–4 μ. as well as the 6–7 μ. efferent fibres to a spindle may innervate a number of intrafusal muscle fibres (Barker, 1948), there is no *a priori* reason to expect a great difference in their effectiveness. If a difference did exist, however, two types of excitatory processes might have to be postulated for nerve fibres innervating the same structure, such as propagated responses set up by 'larger' fibres and local activation by the smaller fibres. This appears unlikely.

Since large efferent nerve fibres can cause discharges during contraction in some spindle receptors without excitation of intrafusal elements, an explanation must be sought in an effect produced on the spindle by activation of the extrafusal muscle fibres. The most apparent assumption is that some spindles, by the peculiarity of their insertion, may lie 'in series' with certain contracting muscle fibres so that they are pulled upon during contraction. Although the experimental findings show that under most conditions spindles respond as though they were in parallel to the contracting muscle fibres, some variations in the mode of their attachments are likely, particularly in complex muscles. In addition to such explanations certain of these responses may be due to tension changes on strategically located spindles which may result from forces arising from unequal rates of contraction in elements of the same muscle. In this regard, Gordon & Holbourn (1949) have recently demonstrated variations in the time course of contraction in different portions of the same muscle.

A number of units had a short 'silent' period at the onset of contraction followed by a train of impulses beginning during the tension rise, particularly at high initial tensions (Fig. 5). The onset of discharges probably reflects the beginning of re-extension of the spindle following shortening of the contractile elements. Hill (1949) has shown that the 'activation' of the contractile elements in muscle begins abruptly at the end of the latent period. His analysis of the intensity and duration of this contractile 'activation', by the application of sudden stretches to the muscle during different periods of the twitch response, indicates that the intensity of the 'active state' begins to decline before the twitch tension recorded from the tendon has reached a maximum. Thus, tension changes within the muscle during contraction may be reflected in the spindle discharge before they are recorded at the tendon. If such an explanation is correct for this type of discharge occurring during a twitch, then one may assume that the discharge during a tetanus results from a rapid series of re-extensions. This would imply an intermittence in the 'active state' of the contractile elements at frequencies as high as 100/sec. Support for such a view is provided by the observation that certain B units discharge at the frequency of stimulation during a tetanus, even if the latter is considerably higher than that required to cause fusion of the tension response recorded at the tendon.

The 'early discharge' has been found in a large number of stretch afferents of both the A and B type. This brief, high-frequency burst of impulses is set up with a short latency after motor activation of the muscle. It is not clear whether this discharge has any relation to the secondary centripetal discharge recorded in the dorsal roots after excitation of the muscles through the ventral root, as found by Lloyd (1942). His calculation of the latency of the latter discharge indicates that its onset occurs somewhat earlier than the early discharge. Both processes, however, are set up by muscle contraction and are abolished by paralytic doses of curare. The function of the early discharge is not known, but its frequent occurrence suggests that it may have some significance.

The conduction velocities in fibres from A and B receptors are similar, indicating that impulses from both type endings travel in fibres of similar diameter. The calculated diameters of most stretch receptor fibres examined fall into group I of the histological spectrum (Lloyd & Chang, 1948). The fastest conduction velocities are in accord with Lloyd's observations (1943) on the maximum velocity of afferent fibres responding to brief stretch. Such fibres from the gastrocnemius have an average maximum velocity of 116 m./sec. and set up the reflex response to brief stretch through arcs of two neurones.

It is not yet certain what type of reflex effects A and B fibres may have. On excitation of the myotatic reflex by brief, near-threshold stretch the afferent discharge will be largely set up in A units, since these usually have lower thresholds to stretch than B receptors. However, depending on the rate and magnitude of stretch a number of B endings will also be excited. When reflex effects are studied by electrical stimulation of group I fibres in muscle nerves, it is likely that A and B fibres are stimulated in proportion to their relative numbers, since no threshold differences to this type of excitation can be expected. Assuming that A and B fibres produce different effects, like excitation and inhibition, the reflex response to electrical stimulation of all group I fibres would depend on the interaction between these effects.

Most B fibres have no continuous discharge during moderate amounts of steady stretch but may respond to small increments, if suddenly applied. During reflexly maintained contraction, such as that concerned with posture, only a fraction of the motor units are excited and the moderate tension developed is sustained and without sudden fluctuation. Under these conditions the afferent discharge from stretch receptors should be mainly in the A fibres. It seems reasonable to assume that the discharge in A units is responsible for this type of reflex excitation.

Following the stretch reflex activation of a muscle, there is a period of 'silence' in the impulses from muscle fibres (Denny-Brown, 1928), not only in the muscle which was stretched, but also in adjacent muscles. The afferent discharge evoked during the reflex contraction is largely in B units, while activity in A fibres ceases or diminishes in rate. It has been suggested that the 'silent period' observed in the adjacent muscles depends on an inhibitory effect produced by the B fibres. It therefore seems likely that the reflex effects of A units are excitatory and that the B fibres may produce, in part at least, some inhibition. However, there has not yet been a direct demonstration of different effects produced by A and B fibres.

SUMMARY

1. Responses of over 700 individual stretch afferents have been observed from various hindlimb muscles of cat, in particular from the soleus. By their discharge patterns during contraction these afferents have been classified as A and B units according to Matthews's (1933) nomenclature.

2. The A receptors usually have a low threshold to stretch and cease to discharge during contraction, particularly when external muscle shortening occurs. They are presumed to arise from muscle spindles.

3. Under certain conditions the A units may show discharges during contraction. These responses may be set up by efferent small-nerve fibres. A units may also show responses during contraction when only larger, twitch-producing, efferent nerve fibres are excited. These responses usually occur only when the muscle is under high initial tension. Such discharges during contraction are not thought to be due to nervous activation of the muscle elements within the spindle, but rather to tension changes on the spindle produced by the contracting extrafusal muscle fibres. It is concluded that intrafusal muscle fibres in the cat are not innervated by large motor-nerve fibres which cause the muscle twitch responses.

4. B-type receptors usually showed a higher threshold to stretch, and their discharge rate was accelerated during contraction. They are considered to arise from tendon organs (Matthews).

5. Conduction velocities of 200 individual stretch afferents from the soleus ranged from 60 to 125 m./sec. with a peak between 90 and 110 m./sec. These correspond to the distinct large group of the afferent fibre diameter spectrum from this muscle nerve. No difference in conduction velocity between A and B fibres was found, indicating that impulses from both type receptors travel in fibres of similar diameter.

6. A discharge arising from many A and B stretch-receptors has been described, consisting of one to five impulses at high frequency occurring with brief latency after stimulation of the motor outflow to muscles. This has been termed the 'early discharge'. Its onset may occur within 1·0 msec. after the earliest onset of the muscle action potential, and it is believed to result from early tension changes within the muscle.

7. The role of different stretch afferent fibres in reflex function is briefly discussed.

This work was supported by a grant from the Rockefeller Foundation and one of us (C.C.H.) was supported by the National Foundation for Infantile Paralysis. We wish to thank Dr S. A. Talbot for his valuable help, particularly in the design of much of the equipment.

REFERENCES

Barker, D. (1948). *Quart. J. micr. Sci.* **89**, 143.

Blair, E. A. & Erlanger, J. (1936). *Amer. J. Physiol.* **114**, 309.

Clark, D. A. (1931). *Amer. J. Physiol.* **96**, 296.

Denny-Brown, D. (1928). *Proc. Roy. Soc.* B, **103**, 321.

Eccles, J. C. & Sherrington, C. S. (1930). *Proc. Roy. Soc.* B, **106**, 326.

Fulton, J. F. & Pi-Suñer, J. (1928). *J. Physiol.* **83**, 554.

Gasser, H. S. & Grundfest, H. (1939). *Amer. J. Physiol.* **127**, 393.

Gordon, G. & Holbourn, A. H. S. (1949). *J. Physiol.* **110**, 26.

Hill, A. V. (1949). *Proc. Roy. Soc.* B, **136**, 399.

Hunt, C. C. & Kuffler, S. W. (1951). *J. Physiol.* **113**, 283.

Hursh, J. B. (1939). *Amer. J. Physiol.* **127**, 131.

Katz, B. (1949). *J. exp. Biol.* **26**, 201.

Kuffler, S. W., Hunt, C. C. & Quilliam, J. P. (1951). *J. Neurophysiol.* **14**, 29.

Lloyd, D. P. C. (1942). *J. Neurophysiol.* **5**, 153.

Lloyd, D. P. C. (1943). *J. Neurophysiol.* **6**, 317.

Lloyd, D. P. C. & Chang, H. T. (1948). *J. Neurophysiol.* **11**, 199.

Matthews, B. H. C. (1931a). *J. Physiol.* **61**, 64.

Matthews, B. H. C. (1931b). *J. Physiol.* **62**, 153.

Matthews, B. H. C. (1933). *J. Physiol.* **78**, 1.

ACTION POTENTIAL

Though the first assumptions that nervous activity is based on electrical phenomena were made early in the 1700's, the opinion that the nervous impulse had a negative potential inside and a positive potential outside was not advanced until Galvani's experiments were published in 1791 (22). It was subsequently discovered that a potential change moved along an active nerve fiber. By 1850 Helmholtz (23) had measured the conduction velocity of this nerve impulse.

In 1922 Gasser and Erlanger (24) introduced the cathode tube oscillograph into the physiological laboratory to replace the somewhat less sensitive and more unwieldy capillary electrometer formerly used. They studied the compound action potential and, later, saltatory conduction (25). For their work Gasser and Erlanger received a Nobel prize in 1944. In the mid-1930's the action potential in *Nitella,* the giant plant cell, was investigated and the line of study leading to the present concepts of the action potential was set in motion.

Once the transducer mechanisms of the muscle receptor have converted mechanical energy into an electrical action potential, that action potential must be propagated along the afferent nerve to the spinal cord. Single vertebrate nerve cells were difficult to study until the techological advances of the 1930's. Until 1936 those measurements which had been done were of impedance, conduction velocity, shape and duration of the action current, and various other electrical measures across a whole nerve fiber. In 1936, J. Z. Young (26) rediscovered that the giant nerve axons of the squid *Loligo forbesi* were about a millimeter in diameter, making them accessible to study with intracellular electrodes. (The original report had been made by L. W. Williams in 1909 in a privately published doctoral thesis; [27].)

In 1939, capitalizing on Young's report and information that had been obtained from pioneering studies on single cells of *Nitella,* Hodgkin and Huxley (28), and independently and practically simultaneously Cole and Curtis, succeeded in the difficult task of recording across the membrane of the giant nerve fibers. In this way the electrical properties of the membrane itself were directly studied. The Cole and Curtis study aimed at detecting the impedance changes as an action potential passed the site on the membrane where the recording electrodes were located.

Hodgkin and Rushton reported in 1946 their findings on a quantitative determination of the electrical constants of an unmyelinated axon and also demonstrated passive local potentials in the regions of stimulating electrodes. Such findings relating to the cable properties of the axon have been essential for interpreting data obtained from intracellular recordings in other preparations.

Hodgkin and Huxley, whose work in England was interrupted by World War II, continued studies on the single giant axon preparation. In 1952, with Katz, they demonstrated that the action potential is accompanied by a sudden increase in membrane conductance—first to sodium and then to potassium (29). Using the information that they had gathered from an elegant sequence of experiments, Hodgkin and Huxley managed to formulate equations which accurately predicted the form of the action potential.

One of the technical advances which allowed the collection of the detailed data necessary for equations describing the action potential was the voltage clamp, introduced by Marmont (30). When the membrane is depolarized to a threshold voltage, a spike is inevitable, and it is normally not possible to measure the electrical properties of the membrane during the short duration of the spike. The voltage clamp utilizes negative feedback circuitry which passes current across the membrane to counteract the events underlying the action potential. This allows the membrane voltage to be controlled at all levels by the experimentor, making it possible to collect data as to the underlying currents and conductances. For their work on the squid axon, Hodgkin and Huxley shared with Eccles the 1963 Nobel Prize in Physiology.

Recent refinements of technique have resulted in the discovery that the axoplasm can be extruded from a giant axon with the membrane still able to produce an action potential (31). These advances have stimulated the performance of a large number of experiments in which artificial solutions are substituted for the axoplasm to test the effects of physical phenomena on the properties of biological membranes.

REFERENCES

22. Galvani, A. De viribus electricitatis in motu musculari. *Commentarius De Bononiensi Scientiarum et Artium Institute atque Commentarii* 7: 363 (1791).

23. Helmholtz, H. von. Messungen uber den zeitlichen Verlauf der Zuchung animalischer Muskeln und die fortpflanzungsgeschwindigkeit der Reizung in den Nerven. *Arch. Anat. Physiol.* 277 (1850).

24. Gasser, H. S., and J. Erlanger. A study of the action currents of nerve with the cathode ray oscillograph. *Am. J. Physiol.* 62: 496–524 (1922).

25. Gasser, H. S., and J. Erlanger. The role played by the sizes of the constituent fibers of a nerve trunk in determining the form of its action potential wave. *Am J. Physiol.* 80: 522–547 (1927).

26. Young, J. Z. Structure of nerve fibres and some synapses in some invertebrates. *Cold Spr. Harbor Symp. Quant. Biol.* 4: 1–6 (1936).

27. Williams, L. W. *The Anatomy of the Common Squid,* Loligo Pealii (Leseur), Leiden, 1909.

28. Hodgkin, A. L., and A. F. Huxley. Action potentials recorded from inside a nerve fibre. *Nature (London)* **144:** 710–711 (1939).

29. Hodgkin, A. L., A. F. Huxley, and B. Katz. Measurement of current-voltage relations in the membrane of the giant axon of *Loligo. J. Physiol.* **116:** 424–448 (1952).

30. Marmont, G. Studies on, the axon membrane: I. A new method. *J. Cell. Comp. Physiol.* **34:** 351–382 (1949).

31. Baker, P. F., A. L. Hodgkin, and T. I. Shaw. Replacement of the axoplasm of giant nerve fibres with artificial solutions *J. Physiol.* **164:** 330–354 (1962).

32. Baker, P. F., A. L. Hodgkin, and T. I. Shaw. The effects of changes in internal ionic concentrations on the electrical properties of perfused giant axon. *J. Physiol.* **164:** 355–374 (1962).

BIBLIOGRAPHY

Erlanger, J. and H. S. Gasser. The compound nature of the action current of nerve as disclosed by the cathode ray oscillograph. *Am. J. Physiol.* **70:** 624–666 (1924).

Cole, K. S., and H. J. Curtis. Electric impedance of *Nitella* during activity. *J. Gen. Physiol.* **22:** 37–64 (1938).

Curtis, H. J., and K. S. Cole. Membrane resting and action potentials from the squid giant axon. *J. Cell. Comp. Physiol.,* **19:** 135–144 (1942).

Ling, G., and R. W. Gerard. The normal membrane potential of frog sartorius fibers. *J. Cell. Comp. Physiol.* **34:** 383–396 (1949).

Oikawa, T., C. S. Spyropoulos, I. Tasaki, and T. Teorell. Methods for perfusing the giant axon of *Loligo pealii. Acta Physiol. Scand.* **52:** 195–196 (1961).

Tasaki, I. Permeability of squid axon membrane to various ions. *J. Gen. Physiol.* **46:** 755–772 (1963).

Hodgkin, A. L. *The Conduction of the Nervous Impulse.* Charles C. Thomas, Springfield, Illinois, 1964.

SUGGESTED TEXTS

Ruch *et al.* Chapters 1–3.

Ochs, S. Chapters 1–7.

Mountcastle, V. Chapters 50–54.

ELECTRIC IMPEDANCE OF THE SQUID GIANT AXON DURING ACTIVITY*

By KENNETH S. COLE AND HOWARD J. CURTIS

(*From the Department of Physiology, College of Physicians and Surgeons, Columbia University, New York, and the Marine Biological Laboratory, Woods Hole*)

(Accepted for publication, January 11, 1939)

The permeability of a membrane to a penetrating substance is given quantitatively by the amount of the substance which crosses a unit area of the membrane in unit time under the action of a unit force. In simple cases of ionized substances both the amount of substance and the force acting may be expressed in electrical terms. Then the permeability may be ultimately converted into coulombs per second for a square centimeter and a potential difference of 1 volt, which is the conductance, in reciprocal ohms, for a square centimeter. Marine eggs have been measured before and after fertilization and a number of tissues have been measured during activity, but the attempts to interpret the observed conductance changes have not been particularly satisfactory. Since it is quite generally believed that the depolarization of a nerve fiber membrane, during excitation and propagation, involves an increased permeability to ions there have been many attempts to detect and to measure this change as an increase in the electrical conductivity. A decrease in the longitudinal low frequency impedance of frog sciatic nerve during activity was found by Lullies (1930) (also Cole and Curtis, 1936), and a similar change was found in the transverse impedance of the squid giant fiber (Curtis and Cole, 1938). In these cases the measuring current was also the stimulating current and it was not possible to analyze the changes satisfactorily. In *Nitella*, Blinks (1936) showed with direct current transients that on excitation the membrane impedance decreased under the cathode, but it was not possible to separate the change into resistance and capacity components.

* Aided by a grant from The Rockefeller Foundation.

Cole, K. S., and H. J. Curtis. Electric impedance of the squid giant axon during activity. *J. Gen. Physiol.* **22:** 649–670, **1939.**

Recently the transverse alternating current impedance of *Nitella* has been measured during the passage of an impulse which originated several centimeters away (Cole and Curtis, 1938 *b*). These measurements showed that the membrane capacity decreased 15 per cent or less while the membrane conductance increased to about 200 times its resting value. Also this conductance increase and the membrane electromotive force decrease occurred at nearly the same time, which was late in the rising phase of the monophasic action potential. Similar measurements have now been made on Young's giant nerve fiber preparation from the squid (Young, 1936). These were undertaken first, to determine whether or not a functional nerve propagates an impulse in a manner similar to *Nitella*, and second, because the microscopic structure of the squid axon corresponds considerably better than that of *Nitella* to the postulates upon which the measurements are interpreted.

The squid axon has about the same membrane capacity (Curtis and Cole, 1938) as other nerve fibers (Cole and Curtis, 1936) and *Nitella* (Curtis and Cole, 1937). The large diameter of the axon, 0.5 mm. or more, makes it particularly favorable material since, for a given membrane conductance change, the magnitude of the observed transverse impedance change is proportional to the fiber diameter. It is also relatively easy to obtain considerable lengths of the axon which can be kept functional for hours.

The experimental procedure and the technique of analysis are fundamentally the same as those used for *Nitella* during activity, although variations have been necessary or possible because of the relatively short time intervals involved. We will present and discuss here only observations made during the passage of an impulse which has been initiated at a distant point.

Material and Dissection

The Atlantic squid, *Loligo pealii*, was used at Woods Hole for these experiments. From early May until late June excellent animals were available, but later they were smaller, not so numerous, and did not live long in the aquarium. The measuring cell was designed for an axon diameter between 530μ and 580μ and this was usually to be found in squid having a mantle length between $10\frac{1}{2}$ and $11\frac{1}{2}$ inches. Slender animals were preferred because the axons were of nearly uniform diameter over their usable length.

It seemed fairly certain that body fluids had an injurious effect, so the mantle was removed from the rest of the animal under running sea water. It was slit along the ventral mid-line, and laid out flat. The preganglionic stellate and fin nerves were then cut on each side and the mantle freed from the rest of the body. The mantle was placed on a large glass absorption cell, cooled by circulating water and illuminated from underneath, and the hindmost stellar nerve dissected out. The nerve was freed at the stellate ganglion, ligated with silk thread, and then separated from the fin nerve and the mantle up to the point where it entered the muscle. It was again ligated and cut free. The small fibers were then teased away from the giant axon in sea water in a Petri dish. The two silk threads were held against the bottom by clips on opposite sides of the dish after the nerve had been stretched until the giant axon was nearly straight. Under a binocular dissecting microscope, the small fibers were all cut near one end with a sharp pointed double edged scalpel and then pulled slightly to one side and cut free where they looped around the giant axon. The axon has a number of small branches which must be cut at a short distance from it. These can often be pulled free without immediately killing the nerve, but degeneration will usually progress slowly from that point. The fibers which remained in good condition for considerable time were usually very turgid after dissection. A 3 cm. length of axon was necessary but it was usually possible to get 6 or 8 cm. in good condition.

After the axon was placed in the measuring cell, the sea water circulation was started, and preliminary measurements made. If the impedance, the threshold for excitation, and the impedance change on excitation became constant within an hour, measurements were started. If not, the fiber was discarded because experience showed that the impedance and impedance change would decrease and the threshold for excitation would increase more or less steadily until after 4 to 6 hours the fiber failed. Under favorable conditions, the axons would have quite constant electrical characteristics for 6 to 8 hours and one remained excitable for 36 hours.

Some experiments were made at room temperature, but the majority were between 2°C. and 4°C. where the conduction velocity was less, a higher bridge input and consequent greater sensitivity could be used, and the axon survival was better. When monophasic action potentials were desired, one end of the axon was dipped in iso-osmotic KCl for a few minutes.

Measuring Cell

The measuring cell, shown in Fig. 1, is very similar to that used for *Nitella*. The axon was placed in the trough, 570μ wide and 560μ deep, cut in the top of a sheet of Victron. The entire cell was mounted on a metal box which was maintained at constant temperature by circulating water. After the axon was in place, the cell was covered with a thin microscope cover glass and sea water circulation was started through the cell by a siphon. This maintained a slight negative pressure in the trough and so held the cover glass in place. The cell assembly was mounted on the bridge panel in an insulating shield to lessen temperature changes.

The stimulating electrodes, a, impedance electrodes, b, b', and potential electrodes, c, c', were all platinized platinum. The impedance electrodes should be wide to minimize electrode polarization corrections at low frequencies and the effect of the "fringing" of the current at the electrode edges, but narrow to include as short a length of the axon as possible. The electrode width of 570μ was a fairly satisfactory compromise. The polarization was considerable below 1 kc.,[1] but the duration of the impedance change was short enough to make the interpretation of lower frequency measurements difficult, and the time of transit of a given point of the impulse past the electrode region was about 0.1 millisecond which was too short for the bridge amplifier to follow faithfully. The electrode wells used for the resting squid axon (Curtis and Cole, 1938) were not tried because of the loss in sensitivity and difficulty of construction involved.

The potential electrodes, c, c, c', c', were all 140μ wide. The "monophasic" potentials, V, were measured between the grounded impedance electrode, b, and the farther c' electrode on an inactive portion of the axon (see Fig. 9 a).

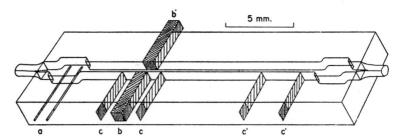

FIG. 1. Measuring cell for squid giant axon. The central trough is for the axon and the connections for circulating sea water are at each end. The axon is stimulated with electrodes, a, the transverse impedance measured between electrodes, b, b', and the action potentials between various combinations of b, c, and c'.

On the basis of simple cable theory which has been discussed ($Nitella$[2]), the monophasic action potential is proportional to the potential difference across the membrane and its slope or first derivative is proportional to the current flow parallel to the fiber axis. The density of current flow across the membrane is then given by the second derivative. For $Nitella$, the first and second derivatives were usually calculated from the monophasic action potential, but this was not a particularly satisfactory procedure. The disadvantages were even greater with the squid axon. The oscillograph time scale was not linear and completely monophasic action potentials were seldom obtained, so the extra potential electrodes were added to record the approximate derivatives directly. As is shown on p. 663, the potential difference between electrodes c, c (see Fig. 9 b) is approxi-

---

[1] Kilocycles per second.

[2] Cole, K. S., and Curtis, H. J., 1938–39, $J. Gen. Physiol.$, **22**, 58.

mately the first derivative,[3] V_t, of the potential at the impedance electrodes. Also the potential difference between the mid-point of a high resistance across the electrodes c, c and the ground electrode b (see Fig. 9 c) gives the approximate second derivative,[3] V_{tt}, at the same point.

Conduction velocities were measured by the separation between the V_t potential at electrodes c, c and that at c', c' when these were recorded on the same film.   If there was an inactive end under one c' electrode, the V potentials between this electrode and each of the c electrodes, were used to determine the conduction velocity.

Electrical Apparatus

The ellipse and motion picture technique, as used for the *Nitella* experiments, gave complete information on each excitation and would have been ideal for these experiments if the short duration of the action had not made it completely impractical.   The next best system considered was the *"Lichtbandmethode"* of Hō-zawa (1935), using the Schering bridge in which either the reactance or resistance component of an impedance change can be recorded independently of the other component.   The objections to its use were primarily practical ones for, after it was recognized that the Wheatstone bridge could be used, it was obviously inadvisable to attempt to design, construct, and learn to operate a new bridge for the investigation of a phenomenon that was not known to exist.   The alternating current Wheatstone bridge which was used and the method of making steady state impedance measurements with it have been described (Cole and Curtis, 1937).   A schematic diagram of the equipment is shown in Fig. 2.

The strength of the bridge current was kept as low as possible because it was found that even relatively small currents can cause local changes in the portion of the axon between the impedance electrodes.   By maintaining 50 to 100 mv. across the impedance electrodes for a number of minutes, the impedance change on excitation was diminished and only a partial recovery was possible.   But if the axon was then moved along the trough so that a different section was between the electrodes, the impedance change was as large as ever.   During a run, the voltage across the axon was not allowed to exceed 20 mv. and this was maintained for as short a time as possible.

As a result of the low input voltage requirement, an adequate sensitivity could be obtained only by the use of considerable detector amplification.   An ordinary audio frequency bridge output amplifier was satisfactory for *Nitella*, which has a transverse characteristic frequency[4] of 1 kc., but this did not go to high enough frequencies for the squid axon where the characteristic frequency is about 30 kc. The amplifier was first replaced by a conventional radio superheterodyne mixer, to convert the bridge output to 175 kc., and a transformer coupled amplifier tuned to this frequency.   This arrangement introduced very serious distortion when the

---

[3] $V_t = \partial V/\partial t$; $V_{tt} = \partial^2 V/\partial t^2$

[4] The frequency at which the series reactance is a maximum (Cole, 1932).

amplifier was sharply tuned so that a bridge frequency as low as 20 kc. could be used.   A balanced modulator was then substituted for the simple mixer and the amplifier tuning broadened as much as possible.   A bridge frequency of 2 kc. could then be used and the distortion was greatly decreased.

A differential resistance-capacity coupled amplifier with degeneration in the common mode was used for the action potentials.   The output of either this amplifier or the 175 kc. bridge amplifier could be switched to the vertical deflecting plates of the cathode ray oscillograph through a single stage untuned power amplifier.

The conversion of all bridge output frequencies to 175 kc. before they were impressed on the oscillograph as well as the short time intervals involved precluded

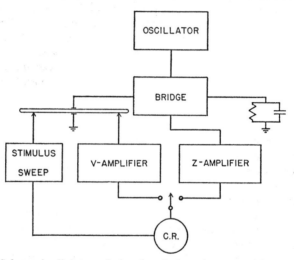

Fig. 2. Schematic diagram of the electrical equipment.   The axon is at the left, and the balancing resistance and capacity at the right, of the bridge.   The action potential and bridge amplifiers are represented by V-amplifier and Z-amplifier respectively and the cathode ray oscillograph by C. R.

the use of the *Nitella* motion picture and ellipse technique, but the use of a horizontal sweep circuit was convenient since the axon could be stimulated between one and ten times per second as was usually done.   The stimulus was a short shock which was taken from the sweep circuit in such a manner that it was applied at the start of the sweep, and a shielded transformer was used in the stimulus circuit to reduce the shock artifact.

Procedure

Experimental.—After the axon was placed in the measuring cell and had become steady, the resting parallel resistance and capacity were measured at 9 frequencies

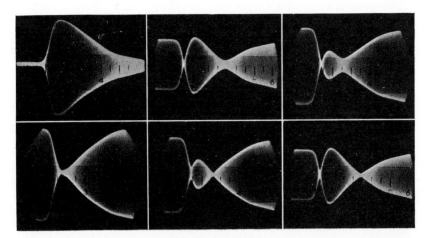

FIG. 3. Bridge output during the passage of an impulse with the bridge balanced for the impedance of the axon first at rest and then at various times during the action.   Frequency 50 kc.; maximum change, 7 per cent.

from 2 kc. to 1000 kc.   At one frequency, the bridge would then be balanced with the oscillograph which gave a narrow horizontal trace each sweep, when the stimulus was below threshold.   After the threshold was reached, the bridge went off balance when the action came between the impedance electrodes, and the oscillograph line broadened into a band.   Then as the axon recovered, the bridge returned to balance and the band narrowed down to the resting line again as shown in Fig. 4.   The width of the band at any point is proportional to the magnitude of the change of impedance, but does not give any information as to the relative values of the resistance and capacity components of this change.   The resistance and capacity of the known arm of the bridge were then altered so that, although the bridge is no longer balanced at rest, it would be balanced at some particular point during the activity as shown in Fig. 3.   In this way the resistance and capacity were measured during the action at a series of ten or fifteen points along a scale on the face of the oscillograph which was calibrated in milliseconds.

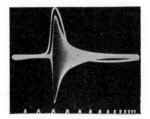

FIG. 4. Double exposure of the 2 per cent maximum bridge unbalance at 20 kc. and the monophasic action potential at one of the impedance electrodes. The time marks at the bottom are 1 millisecond apart.

The relation between the impedance change and the action potential was recorded photographically as shown in Fig. 4 (Cole and Curtis, 1938 a).   The impedance change was first exposed for about ten sweeps, the oscillograph was then switched from the bridge amplifier to action potential amplifier, the bridge oscillator turned off, and without change of the sweep circuit or stimulus, a second exposure of two or three sweeps of the action potential was made a second later on the same film.   The resistance and capacity were also measured both at rest and at the time of the maximum impedance change.

These measurements during activity were made at frequencies of 5, 10, 20, 50, 100 kc. and sometimes 200 and 500 kc.   Finally, another complete frequency run was taken on the axon at rest to show what changes had taken place during the experiment, and if these were too large the experiment was discarded.   The conduction velocity and the amplification of the action potential amplifier were measured and a time record was made to calibrate the sweep circuit.

When the axon was removed from the cell at the end of the experiment it was carefully examined and the diameter measured at the point which was between the impedance electrodes.   The cell was filled with sea water and resistance and capacity data were taken at low frequencies, to determine the electrode polarization, and at high frequencies, to measure the static capacity of the cell.

Analytical.—The data on parallel resistance and capacity, R_p and C_p, were corrected for the electrode polarization and static capacity of the cell (Cole and Curtis, 1937) and the series resistance and reactance, R_s and X_s, were calculated by

$$R_s = R_p/(1 + R_p^2 C_p^2 \omega^2): X_s = R_p^2 C_p \omega/(1 + R_p^2 C_p^2 \omega^2)$$

The frequency impedance locus, which is the path followed when X_s is plotted against R_s, as the frequency of the measuring current is varied (Cole, 1928, 1932), was plotted for the resting fiber (Fig. 5). The properties of the resting axon have been calculated from the extensions of the Rayleigh equation which have been used for single cylindrical cells (Curtis and Cole, 1937, 1938; Cole and Curtis, 1938 *b*). The average membrane capacity at 1 kc. is 1.80 μf./cm.² with an average phase angle of 71°.   The average internal specific resistance is 71 ohms cm. or about 2.9 times that of sea water.

At each frequency, the value of R_s and X_s during activity may be plotted in the same manner and trace a path which is called the time impedance locus.   The points of maximum change at five frequencies are shown in Fig. 5 and all of the 10 kc. points taken at different times during the action of another axon are shown on a larger scale in Fig. 6. If the only change during activity were a decrease of membrane resistance, then the time impedance locus at each frequency would be

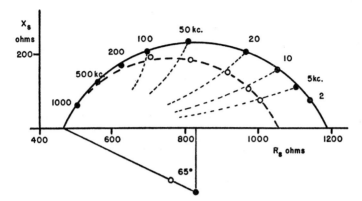

FIG. 5. Impedance loci of series resistance, R_s, vs. series reactance, X_s, in ohms. The solid circles which lie on the solid frequency locus are obtained from resting nerve at the indicated frequencies, and the open circles are the points of maximum change which lie on the heavy broken line representing the frequency locus. The light broken lines forming circular arcs are the theoretical time loci for a pure membrane resistance decrease at each of five frequencies.

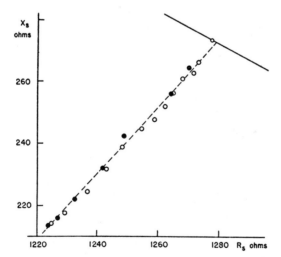

FIG. 6. Time impedance locus of series resistance, R_s, vs. series reactance, X_s, at 10 kc. during the passage of an impulse. The solid circles were taken during the impedance decrease on excitation and the open circles during the increase on recovery. The broken line represents part of a circular arc which is the theoretical locus for a pure membrane resistance change and the solid line is a portion of the resting frequency locus.

155

an arc of a circle passing through the resting point and tangent to the resistance axis at the infinite frequency extrapolation as shown in equation (8) and Fig. 11 of the *Nitella* paper.[5] This is true as a rough approximation and the minimum membrane resistances have been calculated by *Nitella* equation (6). These minimum values range from 14.7 to 53.5 ohm cm.^{2} with an average of 28 ohm cm.^{2} This minimum value is independent of frequency and it is further found that the time variation of the membrane resistance during the passage of the impulse is approximately the same for all frequencies.

The departures from these arcs are then due to a decrease of the membrane capacity during activity, which can be calculated by *Nitella* equation (9). The capacity decrease in Fig. 5 depends upon the frequency and reaches a maximum of nearly 10 per cent at 50 kc. At the other extreme is the negligible capacity change which was found from the data in Fig. 6. The average capacity decrease for all experiments is about 2 per cent. It is usually found, as can be seen in Fig. 3 that the bridge balance is not the same on the rising and falling portions of the impedance change and this means that the time locus does not retrace its initial path during recovery. Because of this the calculated capacity decrease lags slightly behind the resistance decrease during the passage of the impulse. On the other hand the impedance change records made at different frequencies are practically identical. This means that the apparent capacity change either depends upon frequency or is an artifact introduced by the bridge and its amplifier. The latter possibility will be considered later (p. 661).

It is convenient to work with the oscillograph records of the impedance change as far as possible. Since bridge balance measure-

---

[5] In the *Nitella* paper, the sentence which includes equation (8) is incorrect and should read as follows, "By eliminating r_4 we find

$$r^2 + x^2 - 2r_\infty r - [(\bar{r} - r_\infty)^2 + \bar{x}^2]x/\bar{x} + r_\infty^2 = 0$$

which is the equation of a circle having its center at the point,

$$r_\infty, \ [(\bar{r} - r_\infty)^2 + \bar{x}^2]/2\bar{x}$$

and the radius,

$$[(\bar{r} - r_\infty)^2 + \bar{x}^2]/2\bar{x}."$$

ments during the impulse indicate that the change of membrane capacity is small, equation (4) shows that the width of the impedance band on the oscillograph should be approximately proportional to the change of membrane conductance. It has been found experimentally that both the "balance" and "unbalance" data give nearly the same time course for the membrane conductance. The average time of rise to maximum conductance is between 250 and 300 μsec., but this value cannot be accepted until its accuracy has been established (see below).

Distortions and Corrections

The ideal measuring equipment would record accurately the properties of an infinitesimal length of axon, regardless of adjacent portions and independent of what happened the instant before. But in these experiments the impedance and the action potential have been measured over at least a half millimeter length of axon, while the responses of the bridge and the amplifiers may be expected to lag behind the phenomena.

Lines of current flow resulting from the action potential which would otherwise be confined to the sea water in the trough will enter and leave the impedance electrodes as the action passes them. This may alter the speed of propagation (Hodgkin, 1939) and modify other characteristics of the impulse in this region, but no attempt has been made to estimate the magnitude of these effects.

Impedance.—The effects of electrode length and current spread on the impedance measurements are the same as for the *Nitella* cell. If a perfectly sharp change of membrane conductance moved between the impedance electrodes, the observed change of impedance would be spread over the entire effective electrode length, including the region of current spread beyond the ends of the electrodes. As for the *Nitella* cell, this effect has been investigated by measuring the resistance as a cylindrical glass rod was moved along the trough with its end passing through the electrode region. The square cut end of the rod was then equivalent to the sharp transition from a non-conducting to a conducting fiber which corresponded to a sudden drop of membrane resistance.

The results of Fig. 7 show that although the actual electrode length was 570μ, and 90 per cent of the change was confined to 1000μ, the entire electrode region was over 1600μ long. If the rod moved at 12 meters per second, the 90 per cent change would require 83μsec. and the whole over 130μsec. This is a considerable portion of the time of rise of the impedance change as observed on axons having this velocity and so must be considered.

For a steady state, the deflection of the oscillograph was proportional to the difference between the impedances of the known and unknown arms of the bridge, but the response to a rapid change of impedance must also be determined. After the bridge has been thrown off balance, the currents in the bridge, oscillator, and detector circuits will change only as fast as the inductances, capacities, and resistances will permit, and the voltage appearing across the detector will be distorted.   Rough calculations indicate that under ideal conditions this effect would have a time constant of no more than a few micro-seconds.   And when bridge output voltage is applied to the modulator and amplifier further distortion may be expected for, so far as changes of amplitude are concerned, this system is equivalent to an audio frequency amplifier.   The combined characteristics of the bridge, modulator, and amplifier have been determined by recording the response to a sudden unbalance of the bridge.   The bridge was balanced with a high resist-

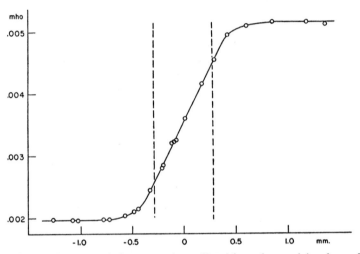

Fig. 7. Conductance of the measuring cell, with a glass rod in place of the squid axon.   The rod is introduced between the electrodes and is moved to the right so its left end goes through the electrode region.   The electrode boundaries are given by the broken lines and the abscissae are distances in millimeters between the left end of the rod and the center of the electrodes.

ance shunt on the known arm of the bridge.   One circuit on a Lucas spring rheotome then started the oscillograph sweep and a millisecond later a second circuit removed the shunt and so threw the bridge off balance.   The record shown in Fig. 8 a has a complicated form, which has not been satisfactorily explained, but it may be roughly approximated by an exponential having a time constant of 100 μ sec.

It would be difficult to obtain directly the oscillograph response to a sudden change of membrane conductance moving past the impedance electrodes with a velocity of 12 meters per second, but it has been calculated by combining the data of Figs. 7 and 8 *a* in Duhamel's integral or the principle of superposition.[6,7] With the response of the oscillograph to a known cause, it is theoretically possible to determine the cause of any other effect, but the practical difficulties are considerable and several methods for the correction of the experimental curves have been tried and found unsatisfactory. For example, the desired curve may be approximated by an exponential with a time constant of 0.125 millisecond and the data corrected by the subtangent method (*cf.* Lucas, 1912; Rushton, 1937) as has been done in Fig. 10. In general these corrections have shortened the apparent time of rise of the membrane conductance to 100 μsec. or less, but have usually increased its maximum value by only about 10 per cent.

It should also be pointed out that the data obtained by balancing the bridge at different points of the impedance change are subject to the same distortions by the bridge, modulator, and amplifier. It is to be expected that there will be a phase alteration introduced during and for a short time after a rapid impedance change, and this would require false capacity and resistance changes for the apparent balance point. The magnitude of this effect has not been investigated in detail, and it is difficult to estimate how much of the apparent change of membrane capacity may be due to it.

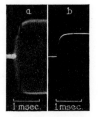

FIG. 8. (*a*) Response of the bridge and the bridge amplifier to a sudden unbalance at 20 kc. (*b*) Response of the action potential amplifier to a suddenly applied potential.

Action Potentials.—A strictly monophasic action potential was never obtained probably due to some remaining activity of the distant end or a lack of uniformity of the axon in the region between the two electrodes. For this reason and because it is preferable to make as many of the measurements in the immediate neighborhood of the impedance electrodes as possible, the integral of the first derivative curve is more satisfactory. The first derivative curve is an approximation as is discussed on p. 664. The two portions of the rising phase of the monophasic action potential have an average time constant of about 110 μsec. corresponding to a length of about 1.3 mm. This is very close to 1.25 mm., the half separation of the V_t electrodes. Thus we find by equation (9) that the recorded V_t curve should be more than 60 per cent wider at the half maximum than the actual V_t. If we now differentiate this curve to obtain V_{tt}, we compute by equation (10) that the two maxima would be separated by 2.5 mm. or 210μsec. if the rising portion is a double exponential, whereas without distortion the reversal for this curve

[6] Webster, A. G., 1927, Partial differential equations of mathematical physics, Leipsic, Teubner, p. 172.

[7] Bush, V., 1929, Operational circuit analysis, New York, John Wiley and Sons, p. 68.

should take place instantaneously. On the other hand, using the three electrode connection, the reversal time would be 175 μsec. and values of from 180 to 200μ sec. have been found. A simple method has not been found for applying corrections for the electrode separations, and no attempt has been made to construct any complete curves.

After the potential is on the electrodes, there is still the action potential amplifier distortion to consider. This also was determined with the spring rheotome which applied a known potential to input of the amplifier. The response curve shown in Fig. 8 *b*, is approximately an exponential with a time constant of 80 μsec. The monophasic action potential record of Fig. 10 has been corrected for this time constant by the subtangent method.

Theory

Membrane Conductance.—The output voltage of the bridge and the oscillograph deflection are proportional to

$$Y = 2 \left| \frac{z - \bar{z}}{z + \bar{z}} \right|, \tag{1}$$

where $\bar{z}$ is the impedance at balance and z is the impedance off balance. When the resting impedance is $\bar{z}$ and the membrane conductance changes by an amount λ without change of membrane capacity, the impedance becomes by *Nitella* equation (7),

$$z = \frac{a\sigma\lambda r_\infty + z}{a\sigma\lambda + 1}, \tag{2}$$

where a is the fiber radius, σ is a complex constant involving z, and r_∞ is the infinite frequency resistance. We then have, approximately,

$$Y = \frac{2\beta\lambda}{1 + \beta\lambda}, \tag{3}$$

where

$$\beta = \left| \frac{a\sigma(z - r_\infty)}{2z} \right|,$$

so if $\beta\lambda$ is small the oscillograph deflection is proportional to the change of membrane conductance. In practice, the maximum change of conductance λ_0 was determined from bridge balance measurements at rest and maximum change. If the oscillograph deflection at the maximum is Y_0 then

$$Y_0 = \frac{2\beta\lambda_0}{1 + \beta\lambda_0},$$

and when λ is calculated by

$$\lambda = Y\lambda_0/Y_0$$

the fractional error in this procedure is given by

$$\frac{Y\lambda_0/Y_0 - \lambda}{\lambda} = \frac{Y_0 - Y}{2 - Y_0}. \tag{4}$$

The average value of Y_0 was about 8 per cent at low frequencies, so that the maximum error in the membrane conductance change was about 4 per cent for the smallest changes and became less nearer the maximum.

Action Potential Derivatives.—At a particular instant let the action potential at each point, x, along the axon be $V(x)$. The potential at a neighboring point, $x + \delta$, is then given by Taylor's expansion,

$$V(x + \delta) = V(x) + \delta \dot{V}(x) + \frac{\delta^2}{2!} \overset{''}{V}(x) + \frac{\delta^3}{3!} \overset{'''}{V}(x) + \cdots,$$

where $\overset{'}{V}$, $\overset{''}{V}$, etc. are the first, second, etc. total derivatives with respect to the independent variable, x in this case. The difference in potential V_1 between two electrodes at a distance on either side of the point x (see Fig. 9 b) is

$$V_1 = V(x + \delta) - V(x - \delta) = 2\delta \dot{V}(x) + \frac{2\delta^2}{3!} \overset{'''}{V}(x) + \cdots \tag{5}$$

and if δ, $\overset{'''}{V}$, and successive derivatives are sufficiently small,

$$V_1 = 2\delta \dot{V}(x) \tag{6}$$

Thus the extreme case of a diphasic potential with electrodes close together is proportional to the first derivative, $\overset{'}{V}$, with respect to moving coordinates and also with respect to time at a fixed point, V_t, if the velocity is constant.

Similarly when the circuit of Fig. 9 c is used, the potential at the midpoint of the resistor connected between points $x + \delta$, and $x - \delta$ is

$$\tfrac{1}{2}[V(x + \delta) + V(x - \delta)]$$

and the potential difference between this point and the center point, x, is

$$V_2 = \tfrac{1}{2}[V(x + \delta) + V(x - \delta)] - V(x) = \frac{\delta^2}{2!} \overset{''}{V}(x) + \frac{\delta^4}{4!} \overset{''''}{V}(x) + \cdots \tag{7}$$

which is proportional to $\overset{''}{V}(x)$ if δ, $\overset{'''}{V}$, and successive derivatives are small, or

$$V_2 = \frac{\delta^2}{2!} \overset{''}{V}(x). \qquad (8)$$

The question of how small δ must be depends of course upon $V(x)$ and we shall consider the errors which may be introduced in the rising phase. For purposes of calculation this part of $V(x)$ will be assumed to be made up of two identical exponentials symmetrically placed

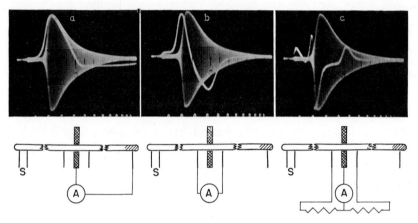

FIG. 9. Double exposures of the impedance change at 10 kc. on each with the action potential in each picture from the circuit shown below it. (a) is V, the monophasic potential, (b) is V_t, the first derivative or axial current, and (c) is V_{tt} the second derivative or membrane current. The time marks at the bottom are 1 millisecond apart.

with respect to the half maximum point, which will be taken as the origin. Then on the upper half

$$V(x) = 1 - e^{-x/\lambda},$$

and on the lower

$$V(-x) = -(1 - e^{x/\lambda}),$$

where λ is the characteristic length. When $x > \delta$,

$$V(x + \delta) - V(x - \delta) = e^{-x/\lambda}(e^{\delta/\lambda} - e^{-\delta/\lambda}), \qquad (9)$$

and if x is the point of half maximum of this potential,

$$e^{x/\lambda} = e^{\delta/\lambda} + 1.$$

If δ/λ is small the width of the true $\overset{'}{V}$ at half maximum is increased by δ, and when $\delta = \lambda$ the width is 62 per cent too large.   Obtaining $\overset{''}{V}$ by direct differentiation of this approximate $\overset{'}{V}$ we find that the maximum occurs at $x = -\delta$ and the minimum at $x = \delta$ so that the peaks are separated by 2δ whereas there should be a discontinuity with reversal of sign at $x = 0$.   A similar error is found in the value of $\overset{''}{V}$ measured directly from the three electrodes, the minimum being at the value of $x < \delta$ given by

$$\delta/\lambda = x/\lambda + \log_e \cosh x/\lambda \tag{10}$$

When δ/λ is small the separation of the peaks is 2δ but when $\delta = \lambda$ the separation is 1.49δ.

DISCUSSION AND CONCLUSIONS

The values for the capacity and phase angle of the membrane and the internal resistance of the resting axon given above are somewhat different from those which were found before (Curtis and Cole, 1938), but this is not particularly surprising.   Although the material in the present work was in considerably better condition, the electrodes were short and the data were calculated on the assumption that end effects were negligible, and it was found for muscle that the measured phase angle was less for short electrodes than for long (Cole and Curtis, 1936).   It has been assumed in calculations on transverse impedance measurements that the resting axon membrane is non-conducting.   The value of 1000 ohm cm.^{2} obtained by Cole and Hodgkin (1939), more than justifies that assumption.   There are considerable differences between the values of the internal specific resistances which have been measured but we are not in a position to explain them.

Turning now to the impedance change during activity, it is first necessary to show that this is a real effect and not an artifact resulting from the stimulus or the action potential.   The stimulus may be eliminated because the effect is entirely all-or-none.   The bridge balance remains unchanged until the stimulus reaches threshold, and then the unbalance picture remains unaltered as the stimulus is further increased except that it moves forward with the action potential because the point of stimulation moves closer to the impedance electrodes. Any possible effect due directly to the action potential is eliminated for several reasons. The only action potential which would be effective is that appearing across the impedance electrodes, which should be zero in a perfect axon. In practice this potential was always present, although it was small and did not come through the bridge amplifier. However, it was never the same in any two axons and yet the impedance change always had the same form. Most conclusive, however, is the fact that the amplitude of the unbalance picture was directly proportional to the bridge input voltage from the oscillator while the action potential was unaffected.

In spite of the shortcomings of the apparatus and the difficulty of correcting for them, the general nature and magnitude of the impedance change seems quite certain. The decrease of the extrapolated zero frequency resistance (Fig. 5) might be due to a change of either the volume of the axon or the resistance of the external medium, but these factors should alter the extrapolated infinite frequency resistance which is unchanged. The phase angle of the membrane is unchanged and the membrane capacity does not change alone because this would merely move each point along the resting curve. Consequently we must assume that there is a change of the membrane resistance which falls from a resting value of 1000 ohm cm.^{2} to a minimum value which is probably 10 per cent and perhaps 20 per cent below the average uncorrected value of 28 ohm cm.^{2}. The 2 per cent decrease of membrane capacity is of quite a different order of magnitude, but even this value should not be taken too seriously because there are indications that the actual change may be somewhat less.

We may reason, as we did for *Nitella*, that the conductance is a measure of the ion permeable aspect of the membrane and we see that the maximum conductance is far from a complete permeability. And indeed the capacity, which represents the ion impermeable portion of the membrane, has not been encroached upon by more than 2 per cent. Thus if the change on excitation is uniform throughout the structure of the membrane it must be so delicate as to leave the capacity and phase angle nearly unchanged and conversely if there are drastic changes they must be confined to a small fraction of the membrane area. The time constant of the resting membrane is of the order of 1 millisecond which is equivalent (*Nitella*)[8] to a thousand ions per second crossing the membrane for each ion pair separated by the membrane, and the time constant of 0.03 millisecond at the maximum then gives a permeability of some thirty thousand ions per ion pair.

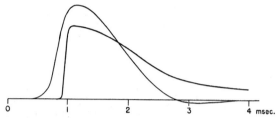

FIG. 10. Membrane conductance increase (heavy line) after approximate corrections for electrode length and bridge amplifier response and monophasic action potential (light line) obtained from the first derivative after approximate correction for action potential amplifier response.

The time course of the membrane conductance is best discussed in connection with the action potential, but before doing so we should submit some proof that the oscillograph sweep circuit, which gave the horizontal time scale, did not alter in the interval between the impedance and action potential exposures. To do this, the two have been taken simultaneously by applying the V_t potential, of Fig. 9 *b*, to the vertical plates and bridge output to the horizontal plates with the result shown in Fig. 11. It is here seen as in Fig. 9 *b*, that the potential rises to its maximum value before the bridge goes off balance. It is then clear that the conductance does not start to increase until the point of inflection on the *V*, or membrane potential, curve, Fig. 9 *a*, which is the reversal point of the V_{tt}, or membrane current, curve, Fig. 9 *c*. The small "foot" at the start of the membrane conductance pictures is due in part to the spread

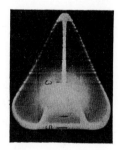

FIG. 11. The first derivative action potential, V_t, vertical, against the bridge unbalance at 20 kc., horizontal, during the passage of an impulse.

of the measuring current beyond the impedance electrodes which gives a similar foot in Fig. 7, but it seems fairly certain that there is

[8] Cole, K. S., and Curtis, H. J., 1938–39, *J. Gen. Physiol.*, **22**, 51.

at least a measurable increase in conductance before the large and rapid increase takes place. The action potential corrections do not permit an accurate placement of this change, but it seems slightly to precede the reversal of the membrane current. This effect may be the impedance counterpart of the phenomenon preceding excitation at the cathode which has been observed by Katz (1937) and Hodgkin (1938).

The difficulties of determining the time of rise of the membrane conductance have already been discussed and the only conclusion to be made at present is that it is probably at least as short as 100 μsec. and perhaps even shorter. In contrast to the *Nitella* results, it will be noticed that for the squid axon the recovery of the action potential is completed considerably before that of the membrane resistance, but it seems likely that when this difference can be explained the whole phenomenon of excitation and conduction will be fairly well understood.

It should be possible, at this point, to determine the time course of the membrane electromotive force, by *Nitella* equation (16), and so obtain a complete picture of the electrical behavior of the membrane during activity. These calculations on *Nitella* were found to be very sensitive to small errors, so it seems best to avoid this procedure until other means have been exhausted and better squid data are available.

It seems apparent, however, from the data now available that, as was found for *Nitella*, the foot of the monophasic action potential up to the point of inflection represents a purely passive discharge into the active region following. Up to this point, the axon acts like a communication cable and although the conditions for the breakdown are being approached the axon has not yet exhibited any biological characteristics. At the point of inflection, we have the increase of conductance and decrease of electromotive force which give rise to the constant velocity and all-or-none behavior so characteristic of the propagated disturbance in excitable tissues.

The similarity of the impedance changes in the activity of *Nitella* and the squid axon is so striking as to add further proof that the phenomena of excitation and conduction are fundamentally the same in these forms. Since the action potentials of these forms are comparable with those of other nerve fibers and the membrane capacities of many cells, including the *Nitella* and the squid, cat sciatic, and frog sciatic axons, are nearly the same (*cf.* Cole, 1939) we may assume for the present that there are impedance changes in other nerve fibers and that the mechanisms of excitation and propagation are all quite similar.   In the future the impedance changes should be measured more accurately in *Nitella* and in squid and should be looked for in other forms, and the effects of various chemical and physical changes of environment should be investigated.   There are a few preliminary observations on subthreshold phenomena and drug action but these are too incomplete to be discussed at the present time.

SUMMARY

Alternating current impedance measurements have been made over a wide frequency range on the giant axon from the stellar nerve of the squid, *Loligo pealii*, during the passage of a nerve impulse. The transverse impedance was measured between narrow electrodes on either side of the axon with a Wheatstone bridge having an amplifier and cathode ray oscillograph for detector.   When the bridge was balanced, the resting axon gave a narrow line on the oscillograph screen as a sweep circuit moved the spot across.   As an impulse passed between impedance electrodes after the axon had been stimulated at one end, the oscillograph line first broadened into a band, indicating a bridge unbalance, and then narrowed down to balance during recovery.   From measurements made during the passage of the impulse and appropriate analysis, it was found that the membrane phase angle was unchanged, the membrane capacity decreased about 2 per cent, while the membrane conductance fell from a resting value of 1000 ohm cm.^{2} to an average of 25 ohm cm.^{2}

The onset of the resistance change occurs somewhat after the start of the monophasic action potential, but coincides quite closely with the point of inflection on the rising phase, where the membrane current reverses in direction, corresponding to a decrease in the membrane electromotive force.   This E.M.F. and the conductance are closely associated properties of the membrane, and their sudden changes constitute, or are due to, the activity which is responsible for the all-or-none law and the initiation and propagation of the nerve impulse. These results correspond to those previously found for *Nitella* and lead us to expect similar phenomena in other nerve fibers.

We wish to express our appreciation of the valuable assistance of Mr. J. M. Spencer in all parts of this work.

BIBLIOGRAPHY

Blinks, L. R., 1936, *J. Gen. Physiol.*, **20**, 229.

Bush, V., 1929, Operational circuit analysis, New York, John Wiley and Sons.

Cole, K. S., 1928, *J. Gen. Physiol.*, **12**, 29; 1932, **15**, 641; 1939, Tabulae Biologicae, Cellula, in press.

Cole, K. S., and Curtis, H. J., 1936, Electric impedance of nerve and muscle, in Cold Spring Harbor symposia on quantitative biology, Cold Spring Harbor, Long Island Biological Association, **4**, 73. 1937, *Rev. Scient. Instr.*, **8**, 333. 1938 *a*, *Nature*, **142**, 209. 1938 *b*, *J. Gen. Physiol.*, **22**, 37.

Cole, K. S., and Hodgkin, A. L., 1939, *J. Gen. Physiol.*, **22**, 671.

Curtis, H. J., and Cole, K. S., 1937, *J. Gen. Physiol.*, **21**, 189; 1938, **21**, 757.

Hodgkin, A. L., 1938, *Proc. Roy. Soc. London, Series B*, **126**, 87. 1939, *J. Physiol.*, **94**, 560.

Hōzawa, S., 1935, *Z. Biol.*, **96**, 586.

Katz, B., 1937, *Proc. Roy. Soc. London, Series B*, **124**, 244.

Lucas, K., 1912, *J. Physiol.*, **44**, 225.

Lullies, H., 1930, *Arch. ges. Physiol.*, **18**, 215.

Rushton, W. A. H., 1937, *Proc. Roy. Soc. London, Series B*, **123**, 382.

Young, J. Z., 1936, Structure of nerve fibers and synapses in some invertebrates, in Cold Spring Harbor symposia on quantitative biology, Cold Spring Harbor, Long Island Biological Association, **4**, 1.

Webster, A. G., 1927, Partial differential equations of mathematical physics, Leipsic, Teubner.

The electrical constants of a crustacean nerve fibre

By A. L. Hodgkin and W. A. H. Rushton

The Physiological Laboratory, Cambridge

(*Communicated by E. D. Adrian, F.R.S.—Received* 3 *October* 1945)

Theoretical equations are derived for the response of a nerve fibre to the sudden application of a weak current. The equations describe the behaviour of the nerve fibre in terms of the membrane resistance and capacity, the axoplasm resistance and the resistance of the external fluid. Expressions are given which allow these four constants to be calculated from experimental observations.

Axons from *Carcinus maenas* were used in preliminary experiments. Quantitative determinations were made on a new single-fibre preparation—the 75μ diameter axon from the walking leg of the lobster (*Homarus vulgaris*). Currents with a strength of one-third to one-half threshold were used in the quantitative determinations.

The behaviour of lobster axons agreed with theoretical predictions in the following respects: (*a*) the steady extrapolar potential declined exponentially with distance; (*b*) the voltage gradient midway between two distant electrodes was uniform; (*c*) the rise and fall of the extrapolar potential at different distances conformed to the correct theoretical curves.

The extrapolar potential disappeared when the axon was treated with a solution of chloroform, indicating that the surface membrane was destroyed by this treatment, and that the potential recorded was in fact derived from the membrane.

The ratio of the internal to external resistance per unit length was found to be about 0·7.

The absolute magnitude of the action potential at the surface membrane was estimated at about 110 mV.

The specific resistance of the axoplasm had an average value of 60Ω cm., which was roughly three times that of the surrounding sea water.

The calculated resistance of one square centimetre of membrane was found to vary from 600 to 7000Ω in thirteen experiments.

The membrane capacity was of the order of $1·3\mu$F cm.$^{-2}$.

No trace of inductive behaviour could be observed in the majority of the experiments. But three axons with low membrane resistances showed effects which could be attributed either to inductance or to a small local response. The absence of inductive behaviour in axons with high membrane resistance does not prove the absence of an inductive element. Currents with a strength several times greater than threshold often produced oscillating potentials at the cathode.

A local response was always observed when the strength of current approached threshold. The response had a striking inflected form if the current strength was near threshold and its duration less than the utilization time.

Indirect evidence indicates that the membrane resistance falls to a low value during activity.

Hodgkin, A. L., and W. A. H. Rushton. The electrical constants of a crustacean nerve fibre. *Proc. Roy. Soc.* **133B**: 444–479, 1946.

Experiments with non-medullated nerve fibres have shown that a sub-threshold electric current produces two quite distinct effects (Hodgkin 1938; Pumphrey, Schmitt & Young 1940). Currents with a strength less than half-threshold produce a voltage which behaves as though it were due to the passive accumulation of charge at the nerve membrane. This voltage varies linearly with the applied current and is sometimes called an electrotonic potential. Currents with a strength greater than half-threshold evoke an additional wave of negativity which is non-linear and which behaves as though it were a subliminal response in the cathodic part of the nerve fibre. The present paper is concerned with an analysis of the first of these effects and contains only qualitative observations of the second. There are several reasons for believing in the importance of such an analysis. In the first place a physical understanding of the passive behaviour of nerve is essential to any theory of excitation. Thus a strength-duration curve cannot be explained until the time course of the voltage across the excitable membrane is known. Nor can the mechanism of excitation by the action potential be fully understood until there exists a thorough knowledge of the effect of applied currents on a single nerve fibre. A physical analysis is also interesting because it provides an insight into the structure of the surface membrane. Physical chemists are now able to prepare very thin films of lipoid material between two aqueous phases (Dean 1939), and it is clearly of the utmost importance to compare the electrical resistance and capacity of such films with those of the surface membrane in the living cell. The membrane resistance is also interesting from a more general point of view. Many biological processes depend upon the movement of ions through cell membranes, and the rate at which ions are transferred across a membrane should be related to its electrical resistance. Our results may, therefore, be of use to those who study the ionic movements that occur in the processes of growth, secretion and respiration. But perhaps the most important reason for making an analysis of the passive properties of a nerve fibre is that such an analysis must precede an understanding of the more complicated electrical changes which make up the nervous impulse itself.

Certain assumptions about the electrical structure of a nerve fibre must be made before any analysis can be started. The basic assumption of our work is that the structure of a non-medullated nerve fibre is similar to that of other cells which are known to have an interior of conducting protoplasm and a thin surface membrane with a high leakage resistance and a large capacity per unit area (Höber 1910; Fricke & Morse 1925; Cole 1937, etc.). If this general type of structure is granted, it follows that the passive behaviour of a new fibre must be governed by the equations of cable theory (Cremer 1899; Hermann 1905; Rushton 1934; Bogue & Rosenberg 1934; Cole & Curtis 1938, and others). The quantitative behaviour of the fibre should be determined by four electrical constants, viz.

(1) The electrical resistance of the fluid outside the nerve fibre.
(2) The electrical resistance of the axoplasm.
(3) The electrical capacity of the surface membrane.
(4) The electrical resistance of the surface membrane.

One other parameter, the membrane inductance, may have to be added (Cole 1941), but will not be considered in the initial stages of this paper. There already exists a considerable amount of information about the magnitude of three of these quantities. The external resistance can be calculated from the volume and conductivity of the fluid bathing the nerve fibre; the cell interior appears to have a resistivity two or three times as great as that of the external fluid and the surface membrane to have a capacity of about $1\mu F/sq.cm$. Very little is known about the membrane resistance and measurements have so far been confined to a few plant cells (Blinks 1937) and one animal cell, the giant nerve fibre of the squid (Cole & Hodgkin 1939; Cole 1940).* The determination of the membrane resistance was therefore the first aim of our experiments and measurement of the remaining constants was originally regarded as of secondary importance. But it so happens that one constant cannot be determined without making measurements of at least two others. An attempt was therefore made to determine all four quantities simultaneously on a single fibre. Four sets of measurements had to be made since there were four unknowns to be evaluated, and after several trials we chose the following methods:

(1) The extent of spread of potential in the extrapolar region.

(2) The rate of rise of potential in the extrapolar region.

(3) The ratio of the applied current to the voltage recorded between cathode or anode and a distant extrapolar point.

(4) The voltage gradient in the region midway between two distant electrodes.

Axons with a diameter of 30μ from *Carcinus maenas* (Hodgkin 1938) were used initially. This work served to develop the experimental technique, but the extent of spread of potential was thought too small for accurate measurement. A search was therefore made for a fibre with a larger diameter and a suitable preparation was eventually found in the walking legs of the lobster (*Homarus vulgaris*). The meropodite of the walking legs contains a few fibres which have a diameter of 75μ and are robust enough to permit isolation without damage. This preparation was used in the majority of experiments. Electrical measurements were made by applying rectangular pulses of current and recording the potential response photographically. About fifteen sets of film were obtained in May and June of 1939, and a preliminary analysis was started during the following months. The work was then abandoned and the records and notes stored for six years. A final analysis was made in 1945 and forms the basis of this paper. A certain amount of biophysical work has proceeded during the interval, but no one seems to have repeated these particular experiments.

Nomenclature

The passive spread of potential which occurs in nerve fibres is sometimes described by the term polarization potential and sometimes electrotonus or electrotonic potential. Both words are unfortunate. Electrotonus implies that the

---

* An estimate of the plasma membrane resistance in the frog's egg has been made by Cole & Guttman (1942).

axon is in a state of enhanced physiological activity: polarization potential that the change of voltage is due to an alteration of ionic concentration in the vicinity of the membrane. Weak currents do not necessarily evoke an active or tonic response; nor is it at all certain that there is a significant polarization in the sense of Nernst (1908) or Warburg (1899). For it seems likely that the change of voltage with current is due to a frictional resistance opposing the motion of ions and not to changes in ionic concentration. We have therefore avoided the use of both terms so far as is possible and have used instead words such as membrane potential or extrapolar potential according to the context.

Wherever possible we have used the same symbols as Cole and his colleagues. λ has been employed as a space constant and should not be confused with the λ of Hill's theory of excitation (Hill 1936). The dual use of symbols is unfortunate but cannot be avoided, since both American and British writers have used λ as a space constant (e.g. Cole & Curtis 1938; Rushton 1934).

THEORETICAL SECTION

Assumptions

(1) The axon has a uniform cable-like structure with a conducting core, an external conducting path and a surface membrane with resistance and capacity.

(2) The axon is sufficiently thin and the membrane resistance sufficiently high for the flow of current in core and interstitial fluid to be strictly parallel. An alternative statement of this assumption is that at any given distance along the nerve the potential is constant throughout the core or throughout the external fluid.

(3) The axoplasm and external fluid behave as pure ohmic resistances.

(4) The membrane resistance is constant when the current density through the membrane is small.

(5) The membrane capacity behaves like a pure dielectric with no loss.

These are general assumptions which allow the differential equations for current or potential to be written. Each assumption is really an approximation, but we shall show later that no very serious errors are likely to result from their use. Certain experimental conditions must also be defined in order to allow the differential equations to be solved. These may be stated in the following way:

(1) The extrapolar and interpolar lengths are sufficiently long to be taken as infinite.

(2) The electrodes are sufficiently fine to be considered of zero breadth.

(3) A current of rectangular wave form is passed through the nerve.

Symbols and definitions

Variables

x is distance along axon in cm.

t is time in seconds.

i_1 is the current in amperes flowing through the external fluid (figure 1).

i_2 is the current in amperes flowing through the axis cylinder.

I is the total current in amperes flowing through the fibre and external fluid $(I = i_1 + i_2)$.

i_m is the current penetrating the surface membrane at any point in ampere cm.$^{-1}$.

V_1 is the potential in volts of the external fluid with respect to a distant point
$$\left(V_1 = -\int_{-\infty}^{x} r_1 i_1 \, dx \right).$$

V_2 is the potential in volts of the axis cylinder with respect to a distant point
$$\left(V_2 = -\int_{-\infty}^{x} r_2 i_2 \, dx \right).$$

V_m is the change in potential difference across the surface membrane which results from the flow of current $(V_m = V_1 - V_2)$.

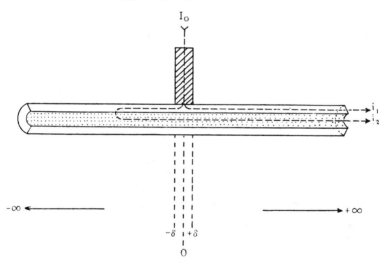

FIGURE 1. Geometry of system considered in theoretical section.

Basic constants

a is the radius of the axis cylinder in cm.

R_2 is the specific resistivity of the axoplasm in Ω cm.

R_4 is the resistance × unit area of the surface membrane in Ω cm.^{2}.

C_M is the capacity per unit area of the surface membrane in F cm.$^{-2}$.

Practical constants

r_1 is the resistance per unit length of the external fluid in Ω cm.$^{-1}$.

r_2 is the resistance per unit length of the axis cylinder in Ω cm.$^{-1}$ $(r_2 = R_2/\pi a^2)$.

r_4 is the resistance × unit length of the surface membrane in the axon in Ω cm. $(r_4 = R_4/2\pi a)$.

c is the capacity per unit length of the surface membrane in the axon in F cm.$^{-1}$
   ($c = C_M \times 2\pi a$).

$\lambda = \sqrt{(r_4/r_1 + r_2)}$, and is the characteristic length in cm.

$m = r_1 r_2/r_1 + r_2$, and is the parallel resistance of the axis cylinder and external
   fluid in Ω cm.$^{-1}$.

$y = m\lambda r_1/2r_2 = r_1^2 \lambda/2(r_1 + r_2)$.

$\tau_m = r_4 c = R_4 C_M$, and is the characteristic time of the surface membrane in seconds.

Miscellaneous

δ is equal to half the electrode width (figure 1). This quantity will eventually be
made vanishingly small, but is introduced in order to deal with discontinuities.
X, T, U, ξ and I_0 are best defined as they are introduced.

Theory

A number of useful equations follow at once from the definitions:

$$\frac{\partial V_1}{\partial x} = -r_1 i_1, \tag{1.0}$$

$$\frac{\partial V_2}{\partial x} = -r_2 i_2, \tag{1.1}$$

$$\frac{\partial V_m}{\partial x} = (r_1 + r_2) i_2 - I r_1. \tag{1.2}$$

$$V_m = \left(\frac{r_1 + r_2}{r_1}\right) V_1 + r_2 \int_{-\infty}^{x} I \, dx. \tag{1.3}$$

In the extrapolar region $I = 0$ so that (1.3) can be simplified to

$$V_m = \left(\frac{r_1 + r_2}{r_1}\right) V_1. \tag{1.4}$$

The total current through the membrane can be obtained in two ways:

$$i_m = \frac{\partial i_2}{\partial x}, \tag{1.5}$$

$$i_m = \frac{V_m}{r_4} + c\frac{\partial V_m}{\partial t}. \tag{1.6}$$

Hence

$$\frac{V_m}{r_4} + c\frac{\partial V_m}{\partial t} = \frac{\partial i_2}{\partial x}, \tag{1.7}$$

and on substituting from (1.2)

$$\frac{V_m}{r_4} + c\frac{\partial V_m}{\partial t} = \frac{1}{r_1 + r_2}\frac{\partial^2 V_m}{\partial x^2} + \frac{r_1}{r_1 + r_2}\frac{\partial I}{\partial x}, \tag{2.0}$$

or

$$-\lambda^2\frac{\partial^2 V_m}{\partial x^2} + \tau_m\frac{\partial V_m}{\partial t} + V_m = r_1\lambda^2\frac{\partial I}{\partial x}. \tag{2.1}$$

Now $\partial I/\partial x$ vanishes except at the electrode, since $I = 0$ for $-\infty < x < -\delta$ and $I = I_0$ for $\delta < x < \infty$. Hence the following equation (2·2) applies to the regions $-\infty < x < -\delta, \delta < x < \infty$:

$$-\lambda^2 \frac{\partial^2 V_m}{\partial x^2} + \tau_m \frac{\partial V_m}{\partial t} + V_m = 0. \tag{2·2}$$

This equation must now be solved for the particular case where I is a constant current I_0 starting abruptly at $t = 0$.

The boundary conditions are

$V_m = 0$ everywhere $-\infty < t < 0$, $V_m = 0$ always when $x = \pm \infty$.

There are also two continuity conditions. First, V_m is always a continuous function of x, since a discontinuity in V_m would mean that an infinite current must flow through the nerve. Secondly, i_2 is also a continuous function of x since the current density through the membrane cannot be infinite when $t \neq 0$. Introduce new variables $X = x/\lambda$, $T = t/\tau_m$, $U = V_m e^T$. Equation (2·2) can now be written

$$-\frac{\partial^2 V_m}{\partial X^2} + \frac{\partial V_m}{\partial T} + V_m = 0, \tag{2·3}$$

or

$$-\frac{\partial^2 U}{\partial X^2} + \frac{\partial U}{\partial T} = 0. \tag{2·4}$$

The operator q^2 may be substituted directly for $\partial/\partial T$ since $U = 0$ when $T = 0$. Hence

$$\frac{\partial^2 U}{\partial X^2} = q^2 U. \tag{3·0}$$

The solutions of (3·0) are

$$U = A e^{qX} + B e^{-qX}, \qquad \text{when} \quad -\infty < X < -\delta/\lambda,$$
$$U = A_1 e^{qX} + B_1 e^{-qX}, \qquad \text{when} \quad \delta/\lambda < X < \infty.$$

But the second boundary condition indicates that $U \neq \infty$ when $X = \pm \infty$, so $B = 0 = A_1$.

From the first continuity condition it follows that $A = B_1$, since

$$U_{X=\delta/\lambda} = U_{X=-\delta/\lambda},$$

when δ/λ is made vanishingly small. Hence

$$U = A e^{qX} \quad \text{for} \quad -\infty < X < -\delta/\lambda, \tag{3·1}$$
$$U = A e^{-qX} \quad \text{for} \quad \delta/\lambda < X < \infty. \tag{3·2}$$

The value of A can be found by applying the continuity of i_2 to equation (1·2). For

$$\left(\frac{\partial V_m}{\partial x}\right)_{x=\delta} - \left(\frac{\partial V_m}{\partial x}\right)_{x=-\delta} = (r_1+r_2)\{(i_2)_{x=\delta} - (i_2)_{x=-\delta}\} - r_1(I_{x=\delta} - I_{x=-\delta}),$$

whence

$$\left(\frac{\partial U}{\partial X}\right)_{X=\delta/\lambda} - \left(\frac{\partial U}{\partial X}\right)_{X=-\delta/\lambda} = -r_1 I_0 \lambda e^T,$$

which in the operational form becomes $-r_1\lambda I_0 \dfrac{q^2}{q^2-1}$. But from (3·1) and (3·2)

$$\left(\frac{\partial U}{\partial X}\right)_{X=\delta/\lambda} - \left(\frac{\partial U}{\partial X}\right)_{X=-\delta/\lambda} = -2qA.$$

So
$$U = \frac{r_1\lambda I_0}{4}\left\{\frac{1}{q-1}+\frac{1}{q+1}\right\}e^{qX} \quad \text{for} \quad -\infty < X < -\delta/\lambda, \tag{3·3}$$

and
$$U = \frac{r_1\lambda I_0}{4}\left\{\frac{1}{q-1}+\frac{1}{q+1}\right\}e^{-qX} \quad \text{for} \quad \delta/\lambda < X < \infty. \tag{3·4}$$

The interpretations of the operational expressions in (3·3) and (3·4) are known (Jeffreys 1931). When they are substituted, the following equations for V_m are obtained:

$$V_m = \frac{r_1\lambda I_0}{4}\{e^X[1+\mathrm{erf}\,(X/2\sqrt{T}+\sqrt{T})]-e^{-X}[1+\mathrm{erf}\,(X/2\sqrt{T}-\sqrt{T})]\},$$
$$\text{when} \quad -\infty < X < 0, \quad (4·0)$$

and
$$V_m = \frac{r_1\lambda I_0}{4}\{e^{-X}[1-\mathrm{erf}\,(X/2\sqrt{T}-\sqrt{T})]-e^X[1-\mathrm{erf}\,(X/2\sqrt{T}+\sqrt{T})]\},$$
$$\text{when} \quad 0 < X < \infty, \quad (4·1)$$

where
$$\mathrm{erf}\,Z = \frac{2}{\sqrt{\pi}}\int_0^Z e^{-\omega^2}\,d\omega.$$

These expressions satisfy equation (2·3) and the boundary conditions. Campbell & Foster (1931, p. 162) give an expression which is equivalent to (4·1) for the response of a non-inductive cable to the sudden application of current.

The solutions for the case when the applied current is maintained for a long time and then broken suddenly at $t = 0$ can be written down at once from the superposition theorem. They are

$$V_m = \frac{r_1\lambda I_0}{4}\{e^X[1-\mathrm{erf}\,(X/2\sqrt{T}+\sqrt{T})]+e^{-X}[1+\mathrm{erf}\,(X/2\sqrt{T}-\sqrt{T})]\},$$
$$\text{when} \quad -\infty < X < 0, \quad (4·2)$$

and
$$V_m = \frac{r_1\lambda I_0}{4}\{e^{-X}[1+\mathrm{erf}\,(X/2\sqrt{T}-\sqrt{T})]+e^X[1-\mathrm{erf}\,(X/2\sqrt{T}+\sqrt{T})]\},$$
$$\text{when} \quad 0 < X < \infty. \quad (4·3)$$

Equations (4·0), (4·1) and (4·2), (4·3) are symmetrical pairs differing only in the sign of X. Thus it is necessary to compute only one set of curves in order to describe the distribution of potential for the make or break of a constant current. And the curves for the break of current can be obtained from those for the make by a direct application of the superposition theorem. Equation (4·1) is the most convenient to compute, since it deals with positive values of X. An evaluation of the essential part of (4·1) is given in table 1 and the results are plotted graphically in figure 2.

TABLE 1. TABLE OF THE FUNCTION $\{e^{-X}[1 - \mathrm{erf}\,(X/2\sqrt{T} - \sqrt{T})] - e^{X}[1 - \mathrm{erf}\,(X/2\sqrt{T} + \sqrt{T})]\}$ FOR DIFFERENT VALUES OF X AND T

	$T=0\cdot01$	$0\cdot04$	$0\cdot16$	$0\cdot36$	$0\cdot64$	$1\cdot0$	$1\cdot44$	$1\cdot96$	$2\cdot56$	$3\cdot24$	$4\cdot00$	$6\cdot25$	∞
$X=0$	0·2249	0·4454	0·8567	1·208	1·484	1·685	1·821	1·904	1·953	1·987	1·991	1·999	2·000
0·1	0·0795	0·2743	0·673	1·020	1·294	1·496	1·631	1·714	1·763	1·788	1·801	1·800	1·810
0·2	0·0200	0·1561	0·5201	0·855	1·126	1·325	1·459	1·542	1·590	1·616	1·628	1·636	1·637
0·3	0·0035	0·0816	0·3926	0·712	0·976	1·172	1·305	1·387	1·435	1·460	1·473	1·481	1·482
0·4	0·0004	0·0390	0·2921	0·588	0·842	1·034	1·165	1·247	1·294	1·320	1·332	1·340	1·341
0·5	—	0·0170	0·2125	0·483	0·725	0·911	1·040	1·120	1·167	1·192	1·204	1·212	1·213
0·6	—	0·0067	0·1513	0·392	0·621	0·801	0·926	1·006	1·052	1·077	1·089	1·097	1·098
0·7	—	0·0024	0·1055	0·316	0·530	0·702	0·824	0·903	0·948	0·972	0·984	0·992	0·993
0·8	—	0·00076	0·0718	0·252	0·450	0·614	0·732	0·809	0·853	0·878	0·890	0·898	0·899
0·9	—	—	0·0474	0·2000	0·381	0·537	0·651	0·725	0·769	0·793	0·804	0·812	0·813
1·0	—	—	0·0311	0·1554	0·319	0·467	0·577	0·649	0·691	0·715	0·727	0·735	0·736
1·2	—	—	0·0122	0·0937	0·224	0·351	0·451	0·517	0·560	0·583	0·594	0·601	0·602
1·5	—	—	0·0026	0·0401	0·125	0·225	0·309	0·369	0·407	0·428	0·438	0·445	0·446
2·0	—	—	0·0001	0·0086	0·0435	0·1008	0·159	0·205	0·236	0·254	0·263	0·270	0·271
2·5	—	—	—	−0·0012	0·0129	0·0415	0·0773	0·1113	0·1347	0·1494	0·1574	0·1636	0·1642
3·0	—	—	—	—	0·0033	0·0174	0·0364	0·0581	0·0754	0·0870	0·0937	0·0988	0·0996

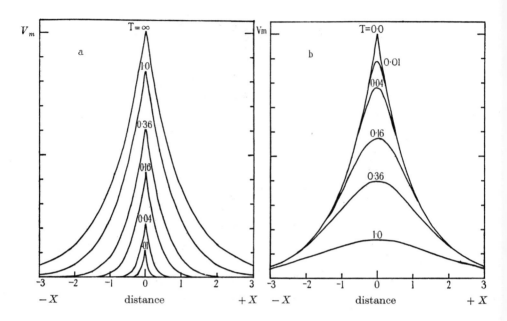

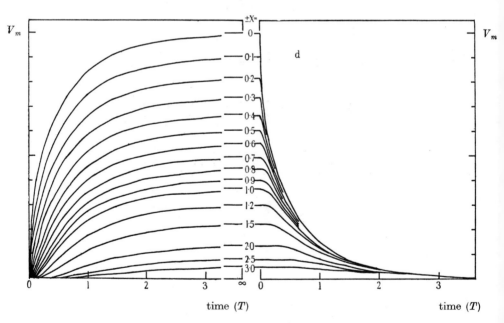

FIGURE 2. Theoretical behaviour of potential difference across nerve membrane (V_m). a, b, spatial distribution of potential at different times; c, d, time course of potential at different distances from electrode; a, c, current made at $T=0$; b, d, current maintained for a long time and then broken at $T=0$.

A great simplification of the mathematical theory can be achieved by considering the total charge in the region of the electrode instead of the membrane potential. Define total charge by a new variable

$$\xi = c \int_{-\infty}^{\beta} V_m \, dx, \tag{5.0}$$

where β is sufficiently large to allow the integration to include all the charge in the electrode region. β can be considered as infinite provided that the integration does not include the region of the second electrode. Integration of equation (2.1) from $-\infty$ to β gives

$$\tau_m \frac{\partial \xi}{\partial t} + \xi = r_1 c \lambda^2 I_0, \tag{5.1}$$

since

$$\int_{-\infty}^{\beta} \partial V_m / \partial t \, dx = \frac{\partial}{\partial t} \left[\int_{-\infty}^{\beta} V_m \, dx \right]$$

and $\dfrac{\partial V_m}{\partial x} = 0$ when $x = -\infty$ and $x = +\beta$. The solutions of (5.1) are

$$\xi = r_1 c \lambda^2 I_0 (1 - e^{-t/\tau_m}) \tag{5.2}$$

for a constant current made at $t = 0$ and

$$\xi = r_1 c \lambda^2 I_0 e^{-t/\tau_m} \tag{5.3}$$

for a constant current broken at $t = 0$. Unfortunately, these simple equations are of little practical use, since ξ can only be obtained indirectly from the experimental results.

The extrapolar potential

Equations (4.0) and (4.2) can be applied directly to the experimental results since $V_m = \dfrac{r_1 + r_2}{r_1} V_1$, $X = x/\lambda$ and $T = t/\tau_m$.

The most convenient expressions for the make of current are

$$V_1 = (V_1)_{\substack{t=\infty \\ x=0}} \tfrac{1}{2} \{ e^X [1 + \mathrm{erf}\,(X/2\sqrt{T} + \sqrt{T})] - e^{-X}[1 + \mathrm{erf}\,(X/2\sqrt{T} - \sqrt{T})] \}, \tag{6.0}$$

where

$$(V_1)_{\substack{t=\infty \\ x=0}} = \frac{r_1^2 \lambda I_0}{2(r_1 + r_2)} = y I_0, \tag{6.1}$$

y being thus defined in the table of practical constants,

$$(V_1)_{t=\infty} = (V_1)_{\substack{t=\infty \\ x=0}} e^X, \tag{6.2}$$

and

$$(V_1)_{x=0} = (V_1)_{\substack{t=\infty \\ x=0}} \mathrm{erf}\,(\sqrt{T}). \tag{6.3}$$

For the break of current the relevant expressions are

$$V_1 = (V_1)_{\substack{t=0 \\ x=0}} \tfrac{1}{2} \{ e^X [1 - \mathrm{erf}\,(X/2\sqrt{T} + \sqrt{T})] + e^{-X}[1 + \mathrm{erf}\,(X/2\sqrt{T} - \sqrt{T})] \}, \tag{6.4}$$

and

$$(V_1)_{x=0} = (V_1)_{\substack{t=0 \\ x=0}} [1 - \mathrm{erf}\,(\sqrt{T})]. \tag{6.5}$$

The mid-interpolar gradient

The expressions given in the preceding paragraph allow λ, τ_m and y to be determined from experimental observations of the extrapolar potential. The constant m can be obtained from a measurement of the voltage gradient in the interpolar region at a large distance from either electrode. For equation (4·1) shows that $\left(\dfrac{\partial V_m}{\partial x}\right)_{x=\beta} = 0$ when $\beta \gg \lambda$. Hence differentiation of (1·3) gives

$$-\left(\frac{\partial V_1}{\partial x}\right)_{x=\beta}\bigg/ I_0 = \frac{r_1 r_2}{r_1 + r_2} = m. \tag{7·0}$$

Determination of basic constants

Convenient expressions for determining the basic constants are

$$R_2 = \pi a^2 m(1 + m\lambda/2y), \tag{8·0}$$

$$R_4 = 2\pi a \lambda^2 m(2 + m\lambda/2y + 2y/m\lambda), \tag{8·1}$$

$$C_M = \tau_m/R_4. \tag{8·2}$$

An expression for the resistivity of the external fluid is not given because there was no easy way of determining the volume of fluid surrounding the nerve fibre. Nor would this quantity have been of great interest. But it is desirable to have an index of the amount of short-circuiting introduced by the external fluid and the ratio r_2/r_1 has been used for this purpose. It can be computed by the relation

$$r_2/r_1 = m\lambda/2y. \tag{8·3}$$

VALIDITY OF ASSUMPTIONS

We are now in a better position to assess the errors which are introduced by the approximations made in the theory. The assumption of parallel current flow is not likely to involve any serious error provided that the current spreads over a length which is several times greater than the diameter of the axon. This condition was satisfied experimentally, since the average value for the space constant λ was twenty times greater than the axon diameter. The assumption of zero breadth for the electrode can be justified in the same way, since λ/δ was also of the order of twenty. Both approximations are doubtful at short time intervals. Thus figure 2 shows that the effective space constant is only $\lambda/5$ when t/τ_m is 0·04. But it can be said that the cable equations apply with reasonable accuracy provided $t/\tau_m > 0·04$.

In practice anode and cathode were separated by about 8 mm. of nerve; theory assumes them to be an infinite distance apart. But interference between the two electrode regions must have been negligible, since 8 mm. was equivalent to 5λ in an average experiment and e^{-5} is 0·007. A similar argument applies to the recording electrodes which were also 8 mm. apart.

The assumption that the internal and external resistances obey Ohm's law is fully justified by earlier work (see, for instance, Cole & Hodgkin 1939) and finds further confirmation in the measurements of mid-interpolar gradient which will be described presently. The constancy of the membrane resistance might be questioned in view of Cole & Curtis's (1941) demonstration of the rectifying properties of the surface membrane. But any rectifier behaves as a linear element if it is examined with a sufficiently weak current. And we shall show later that the measuring currents used were probably small enough to keep the membrane in a linear part of its characteristic.

Some error must have been introduced by assuming that the membrane capacity behaved like a pure dielectric. The magnitude of the error cannot be estimated in any simple way, but it is not likely to have been very large. For a.c. measurements give a value of 76° for the phase angle of the dielectric of the membrane in the squid axon (Curtis & Cole 1938). This suggests that the membrane capacity would be reduced by 30 % when the frequency was increased tenfold. Most of the records dealt with here could be reproduced fairly accurately by a Fourier synthesis containing a tenfold range of frequencies and so would not have been greatly affected by imperfections in the membrane capacity.

METHOD

Material

Single-nerve fibres with a diameter of 60–80μ were obtained from the walking legs of the common lobster (*Homarus vulgaris*). Live lobsters were bought from a fishmonger and kept in an aquarium filled with circulating sea water. The animals were in poor condition when first obtained, but they recovered after a few hours in the aquarium and were able to live there for several weeks. Axons were obtained from the first two pairs of walking legs which are chelate and appear to be better supplied with large fibres than the last two which have no terminal claw. The nerve was dissected from the meropodite and teased apart in a Petri dish of sea water. *Homarus* nerve contains much connective tissue, and separation of a single fibre proved to be a more laborious process than in a *Carcinus* preparation. More time had to be spent in cutting away connective tissue, and no attempt could be made to pull fibres apart until they had been freed from the strands of connective tissue which bound them together. All loose material was removed from the isolated axon whose length varied from 25 to 40 mm. Fibres with branches were never employed.

The method of isolating *Carcinus* axons was similar to that employed in earlier work (Hodgkin 1938) and need not be described again.

Apparatus

A general plan of the equipment used is shown in figure 3. The axon was kept in paraffin oil and was gripped at each end by the tips of insulated forceps (AA'). It was held in a horizontal position and could be observed from above by means of a binocular microscope. The axon rested on the wick electrodes B, D, and made contact with the tip of electrode C. Electrodes B and D made contact over a length of about 250μ, and electrode C over approximately 100μ. These three electrodes consisted of small glass tubes containing sea water and silver wires which had been coated electrolytically with chloride. One end of the glass tube was sealed with wax; the other was drawn out into a coarse capillary and plugged with agar sea water. Connexion to the nerve was made through fine agar wicks which projected for about 5 mm. beyond the tip of the glass capillary. The wicks were built by allowing agar sea water to solidify around a fine silk thread. Silver chloride electrodes were sufficiently non-polarizable, since a 5MΩ resistance in series with the electrodes ensured that the current was entirely unaffected by residual electrode polarization. Electrode E did not need to be non-polarizable, since it was used only for recording transient pulses with an amplifier of high input impedance. This electrode consisted of a fine glass tube into which a platinum wire was sealed; one end of the tube was drawn out into a fine glass capillary, ground square and the whole filled with sea water. The diameter of the tip was about 50μ and the region of contact with the nerve fibre of the same order of magnitude.

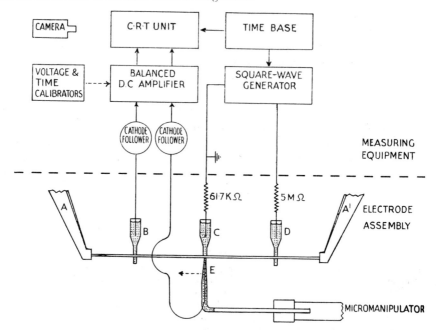

FIGURE 3. General plan of equipment. For letter references, see text.

Electrode E was held in a micromanipulator carriage and could be moved along the nerve fibre by turning one of the vernier controls on the manipulator. The electrode slid smoothly along the fibre provided that all loose connective tissue had been removed and that the direction of movement was parallel to the axis of the fibre. The position of the electrode was determined by a scale on the manipulator which was calibrated to read in fractions of a millimetre. This method of measurement was checked periodically by observing the motion of the electrode under the binocular microscope. The movement of the electrode was found to be the same as that given by the scale on the screw adjustment. Back-lash could be taken as zero, since it was less than 10 micra.

All electrical measurements were made by applying a rectangular pulse of current to the axon and recording the resulting potential changes with an amplifier and oscillograph. The rectangular pulse was generated by means of an arrangement of thyratrons (R.C.A. 885) and a multivibrator of the type described by Schmitt (1938). The wave form of the rectangular pulses was tested by connecting the pulse output to the plates of a cathode-ray tube. This showed that the deflexion was 90 % complete in less than 10μsec. The pulse could be synchronized with the sweep circuit and its duration varied between 10 and $10^6\mu$sec. A low-resistance attenuator was used for varying the magnitude of the pulse applied to the nerve. One terminal of the pulse generator was connected to earth; the other became positive for the duration of the pulse. The positive-going terminal was connected to electrode D through $5\mathrm{M}\Omega$ and the other terminal (earth) to electrode C through a monitoring resistance of $61,700\Omega$. The 5-megohm resistance ensured that a constant current was passed through the nerve, while the monitoring resistance was used to measure the current through the nerve fibre. The pulses of current were repeated at a rate of about one a second.

Electrical changes were recorded with a balanced d.c. amplifier designed by Dr Rawdon Smith of the Psychological Laboratory, Cambridge. This consisted of three pairs of pentodes with separate anode loads and common cathode resistances. The line voltages were arranged so that the anode of one stage could be connected to the grid of the next. In this way the undesirable resistance chains usually associated with d.c. amplifiers were avoided. Occasional checks showed that the differential action of the amplifier was better than one part in five hundred (i.e. when both inputs were raised 1 V above earth the oscillograph deflexion was equivalent to less than 2 mV difference between inputs). Initial checks with a signal generator indicated that the response of the amplifier was substantially flat between 0 and 50 kcyc./sec. In order to increase the input impedance the recording leads were connected to the grids of two cathode followers which were placed at a distance of 15 cm. from the preparation. Calibrations of the input stage and the whole amplifier were made by applying the rectangular pulse to the grids of the input stage through a resistance of the same magnitude as that involved in recording from the nerve. This test showed that the deflexion produced was 90 % complete in about 30 μsec., and the system was therefore sufficiently rapid for the investigation of phenomena lasting several milliseconds. The d.c. input impedance was greater than $10^{10} \Omega$ and the grid current less than 10^{-10} amp.

The time base was calibrated by applying the output from a 500 cyc./sec. oscillator to the amplifier. Voltage calibrations were made by photographing the series of oscillograph lines produced by varying the position of a decade resistance attenuator. In this way a calibration grid was obtained and could be compared with the experimental results. In general the experimental records fell in a region which was linear to within 2 % and so could be analysed without correction. Corrections had occasionally to be made but did not materially affect the results, since the amount of instrumental distortion rarely exceeded 5 %. All photographic records were taken on film and were traced on to graph paper after they had been enlarged about ten times.

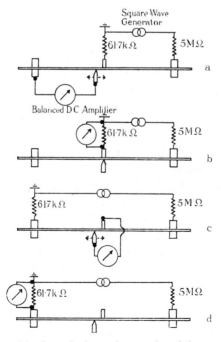

FIGURE 4. Arrangement of leads and electrodes employed in a quantitative experiment. a, system used for determining λ and τ_m; b, system used in conjunction with a for determining y; c, d, system used for determining m.

A typical experiment

The sequence of events in a quantitative experiment must now be described. The isolated axon was mounted on the electrode system and raised into a layer of aerated mineral oil which floated on the surface of the sea water. The recording electrode was brought into contact with the axon and a preliminary test made to ensure that the action potential was propagated normally throughout the whole fibre. The strength of current was reduced until it was below half-threshold and the potential response observed visually on the C.R.T. The duration of the rectangular wave was adjusted until it was sufficient to allow the membrane voltage to reach its equilibrium value. A test was made to ensure that the recording electrode slid smoothly along the axon. A series of photographic records of the extrapolar potential was then obtained with the arrangement of electrodes shown in figure 4a; in general these were similar to those in figure 6. One set of records was made with the movable electrode receding from the cathode and another with it approaching. There was sometimes a difference of 5 or 10 % between the two sets of records, but as a rule they agreed closely with one another. The current through the axon was determined with the arrangement of electrodes shown in figure 4b and a typical record is given in figure 6. This observation also provided a routine check of the squareness of the current wave form through the nerve fibre. The next operation was to determine the voltage gradient in the mid-interpolar stretch using the arrangement of figure 4c. The recording electrode was moved along the axon and a series of records similar to those in figure 9a obtained. The current through the axon was again determined; the arrangement of leads being that of figure 4d and a typical record that of figure 9b. At the end of each experiment the fibre diameter was measured in the following way. The axon was lowered into sea water and transferred to a hollow-ground slide; it was then examined with a microscope using a $\frac{1}{8}$ in. objective and an eyepiece micrometer. Some variation in diameter was always encountered, but this rarely exceeded 5 %.

Results

Preliminary experiments

Local response and passive spread of potential

In attempting to measure the membrane resistance it is important to ensure that measurements are made in the linear part of the nerve characteristic, and that the results are not complicated by the non-linear phenomena of local response and rectification. From this point of view currents which are much weaker than threshold should be employed. On the other hand, as the current is reduced the amplification must be increased and errors from other sources increase. This fact will be appreciated by anyone who has worked with a single-fibre preparation and a high-gain d.c. amplifier. It is sufficient to mention the difficulties which arise from stray interference, shock artifact and the irregular drifts in voltage which occur in the amplifier and in the nerve and electrode system. Preliminary tests indicated that a reasonable compromise would be to use currents with a strength of 0·4–0·5 threshold. An absolute value for the resulting current density through the membrane cannot be given, since it varied with the excitability and membrane resistance of individual axons. But a rough estimate is that the current density under the electrode was of the order of $5 \mu A \, cm.^{-2}$. The total current through the axon was roughly $0·1 \mu A$. The absence of any significant response in the region below half-threshold is illustrated by an experiment with a *Carcinus* fibre (figure 5). Here the behaviour of the axon is shown for different strengths of applied current. Anodic or weak cathodic currents appear to affect only the passive charging process;

for all the curves have the same shape and their amplitude is roughly proportional to the applied current. And the shape of the curves is of a type which is to be expected from a process involving passive charge and discharge of the membrane capacity. The picture changed completely when the applied current approached threshold. At 0·9 threshold the cathodic potential showed a fast creep, and at 1·0 the curves turned upwards as if to give rise to a propagated impulse. But a true

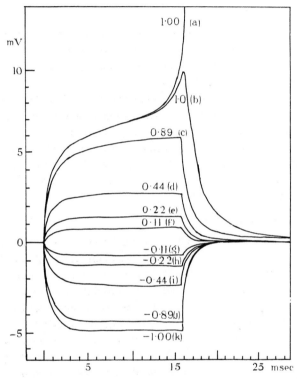

FIGURE 5. Response of *Carcinus* axon to rectangular waves of current of different intensity; recorded at a polarizing electrode of width about 200 μ. The numbers on each record give the strength of current relative to threshold. Depolarization of the nerve is shown as positive.

action potential did not result in every case. Owing to the spontaneous play in excitability, a stimulus does not invariably evoke an impulse until its strength is slightly greater than threshold. In fact, a threshold shock is normally defined as one which produces impulses on 50 % of occasions. Record *b* shows what happens when a threshold shock failed to evoke an impulse. The potential turned upwards as if to give rise to a spike, but it failed to reach a critical level and died out as a localized wave. Inflected local responses of this kind only occurred when the current was nearly threshold but their onset was completely gradual. Thus all transitions between records *b* and *c* could be obtained by careful adjustment of the strength of current.

The striking form of local response illustrated by this experiment was observed on a large number of occasions and will be described in greater detail later. For the moment our chief concern is that it did not occur when the current was less than half-threshold.

Measurement of the curves in figure 5 indicated that there were small deviations from linearity in the region below half-threshold. At present there is no evidence to show whether these deviations were reproducible, and they may well have been instrumental in origin.

The effect of long pulses of current

The observations of Cole & Hodgkin (1939) on membrane resistance were made with currents lasting several seconds, while the duration of the currents used in the present work was of the order of 20 msec. It is legitimate to ask whether the two methods of measurement give comparable results. One or two experiments with long pulses were made in order to answer this question. The point at issue is whether the steady potential which is established in a few milliseconds is really constant, or whether there may not be a creep of potential which is too slow to register on the time scale used. Records showing the effect of pulses lasting 300 msec. were therefore made on a slow time base. The result was unequivocal, since the potential attained its maximum in a few milliseconds and then remained constant for the duration of the pulse.

Experiments with dead nerve fibres

Measurements of the extrapolar potential are liable to be complicated by errors and artifacts of various kinds (cf. Bogue & Rosenberg 1934). A number of control experiments were therefore made in order to ensure that the potential recorded in the extrapolar region was entirely due to accumulation of charge at the nerve membrane. In general, we found that the spread of potential in the extrapolar region was reduced progressively as the fibre lost its physiological activity, and that it finally fell to a low value when the fibre became inexcitable. A very striking demonstration of this general type of behaviour can be obtained by allowing the axon to come into contact with a solution of chloroform. Figure 6 illustrates an experiment of this kind. Records b–g show the spread of potential in the extrapolar region of a normal axon, and demonstrate the passive accumulation of charge at the surface membrane. The fibre was then dipped into sea water which had been shaken with chloroform. It was left in this solution for 1 or 2 min. and raised into oil. The result was extremely striking; for the potential change at the cathode was reduced to one-twentieth of its former value and was abolished at all other points. Records a and A are an index of the current through the axon, which was unchanged by the chloroform treatment. This experiment illustrates the delicate nature of the surface membrane and provides a convincing demonstration of the virtual absence of artifacts. The small potential which is recorded at the cathode in B may be attributed either to a residual membrane resistance or to the finite thickness of the nerve fibre. Close examination of the original records revealed a rapid spike which occurred at the beginning and end of the square wave, but was too faint for reproduction. This persisted after chloroform treatment and must be regarded as an artifact caused by capacitative coupling between the polarizing and recording leads. The spike was ignored in analysing the records, but served a useful purpose in defining precisely the beginning and end of the applied current.

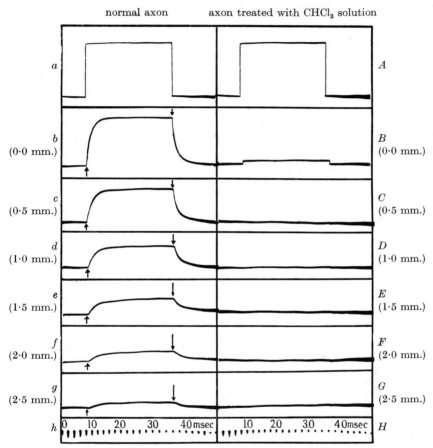

FIGURE 6. Effect of chloroform solution on spread of membrane potential in *Homarus* axon. *a*, *A*, current through normal and chloroform treated axon, measured as voltage across 61,700 Ω resistance in series with axon; *b–g*, potential recorded in extrapolar region of normal axon; the distance from the cathode is shown by the figures in brackets; *B–G*, potentials recorded in the same way after application of chloroform solution; *h*, *H*, 500 cyc./sec. time calibration. The vertical arrows indicate the beginning and end of the square wave of current and were marked from a capacitative artifact which appeared on the original records. Records *a* to *c* have been retouched. The amplification was the same in all records and the amplitude of the wave in *b* was approximately 4·5 mV. Records taken from experiment 13.

The measurement of λ

Equation (6·2) shows that there should be an exponential relation between the steady potential in the extrapolar region and the distance from the cathode. Hence a straight line with slope $(\log_{10} e)/\lambda$ should result when the $\log_{10}$ of the potential is plotted against distance. This method was used in all the experiments and is illustrated by figure 7. In drawing a straight line through the experimental points, more weight was placed on observations near the cathode, since the percentage error increased as the recorded voltage decreased. Figure 8 proves that this procedure gave satisfactory results. Here the results of all the experiments are plotted on a linear scale: the ordinate giving the potential as a fraction of the potential at the cathode and the abscissa giving distance as a fraction of the space constant. If equation (6·2) were obeyed perfectly all the points should fall on an exponential curve which is drawn as a solid line. In practice there are deviations, but in no case are they at all serious. Hence this set of observations demonstrates the validity of the theory and of the method of measurement employed.

Table 2 shows that the average value for λ was 1·6 mm., but that its magnitude varied considerably in individual experiments. As will appear later the variations are primarily due to differences in the membrane resistance, and the scatter in the results reflects the variable nature of this quantity.

TABLE 2. ELECTRICAL CONSTANTS IN TEN AXONS FROM *HOMARUS VULGARIS*

experi-ment number	axon number	dia-meter μ	λ mm.	y $\Omega \times 10^3$	m MΩ cm.$^{-1}$	τ_m msec.	r_2/r_1	R_2 Ω cm.	R_4 Ω cm.^{2}	C_M μF cm.
1	1	65	1·80	78	0·72	1·6	0·82	43·6	1910	0·83
2	2	80	1·07	49	0·80	1·8	0·87	75·2	927	1·94
3	3	62	1·90	77	0·98	2·4	1·21	65·4	2784	0·87
4	4	76	1·40	80	0·88	5·4	0·76	70·6	1655	3·24
5	5	76	1·82	134	0·86	3·7	0·59	63·0	2955	1·25
6	6	73	2·95	103	0·90	4·0	1·3	83·6	7330	0·55
7	6	73	2·62	114	0·73	3·3	0·84	55·9	4590	0·71
8	6	73	1·95	55	0·76	1·3	1·35	74·6	2720	0·46
9	7	87	1·31	54	0·59	0·76	0·72	61·2	1150	0·66
10	8	78	1·29	137	0·74	1·9	0·35	48·1	1590	1·23
11	8	78	0·81	112	0·71	0·91	0·26	43·2	706	1·29
12	9	73	0·92	40	0·72	0·89	0·84	55·6	564	1·58
13	10	80	1·15	55	0·66	2·5	0·69	56·6	905	2·73
average value		75	1·61	81	0·83	2·3	0·81	60·5	2290	1·33

Square brackets indicate that successive measurements were made on the same nerve fibre; curve brackets that they were made on the same stretch of the same fibre. Temperature: 15–20° C. Strength of current: 0·4–0·5 threshold. The values given for τ_m are the mean of four measurements.

The measurement of y

The constant y has the dimensions of a resistance and is given by the ratio of the steady voltage at the cathode to the applied current (see equation (6·1)). The method of measurement is clarified by referring to figure 6. Here b gives the voltage at the cathode and a the voltage across 61,700 Ω. Hence $y = 61,700 \times b/a$ Ω, where b/a is the ratio of the observed voltages. In this case y was 55,400 Ω, which was rather smaller than that usually obtained (see table 2).

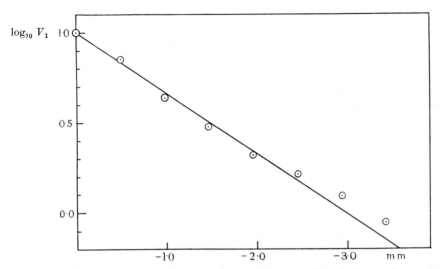

FIGURE 7. Equilibrium distribution of extrapolar potential. Ordinate: $\log_{10}$ potential. Abscissa: distance of recording electrode from cathode in mm. The distance is shown as negative in order to conform to the convention used in the theoretical section.

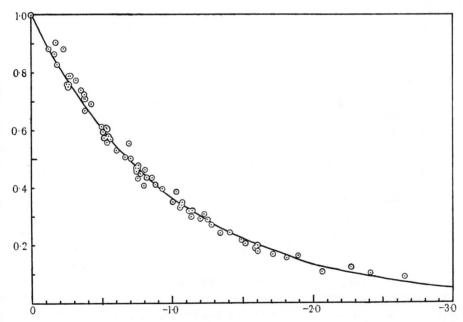

FIGURE 8. Equilibrium distribution of extrapolar potential in thirteen experiments. Ordinate: potential as a fraction of the potential at the cathode. Abscissa: distance as a fraction of the measured space constant λ. The solid line is drawn according to equation (6·2).

189

The measurement of m

m has been defined as the parallel resistance of core and external fluid. It was determined by measuring the voltage gradient midway between two distant electrodes and dividing the gradient by the current through the nerve. Typical records for determining m are given in figure 9. According to theory all these records should be perfectly rectangular, since the membrane impedance is not involved in the mid-interpolar region. The records actually show a slight creep, which can be explained in various ways. It might have been due to some capacitative property of the axoplasm or to irregularities in the diameter of the axis cylinder; or it could be attributed to the fact that the electrodes were not really an infinite distance apart as assumed in the theory. Whatever its explanation, the effect is not of present importance, since it makes little difference whether the maximum or the sudden rise is used for analysis. On the whole it seemed best to measure the sudden rise, since any effects introduced by the membrane were avoided by this procedure. The deflexion observed at any point could be expressed as a resistance by comparing it with the effect produced by the monitoring resistance. It was therefore possible to plot resistance against electrode separation as has been done in figure 10, which illustrates three typical experiments. The observed points fall very close to straight lines as they should according to theory. A direct measurement of m is given by the slope of the best straight line through the experimental points. The random nature of the errors involved seemed to justify a statistical treatment and m was therefore determined by the standard 'least square' formula.

The measurement of τ_m

The spatial and temporal distribution of the extrapolar potential are determined by the two constants λ and τ_m. λ has already been obtained so that τ_m can be determined by comparing experimental and theoretical curves. But first it must be established that the experimental records agree with the rather complicated equations of cable theory. Practice and theory are usually related by comparing experimental points with a theoretical curve. Here the situation is more complicated, since the experimental observations consist of a family of curves instead of a single set of points. In other words a three-dimensional surface has been found and must be compared with a theoretical surface. This imposes a much more drastic test on the theoretical equations, since only one parameter, τ_m, can be varied to make a number of curves coincide. In such a case it would be too much to hope for complete agreement at every point on the nerve. Nevertheless, agreement between theory and practice is reasonably good, as may be seen from figure 11. Here tracings of the voltage-time records at different distances are compared with the corresponding theoretical curves for those distances. Only a finite number of theoretical curves was computed and it was therefore impossible to use a theoretical curve which corresponded exactly with the experimental one. Thus C is the experimental curve for $x/\lambda = 0.38$ and d the theoretical curve for

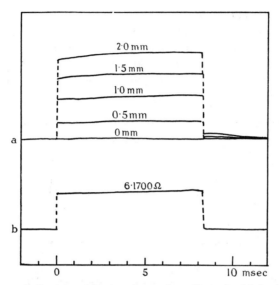

FIGURE 9. *a*, voltage gradient in mid-interpolar region. Records obtained with arrangement of figure 4*c* and with measuring electrodes separated by distances of 0–2·0 mm. *b*, voltage across 61,700Ω using the same strength of current as that in *a*. Electrode arrangement as in figure 4*d*.

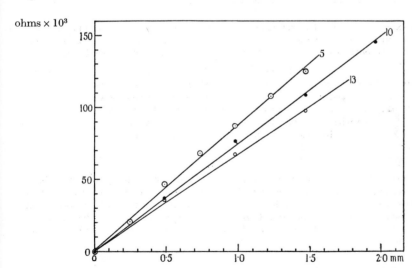

FIGURE 10. Resistance length relation in the mid-interpolar region. Ordinate: resistance, measured from records of the type shown in figure 9. Abscissa: distance between recording leads. The numbers on the straight lines refer to the experiments in table 2. The current was led into the nerve through electrodes about 16 mm. apart.

191

$x/\lambda = 0.4$. But the small differences introduced by this method of plotting do not materially alter the general picture of close agreement between theory and practice. Nor do they obscure the fact that there are certain real differences between the two sets of curves. Thus the record at the cathode rises more slowly than the corresponding theoretical curve, while the descending curves agree closely at the cathode but diverge at larger distances.

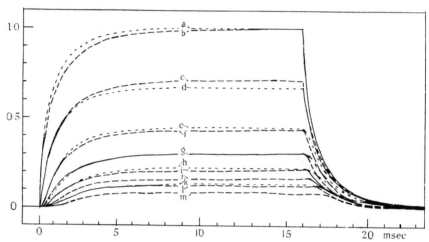

FIGURE 11. Experimental and theoretical curves showing rise and fall of extrapolar potential at different distances from cathode. Experiment 10 (table 2); $\lambda = 1.29$ mm. Abscissa: time in msec. Ordinate: potential expressed as a fraction of the equilibrium potential at the cathode.

a. Theoretical curve with $-x/\lambda = 0.0$	*h.* Theoretical curve with $-x/\lambda = 1.5$
b. Experimental curve with $-x/\lambda = 0.0$	*i.* Experimental curve with $-x/\lambda = 1.52$
c. Experimental curve with $-x/\lambda = 0.38$	*j.* Experimental curve with $-x/\lambda = 1.89$
d. Theoretical curve with $-x/\lambda = 0.4$	*k.* Theoretical curve with $-x/\lambda = 2.0$
e. Theoretical curve with $-x/\lambda = 0.8$	*l.* Experimental curve with $-x/\lambda = 2.27$
f. Experimental curve with $-x/\lambda = 0.76$	*m.* Experimental curve with $-x/\lambda = 2.65$
g. Experimental curve with $-x/\lambda = 1.14$	
Theoretical curve with $-x/\lambda = 1.2$	

Theoretical curves drawn according to equations (6·0) and (6·4) with τ_m taken as 2·10 msec. Arrangement of electrodes as in figure 4*a*. Rectangular pulse with strength about 40 % threshold. The abscissa is not quite linear and the theoretical curves have been plotted according to the actual scale and not to a hypothetical linear scale; time calibrations derived from 500 cyc./sec. oscillator. A continuous line indicates that theoretical and experimental curves coincide.

The general coincidence between theory and experiment illustrated by figure 11 was only obtained because the theoretical curves were plotted with the correct time constant which in this case happened to be 2·10 msec. This value was obtained by a laborious process of trial and error which was too cumbersome for use in every experiment. It was therefore necessary to find a swifter method of computation. One possibility is to make use of the equations for total charge. This method was of little general use, but will be described briefly because it is of considerable theoretical interest. Equations (5·2) and (5·3) show that the total charge obeys simple exponential laws. It follows immediately that the total extrapolar charge, which is proportional to $\int_{-\infty}^{0} V_1\,dx$, must also obey exponential charging laws. This quantity can be obtained by graphical integration of the potential in the extrapolar region and may then be plotted against time. The result of such an analysis is given in figure 12. Here the theoretical curve for the rise of a charge is drawn with a time constant of 2·02 msec. and for the fall with a time constant of 1·65 msec. The charging process obviously agrees closely with theory, but there is a definite deviation in the process of discharge. Further, the time constant for the charging process agrees with that found previously (2·10 msec.), whereas the discharge constant is appreciably smaller. The reason for these discrepancies is not clear, but they may arise from an apparently trivial circumstance. During the charging process the potential is relatively large and occupies a small area, whereas the converse situation holds during the period of discharge (see figures 2 a, b). This means that graphical integration is much less susceptible to cumulative errors in the former case than it is in the latter. The discharge curve may therefore be a less reliable index of the behaviour of the nerve than the corresponding charging curve. Whatever the explanation, this method will not be pursued further, since it proved too laborious for use in more than one experiment.

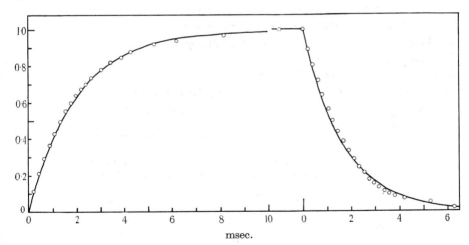

FIGURE 12. Time course of total membrane charge in extrapolar region. Abscissa: time in msec. Ordinate: $\int_{-\infty}^{0} V_1\,dx$ in arbitrary units. The circles are experimental points computed by graphical integration of photographic records from experiment 10. The solid line is a plot of equations (5·2) and (5·3) with $\tau_m = 2·02$ and 1·65 msec. for the rise and fall, respectively.

A simple method of measuring the membrane time constant is to ignore all observations except those at the cathode and find the time constant by comparing a single theoretical curve with the correct equation ((6·3) or (6·5)). This can be done for both charging and discharging processes and has the advantage of simplicity. But it suffers from two serious disadvantages. In the first place it ignores a great deal of valuable information, and in the second it is liable to magnify the errors which arise from the finite width of the electrode. The general effect of electrode width is to lengthen the apparent time constant; for the effective cathode occurs on the interpolar side of the electrode and the effective recording point on the extrapolar side. With a cathode of width $\lambda/10$ the apparent time constant should be 10 % larger than the true time constant. But no worth-while correction can be made, since the exact current distribution at the electrode is unknown. Time constants measured by this method should therefore be regarded as only approximately correct.

Another method of measuring the time constant depends upon a remarkable property of equations (6·0) and (6·4). If the time to reach half-maximum is plotted against distance, a curve is obtained which is very nearly a straight line with a slope of $2\lambda/\tau_m$. An alternative statement of this result is that the half-value potential propagates at a constant velocity of $2\lambda/\tau_m$.* Since λ is known, τ_m can be obtained by measuring the velocity of propagation from the experimental records.

Seven methods of measuring τ_m from the experimental data have now been described:

(1) Trial and error to find best overall fit of experimental curves.
(2) Rate of rise of total charge in extrapolar region.
(3) Rate of fall of total charge in extrapolar region.
(4) Rate of rise of potential at cathode.
(5) Rate of fall of potential at cathode.
(6) Propagation velocity of half-value potential following make of current.
(7) Propagation velocity of half-value potential following break of current.

All seven methods were applied to one experiment, with the following results:

method	apparent time constant (msec.)	method	apparent time constant (msec.)
1	2·10	5	2·10
2	2·02	6	1·63
3	1·65	7	1·40
4	2·67	average	1·93

The last four methods were applied as a routine procedure to all the experiments, with results which are shown in table 3. The agreement between different methods is often poor and the variations seem to be entirely random in nature. But there is little doubt as to the order of magnitude of the time constant, and it is this that is of interest at the moment.

* A footnote in Bogue & Rosenberg's (1934) paper suggests that this relation was known to Cremer.

TABLE 3. VALUES OF MEMBRANE TIME CONSTANT (τ_m) OBTAINED
BY FOUR DIFFERENT METHODS

| experiment number | τ_m in msec. determined by method | | | | τ_m in msec. average |
	4	5	6	7	
1	1·97	1·71	1·28	1·40	1·6
2	1·28	1·49	2·48	1·96	1·8
3	3·09	2·34	2·49	1·80	2·4
4	3·85	6·22	6·00	5·40	5·4
5	4·51	3·91	3·33	3·06	3·7
6	2·90	2·67	5·64	4·86	4·0
7	3·46	3·11	3·28	3·18	3·3
8	0·81	0·84	1·81	1·59	1·3
9	0·73	0·91	0·78	0·63	0·76
10	2·67	2·10	1·63	1·40	1·9
11	1·24	1·22	0·65	0·54	0·91
12	1·17	1·36	0·56	0·49	0·89
13	2·43	3·50	1·82	2·12	2·5
average	2·31	2·40	2·44	2·19	2·34

The relative magnitude of internal and external resistances

The ratio of the internal to external resistance per unit length (r_2/r_1) is important, because it allows us to estimate the absolute magnitude of potential changes at the nerve membrane. Equation (1·4) was derived without reference to the properties of the surface membrane, and it may therefore be applied to any region of nerve which does not form part of an external circuit. In general

(potential change at membrane)
$$= \text{(potential change recorded externally)} \times (1 + r_2/r_1).$$

r_2/r_1 was obtained from the experimental results by equation (8·3) and calculated values are given in table 2. Action potentials were measured in five of these experiments, and the absolute magnitude of the electrical change at the surface membrane could therefore be estimated. The average value for the membrane action potential was found to be 110 mV and the extremes 135 and 87 mV. This result is in good agreement with the direct measurements which have been made with a micro-electrode in squid axons (Curtis & Cole 1942; Hodgkin & Huxley 1939).

The measurement of r_2/r_1 was subject to a small systematic error. In the theory it was assumed that the electrode was infinitesimal in width, whereas it actually had an effective width of 100–150μ. The measured value for r_2/r_1 would therefore exceed the true value by an amount which we estimate roughly at 10 %.

The axoplasm resistivity (R_2)

The resistivity of the axoplasm can be computed by equation (8·0):

$$R_2 = \pi a^2 m(1 + m\lambda/2y).$$

It would be unwise to expect great accuracy or consistency in the calculated value of R_2, since four separate measurements enter into its determination, and the final result is subject to the errors which arise from the assumption of infinitesimal electrode width. A rough estimate of the total error in R_2 is that it amounts to $\pm 30 \%$. Table 2 shows that the average value of R_2 was $60 \cdot 5 \Omega$ cm. and the limits $43 \cdot 2$ and $83 \cdot 6 \Omega$ cm. The average value of the axoplasm resistivity was, therefore, about three times as great as that of the surrounding sea water. This result is similar to those obtained for other cells. Measurements with transverse electrodes gave an average value of four times sea water for the resistivity of squid axoplasm (Cole & Curtis 1938), and observations with axial electrodes an average of $1 \cdot 4$ times sea water for the same material (Cole & Hodgkin 1939). Red and white blood corpuscles have a resistivity of twice plasma, frog's sartorius muscle one of about three times Ringer and various echinoderm eggs a resistivity of four to eleven times sea water (for references see Cole & Cole (1936) and Bozler & Cole (1935)).

The membrane resistance

The resistance × unit area of the surface membrane is determined by equation (8·1):

$$R_4 = 2\pi a \lambda^2 m (2 + m\lambda/2y + 2y/m\lambda).$$

Table 2 shows that the ratio r_2/r_1 which is equal to the factor $m\lambda/2y$ usually lies between $\frac{2}{3}$ and $\frac{3}{2}$. This means that a large error in $m\lambda/2y$ will have only a small effect on R_4. Suppose, for example, that the true value of $m\lambda/2y$ is $1 \cdot 0$ and that it is measured as $1 \cdot 5$. In the first case the factor in brackets in (8·1) would be $4 \cdot 0$ and in the second $4 \cdot 17$; hence the error in R_4 would only be 4%. A similar line of argument shows that the measured value of R_4 will only be very slightly affected by the assumption of infinitesimal electrode width. The accuracy of the R_4 determination is, therefore, primarily controlled by the measurement of λ^2, a and m. The errors in λ^2 are likely to be of the order of $\pm 30 \%$, and almost certainly swamp the errors in a and m. A conservative estimate of the accuracy of the measurements in table 2 is that the values given for R_4 are correct to within 50%. The observed variation was much greater than this, and successive measurements on one axon showed that the membrane resistance declined progressively during the course of an experiment. Thus axons 6 and 8 had initial resistances of 7330 and 1590Ω cm.², while their final resistances were 2720 and 706Ω cm.². The variable properties of the surface membrane mean that an average or standard value cannot be given for its resistance. All that can be said is that axons with resistances varying from 600 to 7000Ω cm.² are capable of conducting nervous impulses in a normal manner. It is equally impossible to estimate the value of the membrane resistance in the living animal. The natural membrane resistance is not likely to be less than that found *in vitro*, but it may be much higher since Blinks's (1930) work on *Valonia* indicates that the surface resistance falls when cells are handled.

The values for R_4 given in table 2 are considerably larger than those recorded in the squid axon. Cole & Hodgkin (1939) reported values ranging from 400 to 1100Ω cm.² on the basis of resistance-length measurements with direct current, while Cole & Baker (1941 a) obtained an upper limit of 200Ω cm.² from measurements with a.c. and transverse electrodes. On the other hand, Cole & Curtis (1941) give an average value of only 23Ω cm.^{2} from measurements with an internal electrode and d.c. pulses. Finally, Cole & Baker (1941b) calculated a value of 350Ω cm.$^{-2}$ from the result of a.c. measurements with longitudinal electrodes and the assumption of a membrane capacity of $1\cdot1\,\mu$F cm.^{2}. Cole (1941) appears to regard 300Ω cm.^{2} as a more or less average value. The low value of 23Ω cm.^{2} was attributed by Cole & Curtis (1941) to the poor physiological condition of impaled axons, but as they point out it may also have been due to the fact that two constants required in the analysis were assumed and not measured. In any case, there seems to be no doubt that the membrane resistance of $75\,\mu$ lobster axons is several times larger than it is in $500\,\mu$ squid axons. This difference may have some functional significance, since the rate of attaining ionic equilibrium tends to increase with surface-volume ratio, other things being equal. The membrane resistance would therefore need to decrease as the diameter increased if the cell economy demands a constant rate of approach to equilibrium.

The values of membrane resistance encountered in our work suggest that the permeability to ions must be rather low. Some idea of this may be gained by supposing that potassium ions alone can diffuse through the membrane and that permeability is studied by replacing the potassium in the external solution with a radioactive isotope. In this case it is fairly easy to show that approximately 30 min. would elapse before an $80\,\mu$ fibre with a membrane resistance of 7000Ω cm.^{2} reached a state in which one-tenth of its internal potassium was replaced by the radioactive isotope. It would be interesting to see whether the rate of penetration of potassium is of this general order of magnitude.

Our values for the membrane resistance may be compared with those obtained by Dean, Curtis & Cole (1940) on artificial films containing lipoid and protein molecules. These films were of the right electrical thickness, since their capacity was about $1\,\mu$F cm.$^{-2}$, but their electrical resistance was only 50–100Ω cm.^{2}. It is too early to try to correlate this difference with chemical structure, but there is some hope that future work will show what sort of structure is needed to produce a membrane of high resistance.

The magnitude of the membrane capacity

The membrane capacity was determined by the relation

$$C_M = \tau_m/R_4.$$

Both τ_m and R_4 are subject to large errors, so that little confidence can be placed on the exact numerical values obtained for C_M. In fact, it is possible that the variation encountered in table 2 was entirely due to experimental error. But there can be little doubt that the membrane capacity was of the order of $0\cdot5$–$2\cdot0\,\mu$F cm.$^{-2}$. A value of this kind has been obtained in a wide variety of living cells; well-known examples are red blood cells $0\cdot95\,\mu$F cm.$^{-2}$, yeast $0\cdot60\,\mu$F cm.$^{-2}$, echinoderm eggs

0.87–$3.1\,\mu$F cm.$^{-2}$, frog's sartorius muscle c. $1\,\mu$F cm.$^{-2}$, squid nerve $1.1\,\mu$F cm.$^{-2}$, and *Nitella* $0.94\,\mu$F cm.$^{-2}$ (for references and qualifications see Cole 1940).

All these results depend on the use of a.c., transverse electrodes and a theory based on Maxwell's application of Laplace's equation to a suspension of spheres. Our observations were made with pulses of d.c., longitudinal electrodes and a theory based on Kelvin's equations for the submarine cable. So it is pleasing to find even a broad agreement between the two sets of results.

The implications of the membrane capacity of $1\,\mu$F cm.$^{-2}$ are too well known to be repeated. All that need be said is that the result suggests the presence either of a very thin membrane, or of one with a large dielectric constant. If the dielectric constant were 3, the membrane thickness would be $27\,$A; and if the thickness were $1\,\mu$ the dielectric constant would be 1100.

Possible membrane inductance

Cole & Baker (1941 b) have presented experimental evidence which suggests that an inductive element is present in the surface membrane of the squid axon. No sign of inductive behaviour could be observed in the majority of our experiments. But the two sets of observations do not conflict in spite of the apparent contradiction. Cole & Baker's axons had a membrane resistance of about 300Ω cm.^{2}, ours an average of 2300Ω cm.^{2}. The effect of an inductive element would have been profoundly influenced by the value of the membrane resistance, since Cole & Baker's work indicates that the two elements are in series. To take a specific example: assume that the membrane has the equivalent circuit suggested by Cole & Baker, that the capacity is $1\,\mu$F, the inductance $0.2\,$H and the resistance 300Ω cm.^{2}. When a rectangular current is applied to this circuit, the voltage response is oscillatory and the first overshoot is 75 % greater than the final steady value. The response is entirely different if the resistance is increased to 2500Ω cm.^{2}. In this case the wave form is no longer oscillatory, it does not overshoot the steady value, and it differs from a simple exponential solution by less than 0.2 %. The absence of inductive or oscillatory behaviour therefore agrees with Cole & Baker's hypothesis, although it clearly cannot be used in evidence one way or the other. But some of the axons studied had low membrane resistances and should have shown signs of inductive behaviour, if Cole & Baker's picture is correct. This, in fact, is what happened. Figure 13c gives the response of an axon with a resistance of 700Ω cm.^{2} and shows that there is an overshoot of 5 %. There is no equation with which to compare this record, but a theory for total charge can be developed by the method used in deriving (5.1). The resulting expressions allow the membrane inductance (L) to be calculated from the overshoot and predict that the response will only be oscillatory when $L > R_4^2 C_m / 4$. Experiments 9, 11 and 12 (table 2) showed a small overshoot and gave an average value of $0.3\,$H for the membrane inductance. No overshoot was observed in the remaining experiments, and this is to be expected since the factor $R_4^2 C_M / 4$ always exceeded 0.4. Our results are therefore consistent with the existence of an inductive element of about $0.2\,$H cm.^{2}.

But there is an entirely different way of explaining the experimental facts and this must now be considered. In figure 13 a and b the current had been increased until it was of just threshold strength, which means that it was strong enough to produce propagated spikes on 50 % of occasions. The propagated response is shown by a and the critical local response by b. It is arguable that the local response is of the same general nature as the spike, and that the discontinuity in nerve arises because the response to a superthreshold shock is large enough to involve the whole fibre by local circuit action, whereas the subthreshold response cannot spread beyond the cathodic region. It is also arguable that the small overshoot produced by the weak current is of the same general nature as the larger overshoot produced by the threshold current. And the similarity of the two lower curves in figure 13 suggests rather strongly that a common process is involved. According to this train of reasoning the overshoot seen in figure 13c is to be regarded as a vestige of the normal action potential. In this case it cannot be considered as an inductive effect. For the process underlying the action potential must involve energy liberation by the nerve, whereas a pure inductive overshoot would not. The two theories are therefore quite distinct, although no attempt can be made to decide between them until there are precise concepts to replace the general notions of inductance and energy liberation.

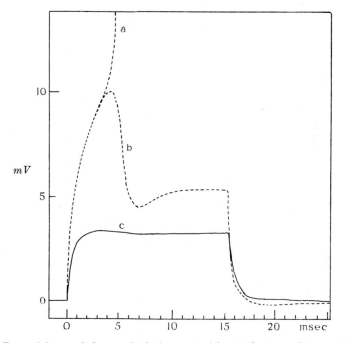

FIGURE 13. Potential recorded at cathode in axon with membrane resistance of $700\varOmega$ cm.² (experiment 11). a, propagated response produced by current of strength 1·00; b, local response produced by current of strength 1·00; c, potential produced by current of strength 0·49. The absolute values given on the ordinate are approximate, but the scale is linear.

The idea of a membrane inductance is certainly useful, whatever its ultimate truth or falsehood. One application was found in the attempt to explain the difference between the action potential and the resting potential (Curtis & Cole 1942; Hodgkin & Huxley 1945). Another is illustrated by figure 14, which shows the effect of strong cathodic currents on a *Carcinus* axon. The records indicate that the wave form of the cathodic potential becomes increasingly oscillatory as

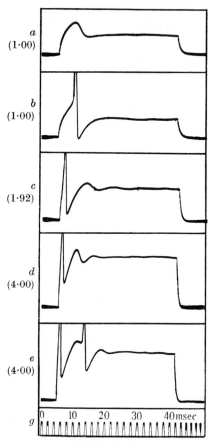

FIGURE 14. Effect of strong cathodic currents on *Carcinus* axon. Relative strength of current shown by bracketed figures. *g*, 500 cyc./sec. time calibration. Propagated spikes retouched.

Two points in figure 14 call for comment. After the oscillations have died out the membrane potential settles down to a steady value which is not proportional to the current but varies more slowly as the current is increased. This is an example of the membrane rectification described by Cole & Curtis (1941) in the squid axon.

In figure 14*e* a second spike arises from the second wave of potential, but a little after its crest. Hodgkin (1938) showed that a spike always started at a distance from the cathode when it arose later than the crest of the local response. Examination of the original records suggested that the same thing was occurring here, although no positive evidence for this conclusion was obtained.

the strength of current is increased. Similar results have been reported by Arvanitaki (1939) in *Sepia* and are to be expected from Cole & Baker's hypothesis. For the membrane resistance decreases progressively as the nerve is depolarized (Cole & Curtis 1941), and the response therefore becomes increasingly oscillatory as the current is raised. The frequency of the oscillations in figure 14 is consistent with an inductance of $0 \cdot 3$ H cm.^{2} and a capacity of 2μF cm.$^{-2}$.

Observations on the local response

The most striking features of the local response were the inflexion and miniature spike which occurred when the duration of the rectangular wave was less than the utilization time. One example has already been described (figure 5), and a more general picture is given by figure 15 which shows the effect produced by threshold pulses of different duration. A large number of photographs were taken and with two exceptions only the responses which just succeed or just fail to propagate have been reproduced. The effect of a current longer than the utilization time is given by c and C. In this case the record shows first the passive charging of the nerve membrane and then a slow creep, which must be regarded as a local response, since it is absent from the anodic wave form (a). If the local activity succeeded in reaching a critical level it turned upwards and gave rise to a propagated action potential. When the critical level was not reached the response died out as a monophasic wave of low amplitude. The form of the propagating responses was not very different when the duration of the rectangular wave was less than the utilization time $(D$ to $H)$, but the responses which failed to propagate showed the characteristic inflexion and miniature spike $(d$ to $h)$. This type of response persisted as the duration of the current was reduced, but at very short times it changed to that characteristic of excitation by short shocks (cf. Hodgkin 1938). An example is given in h and H, but the details of the record cannot be appreciated on the slow time scale used. This set of records suggests that the condition for excitation by currents of different duration is that a critical potential must be reached; they also illustrate the reversibility of the process responsible for the action potential. One is accustomed to think that nothing can stop an impulse once the potential has begun to turn upwards into a spike. Our records indicate that the potential wave may fail to propagate, although it has shown the inflexion normally associated with a spike.

The records which have just been described were obtained from a *Carcinus* axon and may be regarded as typical of this preparation. *Homarus* fibres behaved in a similar manner, but the utilization time was considerably shorter and the rheobasic local response had a more conspicuous humped form. We obtained the impression that the long utilization time and flat local response were associated with a high membrane resistance, and that axons with a low resistance gave the short utilization time and humped local response characterized by figure 13.

In comparing our results with those obtained in whole nerve trunks it should be remembered that the amplitude of the subthreshold potentials was small compared to the spike. Thus the propagated potential was ten times larger than the sub-threshold potential shown in figure 15. The effects we have described would there-fore be difficult to observe in preparations giving spikes only $100\,\mu$V in amplitude.

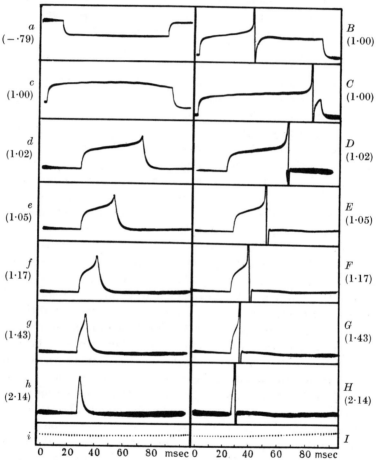

FIGURE 15. Effect of rectangular currents on *Carcinus* axon recorded at polarizing electrode. *a*, polarization produced by anodic current; *c–h*, local responses produced by threshold currents; *B–H*, propagated spikes (retouched) produced by threshold currents; *i, I,* 500 cyc./sec. time calibration. The strength of the current relative to the rheobase is indicated by the bracketed figures. The strength and duration of the current was identical in the pairs *c, C, d, D, ..., h, H.*

The change of membrane resistance during activity

A transient decrease of membrane resistance during activity has been proved by the well-known experiments of Cole & Curtis (1939). One result of this pheno-menon is shown in figure 15 *B*. Here the diphasic action potential arose before the end of the rectangular wave and lasted for about 2 msec. The membrane capacity should be discharged during the spike and must charge again when the resistance returns to its normal value. The spike should therefore be followed by a charging process similar to that which occurred at the beginning of the rectangular wave. This effect is clearly shown by record B but is absent when the action potential arises at the end of the applied current (D to H). In this case the charge disappeared rapidly during the spike and did not reform, because the applied current was removed.

DISCUSSION

The implications of the resistance and capacity measurements have already been discussed. It remains to consider the bearing of our results on studies of electric excitation. The local responses observed in our experiments agree in a remarkable way with the instability described by one of us. Rushton (1932) studied the excitation process in medullated nerve by superimposing a short shock on a rectangular wave. A plot of excitability against time showed that the excitation process followed an inflected time course very similar to that observed in our records of local response. This is another example of the general similarity between the results of excitability studies on medullated nerves and the electrical records obtained in non-medullated nerve fibres. The phenomenon of latency and the excitability effects described by Rushton and by Katz (1937) all find an explanation in the electrical behaviour of isolated crustacean axons. The obvious conclusion is that similar electric effects exist in medullated axons, but that they are too small to be detected in studies of whole nerve trunks. This conclusion is not generally accepted and is likely to remain in dispute until satisfactory records can be obtained from an isolated medullated axon.

Hill (1936) and others have shown that many phenomena can be explained by supposing that the process of excitation is equivalent to the charging of a leaky condenser. This theory is useful in co-ordinating a wide range of observations, but extra assumptions have to be introduced to deal with the phenomena of accommodation, latency and the decay of excitability following a brief stimulus. Our results indicate that the processes underlying excitation are of great mathematical complexity. When the current is weak its spatial and temporal distribution is determined by the cumbersome equations of cable theory; when it is strong an immense complication is introduced by the non-linear effect of the local response. Hill's equations must therefore be regarded as largely empirical in nature. But there can be no doubt that certain facts seem to agree better with Hill's theory than with the cable equations. To take a specific example. It is universally agreed that the criterion for excitation by short shocks is that a fixed quantity of electricity must flow through the nerve. This follows at once from Hill's theory, but not from the equations of cable theory. For the condition which allows a short pulse to produce a constant potential at the cathode in a cable-like system is that a pulse of constant energy must flow through the electrodes. This difficulty and others of a similar kind can be resolved in the following way. The condition for excitation seems to be that the cathodic response must reach a potential at which it can propagate through the nerve by local circuit action. It is easy to suppose that the criterion for propagation is related not to the membrane potential at the cathode but to the total membrane charge in the region of the electrode. In this case a constant quantity relation would be obtained and the behaviour of nerve would approximate to that of a leaky condenser in many respects. According to this view, Hill's 'local potential' is to be identified with the total charge in the electrode region and Hill's constant k with the membrane time constant. The true situation is obviously much more complicated, but this hypothesis provides a simple and convenient way of looking at the excitation process.

We wish to express our indebtedness to the Rockefeller Foundation for defraying the expenses associated with this work and to Professor Gray for allowing us to use the aquarium in the Zoological Laboratory.

REFERENCES

Arvanitaki, A. 1939 *Arch. int. Physiol.* 49, 209.
Blinks, L. R. 1930 *J. Gen. Physiol.* 13, 361.
Blinks, L. R. 1937 *Trans. Faraday Soc.* 33, 991.
Bogue, J. G. & Rosenberg, H. 1934 *J. Physiol.* 82, 353.
Bozler, E. & Cole, K. S. 1935 *J. Cell. Comp. Physiol.* 6, 229.
Campbell, G. A. & Foster, R. M. 1931 *Fourier Integrals for practical applications.* Bell Telephone system Technical publications monograph, B. 584, 162.
Cole, K. S. 1937 *Trans. Faraday Soc.* 33, 966.
Cole, K. S. 1940 *Cold. Spr. Harb. Symp. Quant. Biol.* 8, 110.
Cole, K. S. 1941 *J. Gen. Physiol.* 25, 29.
Cole, K. S. & Baker, R. F. 1941a *J. Gen. Physiol.* 24, 535.
Cole, K. S. & Baker, R. F. 1941b *J. Gen. Physiol.* 24, 771.
Cole, K. S. & Cole, R. H. 1936 *J. Gen. Physiol.* 19, 609.
Cole, K. S. & Curtis, H. J. 1938 *J. Gen. Physiol.* 22, 37.
Cole, K. S. & Curtis, H. J. 1939 *J. Gen. Physiol.* 22, 649.
Cole, K. S. & Curtis, H. J. 1941 *J. Gen. Physiol.* 24, 551.
Cole, K. S. & Guttman, R. M. 1942 *J. Gen. Physiol.* 25, 765.
Cole, K. S. & Hodgkin, A. L. 1939 *J. Gen. Physiol.* 22, 671.
Cremer, M. 1899 *Z. Biol.* 37, 550.
Curtis, H. J. & Cole, K. S. 1938 *J. Gen. Physiol.* 21, 757.
Curtis, H. J. & Cole, K. S. 1942 *J. Cell. Comp. Physiol.* 19, 135.
Dean, R. B. 1939 *Nature*, 144, 32.
Dean, R. B., Curtis, H. J. & Cole, K. S. 1940 *Science*, 91, 50.
Fricke, H. & Morse, S. 1925 *J. Gen. Physiol.* 9, 153.
Hermann, L. 1905 *Pflüg. Arch. ges. Physiol.* 109, 95.
Hill, A. V. 1936 *Proc. Roy. Soc.* B, 119, 305.
Höber, R. 1910 *Pflüg. Arch. ges. Physiol.* 133, 237.
Hodgkin, A. L. 1938 *Proc. Roy. Soc.* B, 126, 87.
Hodgkin, A. L. & Huxley, A. F. 1939 *Nature*, 144, 710.
Hodgkin, A. L. & Huxley, A. F. 1945 *J. Physiol.* 104, 176.
Jeffreys, H. 1931 *Operational methods in mathematical physics*, 2nd ed. Camb. Univ. Press.
Katz, B. 1937 *Proc. Roy. Soc.* B, 124, 244.
Nernst, W. 1908 *Pflüg. Arch. ges. Physiol.* 122, 275.
Pumphrey, R. J., Schmitt, O. H. & Young, J. Z. 1940 *J. Physiol.* 98, 47.
Rushton, W. A. H. 1932 *J. Physiol.* 75, 16P.
Rushton, W. A. H. 1934 *J. Physiol.* 82, 332.
Schmitt, O. H. 1938 *J. Sci. Instrum.* 15, 24.
Warburg, E. 1899 *Ann. Phys., Lpz.*, 67, 493.

A QUANTITATIVE DESCRIPTION OF MEMBRANE CURRENT AND ITS APPLICATION TO CONDUCTION AND EXCITATION IN NERVE

By A. L. HODGKIN and A. F. HUXLEY

From the Physiological Laboratory, University of Cambridge

(*Received* 10 *March* 1952)

This article concludes a series of papers concerned with the flow of electric current through the surface membrane of a giant nerve fibre (Hodgkin, Huxley & Katz, 1952; Hodgkin & Huxley, 1952 *a–c*). Its general object is to discuss the results of the preceding papers (Part I), to put them into mathematical form (Part II) and to show that they will account for conduction and excitation in quantitative terms (Part III).

PART I. DISCUSSION OF EXPERIMENTAL RESULTS

The results described in the preceding papers suggest that the electrical behaviour of the membrane may be represented by the network shown in Fig. 1. Current can be carried through the membrane either by charging the membrane capacity or by movement of ions through the resistances in parallel with the capacity. The ionic current is divided into components carried by sodium and potassium ions (I_{Na} and I_K), and a small 'leakage current' (I_l) made up by chloride and other ions. Each component of the ionic current is determined by a driving force which may conveniently be measured as an electrical potential difference and a permeability coefficient which has the dimensions of a conductance. Thus the sodium current (I_{Na}) is equal to the sodium conductance (g_{Na}) multiplied by the difference between the membrane potential (E) and the equilibrium potential for the sodium ion (E_{Na}). Similar equations apply to I_K and I_l and are collected on p. 505.

Our experiments suggest that g_{Na} and g_K are functions of time and membrane potential, but that E_{Na}, E_K, E_l, C_M and $\bar{g}_l$ may be taken as constant. The influence of membrane potential on permeability can be summarized by stating: first, that depolarization causes a transient increase in sodium conductance and a slower but maintained increase in potassium conductance; secondly, that these changes are graded and that they can be reversed by repolarizing the membrane. In order to decide whether these effects are sufficient to account for complicated phenomena such as the action potential and refractory period, it is necessary to obtain expressions relating

Hodgkin, A. L., and A. F. Huxley. A quantitative description of membrane current and its application to conduction and excitation in nerve. *J. Physiol.* **117**: 500–544, 1952.

the sodium and potassium conductances to time and membrane potential. Before attempting this we shall consider briefly what types of physical system are likely to be consistent with the observed changes in permeability.

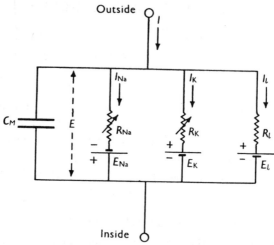

Fig. 1. Electrical circuit representing membrane. $R_{Na}=1/g_{Na}$; $R_K=1/g_K$; $R_l=1/\bar{g}_l$. R_{Na} and R_K vary with time and membrane potential; the other components are constant.

The nature of the permeability changes

At present the thickness and composition of the excitable membrane are unknown. Our experiments are therefore unlikely to give any certain information about the nature of the molecular events underlying changes in permeability. The object of this section is to show that certain types of theory are excluded by our experiments and that others are consistent with them.

The first point which emerges is that the changes in permeability appear to depend on membrane potential and not on membrane current. At a fixed depolarization the sodium current follows a time course whose form is independent of the current through the membrane. If the sodium concentration is such that $E_{Na} < E$, the sodium current is inward; if it is reduced until $E_{Na} > E$ the current changes in sign but still appears to follow the same time course. Further support for the view that membrane potential is the variable controlling permeability is provided by the observation that restoration of the normal membrane potential causes the sodium or potassium conductance to decline to a low value at any stage of the response.

The dependence of g_{Na} and g_K on membrane potential suggests that the permeability changes arise from the effect of the electric field on the distribution or orientation of molecules with a charge or dipole moment. By this we do not mean to exclude chemical reactions, for the rate at which these occur might depend on the position of a charged substrate or catalyst. All that is intended is that small changes in membrane potential would be most unlikely to cause large alterations in the state of a membrane which was composed entirely of electrically neutral molecules.

The next question to consider is how changes in the distribution of a charged particle might affect the ease with which sodium ions cross the membrane. Here we can do little more than reject a suggestion which formed the original basis of our experiments (Hodgkin, Huxley & Katz, 1949). According to this view, sodium ions do not cross the membrane in ionic form but in combination with a lipoid soluble carrier which bears a large negative charge and which can combine with one sodium ion but no more. Since both combined and un-combined carrier molecules bear a negative charge they are attracted to the outside of the membrane in the resting state. Depolarization allows the carrier molecules to move, so that sodium current increases as the membrane potential is reduced. The steady state relation between sodium current and voltage could be calculated for this system and was found to agree reasonably with the observed curve at 0·2 msec after the onset of a sudden depolarization. This was encouraging, but the analogy breaks down if it is pursued further. In the model the first effect of depolarization is a movement of negatively charged molecules from the outside to the inside of the membrane. This gives an initial outward current, and an inward current does not occur until combined carriers lose sodium to the internal solution and return to the outside of the membrane. In our original treatment the initial outward current was reduced to vanishingly small proportions by assuming a low density of carriers and a high rate of movement and combination. Since we now know that the sodium current takes an appreciable time to reach its maximum, it is necessary to suppose that there are more carriers and that they react or move more slowly. This means that any inward current should be preceded by a large outward current. Our experiments show no sign of a component large enough to be consistent with the model. This invalidates the detailed mechanism assumed for the permeability change but it does not exclude the more general possibility that sodium ions cross the membrane in combination with a lipoid soluble carrier.

A different form of hypothesis is to suppose that sodium movement depends on the distribution of charged particles which do not act as carriers in the usual sense, but which allow sodium to pass through the membrane when they occupy particular sites in the membrane. On this view the rate of movement of the activating particles determines the rate at which the sodium con-ductance approaches its maximum but has little effect on the magnitude of the conductance. It is therefore reasonable to find that temperature has a large effect on the rate of rise of sodium conductance but a relatively small effect on its maximum value. In terms of this hypothesis one might explain the transient nature of the rise in sodium conductance by supposing that the activating particles undergo a chemical change after moving from the position which they occupy when the membrane potential is high. An alternative is to attribute the decline of sodium conductance to the relatively slow movement of another particle which blocks the flow of sodium ions when it reaches a certain position in the membrane.

Much of what has been said about the changes in sodium permeability applies equally to the mechanism underlying the change in potassium permeability. In this case one might suppose that there is a completely separate system which differs from the sodium system in the following respects: (1) the activating molecules have an affinity for potassium but not for sodium; (2) they move more slowly; (3) they are not blocked or inactivated. An alternative hypothesis is that only one system is present but that its selectivity changes soon after the membrane is depolarized. A situation of this kind would arise if inactivation of the particles selective for sodium converted them into particles selective for potassium. However, this hypothesis cannot be applied in a simple form since the potassium conductance rises too slowly for a direct conversion from a state of sodium permeability to one of potassium permeability.

One of the most striking properties of the membrane is the extreme steepness of the relation between ionic conductance and membrane potential. Thus g_{Na} may be increased e-fold by a reduction of only 4 mV, while the corresponding figure for g_K is 5–6 mV (Hodgkin & Huxley, 1952a, figs. 9, 10). In order to illustrate the possible meaning of this result we shall suppose that a charged molecule which has some special affinity for sodium may rest either on the inside or the outside of the membrane but is present in negligible concentrations elsewhere. We shall also suppose that the sodium conductance is proportional to the number of such molecules on the inside of the membrane but is independent of the number on the outside. From Boltzmann's principle the proportion P_i of the molecules on the inside of the membrane is related to the proportion on the outside, P_o, by

$$\frac{P_i}{P_o} = \exp[(w + zeE)/kT],$$

where E is the potential difference between the outside and the inside of the membrane, w is the work required to move the molecule from the inside to the outside of the membrane when $E = 0$, e is the absolute value of the electronic charge, z is the valency of the molecule (i.e. the number of positive electronic charges on it), k is Boltzmann's constant and T is the absolute temperature. Since we have assumed that $P_i + P_o = 1$ the expression for P_i is

$$P_i = 1 \bigg/ \left[1 + \exp - \left(\frac{w + zeE}{kT} \right) \right].$$

For negative values of z and with E sufficiently large and positive this gives

$$P_i = \text{constant} \times \exp[zeE/kT].$$

In order to explain our results z must be about -6 since $\dfrac{kT}{e}\left(=\dfrac{RT}{F}\right)$ is 25 mV at room temperature and $g_{\mathrm{Na}} \propto \exp - E/4$ for E large. This suggests that the particle whose distribution changes must bear six negative electronic charges, or, if a similar theory is developed in terms of the orientation of a long molecule with a dipole moment, it must have at least three negative charges on one end and three positive charges on the other. A different but related approach is to suppose that sodium movement depends on the presence of six singly charged molecules at a particular site near the inside of the membrane. The proportion of the time that each of the charged molecules spends at the inside is determined by $\exp - E/25$ so that the proportion of sites at which all six are at the inside is $\exp - E/4\cdot17$. This suggestion may be given plausibility but not mathematical simplicity by imagining that a number of charges form a bridge or chain which allows sodium ions to flow through the membrane when it is depolarized. Details of the mechanism will probably not be settled for some time, but it seems difficult to escape the conclusion that the changes in ionic permeability depend on the movement of some component of the membrane which behaves as though it had a large charge or dipole moment. If such components exist it is necessary to suppose that their density is relatively low and that a number of sodium ions cross the membrane at a single active patch. Unless this were true one would expect the increase in sodium permeability to be accompanied by an outward current comparable in magnitude to the current carried by sodium ions. For movement of any charged particle in the membrane should contribute to the total current and the effect would be particularly marked with a molecule, or aggregate, bearing a large charge. As was mentioned earlier, there is no evidence from our experiments of any current associated with the change in sodium permeability, apart from the contribution of the sodium ion itself. We cannot set a definite upper limit to this hypothetical current, but it could hardly have been more than a few per cent of the maximum sodium current without producing a conspicuous effect at the sodium potential.

PART II. MATHEMATICAL DESCRIPTION OF MEMBRANE CURRENT DURING A VOLTAGE CLAMP

Total membrane current

The first step in our analysis is to divide the total membrane current into a capacity current and an ionic current. Thus

$$I = C_M \frac{dV}{dt} + I_i, \tag{1}$$

where

I   is the total membrane current density (inward current positive);

I_i is the ionic current density (inward current positive);

V   is the displacement of the membrane potential from its resting value (depolarization negative);

C_M is the membrane capacity per unit area (assumed constant);

t   is time.

The justification for this equation is that it is the simplest which can be used and that it gives values for the membrane capacity which are independent of the magnitude or sign of V and are little affected by the time course of V (see, for example, table 1 of Hodgkin et al. 1952). Evidence that the capacity current and ionic current are in parallel (as suggested by eqn. (1)) is provided by the similarity between ionic currents measured with $\dfrac{dV}{dt}=0$ and those calculated from $-C_M\dfrac{dV}{dt}$ with $I=0$ (Hodgkin et al. 1952).

The only major reservation which must be made about eqn. (1) is that it takes no account of dielectric loss in the membrane. There is no simple way of estimating the error introduced by this approximation, but it is not thought to be large since the time course of the capacitative surge was reasonably close to that calculated for a perfect condenser (Hodgkin et al. 1952).

The ionic current

A further subdivision of the membrane current can be made by splitting the ionic current into components carried by sodium ions (I_{Na}), potassium ions (I_K) and other ions (I_l):

$$I_i = I_{Na} + I_K + I_l. \tag{2}$$

The individual ionic currents

In the third paper of this series (Hodgkin & Huxley, 1952b), we showed that the ionic permeability of the membrane could be satisfactorily expressed in terms of ionic conductances (g_{Na}, g_K and $\bar g_l$). The individual ionic currents are obtained from these by the relations

$$I_{Na} = g_{Na}\,(E - E_{Na}),$$
$$I_K = g_K\,(E - E_K),$$
$$I_l = \bar g_l\,(E - E_l),$$

where E_{Na} and E_K are the equilibrium potentials for the sodium and potassium ions. E_l is the potential at which the 'leakage current' due to chloride and other ions is zero. For practical application it is convenient to write these equations in the form

$$I_{Na} = g_{Na}\,(V - V_{Na}), \tag{3}$$
$$I_K = g_K\,(V - V_K), \tag{4}$$
$$I_l = \bar g_l\,(V - V_l), \tag{5}$$

where
$$V = E - E_r,$$
$$V_{Na} = E_{Na} - E_r,$$
$$V_K = E_K - E_r,$$
$$V_l = E_l - E_r,$$

and E_r is the absolute value of the resting potential. V, V_{Na}, V_K and V_l can then be measured directly as displacements from the resting potential.

The ionic conductances

The discussion in Part I shows that there is little hope of calculating the time course of the sodium and potassium conductances from first principles. Our object here is to find equations which describe the conductances with reasonable accuracy and are sufficiently simple for theoretical calculation of the action potential and refractory period. For the sake of illustration we shall try to provide a physical basis for the equations, but must emphasize that the interpretation given is unlikely to provide a correct picture of the membrane.

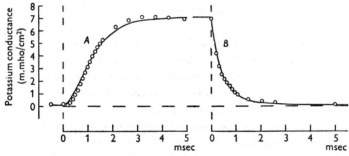

Fig. 2. A, rise of potassium conductance associated with depolarization of 25 mV; B, fall of potassium conductance associated with repolarization to the resting potential. Circles: experimental points replotted from Hodgkin & Huxley (1952b, Fig. 13). The last point of A is the same as the first point in B. Axon 18, 21° C in choline sea water. The smooth curve is drawn according to eqn. (11) with the following parameters:

	Curve A ($V = -25$ mV)	Curve B ($V = 0$)
g_{K0}	0·09 m.mho/cm²	7·06 m.mho/cm²
$g_{K\infty}$	7·06 m.mho/cm²	0·09 m.mho/cm²
τ_n	0·75 msec	1·1 msec

At the outset there is the difficulty that both sodium and potassium conductances increase with a delay when the axon is depolarized but fall with no appreciable inflexion when it is repolarized. This is illustrated by the circles in Fig. 2, which shows the change in potassium conductance associated with a depolarization of 25 mV lasting 4·9 msec. If g_K is used as a variable the end of the record can be fitted by a first-order equation but a third- or fourth-order equation is needed to describe the beginning. A useful simplification is achieved by supposing that g_K is proportional to the fourth power of a variable which obeys a first-order equation. In this case the rise of potassium conductance from zero to a finite value is described by $(1 - \exp{(-t)})^4$, while the fall is given by $\exp{(-4t)}$. The rise in conductance therefore shows a marked inflexion, while the fall is a simple exponential. A similar assumption using a cube instead of a fourth power describes the initial rise of sodium conductance, but a term representing inactivation must be included to cover the behaviour at long times.

The potassium conductance

The formal assumptions used to describe the potassium conductance are:

$$g_K = \bar{g}_K n^4, \tag{6}$$

$$\frac{dn}{dt} = \alpha_n (1 - n) - \beta_n n, \tag{7}$$

where $\bar{g}_K$ is a constant with the dimensions of conductance/cm^2, α_n and β_n are rate constants which vary with voltage but not with time and have dimensions of [time]$^{-1}$, n is a dimensionless variable which can vary between 0 and 1.

These equations may be given a physical basis if we assume that potassium ions can only cross the membrane when four similar particles occupy a certain region of the membrane. n represents the proportion of the particles in a certain position (for example at the inside of the membrane) and $1 - n$ represents the proportion that are somewhere else (for example at the outside of the membrane). α_n determines the rate of transfer from outside to inside, while β_n determines the transfer in the opposite direction. If the particle has a negative charge α_n should increase and β_n should decrease when the membrane is depolarized.

Application of these equations will be discussed in terms of the family of curves in Fig. 3. Here the circles are experimental observations of the rise of potassium conductance associated with depolarization, while the smooth curves are theoretical solutions of eqns. (6) and (7).

In the resting state, defined by $V = 0$, n has a resting value given by

$$n_0 = \frac{\alpha_{n0}}{\alpha_{n0} + \beta_{n0}}.$$

If V is changed suddenly α_n and β_n instantly take up values appropriate to the new voltage. The solution of (7) which satisfies the boundary condition that $n = n_0$ when $t = 0$ is

$$n = n_\infty - (n_\infty - n_0) \exp{(-t/\tau_n)}, \tag{8}$$

where

$$n_\infty = \alpha_n/(\alpha_n + \beta_n), \tag{9}$$

and

$$\tau_n = 1/(\alpha_n + \beta_n). \tag{10}$$

From eqn. (6) this may be transformed into a form suitable for comparison with the experimental results, i.e.

$$g_K = \{(g_{K\infty})^{\frac{1}{4}} - [(g_{K\infty})^{\frac{1}{4}} - (g_{K0})^{\frac{1}{4}}] \exp(-t/\tau_n)\}^4, \tag{11}$$

where $g_{K\infty}$ is the value which the conductance finally attains and g_{K0} is the conductance at $t=0$. The smooth curves in Fig. 3 were calculated from

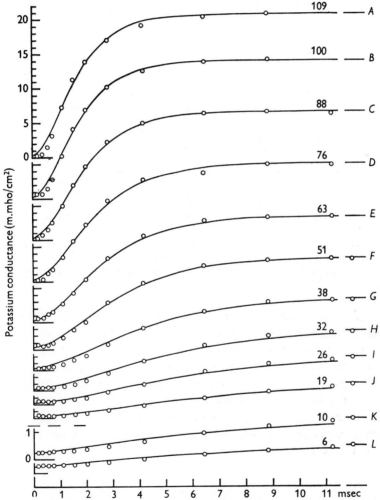

Fig. 3. Rise of potassium conductance associated with different depolarizations. The circles are experimental points obtained on axon 17, temperature 6–7° C, using observations in sea water and choline sea water (see Hodgkin & Huxley, 1952a). The smooth curves were drawn from eqn. (11) with $g_{K0} = 0.24$ m.mho/cm^2 and other parameters as shown in Table 1. The time scale applies to all records. The ordinate scale is the same in the upper ten curves (A to J) and is increased fourfold in the lower two curves (K and L). The number on each curve gives the depolarization in mV.

eqn. (11) with a value of τ_n chosen to give the best fit. It will be seen that there is reasonable agreement between theoretical and experimental curves, except that the latter show more initial delay. Better agreement might have been obtained with a fifth or sixth power, but the improvement was not considered to be worth the additional complication.

The rate constants α_n and β_n. At large depolarizations $g_{K\infty}$ seems to approach an asymptote about 20–50% greater than the conductance at -100 mV.

TABLE 1. Analysis of curves in Fig. 3

Curve	V (mV) (1)	$g_{K\infty}$ (m.mho/cm²) (2)	n_∞ (3)	τ_n (msec) (4)	α_n (msec⁻¹) (5)	β_n (msec⁻¹) (6)
—	$(-\infty)$	(24·31)	(1·000)	—	—	—
A	-109	20·70	0·961	1·05	0·915	0·037
B	-100	20·00	0·953	1·10	0·866	0·043
C	-88	18·60	0·935	1·25	0·748	0·052
D	-76	17·00	0·915	1·50	0·610	0·057
E	-63	15·30	0·891	1·70	0·524	0·064
F	-51	13·27	0·859	2·05	0·419	0·069
G	-38	10·29	0·806	2·60	0·310	0·075
H	-32	8·62	0·772	3·20	0·241	0·071
I	-26	6·84	0·728	3·80	0·192	0·072
J	-19	5·00	0·674	4·50	0·150	0·072
K	-10	1·47	0·496	5·25	0·095	0·096
L	-6	0·98	0·448	5·25	0·085	0·105
—	(0)	(0·24)	(0·315)	—	—	—

Col. 1 shows depolarization in mV; col. 2, final potassium conductance; col. 3, $n_\infty = (g_{K\infty}/\bar{g}_K)^{\frac{1}{4}}$; col. 4, time constant used to compute curve; col. 5, $\alpha_n = n_\infty/\tau_n$; col. 6, $\beta_n = (1-n_\infty)/\tau_n$. The figure of 24·31 was chosen for $\bar{g}_K$ because it made the asymptotic value of n_∞ 5% greater than the value at -100 mV.

For the purpose of calculation we assume that $n=1$ at the asymptote which is taken as about 20% greater than the value of $g_{K\infty}$ at $V = -100$ mV. These assumptions are somewhat arbitrary, but should introduce little error since we are not concerned with the behaviour of g_K at depolarizations greater than about 110 mV. In the experiment illustrated by Fig. 3, $g_{K\infty} = 20$ m.mho/cm² at $V = -100$ mV. $\bar{g}_K$ was therefore chosen to be near 24 m.mho/cm². This value was used to calculate n_∞ at various voltages by means of eqn. (6). α_n and β_n could then be obtained from the following relations which are derived from eqns. (9) and (10):

$$\alpha_n = n_\infty/\tau_n,$$

$$\beta_n = (1-n_\infty)/\tau_n.$$

The results of analysing the curves in Fig. 3 by this method are shown in Table 1.

An estimate of the resting values of α_n and β_n could be obtained from the decline in potassium conductance associated with repolarization. The procedure was essentially the same but the results were approximate because the resting value of the potassium conductance was not known with any accuracy when the membrane potential was high. Fig. 2 illustrates an experiment in which the membrane potential was restored to its resting value after a depolarization of 25 mV. It will be seen that both the rise and fall of the potassium conductance agree reasonably with theoretical curves calculated from eqn. (11) after an appropriate choice of parameters. The rate constants derived from these parameters were (in msec^{-1}): $\alpha_n = 0{\cdot}21$, $\beta_n = 0{\cdot}70$ when $V = 0$ and $\alpha_n = 0{\cdot}90$, $\beta_n = 0{\cdot}43$ when $V = -25$ mV.

In order to find functions connecting α_n and β_n with membrane potential we collected all our measurements and plotted them against V, as in Fig. 4. Differences in temperature were allowed for by adopting a temperature coefficient of 3 (Hodgkin $et\ al.$ 1952) and scaling to 6° C. The effect of replacing sodium by choline on the resting potential was taken into account by displacing the origin for values in choline sea water by $+4$ mV. The continuous curves, which are clearly a good fit to the experimental data, were calculated from the following expressions:

$$\alpha_n = 0{\cdot}01\ (V+10)\Big/\left[\exp\frac{V+10}{10} - 1\right],\tag{12}$$

$$\beta_n = 0{\cdot}125\ \exp\ (V/80),\tag{13}$$

where α_n and β_n are given in reciprocal msec and V is the displacement of the membrane potential from its resting value in mV.

These expressions should also give a satisfactory formula for the steady potassium conductance ($g_{K\infty}$) at any membrane potential (V), for this relation is implicit in the measurement of α_n and β_n. This is illustrated by Fig. 5, in which the abscissa is the membrane potential and the ordinate is $(g_{K\infty}/\bar{g}_K)^{\frac{1}{4}}$. The smooth curve was calculated from eqn. (9) with α_n and β_n substituted from eqns. (12) and (13).

Fig. 4 shows that β_n is small compared to α_n over most of the range; we therefore do not attach much weight to the curve relating β_n to V and have used the simplest expression which gave a reasonable fit. The function for α_n was chosen for two reasons. First, it is one of the simplest which fits the experimental results and, secondly, it bears a close resemblance to the equation derived by Goldman (1943) for the movements of a charged particle in a constant field. Our equations can therefore be given a qualitative physical basis if it is supposed that the variation of α and β with membrane potential arises from the effect of the electric field on the movement of a negatively charged particle which rests on the outside of the membrane when V is large and positive, and on the inside when it is large and negative. The analogy cannot be pressed since α and β are not symmetrical about $E = 0$, as they should be if Goldman's theory held in a simple form. Better agreement might

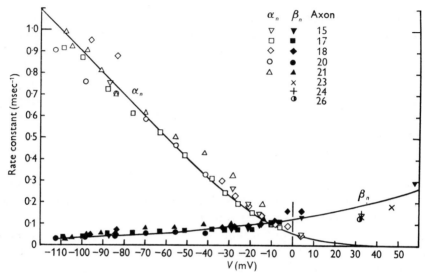

Fig. 4. Abscissa: membrane potential minus resting potential in sea water. Ordinate: rate constants determining rise (α_n) or fall (β_n) of potassium conductance at 6° C. The resting potential was assumed to be 4 mV higher in choline sea water than in ordinary sea water. Temperature differences were allowed for by assuming a Q_{10} of 3. All values for $V < 0$ were obtained by the method illustrated by Fig. 3 and Table 1; those for $V > 0$ were obtained from the decline of potassium conductance associated with an increase of membrane potential or from repolarization to the resting potential in choline sea water (e.g. Fig. 2). Axons 17–21 at 6–11° C, the remainder at about 20° C. The smooth curves were drawn from eqns. (12) and (13).

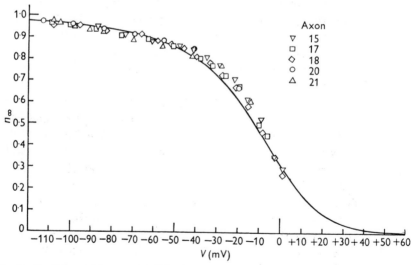

Fig. 5. Abscissa: membrane potential minus resting potential in sea water. Ordinate: experimental measurements of n_∞ calculated from the steady potassium conductance by the relation $n_\infty = \sqrt[4]{(g_{K\infty}/\bar{g}_K)}$, where $\bar{g}_K$ is the 'maximum' potassium conductance. The smooth curve is drawn according to eqn. (9).

be obtained by postulating some asymmetry in the structure of the membrane, but this assumption was regarded as too speculative for profitable consideration.

The sodium conductance

There are at least two general methods of describing the transient changes in sodium conductance. First, we might assume that the sodium conductance is determined by a variable which obeys a second-order differential equation. Secondly, we might suppose that it is determined by two variables, each of which obeys a first-order equation. These two alternatives correspond roughly to the two general types of mechanism mentioned in connexion with the nature of inactivation (pp. 502–503). The second alternative was chosen since it was simpler to apply to the experimental results.

The formal assumptions made are:

$$g_{Na} = m^3 h \bar{g}_{Na}, \tag{14}$$

$$\frac{dm}{dt} = \alpha_m (1 - m) - \beta_m m, \tag{15}$$

$$\frac{dh}{dt} = \alpha_h (1 - h) - \beta_h h, \tag{16}$$

where $\bar{g}_{Na}$ is a constant and the α's and β's are functions of V but not of t.

These equations may be given a physical basis if sodium conductance is assumed to be proportional to the number of sites on the inside of the membrane which are occupied simultaneously by three activating molecules but are not blocked by an inactivating molecule. m then represents the proportion of activating molecules on the inside and $1 - m$ the proportion on the outside; h is the proportion of inactivating molecules on the outside and $1 - h$ the proportion on the inside. α_m or β_h and β_m or α_h represent the transfer rate constants in the two directions.

Application of these equations will be discussed first in terms of the family of curves in Fig. 6. Here the circles are experimental estimates of the rise and fall of sodium conductance during a voltage clamp, while the smooth curves were calculated from eqns. (14)–(16).

The solutions of eqns. (15) and (16) which satisfy the boundary conditions $m = m_0$ and $h = h_0$ at $t = 0$ are

$$m = m_\infty - (m_\infty - m_0) \exp(-t/\tau_m), \tag{17}$$

$$h = h_\infty - (h_\infty - h_0) \exp(-t/\tau_h), \tag{18}$$

where

$$m_\infty = \alpha_m/(\alpha_m + \beta_m) \quad \text{and} \quad \tau_m = 1/(\alpha_m + \beta_m),$$
$$h_\infty = \alpha_h/(\alpha_h + \beta_h) \quad \text{and} \quad \tau_h = 1/(\alpha_h + \beta_h).$$

In the resting state the sodium conductance is very small compared with the value attained during a large depolarization. We therefore neglect m_0 if the depolarization is greater than 30 mV. Further, inactivation is very nearly complete if $V < -30$ mV so that h_∞ may also be neglected. The expression for the sodium conductance then becomes

$$g_{\text{Na}} = g'_{\text{Na}} \left[1 - \exp\left(-t/\tau_m\right)\right]^3 \exp\left(-t/\tau_h\right), \qquad (19)$$

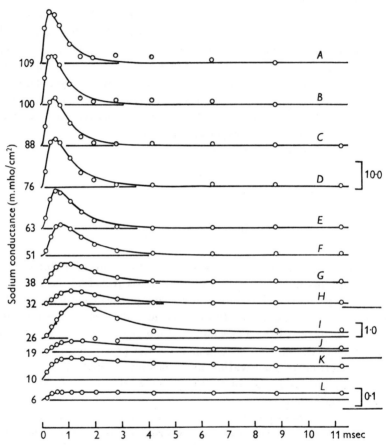

Fig. 6. Changes of sodium conductance associated with different depolarizations. The circles are experimental estimates of sodium conductance obtained on axon 17, temperature 6–7° C (cf. Fig. 3). The smooth curves are theoretical curves with parameters shown in Table 2; A to H drawn from eqn. 19, I to L from 14, 17, 18 with $\bar{g}_{\text{Na}} = 70.7$ m.mho/cm². The ordinate scales on the right are given in m.mho/cm². The numbers on the left show the depolarization in mV. The time scale applies to all curves.

where $g'_{\text{Na}} = \bar{g}_{\text{Na}} m_\infty^3 h_0$ and is the value which the sodium conductance would attain if h remained at its resting level (h_0). Eqn. (19) was fitted to an experimental curve by plotting the latter on double log paper and comparing it with a similar plot of a family of theoretical curves drawn with different ratios of τ_m to τ_h. Curves A to H in Fig. 6 were obtained by this method and gave the

TABLE 2. Analysis of curves in Fig. 6

Curve	V (mV)	g'_{Na} (m.mho/cm²)	m_∞	τ_m (msec)	α_m (msec⁻¹)	β_m (msec⁻¹)	τ_h (msec)	h_∞	α_h (msec⁻¹)	β_h (msec⁻¹)
—	(−∞)	(42·9)	(1·00)	—	—	—	—	—	—	—
A	−109	40·3	0·980	0·140	7·0	(0·14)	0·67	(0)	(0)	1·50
B	−100	42·6	0·997	0·160	6·2	(0·02)	0·67	(0)	(0)	1·50
C	−88	46·8	1·029	0·200	5·15	(−0·14)	0·67	(0)	(0)	1·50
D	−76	39·5	0·975	0·189	5·15	0·13	0·84	(0)	(0)	1·19
E	−63	38·2	0·963	0·252	3·82	0·15	0·84	(0)	(0)	1·19
F	−51	30·7	0·895	0·318	2·82	0·33	1·06	(0)	(0)	0·94
G	−38	20·0	0·778	0·382	2·03	0·58	1·27	(0)	(0)	0·79
H	−32	15·3	0·709	0·520	1·36	0·56	1·33	(0)	(0)	0·75
I	−26	7·90	0·569	0·600	0·95	0·72	(1·50)	(0·029)	(0·02)	(0·65)
J	−19	1·44	0·323	0·400	0·81	1·69	(2·30)	(0·069)	(0·03)	(0·40)
K	−10	0·13	0·145	0·220	0·66	3·9	(5·52)	(0·263)	(0·05)	(0·13)
L	−6	0·046	0·103	0·200	0·51	4·5	(6·73)	(0·388)	(0·06)	(0·09)
—	(0)	(0·0033)	(0·042)	—	—	—	—	(0·608)	—	—

Values enclosed in brackets were not plotted in Figs. 7–10 either because they were too small to be reliable or because they were not independent measurements obtained in this experiment.

values of g'_{Na}, τ_m and τ_h shown in Table 2. Curves I to L were obtained from eqns. (17) and (18) assuming that h_∞ and τ_h had values calculated from experiments described in a previous paper (Hodgkin & Huxley, 1952 c).

The rate constants α_m and β_m. Having fitted theoretical curves to the experimental points, α_m and β_m were found by a procedure similar to that used with α_n and β_n, i.e.

$$\alpha_m = m_\infty / \tau_m, \quad \beta_m = (1 - m_\infty)/\tau_m,$$

the value of m_∞ being obtained from $\sqrt[3]{g'_{Na}}$ on the basis that m_∞ approaches unity at large depolarizations.

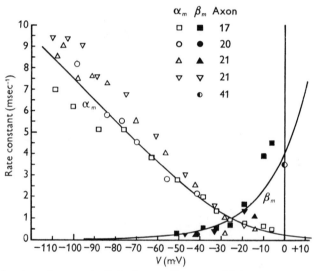

Fig. 7. Abscissa: membrane potential minus resting potential in sea water. Ordinate: rate constants (α_m and β_m) determining initial changes in sodium conductance at 6° C. All values for $V < 0$ were obtained by the method illustrated by Fig. 6 and Table 2; the value at $V = 0$ was obtained from the decline in sodium conductance associated with repolarization to the resting potential. The temperature varied between 3 and 11° C and was allowed for by assuming a Q_{10} of 3. The smooth curves were drawn from eqns. (20) and (21).

Values of α_m and β_m were collected from different experiments, reduced to a temperature of 6° C by adopting a Q_{10} of 3 and plotted in the manner shown in Fig. 7. The point for $V = 0$ was obtained from what we regard as the most reliable estimate of the rate constant determining the decline of sodium conductance when the membrane is repolarized (Hodgkin & Huxley, 1952b, table 1, axon 41). The smooth curves in Fig. 7 were drawn according to the equations:

$$\alpha_m = 0 \cdot 1 \ (V + 25) \bigg/ \left(\exp \frac{V + 25}{10} - 1 \right), \tag{20}$$

$$\beta_m = 4 \exp (V/18), \tag{21}$$

where α_m and β_m are expressed in msec^{-1} and V is in mV.

Fig. 8 illustrates the relation between m_∞ and V. The symbols are experimental estimates and the smooth curve was calculated from the equation

$$m_\infty = \alpha_m/(\alpha_m + \beta_m), \tag{22}$$

where α_m and β_m have the values given by eqns. (20) and (21).

The rate constants α_h and β_h. The rate constants for the inactivation process were calculated from the expressions

$$\alpha_h = h_\infty/\tau_h,$$
$$\beta_h = (1 - h_\infty)/\tau_h.$$

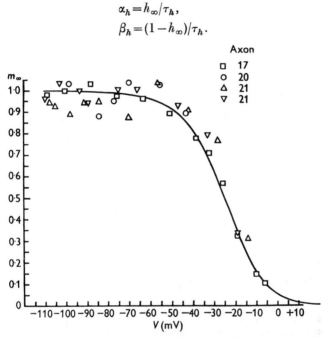

Fig. 8. Abscissa: membrane potential minus resting potential in sea water. Ordinate: m_∞ obtained by fitting curves to observed changes in sodium conductance at different depolarizations (e.g. Fig. 6 and Table 2). The smooth curve is drawn according to eqn. (22). The experimental points are proportional to the cube root of the sodium conductance which would have been obtained if there were no inactivation.

Values obtained by these equations are plotted against membrane potential in Fig. 9. The points for $V < -30$ mV were derived from the analysis described in this paper (e.g. Table 2), while those for $V > -30$ mV were obtained from the results given in a previous paper (Hodgkin & Huxley, 1952 c). A temperature coefficient of 3 was assumed and differences in resting potential were allowed for by taking the origin at a potential corresponding to $h_\infty = 0.6$.

The smooth curves in this figure were calculated from the expressions

$$\alpha_h = 0.07 \exp (V/20), \tag{23}$$

and

$$\beta_h = 1 \Big/ \left(\exp \frac{V+30}{10} + 1\right). \tag{24}$$

The steady state relation between h_∞ and V is shown in Fig. 10. The smooth curve is calculated from the relation

$$h_\infty = \alpha_h/(\alpha_h + \beta_h), \tag{25}$$

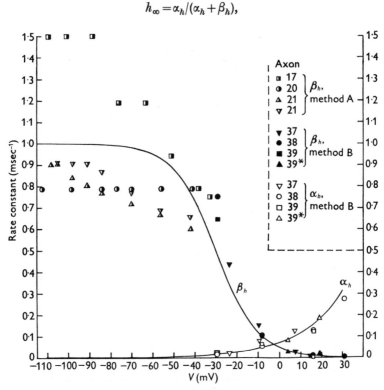

Fig. 9. Rate constants of inactivation (α_h and β_h) as functions of membrane potential (V). The smooth curves were calculated from eqns. (23) and (24). The experimental values of α_h and β_h were obtained from data such as those in Table 2 of this paper (method A) or from the values of τ_h and h_∞ given in Table 1 of Hodgkin & Huxley (1952c) (method B). Temperature differences were allowed for by scaling with a Q_{10} of 3. Axon 39 was at 19° C; all others at 3–9° C. The values for axons 37 and 39* were displaced by $-1\cdot5$ and -12 mV in order to give $h_\infty = 0\cdot6$ at $V = 0$.

with α_h and β_h given by eqns. (23) and (24). If $V > -30$ mV this expression approximates to the simple expression used in a previous paper (Hodgkin & Huxley, 1952 c), i.e.

$$h_\infty = 1 \bigg/ \left(1 + \exp \frac{V_h - V}{7}\right),$$

where V_h is about -2 and is the potential at which $h_\infty = 0\cdot5$. This equation is the same as that giving the effect of a potential difference on the proportion of negatively charged particles on the outside of a membrane to the total number of such particles on both sides of the membrane (see p. 503). It is therefore consistent with the suggestion that inactivation might be due to the movement of a negatively charged particle which blocks the flow of sodium ions when it reaches the inside of the membrane. This is encouraging, but it must be mentioned that a physical theory of this kind does not lead to satisfactory functions for α_h and β_h without further *ad hoc* assumptions.

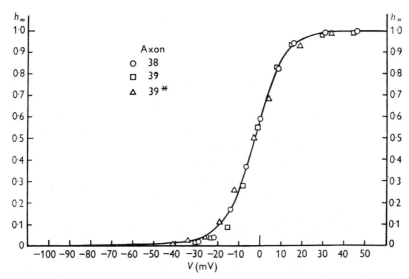

Fig. 10. Steady state relation between h and V. The smooth curve is drawn according to eqn. (25). The experimental points are those given in Table 1 of Hodgkin & Huxley (1952c). Axon 38 (5° C) as measured. Axon 39 (19° C) displaced -1.5 mV. Axon 39* (3° C, fibre in derelict state) displaced -12 mV. The curve gives the fraction of the sodium-carrying system which is readily available, as a function of membrane potential, in the steady state.

PART III. RECONSTRUCTION OF NERVE BEHAVIOUR

The remainder of this paper will be devoted to calculations of the electrical behaviour of a model nerve whose properties are defined by the equations which were fitted in Part II to the voltage clamp records described in the earlier papers of this series.

Summary of equations and parameters

We may first collect the equations which give the total membrane current I as a function of time and voltage. These are:

$$I = C_M \frac{dV}{dt} + \bar{g}_K n^4 (V - V_K) + \bar{g}_{Na} m^3 h (V - V_{Na}) + \bar{g}_l (V - V_l), \tag{26}$$

where

$$dn/dt = \alpha_n(1-n) - \beta_n n, \tag{7}$$

$$dm/dt = \alpha_m(1-m) - \beta_m m, \tag{15}$$

$$dh/dt = \alpha_h(1-h) - \beta_h h, \tag{16}$$

and

$$\alpha_n = 0 \cdot 01 \ (V + 10) \Big/ \Big(\exp \frac{V + 10}{10} - 1\Big), \tag{12}$$

$$\beta_n = 0 \cdot 125 \exp (V/80), \tag{13}$$

$$\alpha_m = 0 \cdot 1 \ (V + 25) \Big/ \Big(\exp \frac{V + 25}{10} - 1\Big), \tag{20}$$

$$\beta_m = 4 \exp (V/18), \tag{21}$$

$$\alpha_h = 0 \cdot 07 \exp (V/20), \tag{23}$$

$$\beta_h = 1 \Big/ \Big(\exp \frac{V + 30}{10} + 1\Big). \tag{24}$$

Equation (26) is derived simply from eqns. (1)–(6) and (14) in Part II. The four terms on the right-hand side give respectively the capacity current, the current carried by K ions, the current carried by Na ions and the leak current, for 1 cm² of membrane. These four components are in parallel and add up to give the total current density through the membrane I. The conductances to K and Na are given by the constants $\bar{g}_K$ and $\bar{g}_{Na}$, together with the dimensionless quantities n, m and h, whose variation with time after a change of membrane potential is determined by the three subsidiary equations (7), (15) and (16). The α's and β's in these equations depend only on the instantaneous value of the membrane potential, and are given by the remaining six equations.

Potentials are given in mV, current density in μA/cm², conductances in m.mho/cm², capacity in μF/cm², and time in msec. The expressions for the α's and β's are appropriate to a temperature of 6·3° C; for other temperatures they must be scaled with a Q_{10} of 3.

The constants in eqn. (26) are taken as independent of temperature. The values chosen are given in Table 3, column 2, and may be compared with the experimental values in columns 3 and 4.

Membrane currents during a voltage clamp

Before applying eqn. (26) to the action potential it is well to check that it predicts correctly the total current during a voltage clamp. At constant voltage $dV/dt = 0$ and the coefficients α and β are constant. The solution is then obtained directly in terms of the expressions already given for n, m and h (eqns. (8), (17) and (18)). The total ionic current was computed from these for a number of different voltages and is compared with a series of experimental curves in Fig. 11. The only important difference is that the theoretical current has too little delay at the sodium potential; this reflects the inability of our equations to account fully for the delay in the rise of g_K (p. 509).

'Membrane' and propagated action potentials

By a 'membrane' action potential is meant one in which the membrane potential is uniform, at each instant, over the whole of the length of fibre

TABLE 3

| Constant (1) | Value chosen (2) | Experimental values | | Reference (5) |
		Mean (3)	Range (4)	
C_M (μF/cm^2)	1·0	0·91	0·8 to 1·5	Table 1, Hodgkin et al. (1952)
V_{Na} (mV)	−115	−109	−95 to −119	p. 455, Hodgkin & Huxley (1952a)
V_K (mV)	+12	+11	+9 to +14	Table 3, values for low temperature in sea water, Hodgkin & Huxley (1952b)
V_l (mV)	−10·613*	−11	−4 to −22	Table 5, Hodgkin & Huxley (1952b)
$\bar{g}_{Na}$ (m.mho/cm^2)	120	{80 / 160	65 to 90 / 120 to 260	Fully analysed results, Table 2† } Hodgkin & Huxley (1952a) / Fresh fibres, p. 465†
$\bar{g}_K$ (m.mho/cm^2)	36	34	26 to 49	p. 463, Hodgkin & Huxley (1952a)
$\bar{g}_l$ (m.mho/cm^2)	0·3	0·26	0·13 to 0·50	Table 5, Hodgkin & Huxley (1952b)

* Exact value chosen to make the total ionic current zero at the resting potential ($V = 0$).

† The experimental values for $\bar{g}_{Na}$ were obtained by multiplying the peak sodium conductances by factors derived from the values chosen for α_m, β_m, α_h, and β_h.

225

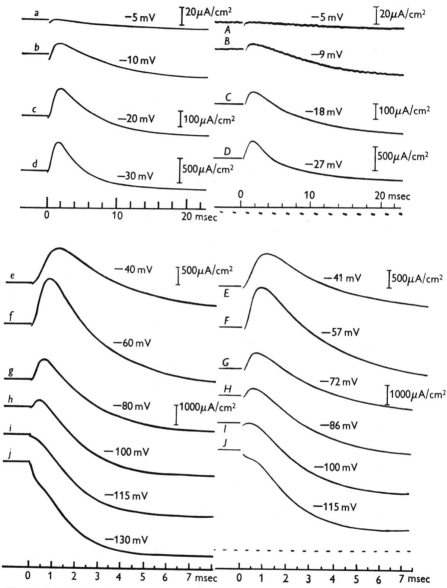

Fig. 11. Left-hand column: time course of membrane current during voltage clamp, calculated for temperature of 4° C from eqn. (26) and subsidiaries and plotted on the same scale as the experimental curves in the right-hand column. Right-hand column: observed time course of membrane currents during voltage clamp. Axon 31 at 4° C; compensated feedback. The time scale changes between d, D and e, E. The current scale changes after b, B; c, C; d, D and f, F.

considered. There is no current along the axis cylinder and the net membrane current must therefore always be zero, except during the stimulus. If the stimulus is a short shock at $t=0$, the form of the action potential should be given by solving eqn. (26) with $I=0$ and the initial conditions that $V=V_0$ and m, n and h have their resting steady state values, when $t=0$.

The situation is more complicated in a propagated action potential. The fact that the local circuit currents have to be provided by the net membrane current leads to the well-known relation

$$i = \frac{1}{r_1+r_2} \frac{\partial^2 V}{\partial x^2},\tag{27}$$

where i is the membrane current per unit length, r_1 and r_2 are the external and internal resistances per unit length, and x is distance along the fibre. For an axon surrounded by a large volume of conducting fluid, r_1 is negligible compared with r_2. Hence

$$i = \frac{1}{r_2} \frac{\partial^2 V}{\partial x^2},$$

or

$$I = \frac{a}{2R_2} \frac{\partial^2 V}{\partial x^2},\tag{28}$$

where I is the membrane current density, a is the radius of the fibre and R_2 is the specific resistance of the axoplasm. Inserting this relation in eqn. (26), we have

$$\frac{a}{2R_2} \frac{\partial^2 V}{\partial x^2} = C_M \frac{\partial V}{\partial t} + \bar{g}_K n^4 (V-V_K) + \bar{g}_{Na} m^3 h (V-V_{Na}) + \bar{g}_l (V-V_l),\tag{29}$$

the subsidiary equations being unchanged.

Equation (29) is a partial differential equation, and it is not practicable to solve it as it stands. During steady propagation, however, the curve of V against time at any one position is similar in shape to that of V against distance at any one time, and it follows that

$$\frac{\partial^2 V}{\partial x^2} = \frac{1}{\theta^2} \frac{\partial^2 V}{\partial t^2},$$

where θ is the velocity of conduction. Hence

$$\frac{a}{2R_2\theta^2} \frac{d^2 V}{dt^2} = C_M \frac{dV}{dt} + \bar{g}_K n^4 (V-V_K) + \bar{g}_{Na} m^3 h (V-V_{Na}) + \bar{g}_l (V-V_l).\tag{30}$$

This is an ordinary differential equation and can be solved numerically, but the procedure is still complicated by the fact that θ is not known in advance. It is necessary to guess a value of θ, insert it in eqn. (30) and carry out the numerical solution starting from the resting state at the foot of the action potential. It is then found that V goes off towards either $+\infty$ or $-\infty$, according as the guessed θ was too small or too large. A new value of θ is then chosen and the procedure repeated, and so on. The correct value brings V back to zero (the resting condition) when the action potential is over.

The solutions which go towards $\pm \infty$ correspond to action potentials travelling slower than normal under a travelling anode or faster than normal under a travelling cathode. We suspect that a system which tends to $-\infty$ for all values of θ after an initial negative displacement of V is one which is incapable of propagating an action potential.

NUMERICAL METHODS

Membrane action potentials

Integration procedure. The equations to be solved are the four simultaneous first-order equations (26), (7), (15), and (16) (p. 518). After slight rearrangement (which will be omitted in this description) these were integrated by the method of Hartree (1932–3). Denoting the beginning and end of a step by t_0 and t_1 $(= t_0 + \delta t)$ the procedure for each step was as follows:

(1) Estimate V_1 from V_0 and its backward differences.

(2) Estimate n_1 from n_0 and its backward differences.

(3) Calculate $(dn/dt)_1$ from eqn. 7 using the estimated n_1 and the values of α_n and β_n appropriate to the estimated V_1.

(4) Calculate n_1 from the equation

$$n_1 - n_0 = \frac{\delta t}{2}\left\{\left(\frac{dn}{dt}\right)_0 + \left(\frac{dn}{dt}\right)_1 - \frac{1}{12}\left[\Delta^2\left(\frac{dn}{dt}\right)_0 + \Delta^2\left(\frac{dn}{dt}\right)_1\right]\right\};$$

$\Delta^2(dn/dt)$ is the second difference of dn/dt; its value at t_1 has to be estimated.

(5) If this value of n_1 differs from that estimated in (2), repeat (3) and (4) using the new n_1. If necessary, repeat again until successive values of n_1 are the same.

(6) Find m_1 and h_1 by procedures analogous to steps (2)–(5).

(7) Calculate $\bar{g}_K n_1^4$ and $\bar{g}_{Na} m_1^3 h_1$.

(8) Calculate $(dV/dt)_1$ from eqn. 26 using the values found in (7) and the originally estimated V_1.

(9) Calculate a corrected V_1 by procedures analogous to steps (4) and (5). This result never differed enough from the original estimated value to necessitate repeating the whole procedure from step (3) onwards.

The step value had to be very small initially (since there are no differences at $t=0$) and it also had to be changed repeatedly during a run, because the differences became unmanageable if it was too large. It varied between about 0·01 msec at the beginning of a run or 0·02 msec during the rising phase of the action potential, and 1 msec during the small oscillations which follow the spike.

Accuracy. The last digit retained in V corresponded to microvolts. Sufficient digits were kept in the other variables for the resulting errors in the change of V at each step to be only occasionally as large as 1 μV. It is difficult to estimate the degree to which the errors at successive steps accumulate, but we are confident that the overall errors are not large enough to be detected in the illustrations of this paper.

Temperature differences. In calculating the action potential it was convenient to use tables giving the α's and β's at intervals of 1 mV. The tabulated values were appropriate to a fibre at 6·3° C. To obtain the action potential at some other temperature T' °C the direct method would be to multiply all α's and β's by a factor $\phi = 3^{(T'-6\cdot3)/10}$, this being correct for a Q_{10} of 3. Inspection of eqn. 26 shows that the same result is achieved by calculating the action potential at 6·3° C with a membrane capacity of ϕC_M μF/cm², the unit of time being $1/\phi$ msec. This method was adopted since it saved recalculating the tables.

Propagated action potential

Equations. The main equation for a propagated action potential is eqn. (30). Introducing a quantity $K = 2R_2\theta^2 C_M/a$, this becomes

$$\frac{d^2 V}{dt^2} = K \left\{ \frac{dV}{dt} + \frac{1}{C_M} [\bar{g}_K n^4 (V - V_K) + \bar{g}_{Na} m^3 h (V - V_{Na}) + \bar{g}_l (V - V_l)] \right\}. \tag{31}$$

The subsidiary equations (7), (15) and (16), and the α's and β's, are the same as for the membrane equation.

Integration procedure. Steps (1)–(7) were the same as for the membrane action potential. After that the procedure was as follows:

(8) Estimate $(dV/dt)_1$ from $(dV/dt)_0$ and its backward differences.

(9) Calculate $(d^2V/dt^2)_1$ from eqn. (31), using the values found in (7) and the estimated values of V_1 and $(dV/dt)_1$.

(10) Calculate a corrected $(dV/dt)_1$ by procedures analogous to steps (4) and (5).

(11) Calculate a corrected V_1 by a procedure analogous to step (4), using the corrected $(dV/dt)_1$.

(12) If necessary, repeat (9)–(11) using the new V_1 and $(dV/dt)_1$, until successive values of V_1 agree.

Starting conditions. In practice it is necessary to start with V deviating from zero by a finite amount (0·1 mV was used). The first few values of V, and hence the differences, were obtained as follows. Neglecting the changes in g_K and g_{Na}, eqn. (31) is

$$\frac{d^2 V}{dt^2} = K \left\{ \frac{dV}{dt} + \frac{g_0}{C_M} V \right\},$$

where g_0 is the resting conductance of the membrane. The solution of this equation is $V = V_0 e^{\mu t}$, where μ is a solution of

$$\mu^2 - K\mu - Kg_0/C_M = 0. \tag{32}$$

When K has been chosen, μ can thus be found and hence V_1, V_2, etc. ($V_0 e^{\mu t_1}$, $V_0 e^{\mu t_2}$, etc.).

After several runs had been calculated, so that K was known within fairly narrow limits, time was saved by starting new runs not from near $V = 0$ but from a set of values interpolated between corresponding points on a run which had gone towards $+\infty$ and another which had gone towards $-\infty$.

Choice of K. The value of K chosen for the first run makes no difference to the final result, but the nearer it is to the correct value the fewer runs will need to be evaluated. The starting value was found by inserting in eqn. (32) a value of μ found by measuring the foot of an observed action potential.

Calculation of falling phase. The procedure outlined above is satisfactory for the rising phase and peak of the action potential but becomes excessively tedious in the falling phase and the oscillations which follow the spike. A different method, which for other reasons is not applicable in the earlier phases, was therefore employed. The solution was continued as a membrane action potential, and the value of d^2V/dt^2 calculated at each step from the differences of dV/dt. From these it was possible to derive an estimate of the values (denoted by z) that d^2V/dt^2 would have taken in a propagated action potential. The membrane solution was then re-calculated using the following equation instead of eqn. (31):

$$\frac{dV}{dt} = -\frac{1}{C_M} \{ \bar{g}_K n^4 (V - V_K) + \bar{g}_{Na} m^3 h (V - V_{Na}) + \bar{g}_l (V - V_l) \} + \frac{z}{K}. \tag{33}$$

This was repeated until the z's assumed for a particular run agreed with the d^2V/dt^2's derived from the same run. When this is the case, eqn. (33) is identical with eqn. (31), the main equation for the propagated action potential.

RESULTS

Membrane action potentials

Form of action potential at 6° C. Three calculated membrane action potentials, with different strengths of stimulus, are shown in the upper part of Fig. 12. Only one, in which the initial displacement of membrane potential was 15 mV, is complete; in the other two the calculation was not carried beyond the middle of the falling phase because of the labour involved and because the solution

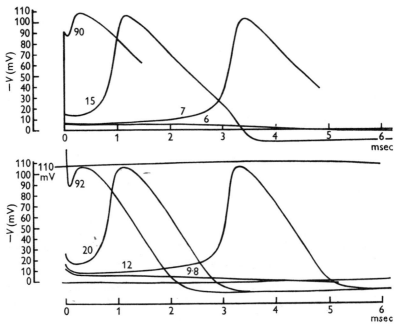

Fig. 12. Upper family: solutions of eqn. (26) for initial depolarizations of 90, 15, 7 and 6 mV (calculated for 6° C). Lower family: tracings of membrane action potentials recorded at 6° C from axon 17. The numbers attached to the curves give the shock strength in $m\mu$coulomb/cm². The vertical and horizontal scales are the same in both families (apart from the slight curvature indicated by the 110 mV calibration line). In this and all subsequent figures depolarizations (or negative displacements of V) are plotted upwards.

had become almost identical with the 15 mV action potential, apart from the displacement in time. One solution for a stimulus just below threshold is also shown.

The lower half of Fig. 12 shows a corresponding series of experimental membrane action potentials. It will be seen that the general agreement is good, as regards amplitude, form and time-scale. The calculated action potentials do, however, differ from the experimental in the following respects: (1) The drop during the first 0·1 msec is smaller. (2) The peaks are sharper.

(3) There is a small hump in the lower part of the falling phase. (4) The ending of the falling phase is too sharp. The extent to which these differences are the result of known shortcomings in our formulation will be discussed on pp. 542–3.

The positive phase of the calculated action potential has approximately the correct form and duration, as may be seen from Fig. 13 in which a pair of curves are plotted on a slower time scale.

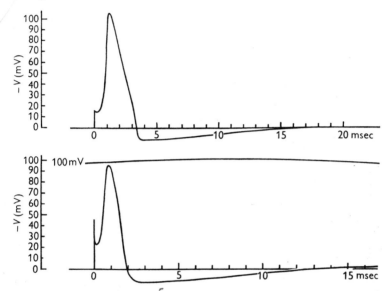

Fig. 13. Upper curve: solution of eqn. (26) for initial depolarization of 15 mV, calculated for 6° C. Lower curve: tracing of membrane action potential recorded at 9·1° C (axon 14). The vertical scales are the same in both curves (apart from curvature in the lower record). The horizontal scales differ by a factor appropriate to the temperature difference.

Certain measurements of these and other calculated action potentials are collected in Table 4.

Form of action potential at 18·5° C. Fig. 14 shows a comparison between a calculated membrane action potential at 18·5° C and an experimental one at 20·5° C. The same differences can be seen as at the low temperature, but, except for the initial drop, they are less marked. In both the calculated and the experimental case, the rise of temperature has greatly reduced the duration of the spike, the difference being more marked in the falling than in the rising phase (Table 4), as was shown in propagated action potentials by Hodgkin & Katz (1949).

The durations of both falling phase and positive phase are reduced at the higher temperature by factors which are not far short of that (3·84) by which the rate constants of the permeability changes are raised ($Q_{10} = 3\cdot0$). This is the justification for the differences in time scale between the upper and lower parts in Figs. 13 and 14.

TABLE 4. Characteristics of calculated action potentials

Type of action potential	Temperature (°C)	Stimulus	Spike height (mV)	Amplitude of positive phase (mV)	Peak conductance (m.mho/cm²)	Duration of rising phase, 20 mV to peak (msec)	Duration of falling phase, peak to V=0 (msec)	Duration of positive phase (msec)	Interval from peak of potential to peak of conductance (msec)	Max. rate of rise (V/sec)
Propagated	18·5	—	90·5	9·7	32·6	0·252	0·67	5·20	−0·016	431
Membrane	18·5	15 mV depolarization	96·8	10·5	30·7	0·275	0·61	5·09	+0·012	564
Membrane	6·3	100 mV depolarization	108·8	—	45·5	—	—	—	+0·16	—
Membrane	6·3	90 mV depolarization	108·5	—	44·8	—	—	—	+0·15	—
Membrane	6·3	15 mV depolarization	105·4	11·2	37·0	0·59	2·21	14·15	+0·15	311
Membrane	6·3	7 mV depolarization	102·1	—	33·4	0·62	—	—	+0·16	277
Membrane	6·3	Anode break	112·1	11·2	53·4	0·50	2·54	14·4	+0·14	414

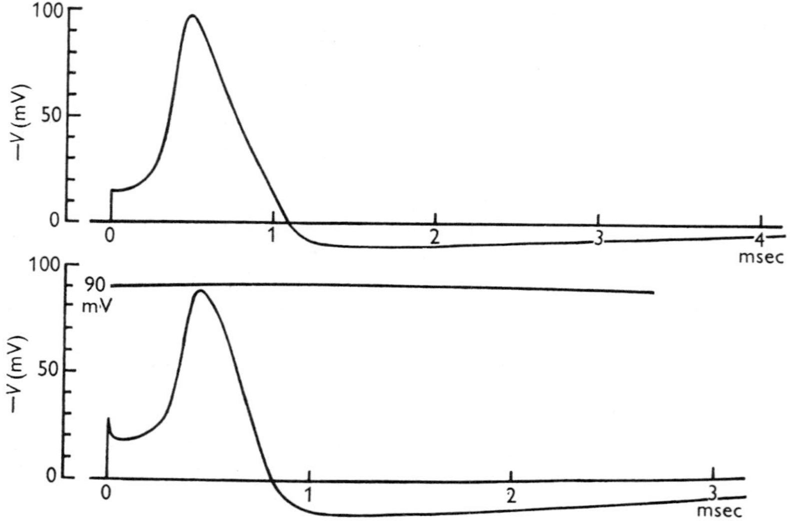

Fig. 14. Upper curve: solution of eqn. (26) for initial depolarization of 15 mV, calculated for 18·5° C. Lower curve: tracing of membrane action potential recorded at 20·5° C (axon 11). Vertical scales are similar. Horizontal scales differ by a factor appropriate to the temperature difference.

Propagated action potential

Form of propagated action potential. Fig. 15 compares the calculated propagated action potential, at 18·5° C, with experimental records on both fast and slow time bases. As in the case of the membrane action potential, the only differences are in certain details of the form of the spike.

Velocity of conduction. The value of the constant K that was found to be needed in the equation for the propagated action potential (eqn. 31) was 10·47 msec⁻¹. This constant, which depends only on properties of the membrane,

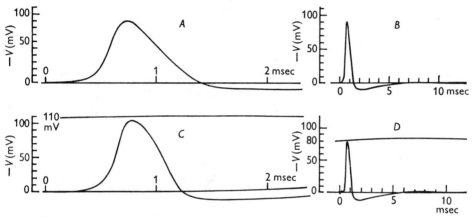

Fig. 15. *A*, solution of eqn. (31) calculated for K of 10·47 msec⁻¹ and temperature of 18·5° C. *B*, same solution plotted on slower time scale. *C*, tracing of propagated action potential on same vertical and horizontal scales as *A*. Temperature 18·5° C. *D*, tracing of propagated action potential from another axon on approximately the same vertical and horizontal scales as *B*. Temperature 19·2° C. This axon had been used for several hours; its spike was initially 100 mV.

determines the conduction velocity in conjunction with the constants of the nerve fibre considered as a cable. The relation is given by the definition of K (p. 524), from which

$$\theta = \sqrt{(Ka/2R_2C_M)}, \tag{34}$$

where θ = conduction velocity, a = radius of axis cylinder, R_2 = specific resistance of axoplasm, and C_M = capacity per unit area of membrane.

The propagated action potential was calculated for the temperature at which the record *C* of Fig. 15 was obtained, and with the value of C_M (1·0 μF/cm²) that was measured on the fibre from which that record was made. Since θ, a and R_2 were also measured on that fibre, a direct comparison between calculated and observed velocities is possible. The values of a and R_2 were 238 μ and 35·4 Ω. cm respectively. Hence the calculated conduction velocity is

$$(10470 \times 0.0238/2 \times 35.4 \times 10^{-6})^{\frac{1}{2}} \text{ cm/sec} = 18.8 \text{ m/sec}.$$

The velocity found experimentally in this fibre was 21·2 m/sec.

Impedance changes

Time course of conductance change. Cole & Curtis (1939) showed that the impedance of the membrane fell during a spike, and that the fall was due to a great increase in the conductance which is in parallel with the membrane capacity. An effect of this kind is to be expected on our formulation, since the entry of Na^+ which causes the rising phase, and the loss of K^+ which causes the falling phase, are consequent on increases in the conductance of the membrane to currents carried by these ions. These component conductances are evaluated during the calculation, and the total conductance is obtained by adding them and the constant 'leak conductance', $\bar{g}_l$.

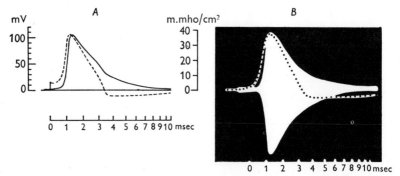

Fig. 16. *A*, solution of eqn. (26) for initial depolarization of 15 mV at a temperature of 6° C. The broken curve shows the membrane action potential in mV; the continuous curve shows the total membrane conductance ($g_{Na} + g_K + \bar{g}_l$) as a function of time. *B*, records of propagated action potential (dotted curve) and conductance change reproduced from Cole & Curtis (1939). The time scales are the same in *A* and *B*.

Fig. 16*A* shows the membrane potential and conductance in a calculated membrane action potential. For comparison, Fig. 16*B* shows superposed records of potential and impedance bridge output (proportional to conductance change), taken from Cole & Curtis's paper. The time scale is the same in *B* as in *A*, and the curves have been drawn with the same peak height. It will be seen that the main features of Cole & Curtis's record are reproduced in the calculated curve. Thus (1) the main rise in conductance begins later than the rise of potential; (2) the conductance does not fall to its resting value until late in the positive phase; and (3) the peak of the conductance change occurs at nearly the same time as the peak of potential. The exact time relation between the peaks depends on the conditions, as can be seen from Table 4.

We chose a membrane action potential for the comparison in Fig. 16 because the spike duration shows that the experimental records were obtained at about 6° C, and our propagated action potential was calculated for 18·5° C. The conductance during the latter is plotted together with the potential in Fig. 17. The same features are seen as in the membrane action potential, the delay between the rise of potential and the rise of conductance being even more marked.

Absolute value of peak conductance. The agreement between the height of the conductance peak in Fig. 16 *A* and the half-amplitude of the bridge output in Fig. 16 *B* is due simply to the choice of scale. Nevertheless, our calculated action potentials agree well with Cole & Curtis's results in this respect. These authors found that the average membrane resistance at the peak of the impedance change was 25 Ω.cm^2, corresponding to a conductance of 40 m.mho/cm^2. The peak conductances in our calculated action potentials ranged from 31 to 53 m.mho/cm^2 according to the conditions, as shown in Table 4.

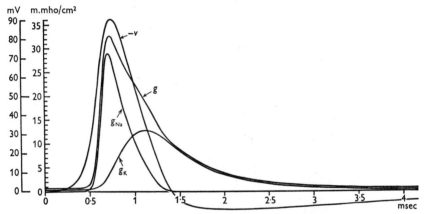

Fig. 17. Numerical solution of eqn. (31) showing components of membrane conductance (*g*) during propagated action potential (– *V*). Details of the analysis are as in Fig. 15.

Components of conductance change. The manner in which the conductances to Na$^+$ and K$^+$ contribute to the change in total conductance is shown in Fig. 17 for the calculated propagated action potential. The rapid rise is due almost entirely to sodium conductance, but after the peak the potassium conductance takes a progressively larger share until, by the beginning of the positive phase, the sodium conductance has become negligible. The tail of raised conductance that falls away gradually during the positive phase is due solely to potassium conductance, the small constant leak conductance being of course present throughout.

Ionic movements

Time course of ionic currents. The time course of the components of membrane current carried by sodium and potassium ions during the calculated propagated spike is shown in Fig. 18 *C*. The total ionic current contains also a small contribution from 'leak current' which is not plotted separately.

Two courses are open to current which is carried into the axis cylinder by ions crossing the membrane: it may leave the axis cylinder again by altering the charge on the membrane capacity, or it may turn either way along the axis cylinder making a net contribution, I, to the local circuit current. The magnitudes of these two terms during steady propagation are $-C_M dV/dt$ and $(C_M/K) d^2V/dt^2$ respectively, and the manner in which the ionic current is divided between them at the different stages of the spike is shown in Fig. 18 B. It will be seen that the ionic current is very small until the potential is well beyond the threshold level, which is shown by Fig. 12 A to be about 6 mV.

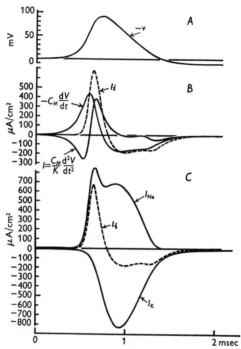

Fig. 18. Numerical solution of eqn. (31) showing components of membrane current during propagated action potential. A, membrane potential $(-V)$. B, ionic current (I_i), capacity current $\left(-C_M \dfrac{dV}{dt}\right)$ and total membrane current $\left(I = \dfrac{C_M}{K}\dfrac{d^2V}{dt^2}\right)$. C, ionic current (I_i), sodium current (I_{Na}) and potassium current (I_K). The time scale applies to all the curves. Details of the analysis are as in Fig. 15.

During this period the current for charging the membrane capacity comes almost entirely from local circuits. The fact that the ionic current does not become appreciable as soon as the threshold depolarization is passed is due partly to the smallness of the currents reached in any circumstances near the threshold, and partly to the delay with which sodium conductance rises when the potential is lowered.

Total movements of ions. The total entry of sodium and loss of potassium can be obtained by integrating the corresponding ionic currents over the whole impulse. This has been done for the four complete action potentials that we calculated, and the results are given in Table 5. It will be seen that the results at 18·5° C are in good agreement with the values found experimentally by Keynes (1951) and Keynes & Lewis (1951), which were obtained at comparable temperatures.

Ionic fluxes. The flux in either direction of an ion can be obtained from the net current and the equilibrium potential for that ion, if the independence principle (Hodgkin & Huxley, 1952 a) is assumed to hold. Thus the outward flux of sodium ions is $I_{Na}/(\exp (V - V_{Na}) F/RT - 1)$, and the inward flux of potassium ions is $- I_K/(\exp (V_K - V) F/RT - 1)$. These two quantities were evaluated at each step of the calculated action potentials, and integrated over the whole impulse. The integrated flux in the opposite direction is given in each case by adding the total net movement. The results are given in Table 5, where they can be compared with the results obtained with radioactive tracers by Keynes (1951) on *Sepia* axons. It will be seen that our theory predicts too little exchange of Na and too much exchange of K during an impulse. This discrepancy will be discussed later.

Refractory period

Time course of inactivation and delayed rectification. According to our theory, there are two changes resulting from the depolarization during a spike which make the membrane unable to respond to another stimulus until a certain time has elapsed. These are 'inactivation', which reduces the level to which

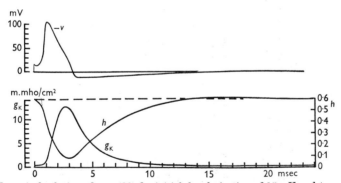

Fig. 19. Numerical solution of eqn. (26) for initial depolarization of 15 mV and temperature of 6° C. Upper curve: membrane potential, as in Fig. 13. Lower curves show time course of g_K and h during action potential and refractory period.

the sodium conductance can be raised by a depolarization, and the delayed rise in potassium conductance, which tends to hold the membrane potential near to the equilibrium value for potassium ions. These two effects are shown in Fig. 19 for the calculated membrane action potential at 6° C. Both curves reach their normal levels again near the end of the positive phase, and finally

TABLE 5. Ionic movements during an impulse. All values are expressed in $\mu\mu$mole/cm^2 and represent the excess over the corresponding movement in the resting state. In the theoretical cases the integration is taken as far as the 3rd intersection with the base line after the spike; it is begun in case (1) when $V = 0.1$ mV; (2) and (3) at the stimulus; (4) when $V = 0$ before the spike. Experimental data from Keynes (1951) for row 6 and from Keynes & Lewis (1951) for rows 5 and 7.

Type of action potential	Temp. (°C)	Stimulus (mV)	Sodium			Potassium		
			Influx	Outflux	Net entry	Influx	Outflux	Net loss
Theoretical (*Loligo*):								
1 Propagated	18·5	—	5·42	1·09	4·33	1·72	5·98	4·26
2 Membrane	18·5	15	5·01	1·02	3·99	1·71	5·78	4·07
3 Membrane	6·3	15	19·30	4·84	14·46	6·17	20·49	14·32
4 Membrane	6·3	Anode break	26·61	9·45	17·16	6·64	23·41	16·77
Experimental:								
5 Propagated (*Loligo*)	22	—	—	—	3·5	—	—	3·0
6 Propagated (*Sepia*)	14	—	10·3	6·6	3·7	0·39	4·7	4·3
7 Propagated (*Sepia*)	22	—	—	—	3·8	—	—	3·6

settle down after a heavily damped oscillation of small amplitude which is not seen in the figure.

Responses to stimuli during positive phase. We calculated the responses of the membrane when it was suddenly depolarized by 90 mV at various times during the positive phase of the membrane action potential at 6° C. These are shown by the upper curves in Fig. 20. After the earliest stimulus the

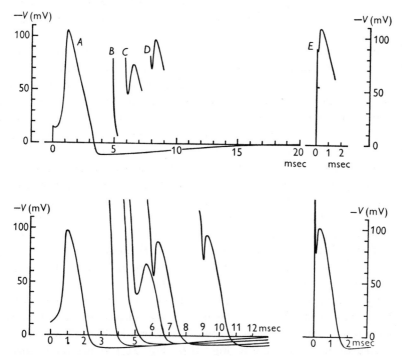

Fig. 20. Theoretical basis of refractory period. Upper curves: numerical solutions of eqn. (26) for temperature of 6° C. Curve *A* gives the response to 15 mμcoulomb/cm² applied instantaneously at $t=0$. Curve *E* gives the response to 90 mμcoulomb/cm² again applied in the resting state. Curves *B* to *D* show effect of applying 90 mμcoulomb/cm² at various times after curve *A*. Lower curves: a similar experiment with an actual nerve, temperature 9° C. The voltage scales are the same throughout. The time scales differ by a factor appropriate to the temperature difference.

membrane potential falls again with hardly a sign of activity, and the membrane can be said to be in the 'absolute refractory period'. The later stimuli produce action potentials of increasing amplitude, but still smaller than the control; these are in the 'relative refractory period'. Corresponding experimental curves are shown in the lower part of Fig. 20. The agreement is good, as regards both the duration of the absolute refractory period and the changes in shape of the spike as recovery progresses.

Excitation

Our calculations of excitation processes were all made for the case where the membrane potential is uniform over the whole area considered, and not for the case of local stimulation of a whole nerve. There were two reasons for this: first, that such data from the squid giant fibre as we had for comparison were obtained by uniform stimulation of the membrane with the long electrode; and, secondly, that calculations for the whole nerve case would have been extremely laborious since the main equation is then a partial differential equation.

Threshold. The curves in Figs. 12 and 21 show that the theoretical 'membrane' has a definite threshold when stimulated by a sudden displacement of membrane potential. Since the initial fall after the stimulus is much less marked in these than in the experimental curves, it is relevant to compare the lowest point reached in a just threshold curve, rather than the magnitude of the original displacement. In the calculated series this is about 6 mV and in the experimental about 8 mV. This agreement is satisfactory, especially as the value for the calculated series must depend critically on such things as the leak conductance, whose value was not very well determined experimentally.

The agreement might have been somewhat less good if the comparison had been made at a higher temperature. The calculated value would have been much the same, but the experimental value in the series at 23° C shown in Fig. 8 of Hodgkin *et al.* (1952) is about 15 mV. However, this fibre had been stored for 5 hr before use and was therefore not in exactly the same state as those on which our measurements were based.

Subthreshold responses. When the displacement of membrane potential was less than the threshold for setting up a spike, characteristic subthreshold responses were seen. One such response is shown in Fig. 12, while several are plotted on a larger scale in Fig. 21 *B*. Fig. 21 *A* shows for comparison the corresponding calculated responses of our model. The only appreciable differences, in the size of the initial fall and in the threshold level, have been mentioned already in other connexions.

During the positive phase which follows each calculated subthreshold response, the potassium conductance is raised and there is a higher degree of 'inactivation' than in the resting state. The threshold must therefore be raised in the same way as it is during the relative refractory period following a spike. This agrees with the experimental findings of Pumphrey, Schmitt & Young (1940).

Anode break excitation. Our axons with the long electrode in place often gave anode break responses at the end of a period during which current was made to flow inward through the membrane. The corresponding response of out theoretical model was calculated for the case in which a current sufficient to bring the membrane potential to 30 mV above the resting potential was suddenly stopped after passing for a time long compared with all the time-constants of the membrane. To do this, eqn. (26) was solved with $I = 0$ and the initial conditions that $V = +30$ mV, and m, n and h have their steady state values for $V = +30$ mV, when $t = 0$. The calculation was made for a temperature

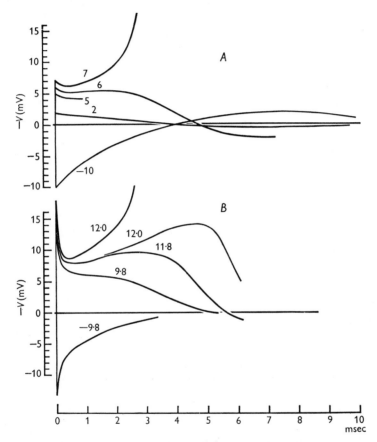

Fig. 21. A, numerical solutions of eqn. (26) for 6° C. The numbers attached to the curves give the initial depolarization in mV (also the quantity of charge applied in mμcoulomb/cm²). B, response of nerve membrane at 6°C to short shocks; the numbers show the charge applied in mμcoulomb/cm². The curves have been replotted from records taken at low amplification and a relatively high time-base speed.

of 6·3° C. A spike resulted, and the time course of membrane potential is plotted in Fig. 22 A. A tracing of an experimental anode break response is shown in Fig. 22 B; the temperature is 18·5° C, no record near 6° being available. It will be seen that there is good general agreement. (The oscillations after the positive phase in Fig. 22 B are exceptionally large; the response of this axon to a small constant current was also unusually oscillatory as shown in Fig. 23.)

The basis of the anode break excitation is that anodal polarization decreases the potassium conductance and removes inactivation. These effects persist for an appreciable time so that the membrane potential reaches its resting value with a reduced outward potassium current and an increased inward sodium current. The total ionic current is therefore inward at $V=0$ and the membrane undergoes a depolarization which rapidly becomes regenerative.

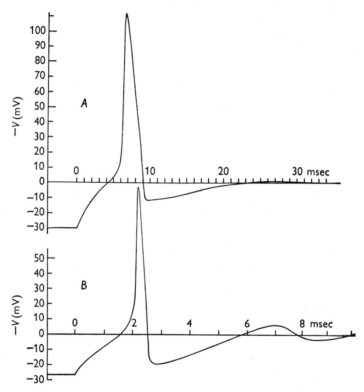

Fig. 22. Theoretical basis of anode break excitation. A, numerical solution of eqn. (26) for boundary condition $-V = -30$ mV for $t < 0$; temperature $6°$ C. B, anode break excitation following sudden cessation of external current which had raised the membrane potential by $26·5$ mV; giant axon with long electrode at $18·5°$ C. Time scales differ by a factor appropriate to the temperature difference.

Accommodation. No measurements of accommodation were made nor did we make any corresponding calculations for our model. It is clear, however, that the model will show 'accommodation' in appropriate cases. This may be shown in two ways. First, during the passage of a constant cathodal current through the membrane, the potassium conductance and the degree of inactivation will rise, both factors raising the threshold. Secondly, the steady state ionic current at all strengths of depolarization is outward (Fig. 11), so that an applied cathodal current which rises sufficiently slowly will never evoke a regenerative response from the membrane, and excitation will not occur.

Oscillations

In all the calculated action potentials and subthreshold responses the membrane potential finally returns to its resting value with a heavily damped oscillation. This is well seen after subthreshold stimuli in Figs. 21A and 24, but the action potentials are not plotted on a slow enough time base or with a large enough vertical scale to show the oscillations which follow the positive phase.

The corresponding oscillatory behaviour of the real nerve could be seen after a spike or a subthreshold short shock, but was best studied by passing a small constant current through the membrane and recording the changes of membrane potential that resulted. The current was supplied by the long internal electrode so that the whole area of membrane was subjected to a uniform current density. It was found that when the current was very weak the potential changes resulting from inward current (anodal) were almost exactly similar to those resulting from an equal outward current, but with opposite sign. This is shown in Fig. 23B and C, where the potential changes are about ± 1 mV. This symmetry with weak currents is to be expected from our equations, since they can be reduced to a linear form when the displacements of all the variables from their resting values are small. Thus, neglecting products, squares and higher powers of δV, δm, δn and δh, the deviations of V, m, n and h from their resting values (0, m_0, n_0 and h_0 respectively), eqn. (26) (p. 518) becomes

$$\delta I = C_M \frac{\mathrm{d}\delta V}{\mathrm{d}t} + \bar{g}_K n_0^4 \delta V - 4\bar{g}_K n_0^3 V_K \delta n + \bar{g}_{Na} m_0^3 h_0 \delta V$$
$$- 3\bar{g}_{Na} m_0^2 h_0 V_{Na} \delta m - \bar{g}_{Na} m_0^3 V_{Na} \delta h + \bar{g}_l \delta V. \qquad (35)$$

Similarly, eqn. (7) (p. 518) becomes

$$\frac{\mathrm{d}\delta n}{\mathrm{d}t} = \frac{\partial \alpha_n}{\partial V} \delta V - (\alpha_n + \beta_n)\,\delta n - n_0 \frac{\partial(\alpha_n + \beta_n)}{\partial V} \delta V,$$

or

$$(p + \alpha_n + \beta_n)\,\delta n = \left\{ \frac{\partial \alpha_n}{\partial V} - n_0 \frac{\partial(\alpha_n + \beta_n)}{\partial V} \right\} \delta V, \qquad (36)$$

where p represents $\mathrm{d}/\mathrm{d}t$, the operation of differentiating with respect to time.

The quantity δn can be eliminated between eqns. (35) and (36). This process is repeated for δm and δh, yielding a fourth-order linear differential equation with constant coefficients for δV. This can be solved by standard methods for any particular time course of the applied current density δI.

Fig. 23 *A* shows the response of the membrane to a constant current pulse calculated in this way. The constants in the equations are chosen to be appropriate to a temperature of 18·5° C so as to make the result comparable with the tracings of experimental records shown in *B* and *C*. It will be seen that the calculated curve agrees well with the records in *B*, while those in *C*, obtained from another axon, are much less heavily damped and show a higher

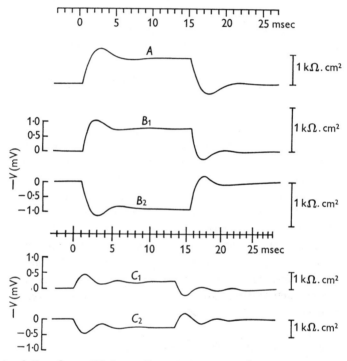

Fig. 23. *A*, solution of eqn. (35) for small constant current pulse; temperature 18·5° C; linear approximation. The curve shows $\delta V/\delta I$ (plotted upwards) as a function of time. *B*, changes in membrane potential associated with application of weak constant currents of duration 15 msec and strength $\pm 1 \cdot 49 \, \mu\text{A/cm}^2$. B_1, cathodic current; B_2, anodic current. Depolarization is shown upward. Temperature 19° C. *C*, similar records from another fibre enlarged to have same time scale. Current strengths are $\pm 0 \cdot 55 \, \mu\text{A/cm}^2$. Temperature 18° C. The response is unusually oscillatory.

frequency of oscillation. A fair degree of variability is to be expected in these respects since both frequency and damping depend on the values of the components of the resting conductance. Of these, g_{Na} and g_{K} depend critically on the resting potential, while $\bar{g}_l$ is very variable from one fibre to another.

Both theory and experiment indicate a greater degree of oscillatory behaviour than is usually seen in a cephalopod nerve in a medium of normal ionic composition. We believe that this is largely a direct result of using the long internal electrode. If current is applied to a whole nerve through a point electrode, neighbouring points on the membrane will have different membrane potentials and the resulting currents in the axis cylinder will increase the damping.

The linear solution for the behaviour of the theoretical membrane at small displacements provided a convenient check on our step-by-step numerical procedure. The response of the membrane at 6·3° C to a small short shock was calculated by this means and compared with the step-by-step solution for an initial depolarization of the membrane by 2 mV. The results are plotted in Fig. 24. The agreement is very close, the step-by-step solution deviating in the direction that would be expected to result from its finite amplitude (cf. Fig. 21).

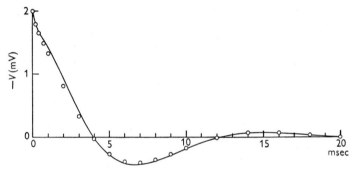

Fig. 24. Comparison of step-by-step solution and linear approximation. Eqn. (26), temperature 6° C; initial displacement of $-V = 2$ mV. Continuous line: step-by-step solution. Circles: linear approximation with same initial displacement.

As pointed out by Cole (1941), the process underlying oscillations in membrane potential must be closely connected with the inductive reactance observed with alternating currents. In our theoretical model the inductance is due partly to the inactivation process and partly to the change in potassium conductance, the latter being somewhat more important. For small displacements of the resting potential the variations in potassium current in 1 cm² of membrane are identical with those in a circuit containing a resistance of 820 Ω in series with an inductance which is shunted by a resistance of 1900 Ω. The value of the inductance is 0·39 H at 25° C, which is of the same order as the 0·2 H found by Cole & Baker (1941). The calculated inductance increases 3-fold for a 10° C fall in temperature and decreases rapidly as the membrane potential is increased; it disappears at the potassium potential and is replaced by a capacity for $E > E_K$.

DISCUSSION

The results presented here show that the equations derived in Part II of this paper predict with fair accuracy many of the electrical properties of the squid giant axon: the form, duration and amplitude of spike, both 'membrane' and propagated; the conduction velocity; the impedance changes during the spike; the refractory period; ionic exchanges; subthreshold responses; and oscillations. In addition, they account at least qualitatively for many of the phenomena of excitation, including anode break excitation and accommodation. This is a satisfactory degree of agreement, since the equations and constants were derived entirely from 'voltage clamp' records, without any adjustment to make them fit the phenomena to which they were subsequently applied. Indeed any such adjustment would be extremely difficult, because in most cases it is impossible to tell in advance what effect a given change in one of the equations will have on the final solution.

The agreement must not be taken as evidence that our equations are anything more than an empirical description of the time-course of the changes in permeability to sodium and potassium. An equally satisfactory description of the voltage clamp data could no doubt have been achieved with equations of very different form, which would probably have been equally successful in predicting the electrical behaviour of the membrane. It was pointed out in Part II of this paper that certain features of our equations were capable of a physical interpretation, but the success of the equations is no evidence in favour of the mechanism of permeability change that we tentatively had in mind when formulating them.

The point that we do consider to be established is that fairly simple permeability changes in response to alterations in membrane potential, of the kind deduced from the voltage clamp results, are a sufficient explanation of the wide range of phenomena that have been fitted by solutions of the equations.

Range of applicability of the equations

The range of phenomena to which our equations are relevant is limited in two respects: in the first place, they cover only the short-term responses of the membrane, and in the second, they apply in their present form only to the isolated squid giant axon.

Slow changes. A nerve fibre whose membrane was described by our equations would run down gradually, since even in the resting state potassium leaves and sodium enters the axis cylinder, and both processes are accelerated by activity. This is no defect in describing the isolated squid giant axon, which does in fact run down in this way, but some additional process must take place in a nerve in the living animal to maintain the ionic gradients which are the immediate source of the energy used in impulse conduction.

After-potentials. Our equations give no account of after-potentials, apart from the positive phase and subsequent oscillations.

Conditions of isolated giant axon. There are many reasons for supposing that the resting potential of the squid giant axon is considerably lower after isolation than when it is intact in the living animal. Further evidence for this view is provided by the observation (Hodgkin & Huxley, 1952c) that the maximum inward current that the membrane can pass on depolarization is increased by previously raising the resting potential by 10–20 mV by means of anodally directed current. Our equations could easily be modified to increase the resting potential (e.g. by reducing the leak conductance and adding a small outward current representing metabolic extrusion of sodium ions). We have not made any calculations for such a case, but certain qualitative results are evident from inspection of other solutions. If, for instance, the resting potential were raised (by 12 mV) to the potassium potential, the positive phase and subsequent oscillations after the spike would disappear, the rate of rise of the spike would be increased, the exchange of internal and external sodium in a spike would be increased, the membrane would not be oscillatory unless depolarized, and accommodation and the tendency to give anode break responses would be greatly reduced. Several of these phenomena have been observed when the resting potential of frog nerve is raised (Lorente de Nó, 1947), but no corresponding information exists about the squid giant axon.

Applicability to other tissues. The similarity of the effects of changing the concentrations of sodium and potassium on the resting and action potentials of many excitable tissues (Hodgkin, 1951) suggests that the basic mechanism of conduction may be the same as implied by our equations, but the great differences in the shape of action potentials show that even if equations of the same form as ours are applicable in other cases, some at least of the parameters must have very different values.

Differences between calculated and observed behaviour

In the Results section, a number of points were noted on which the calculated behaviour of our model did not agree with the experimental results. We shall now discuss the extent to which these discrepancies can be attributed to known shortcomings in our equations. Two such shortcomings were pointed out in Part II of this paper, and were accepted for the sake of keeping the equations simple. One was that the membrane capacity was assumed to behave as a 'perfect' condenser (phase angle 90°; p. 505), and the other was that the equations governing the potassium conductance do not give as much delay in the conductance rise on depolarization (e.g. to the sodium potential) as was observed in voltage clamps (p. 509).

The assumption of a perfect capacity probably accounts for the fact that the initial fall in potential after application of a short shock is much less marked in the calculated than in the experimental curves (Figs. 12 and 21). Some of the initial drop in the experimental curves may also be due to end-effects, the guard system being designed for the voltage clamp procedure but not for stimulation by short shocks.

The inadequacy of the delay in the rise of potassium conductance has several effects. In the first place the falling phase of the spike develops too early, reducing the spike amplitude slightly and making the peak too pointed in shape (p. 525). In the membrane action potentials these effects become more marked the smaller the stimulus, since the potassium conductance begins to rise during the latent period. This causes the spike amplitude to decrease more in the calculated than in the experimental curves (Fig. 12).

The low calculated value for the exchange of internal and external sodium ions is probably due to this cause. Most of the sodium exchange occurs near the peak of the spike, when the potential is close to the sodium potential. The early rise of potassium conductance prevents the potential from getting as close to the sodium potential, and from staying there for as long a time, as it should.

A check on these points is provided by the 'anode break' action potential. Until the break of the applied current, the quantity n has the steady state value appropriate to $V = +30$ mV, i.e. it is much smaller than in the usual resting condition. This greatly increases the delay in the rise of potassium conductance when the membrane is depolarized. It was found that the spike height was greater (Table 4), the peak was more rounded, and the exchange of internal and external sodium was greater (Table 5), than in an action potential which followed a cathodal short shock.

The other important respect in which the model results disagreed with the experimental was that the calculated exchange of internal and external potassium ions per impulse was too large. This exchange took place largely during the positive phase, when the potential is close to the potassium potential and the potassium conductance is still fairly high. We have no satisfactory explanation for this discrepancy, but it is probably connected with the fact that the value of the potassium potential was less strongly affected by changes in external potassium concentration than is required by the Nernst equation.

SUMMARY

1. The voltage clamp data obtained previously are used to find equations which describe the changes in sodium and potassium conductance associated with an alteration of membrane potential. The parameters in these equations were determined by fitting solutions to the experimental curves relating sodium or potassium conductance to time at various membrane potentials.

2. The equations, given on pp. 518–19, were used to predict the quantitative behaviour of a model nerve under a variety of conditions which corresponded to those in actual experiments. Good agreement was obtained in the following cases:

(a) The form, amplitude and threshold of an action potential under zero membrane current at two temperatures.

(b) The form, amplitude and velocity of a propagated action potential.

(c) The form and amplitude of the impedance changes associated with an action potential.

(d) The total inward movement of sodium ions and the total outward movement of potassium ions associated with an impulse.

(e) The threshold and response during the refractory period.

(f) The existence and form of subthreshold responses.

(g) The existence and form of an anode break response.

(h) The properties of the subthreshold oscillations seen in cephalopod axons.

3. The theory also predicts that a direct current will not excite if it rises sufficiently slowly.

4. Of the minor defects the only one for which there is no fairly simple explanation is that the calculated exchange of potassium ions is higher than that found in *Sepia* axons.

5. It is concluded that the responses of an isolated giant axon of *Loligo* to electrical stimuli are due to reversible alterations in sodium and potassium permeability arising from changes in membrane potential.

REFERENCES

COLE, K. S. (1941). Rectification and inductance in the squid giant axon. *J. gen. Physiol.* **25**, 29–51.

COLE, K. S. & BAKER, R. F. (1941). Longitudinal impedance of the squid giant axon. *J. gen. Physiol.* **24**, 771–788.

COLE, K. S. & CURTIS, H. J. (1939). Electric impedance of the squid giant axon during activity. *J. gen. Physiol.* **22**, 649–670.

GOLDMAN, D. E. (1943). Potential, impedance, and rectification in membranes. *J. gen. Physiol.* **27**, 37–60.

HARTREE, D. R. (1932–3). A practical method for the numerical solution of differential equations. *Mem. Manchr lit. phil. Soc.* **77**, 91–107.

HODGKIN, A. L. (1951). The ionic basis of electrical activity in nerve and muscle. *Biol. Rev.* **26**, 339–409.

HODGKIN, A. L. & HUXLEY, A. F. (1952a). Currents carried by sodium and potassium ions through the membrane of the giant axon of *Loligo*. *J. Physiol.* **116**, 449–472.

HODGKIN, A. L. & HUXLEY, A. F. (1952b). The components of membrane conductance in the giant axon of *Loligo*. *J. Physiol.* **116**, 473–496.

HODGKIN, A. L. & HUXLEY, A. F. (1952c). The dual effect of membrane potential on sodium conductance in the giant axon of *Loligo*. *J. Physiol.* **116**, 497–506.

HODGKIN, A. L., HUXLEY, A. F. & KATZ, B. (1949). Ionic currents underlying activity in the giant axon of the squid. *Arch. Sci. physiol.* **3**, 129–150.

HODGKIN, A. L., HUXLEY, A. F. & KATZ, B. (1952). Measurement of current-voltage relations in the membrane of the giant axon of *Loligo*. *J. Physiol.* **116**, 424–448.

HODGKIN, A. L. & KATZ, B. (1949). The effect of temperature on the electrical activity of the giant axon of the squid. *J. Physiol.* **109**, 240–249.

KEYNES, R. D. (1951). The ionic movements during nervous activity. *J. Physiol.* **114**, 119–150.

KEYNES, R. D. & LEWIS, P. R. (1951). The sodium and potassium content of cephalopod nerve fibres. *J. Physiol.* **114**, 151–182.

LORENTE DE NÓ, R. (1947). A study of nerve physiology. *Stud. Rockefeller Inst. med. Res.* **131**, **132**.

PUMPHREY, R. J., SCHMITT, O. H. & YOUNG, J. Z. (1940). Correlation of local excitability with local physiological response in the giant axon of the squid (*Loligo*). *J. Physiol.* **98**, 47–72.

SPINAL CORD POTENTIAL

For many years spinal cord potentials were studied as an index of various neural activities; elaborate hypotheses were developed to attempt to interpret various parts of the spinal cord potential. The characteristic cord potential consists of three main elements: (1) a large initial spike; (2) a smaller and slower negative potential, often with two peaks; and (3) a relatively larger and longer positive potential. Gasser found that if two groups of fibers in a dorsal root were stimulated separately and then simultaneously, the initial spikes would summate; but the secondary negative potentials did not summate and, he reasoned, were therefore produced by elements in the spinal cord (32). Gasser suggested that the secondary potentials arose in spinal internuncial neurons (interneurons).

In 1938, Barron and Matthews (33) described the slow negative dorsal root potential and suggested that it was produced by the interaction of active and passive terminal arborizations of afferent fibers. Earlier, in 1935, Barron and Matthews (34) had observed that occasionally the second of two dorsal root afferent volleys failed to produce the anticipated potential changes recorded from the dorsal aspect of the spinal cord (what is now interpreted as an early discovery of presynaptic inhibition). They also had observed antidromic backfiring into the dorsal root fibers (the dorsal root reflex).

When studies employing the monosynaptic reflex became popular, recording of the spinal cord potentials was more or less dropped by the wayside as the major index of spinal cord activity. That dorsal root potentials and cord dorsum potentials are related to afferent depolarization was well established. For a long time, however, these potentials were regarded as passive processes—the result of electrotonic spread from adjacent active structures. With the realization that the time course of a spinal cord slow potential is approximately the same as that of presynaptic inhibition, and with the recognition that the dorsal root potential and the dorsal root reflex could be explained within the concept of presynaptic inhibition, a resurgence of interest in cord potentials developed.

Wall *et al.* (35) studied the blocking of afferent input that had been observed by Barron and Matthews. They found that after a volley of impulses passed over the dorsal root, impulses arising in the same or adjacent dorsal roots are partly prevented from entering the dorsal columns. The blockade was maximal 15–20 msec. after the initial volley, and the duration of the blockade was enhanced by barbiturates—which were later found to increase the duration of presynaptic inhibition, further supporting a parallel between the events.

Until the 1962 paper by Wall, most authors attributed spinal cord potentials either to the Gasser or the Barron-Matthews explanations. In the paper presented, Wall carefully investigates these two possible origins, demonstrates their inadequacy as a sole explanation, and then presents strong evidence that small cells of the substania gelatinosa do, in fact, produce a major part to the potential.

REFERENCES

32. Gasser, H. S. The control of excitation in the nervous system. *Harvey Lect.* **32:** 169–193 (1937).

33. Barron, D. H., and B. H. C. Matthews. The interpretation of potential changes in the spinal cord. *J. Physiol.* **92:** 276–321 (1938).

34. Barron, D. H., and B. H. C. Matthews. Intermittent conduction in the spinal cord. *J. Physiol.* **85:** 73–103 (1935).

35. Wall, P. E., W. S. McCulloch, J. Y. Lettvin, and W. H. Pitts. Factors limiting the maximum impulse transmitting ability of an afferent system of nerve fibres. *Third London Symposium on Information Theory,* London. Butterworth, (1955) pp. 329–344.

BIBLIOGRAPHY

Eccles, J. C., and J. L. Malcolm. Dorsal root potentials of the spinal cord. *J. Neurophysiol.* **9:** 139–160 (1946).

Brooks, C. McC., and K. Koizumi. Origin of the dorsal root reflex. *J. Neurophysiol.* **19:** 61–74 (1956).

Eccles, J. C. Presynaptic inhibition in the spinal cord. *Prog. Brain Res.* **12:** 65–91 (1964).

Wall, P. D. Presynaptic control of impulses at the first central synapse in the cutaneous pathway. *Prog. Brain Res.* **12:** 92–118 (1964).

THE ORIGIN OF A SPINAL-CORD SLOW POTENTIAL

By P. D. WALL

*From the Department of Biology and Center for Communication Sciences,
Research Laboratory of Electronics, Massachusetts Institute of
Technology, Cambridge, Massachusetts, U.S.A.*

(*Received* 4 *June* 1962)

We want to determine the origin of the slow negative dorsal root potential, which was first described by Barron & Matthews (1938), and subsequently carefully examined by a number of authors, including Eccles & Malcolm (1946), Lloyd & McIntyre (1949) and Bonnet & Bremer (1952). The immediate origin of the dorsal root potential (DRP) is prolonged depolarization of the terminal arborizations of afferent fibres; but the question remains, What is the nature and location of the cause of this depolarization?

Any satisfactory description of the potential's origin must explain the observed properties of the potential. It is evoked by a single volley of impulses in skin nerve fibres, but not by a single volley in large proprioceptive fibres. It is present both in the active fibres that have carried the afferent volley and in their passive neighbours. It can be recorded in ipsilateral dorsal roots up to two segments away from the active root and in the contralateral segment. The potential rises to a peak 20 msec after the arrival of the volley, and then declines for 200 msec. As the size of the afferent volley is increased, the potential reaches a maximal size when only a fraction of the afferent A fibres are active.

The authors cited above, who followed Barron & Matthews, attributed the origin to the activity of internuncials. Wall (1958, 1959) examined the activity of cells in the lamina of dorsal neurones that receive skin afferents and concluded that these cells could not be the origin. Barron & Matthews (1938) had suggested that the potential originated from special properties of the terminal arborization of afferent fibres themselves. This paper will show that no active afferent fibres need be present in the region generating the potential. If neither the larger interneurones nor the afferent fibres is the origin, suspicion naturally turns to the only other neural component of the region, the small cells of substantia gelatinosa, and this paper will present evidence that they are, in fact, the cause of the potential.

Wall, P. D. The origin of a spinal-cord slow potential. *J. Physiol.* **164**: 508–526, 1962.

METHODS

The experiments were carried out on cats anaesthetized with intraperitoneal Dial (allo-barbitone; CIBA) 0·5 ml./kg. Spinal and decerebrate preparations were not used, since the DRPs are resistant to the barbiturate anaesthesia. Cats were paralysed with Flaxedil (gallamine triethiodide; May and Baker) and artificial respiration instituted. Exposed cord temperature was maintained at 38° C. Routine methods were used for recording and stimulating. Micro-electrodes were of the glass, 2 μ, fluid-filled type; the same results were obtained with KCl, K_2SO_4, or Na_2SO_4 solutions in the electrodes. High-input impedance cathode followers were used as the head stage of each recording circuit. Since the potentials to be recorded were of long duration, it was necessary to record low frequencies and, however well the cord was stabilized, low-frequency noise remained in the micro-electrode recordings. This problem was solved by using a 'window' circuit designed by Professor J. Y. Lettvin, which started the oscilloscope trace at a fixed point and allowed wide-band recording for a controllable interval.

Making the lesions. It was necessary to cut the dorsal columns and lateral tracts with the least possible disturbance to the cord. Under a dissecting microscope the surface of the cord to be cut was exposed. A microcautery instrument designed by Dr K. Kornacker was then applied to any visible blood vessels on the pia mater along the intended line of cut. The head of the cautery instrument consists of a V-shaped length of 0·008-in. (0·2 mm) diameter nichrome wire; each arm of the V is 15 mm long and is heated by 1·5 V, d.c. After this extremely local cautery of the blood vessels, the cord is again flooded with oil and a cut is made through the pia. The best instrument for cutting was a fragment of thin razor blade dipped in G.E., SC 87 silicone and held in needle forceps. After the pia was cut, the lesion was completed by picking out white matter to the required depth with watchmakers' forceps.

Locating the micro-electrodes. In constructing the source–sink maps it is necessary to know the location of recording points. Many electrodes were used, one after the other, in order to build up a grid of recording points in the region under examination. The track of each electrode must be located, since electrode penetrations cannot be assumed to be parallel to each other. The method used here is fast and convenient and sufficiently accurate for the purpose. The depth of penetration of each electrode is recorded, and upon reaching its final recording station it is cut off and left *in situ*. Cutting micro-electrodes can be carried out with minimal disturbance under a microscope with fine Castroviejo scissors. A notch is filed in one blade, the micro-electrode lies in this notch, and the other blade of the scissors is brought up against it to cut it. At the end of the experiment the cord is fixed *in situ* with 10 % formalin for 3 hr, and then a large piece of cord containing the micro-electrodes is fixed for a further 24 hr in 10 % formalin. A free-hand section, 1 mm thick, is then cut of a slab of cord containing all the electrodes. This section is then dehydrated in alcohol and cleared in methyl salicylate. The electrodes and the outline of the grey matter are then visible, and depths of penetration can be checked with the known depth, and location of recording points can be made with respect to the surface and the border of grey and white matter. Only those electrode tracks were used when the observed and expected depth of penetration agreed within ± 5 %. A few electrodes had to be rejected because the error was greater, and it was assumed that some accident had occurred either in penetration, cutting or the subsequent manipulations.

Making voltage contour maps and current source–sink maps. The method has been discussed in detail previously (Howland, Lettvin, McCulloch, Pitts & Wall, 1955) and only a brief summary of the stages is presented here. It provides a high-resolution method of locating active sites in nerve tissue. The initial aim was to collect data of the voltage at a large number of points within an area of interest with respect to a fixed distant point. The fixed-reference electrode was a large silver–silver-chloride plate under the skin of the contralateral flank. The data were to be collected at a fixed time after a stimulus. In these experiments the maximal number of recording points was 200, all within an area of 2.0×1.5 mm in the dorsal cord. Recordings were made serially from one point after another, and then the data were pooled as though all points had been recorded from simultaneously. This obviously assumes stability of the preparation, and this was checked by placing the electrodes in the cord in irregular order, to check whether a consistent map was produced independent of the time of observation. The height of the dorsal root potential was also monitored for stability throughout the experiment. We now knew the voltage at all the recording points at a fixed time after the stimulus, and we next obtained the spatial co-ordinates of the recording points by locating the electrodes. At this stage the data were fed to a computer. The computer now took the known data and by interpolation between the known points constructed a regular grid of potential values with equal distances between the points. Finally, each point was examined to determine if it was a source or sink of current by comparing its voltage level with those of the four surrounding equidistant points. If they all have the same value, there is no activity in the region. If the point of interest is in a linearly changing potential field, there is no activity in the region. A source or sink only exists at places where the slope of the spatial distribution of potential is changing. The sum of the second derivatives of the potential in two orthogonal directions gives the intensity of the source or sink. Source–sink maps were made here in a transverse plane across the cord. The third dimension along the longitudinal axis of the cord could be neglected, because it was shown that immediate rostral or caudal sections through the cord contained 'activity' almost identical with the section examined, and therefore the main voltage gradients were in the transverse direction. Sinks are located in the region of depolarized nerve cells.

RESULTS

It is necessary, before starting the direct investigation of the slow potential, to re-examine the Lissauer tract and its associated substantia gelatinosa.

The anatomy and physiology of substantia gelatinosa

The substantia gelatinosa lies as a lamina roofing the dorsal part of the dorsal horn. The lateral part of this lamina is made up of a tract of extremely fine non-myelinated fibres, the dorsolateral fasciculus of Lissauer. It lies sandwiched between the dorsal columns and the lamina of large cells that receive the afferent skin fibres. It is permeated by the terminal arborizations of the incoming afferent fibres and the dendrites of deeper cells. It is found at all levels of the spinal cord and in all vertebrates (Keenan, 1929). From the lumbar enlargement rostrally the substantia gelatinosa is split by the wedge of dorsal columns, but in the sacral and coccygeal segments the lamina clearly extends all the way across the mid line from one side to the other. The region contains a very small number of large marginal cells that lie on the border of the grey and white matter, and a large number of small cells that fail to stain with the ordinary neurological stains and have no Nissl granules in their limited cytoplasm but have the characteristic neural single nucleolus. The anatomy and function of Lissauer tract and substantia gelatinosa have been studied most intensively by Ranson and his colleagues (Ranson & von Hess, 1915; Ranson & Billingsley, 1916; Ranson, 1931) and they presented the following picture. They claimed that fine non-myelinated afferent fibres gather together to make a lateral division of the dorsal root. They believed at the time that the fine fibres were the specific pain fibres, although this opinion is no longer tenable (Douglas & Ritchie, 1962). The lateral division of the dorsal root entered the Lissauer tract and from there the fibres proceeded to the cells of substantia gelatinosa. Section of the lateral division of the dorsal root abolished pain reactions, while section of the medial division of the root had no effect on pain reactions.

We have re-examined the anatomy of the region of the root entrance zone, using Holmes's silver stain. Serial transverse sections of a cat lumbar dorsal root fail to show the migration of the fine fibres into a lateral division as the rootlets approach the cord. Transverse, horizontal, and sagittal sections of the root entrance zone show that the entering roots and Lissauer tract are separate structures with almost no intermingling. A drawing of the region has been included in every edition of Ranson & Clark's text (e.g. Fig. 137, Ranson & Clark, 1953) showing the reputed streaming of non-myelinated fibres into Lissauer's tract. An examination of serial sections through this region shows that the labelled structure is, in fact, the turning of Lissauer's tract in a dorsal direction, which occurs wherever dorsal rootlets are not penetrating into the cord. The region presents signs of an embryological battle for possession of the dorsolateral surface of the cord. The transverse-running dorsal rootlets force the longitudinal-running Lissauer tract ventrally wherever the rootlets penetrate into the cord, and wherever they are not penetrating the Lissauer fibres undulate dorsally. The much reproduced drawing is a transverse section just caudal to the entrance of a rootlet, and shows a rootlet about to plunge into the cord; the structure labelled as the lateral division of the dorsal root is the dorsal extension of Lissauer's tract. In our sections fine non-myelinated fibres can be seen mixed with larger fibres, running toward the dorsal horn, but without any obvious separation. Small numbers of non-myelinated fibres may, indeed, enter the Lissauer tract from the dorsal roots. J. Szentagothai (personal communication) is continuing his extensive investigation of the region (Szentagothai & Kiss, 1949) and presents the following picture. Afferent fibres of all diameters end in the substantia gelatinosa. The region is packed with small cells with many short connexions to each other. Some of the cells send longer axons that run in the Lissauer tract to connect again with other regions of the substantia gelatinosa. The dorsolateral fasciculus of Lissauer is therefore mainly a propriospinal tract for the substantia gelatinosa. Szentagothai has isolated slabs of substantia gelatinosa by undercutting, and he finds no evidence for axons from gelatinosa cells running to other structures. We are left, then, with an apparently self-contained lamina of cells receiving all afferent fibres of all diameters, with massive internal interconnexions, but without axons running to other structures, interposed in the region where the afferent fibres and dendrites of the large secondary cells intermingle.

If this is the anatomical arrangement, and substantia gelatinosa receives afferent fibres of all sizes and there is no apparent lateral division of the dorsal root, it is obviously necessary to repeat the physiological experiments of Ranson & Billingsley (1916), in which a section of a now presumed non-existent lateral division of the dorsal root was reported to abolish pain reactions. In an attempt to duplicate their experiments, cats under light barbiturate or ether anaesthesia were prepared with the cut L7 dorsal root on stimulating electrodes, and the ventral root reflex and heart rate were recorded. They describe making a knife cut into the dorsal-root-cord junction at the ventrolateral angle beneath the root; they mention no special precautions and show no pictures of the lesion. Unfortunately this angle is packed with blood vessels. The junction of the dorsal columns and the lateral columns not only contains Lissauer's tract but is also the main portal for blood vessels supplying the dorsal-horn grey matter. Since most of these vessels are penetrating the surface at exactly the point of Ranson & Billingsley's section, it was not possible to carry out a sub-pial section without also damaging the blood vessels. Dye perfusion of the cord after the section showed ischaemia of the dorsal half of the dorsal-horn grey matter on the side of the lesion, although dorsal columns and ventral horns were still supplied with blood. Physiologically the effect of the lesion was to abolish the heart-rate changes that followed stimulation of L7 dorsal root and to reduce the polysynaptic reflexes severely, while the monosynaptic reflex was only slightly reduced. Conduction of the dorsal columns was only slightly decreased. Since no way could be found to make the described lesion without also affecting the vasculature, the vessels alone were attacked on the surface by the microcautery method described above. Cauterization of half of the visible blood vessels in the pia mater in the angle, without apparent damage to the nerve tissue, produced the same physiological results as the lesion itself. We concluded that the results reported by Ranson & Billingsley (1916) may have been due to a vascular lesion that had abolished the dorsal-horn mechanisms, leaving dorsal column conduction and the medial-running proprioceptive fibres intact. Their results are not consistent with an isolated section of fine fibres, but with destruction of all local spinal mechanisms except the Group I muscle afferents and motor neurones. We can now proceed to investigate the role played by substantia gelatinosa, a system surrounding the first main synapse, and by the Lissauer tract, a propriospinal tract for the substantia gelatinosa, in the generation of the long DRP.

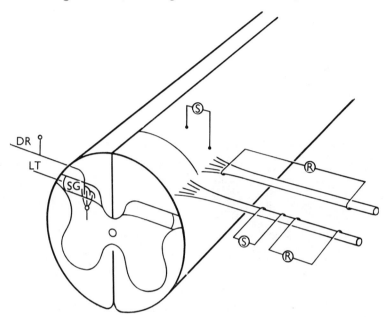

Fig. 1. Left, diagram of the location of the major components: DR, a dorsal root with an afferent fibre shown entering the cord and terminating on the dendrites of a large dorsal interneuron in the region of substantia gelatinosa, SG, which is bounded laterally by the Lissauer tract, LT. On the right the stimulation and recording electrodes are shown. A rootlet of the L6 dorsal root was used for recording the passive DRP. The L7 dorsal root was stimulated. The size of the evoked afferent volley was measured by the recording electrodes on L7. The dorsal columns were divided at the indicated line, between L6 and L7 segments. Stimulating electrodes (S) were placed on the dorsal column in the L6 segment to evoke an antidromic volley recorded on the L7 dorsal root, in order to check that the division of all afferents penetrating from L7 into the L6 segment was complete.

Dorsal root potential produced in de-afferented section of cord

The experimental arrangement is shown in Fig. 1. A square-wave stimulus lasting 0·1 msec was applied to the cut L7 dorsal root. The stimulus was applied once every 2 sec to allow full recovery of the DRP. The size of the afferent volley was measured by electrodes that were also placed on the cut L7 dorsal root. Since the size of the afferent volley was recorded with the use of antidromic impulses, the polarity of the stimulating electrodes was reversed from that used for orthodromic stimulation, so that the cathode of the stimulating electrode pair was always closest to the recording point. The passive DRPs were recorded, as shown, by electrodes placed on the cut L6 dorsal root. All roots were raised into the oil pool covering the cord, to avoid spread of stimulus to neighbouring structures.

The normal passive DRPs are shown in Fig. 2A. They consist of five waves, as described by Lloyd & McIntyre (1949). Initially, there is a fast triphasic wave, negative-positive-negative, and then a somewhat longer positive wave DR IV. The beginning of the long negativity has riding on it a short spike that is the sign of the antidromically-running impulses, the dorsal root reflex of the passive root. Finally, Fig. 2A shows the first 80 msec of the long negative potential, DR V, in which we are interested.

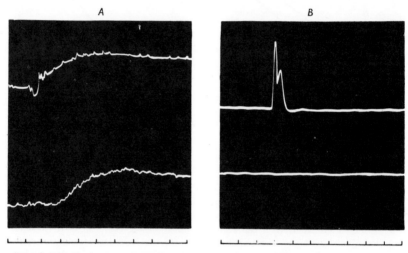

Fig. 2. Effect of removal of afferents from a segment on the DRP. *A*: above, the passive DRP recorded on a rootlet of L 6 dorsal root after a stimulus to L 7 dorsal root in the intact spinal cord. It shows the long negative DRP which follows four small fast early components. The stimulus was given 10 msec after the beginning of the sweep. Time marker, 10 msec. The height of the DRP is 400 μV. Below; the passive DRP recorded as in the upper trace on the L 6 rootlet following the same stimulus to L 7, after complete section of all direct afferents penetrating the segment of the recording root. A prolonged slow wave is still recorded without the preceding fast components, with a delayed onset. The height of the slow wave is reduced to 125 μV. *B*: above, the antidromic volley evoked in the L 7 dorsal root by a stimulus applied to the dorsal columns in L 6 in the intact cord. Time marker, 2 msec. Below; complete absence of antidromic volley in L 7 dorsal root after section of the dorsal column between L 6 and L 7.

In the next stage we removed all active afferent fibres from the region of the recording electrodes. The pathway that carries afferent fibres from an entering root to rostral segment is the dorsal column. The dorsal column was therefore cut by the method described above, between the stimulated fibres of L 7, and the recording rootlet in L 6. The line of section is shown running transversely across the homolateral dorsal column in Fig. 1. The most lateral fibres in the dorsal column were eliminated by cutting the rootlets for 2 mm caudal to the column section. The completeness of the de-afferentation was measured physiologically during the division by placing stimulating electrodes on the dorsal columns at the level of the recording root. Before making the cut, a brief stimulus applied to these electrodes resulted in the appearance of a very large antidromic volley appearing on L7 dorsal root (Fig. 2B above). The gain on the channel recording this antidromic volley was increased until signals as small as 10 μV could be discriminated, and cutting the dorsal columns was continued until absolutely no antidromic volley could be seen to come from above the level of section (Fig. 2B, below). For good measure, in a number of cats the extent of the section was continued to cut the complete contralateral cord and the ipsilateral ventral quadrant. Histological examination showed the cords completely divided, except for the Lissauer tract and ipsilateral funiculus.

The DRP was now recorded in this segment of the cord which had no direct connexion with the stimulated root. The result shown in Fig. 2A (below) shows that there have been three obvious changes. As expected, the first four fast components have disappeared; this is another indication that the first four components result from the direct interaction of active and passive afferent fibres, as previously suggested (Lloyd & McIntyre, 1949; Wall, 1958). A prolonged negative slow wave, however, is still apparent, which differs from the previous one in two respects: first, its onset and peak are delayed approximately 8 msec later than the normal potential; and secondly, the amplitude of the potential is reduced to approximately one quarter of the previously recorded potential. In all other tested respects the potential had the same properties as the potential evoked in the intact cord. The following properties were investigated: threshold, refractory period, recovery period, occlusion, effect of increased barbiturate, and decreased temperature.

The first criticism of these results would be to suggest that the cord was not, in fact, de-afferented of all its A fibres and that the observed potential was the result of a small number of A fibres that had escaped division. An attempt was made, therefore, to imitate the potential by reducing the size of the afferent volley in an intact cord. Figure 3 shows the results of this experiment. Figure 3 (2) shows the size of the afferent volley needed to evoke a slow potential of the same amplitude as that observed in the de-afferented cord. The area under this curve is approximately 15% of the maximal A spike. This number of active fibres should have produced an enormous antidromic spike with the technique used, whereas none was observed. Furthermore, although this potential has the same amplitude as the one observed in the isolated cord, it was not delayed in its onset by the 8 msec observed in the isolated segment, and it is preceded by a positive DR IV. At higher gain the initial three components were also visible. It seems, therefore, reasonable to conclude that the observed potential in the isolated cord was not caused by a small number of intact afferent A fibres.

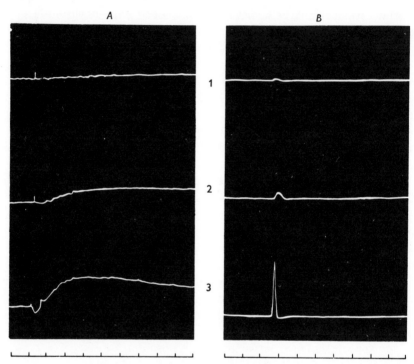

Fig. 3. Relation of the size of the afferent volley to the size of the DRP in an intact cord. Left: the passive DRP recorded on L 6 following stimulation of L 7; 1 is at threshold for the first appearance of the potential, 2 shows the potential at the same height as that recorded from a de-afferented segment, and 3 shows the maximal height recorded. Time marker, 10 msec. Right: the size of the afferent volley required to produce the DRPs shown on the left. The stimulation and recording electrodes were both on L 7, as shown in Fig. 1. 1 shows the size of the afferent volley needed to produce a just visible DRP, 2 shows the size needed to produce a DRP of the same size as that recorded from a de-afferented segment, and 3 shows the size that produces a maximal DRP. Time marker, 2 msec.

If it is not caused by A fibres, could this potential be caused by fine afferent fibres running in the Lissauer tract? As we have already shown, the existence of these fibres in any substantial number is very much in doubt. We can, however, discount the action of even these hypothetical fibres by the two following experiments. First, the threshold stimulus for evoking the potential in the de-afferented cord produced antidromic impulses only in the largest A fibres. Secondly, the potential was evoked in the de-afferented cord, first, by stimulation of the sciatic nerve in the popliteal fossa, and secondly, by stimulation of the intact DRL7, all other roots being cut. The onset of the potential was delayed if the sciatic was stimulated, rather than DRL7. The difference of the two latencies showed that the potential was being evoked by a volley whose leading impulses were travelling at 80 m/sec, and therefore was being produced by A fibres. We thus conclude that a long negative DRP with many of the same properties as the normal Barron & Matthews DR V potential, can be generated in a de-afferented segment of cord by the arrival of a volley of impulses in large fibres in a neighbouring segment.

Development and location of origin of the dorsal root potential

The DRP recorded in the de-afferented segment of cord is completely abolished by dividing the Lissauer tract only, provided that the section is made between the segment of cord which receives the stimulated afferents and the recording segment. This suggests strongly that the potential is being generated as a result of relayed activity transmitted along Lissauer's tract. It also shows that the recorded potential is not produced by passive field spread from the intact segment.

The next series of experiments were designed to show that the location of the origin of the potential was the same in an intact cord and in a de-afferented cord. In Fig. 4A the distribution of the potential is shown in the dorsal half of a transverse section of an intact 6th lumbar segment, 20 msec after a stimulus has been delivered to the cut L7 dorsal root. In Fig. 4B the same experiment has been carried out on a de-afferented L6 segment, 20 msec after the stimulus. The potential map was recorded from many points within the field by fluid-filled micro-electrodes, by the method described above. A general similarity of the contour maps is apparent. There is a steep gradient of decreasing potential paralleling the border of the dorsal columns and grey matter, sinking to a low point just medial to the lateral columns. The development of the potential contour map in a de-afferented segment is shown in Fig. 5. On the left, A, the contour is shown, 10 msec after the stimulus; B is 20 msec after the stimulus; and C is 10 msec later. The DRP reached its maximal amplitude at approximately 28 msec after the stimulus.

While these contour maps suggest that activity developed in a band of tissue paralleling the boundary in the grey matter between the dorsal column and the grey matter, a tremendous increase in the resolution is obtained by reducing the original data to a current-source–sink distribution by the method described above. This method, which measures the second differential of the extracellular voltage distribution, locates the position of entry of current into cells, and locates the presence of sinks of current. The location of the sinks gives the location of active cells. The distribution of activity in an intact segment of cord at the height of the DRP has already been published (Fig. 2, Howland *et al.* 1955). It shows the distribution of the main activity restricted to the region of the substantia gelatinosa. Figure 6 here shows the development of the disturbance in a de-afferented segment of cord. Sinks are indicated by dots,

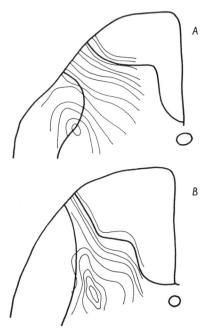

Fig. 4. Potential distribution in a cross-section of an intact cord, *A*, and a de-afferented segment, *B*, 25 msec after a stimulus had been applied to L7 dorsal root. The drawing shows in thick lines the outline of the cord and the white matter of the dorsal quadrant of the L6 segment. 160 recording points were taken with eight electrodes. The fine lines are isopotential lines showing a gradient of potential. The dorsal-to-ventral slope is of increasing negativity. The isopotential contour lines are 50 μV apart in *A* and 25 μV apart in *B*. The general shape of the potential contour map is the same in both the intact and de-afferented cords.

the number indicates intensity. Sources are indicated by dashes. *A*, *B*, and *C* are results observed at 10, 20, and 30 msec after the stimulus. It will be seen that at 10 msec a line of sinks is distributed from the region of the Lissauer tract all along the border between the lateral columns and the grey matter of the dorsal horn. At 20 msec (*B*) there has been a considerable decrease of all activity, but the intense sink located in the region of the Lissauer tract in *A* has begun to extend medially into the cellular

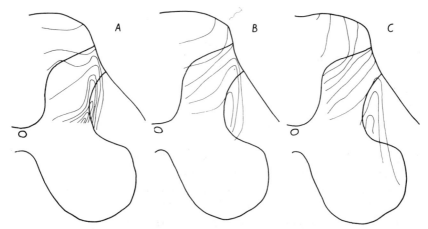

Fig. 5. Potential distribution in a cross-section of a de-afferented segment of cord 10 msec, *A*; 20 msec, *B*; and 30 msec, *C*, after a volley had been fired into the neighbouring intact L 7 segment from its dorsal root. At each time the potential is more negative ventrally than dorsally. The isopotential lines are 25 μV apart. The sequence shows the development of the disturbance in the segment up to the time of the maximal height of the negative dorsal root potential at approximately 30 msec, *C*, after the stimulus.

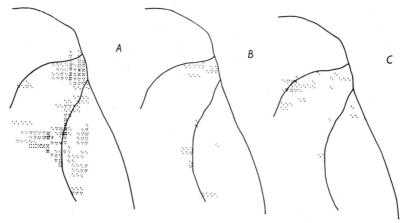

Fig. 6. Source–sink current map showing the distribution of activity in a de-afferented segment of cord 10 msec, *A*; 20 msec, *B*; and 30 msec, *C*, after a volley had been fired into the neighbouring intact L 7 segment from its dorsal root. Sinks of current are shown as dots, and locate the active regions where depolarized cells are present. Sources of current are shown as dashes. 10 msec after the stimulus, *A*, a dense group of current sinks were located along the border of the lateral columns and in the Lissauer tract. In *B* and *C* the more ventral activity fades, while the sinks in the region of the Lissauer tract extend medially into the region of the substantia gelatinosa. The height of the DRP is reached at *C*, and subsequent maps showed a slow fading of this pattern without further changes of location.

region of the substantia gelatinosa. Finally, at 30 msec (*C*), at about the height of the DRP, the activity is now generally spread over the substantia gelatinosa, while the deeper activity has almost completely disappeared. This final distribution of activity is now almost identical with that seen in the intact cord. Later maps show only a slow fading of this activity without any further change of location. It is concluded that in both intact and de-afferented cord segments the disturbance associated with the DRP is located in the region of the substantia gelatinosa, and in the latter case appears to spread into the region from the Lissauer tract.

This method of current-source–sink analysis makes the assumption that the resistance between the recording points is approximately constant. The existence of sudden changes of extracellular resistance would produce spurious sources and sinks. It was particularly necessary to investigate the distribution of resistance in these maps where the most interesting activity occurred at the junction of grey and white matter, where the resistance changes might reasonably be expected. An electrode was therefore placed on the surface of the cord and a sinusoidal potential of low voltage was produced between this electrode and a distant one. The applied sine wave was 20 c/s in one set of experiments and 2000 c/s in another. The maps showed that the applied electrode was the only source of current in the region and no spurious sources or sinks appeared at the boundary of grey and white matter. We therefore concluded that whatever resistance changes occur within the cord are not sufficient to produce the observed results.

Since it was not possible to record in the field of interest with an exactly regular grid of recording points, it was necessary in the computation of the results to interpolate between the actual recording points. Interpolation methods are known to be capable of abolishing existing steps or producing non-existent ones, and it was therefore necessary to check the results by a method that did not involve interpolation. It had been found by Dr K. Kornacker that in frog medulla it was possible in a small area to collect data from a square grid. Small segments of the maps were therefore re-investigated without interpolation. Three electrode tracks, spaced exactly 100 μ apart, were used and, similarly, the recording positions along each tract were spaced 100 μ apart. The results fitted exactly the segments of the larger map from which they were taken. We therefore concluded that the interpolation procedure was not introducing marked errors into the maps.

It is clear from the maps shown in Fig. 6 that activity is arriving in the de-afferented segment, not only from Lissauer's tract but from other systems in the lateral column. Other parts of the cord not shown in these maps showed no significant disturbances. It is believed, for two reasons, that the activity of grey matter generated by impulses arriving in the lateral columns plays no part in the generation of the DRP. First, it will be seen in the maps that this deeper activity is already dying out 20 msec after the stimulus, at a time when the DRP is still increasing. Secondly, after section of the Lissauer tract, which abolishes the DRP, the deeper

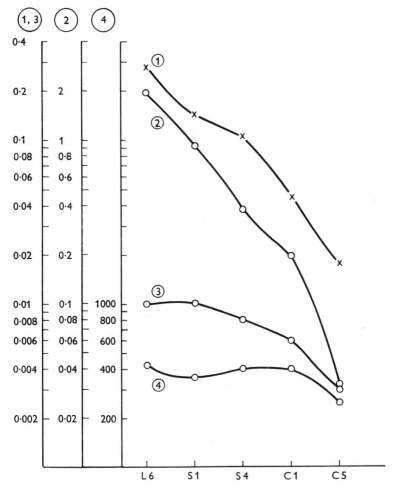

Fig. 7. Changes of size of four variables in segments of the cord from L 6 to the 5th coccygeal; semi-log. scales. 1 is the cross-section area of one half of the spinal cord in the segments denoted on the abscissa; scale in cm². 2 is the cross-section area of the stimulated root in each segment; scale in mm². 3 is the cross-section area of the substantia gelatinosa in one half of the spinal cord in each segment; scale in cm². 4 is the maximal height of the prolonged negative DRP measured in each segment; scale in μV. The relative slopes of these four lines show that while the over-all size of the cord and the dorsal roots is decreasing rapidly, the size of the substantia gelatinosa and DRP remain relatively constant.

activity persists. We were never able to cut both dorsal columns and lateral columns and leave only Lissauer's tract intact, but this is not surprising in view of the pressure and vascular damage, which we could not avoid, during such an operation, to the very fine fibres of the tract. We therefore concluded that the deeper activity is independent of the Lissauer-tract–substantia-gelatinosa activity which seems to generate the DRP.

Relation of dorsal root potential to size of cord structure

Since this DRP requires for its generation a number of nerve impulses in an afferent volley, and yet reaches its maximum when only a fraction of the afferents are active, it is of interest to enquire whether the height of the potential is correlated with the size of any structure in different parts of the spinal cord. Four measures were taken in segments from L 6 to the 5th coccygeal; the height of the DRP, the cross-sectioned areas of the stimulated root, the area of the ipsilateral half of the cord in that segment, and the area of the ipsilateral substantia gelatinosa. The cord was exposed from the lumbar enlargement to the caudal end of the cauda equina. Dorsal roots were dissected out in pairs, the caudal one for stimulation and the rostal for recording the passive DRP. The interelectrode recording distance was held the same for all roots examined. After each experiment the stimulated root was cut free and the segment of cord containing the recording root was excised and fixed in 10 % formalin. Sections were cut, stained, and projected so that the three cross-section areas could be measured by planimeter for each segment. The results are shown in Fig. 7. The most striking result is the relative constancy of both the height of the negative DRP (line 4) and the cross-section area of substantia gelatinosa (line 3) in the lumbar to coccygeal segments, while the expected precipitous decrease of over-all cord size and root size occurs. These results support the more powerful evidence presented above that the substantia gelatinosa may be related to the generation of the negative DRP.

DISCUSSION

The experimental data would fit the following hypothesis for the generation of the DRP. Those afferent fibres that terminate in the dorsal part of the dorsal-horn fire not only the large secondary cells but also the small cells of substantia gelatinosa. The small cells of substantia gelatinosa are interconnected by short axons and by longer running axons in the Lissauer tract. The generation of activity in the small cells fired by the active afferents builds up as a result of mutual bombardment and spreads to neighbouring regions of this continuous sheet of cells. The small cells bombard not only each other, but also the afferent fibres. This bombardment produces the dorsal root reflex during the rising phase of the bombardment and the prolonged depolarization of the terminal arborizations which is the immediate cause of the long DRP.

This hypothesis would explain a number of the curious features of the DRP already discussed in the introduction. A single shock to the large sural nerve fibres generates a massive DRP, while the large afferents from gastrocnemius do not. The morphology of these two types of afferent fibres is similar, but the sural fibres terminate in the region of the substantia gelatinosa, whereas the large-diameter muscle afferents terminate more ventrally (Wall, McCulloch, Lettvin & Pitts, 1956). The generation of the DRP in both active afferent fibres and in their passive neighbours suggests that a third structure on which both terminate is involved, and we have given reasons why the large secondary dorsal cells do not appear to be this third structure (Wall, 1958). The location of the disturbance fits best with the distribution of the small cells. The development of the disturbance in the de-afferented cord fits best with its conduction into the region by the Lissauer tract, which is known to be the propriospinal tract for the small cells. The delay in the appearance of the slow potential in the de-afferented segment fits the expected slow conduction of a volley in the very fine fibres that make up the tract. If all of the delay is attributed to conduction time in this tract, the velocity of conduction would be of the order of 1 m/sec. The close envelopment of the entering afferent fibres by the small cells and the extension of these cells up to the white matter where the myelinated segment of the fibres ends and the non-myelinated terminal arborization begins could explain the relatively large size of the potential recorded on the root. It was suggested in a previous paper (Wall, 1958) that the recorded potential could not be conducted back electrotonically from the fine terminals of the entering fibres. The slow rise to maximum is better explained by the growth of a repetitive discharge rather than by the assumption that an excitatory post-synaptic potential could have such a prolonged rise time. Prolonged-rise excitatory post-synaptic potentials (e.p.s.p.) have never been recorded in vertebrate cells in response to a synchronized volley. The firing pattern of the large secondary cells (Wall, 1959) is not consistent with a slowly rising e.p.s.p. Finally, the distribution of the DRP fits with the distribution of the substantia gelatinosa. This is a continuous sheet of cells spreading up and down the cord. In the thoracic and coccygeal regions it is clear that it spreads across the mid line and is continuous across from one side of the cord to the other. When sections are examined in segments more and more rostral from the coccygeal ones, the enlarging dorsal columns can be seen to split the lamina; but it seems reasonable to assume that the dorsal commissure contains axons interconnecting the two halves of the substantia gelatinosa.

This bilateral extension would explain the delayed contralateral passive DRP. The maintenance of a large-sized DRP in the sacral and upper coccygeal segments is also consistent with the maintenance of the size of substantia gelatinosa in these segments.

The significance of the DRP has increased since it was recognized that presynaptic inhibition (Howland *et al.* 1955; Wall *et al.* 1956) had the same time course as the DRP (Eccles, 1961). The depolarization produced in the terminal arborization may be so severe as to lead to a cathodal block of arriving impulses, or it may diminish the height of the action potential and decrease the excitatory effect of an afferent volley, just as in post-tetanic potentiation the fibre terminations are hyperpolarized (Wall & Johnson, 1958) and the excitatory effect of a volley is increased. The small cells, as the generators of the depolarization, would then act as a modulating mechanism set across the main afferent system at the level of the first synapse. The level of the modulation would be controlled by preceding activity in the same system as in presynaptic inhibition, by activity in surrounding fibres, and by descending systems that may also affect the height of the DRP (Hagbarth & Kerr, 1958).

Finally, one can speculate on the existence elsewhere in the c.n.s. of mechanisms of the type which generate DRP. It is not surprising that the trigeminal nerve shows all the same anatomical and physiological signs that are seen in the spinal nerves. The deep fine fibres of Åstrom (1952) are probably the homologue of Lissauer's tract, and the descending spinal tract is mainly the homologue of the dorsal columns (Wall & Taub, 1962). The terminal arborizations of fibres ending in the nucleus gracilis (Wall, 1958) show a prolonged depolarization after the arrival of an afferent volley. Small cells of unknown function are found scattered in all parts of the central nervous system. Some, such as the Golgi Type II cells of the cerebral cortex, are known to have very short-running axons. However, the extension of our knowledge of these possible analogies must wait on the development of physiological and anatomical methods for marking cells of the substantia gelatinosa type. It would seem very unlikely that the first central synapse of the skin afferent pathway is the only synapse to be surrounded by a modulating group of small cells. The lamination of the dorsal cord neuropile makes the region a favourable one for investigation, but other regions will now be investigated for signs of similar mechanisms.

SUMMARY

1. This paper examines the origin of the long negative dorsal root potential which is a sign of prolonged depolarization of the terminal arborization of afferent fibres. Reasons have been given to show that the

potential cannot be produced by summation of either action potentials or synaptic potentials in the large dorsal horn cells on which the fibres end.

2. It is shown that the potential persists when all direct, active afferent fibres penetrating into the region have been eliminated. It is therefore concluded that the potential cannot be produced by direct interaction of active and passive terminal arborizations, but must be produced by some secondary system.

3. Evidence is presented that the secondary system which is responsible is the small cells of substantia gelatinosa and the Lissauer tract. No evidence could be found that the Lissauer tract consists of the fine fibres from peripheral nerves that have gathered together into a lateral division of the dorsal root.

4. The experiments which designated this system as the 'pain' system were repeated and shown to have alternative interpretations. By source–sink maps the origin of the disturbance producing the dorsal root potential in the de-afferented cord is shown to originate in the Lissauer tract and spread over the region of substantia gelatinosa.

5. Sections of the Lissauer tract abolished the potential in a de-afferented segment of the cord. The size of the dorsal root potential seems related to the size of the substantia gelatinosa in various segments rather than to the over-all size of the segment or the afferent roots.

6. It is therefore suggested that when an afferent volley arrives in the cord both the large secondary cells and the substantia gelatinosa cells are activated. The substantia gelatinosa then generates within itself prolonged activity which spreads to other parts of substantia gelatinosa, partly by the short axons between the small cells and partly by the longer axons that make up Lissauer's tract. The activity of these cells then reflects back on to the afferent fibres. In this way the small cells act as a modulating system surrounding the first synapse between the afferent fibres and the large dorsal horn neurones.

The author is greatly indebted to Dr J. Y. Lettvin, Dr W. S. McCulloch and W. H. Pitts for their interest and help. He would also like to thank Miss Diane Major for the histological preparations, Miss Elizabeth J. Campbell and Miss S. Rosenbaum for the computer programme, and the Computation Centre, M.I.T., for the use of its facilities and the I.B.M. 7090 computer. This work was supported by the U.S. Army Signal Corps, the Air Force Office of Scientific Research, and the Office of Naval Research; in part by the Teagle Foundation, Inc. and Bell Telephone Laboratories, Inc.; and in part by the National Institutes of Health Bethesda, Maryland (Grant B-1865-(C3)).

REFERENCES

ÅSTROM, K. E. (1954). The central course of afferent fibres in the trigeminal, facial and glossopharyngeal nerves and their nuclei in the mouse. *Acta physiol. scand.* Suppl. 106, 209–320.

BARRON, D. H. & MATTHEWS, B. H. C. (1938). The interprétation of potential changes in the spinal cord. *J. Physiol.* **85**, 73–103.

BONNET, J. & BREMER, F. (1952). Les potentials synaptiques et la transmission nerveuse centrale. *Arch. int. Physiol.* **60**, 33–93.

DOUGLAS, W. W. & RITCHIE, X. Z. (1962). Mammalian nonmyelinated nerve fibres. *Physiol. Rev.* **42**, 297–334.

ECCLES, J. C. (1961). The mechanism of synaptic transmission. *Ergebn. Physiol.* **51**, 299–430.

ECCLES, J. C. & MALCOLM, J. L. (1946). Dorsal root potentials of the spinal cord. *J. Neurophysiol.* **9**, 139–160.

HAGBARTH, K. E. & KERR, D. I. B. (1954). Central influences on spinal afferent conduction. *J. Neurophysiol.* **17**, 295–307.

HOWLAND, B., LETTVIN, J. Y., McCULLOCH, W. S., PITTS, W. H. & WALL, P. D. (1955). Reflex inhibition by dorsal root interaction. *J. Neurophysiol.* **18**, 1–17.

KEENAN, E. (1929). The phylogenetic development of substantia gelatinosa rolandi. *K. Akad. Welensch. Te. Amsterdam, Proc. Sect. Sci.* **32**, 466–475.

LLOYD, D. P. C. & McINTYRE, A. K. (1949). On the origin of dorsal root potentials. *J. Gen. Physiol.* **32**, 409–443.

RANSON, S. W. (1931). Cutaneous sensory fibres and sensory conduction. *Arch. Neurol., Chicago,* **26**, 1122–1145.

RANSON, S. W. & BILLINGSLEY, P. R. (1916). The conduction of painful afferent impulses in the spinal nerves. *Amer. J. Physiol.* **40**, 571–589.

RANSON, S. W. & CLARK, S. L. (1953). *The Anatomy of the Nervous System,* 9th ed. Philadelphia: W. B. Saunders.

RANSON, S. W. & VON HESS, C. L. (1915). The conduction within the spinal cord of afferent impulses producing pain and the vasomotor reflexes. *Amer. J. Physiol.* **38**, 129–152.

SZENTAGOTHAI, J. & KISS, T. (1949). Projection of dermatones on the substantia gelatinosa. *Arch. Neurol., Chicago,* **62**, 734–744.

WALL, P. D. (1958). Excitability changes in afferent fibre terminations and their relation to slow potentials. *J. Physiol.* **142**, 1–21.

WALL, P. D. (1959). Repetitive discharge of neurons. *J. Neurophysiol.* **22**, 305–320.

WALL, P. D. & JOHNSON, A. R. (1958). Changes associated with post-tetanic potentiation of a monosynaptic reflex. *J. Neurophysiol.* **21**, 148–158.

WALL, P. D., McCULLOCH, W. S., LETTVIN, J. Y. & PITTS, W. H. (1956). The terminal arborisation of the cats pyramidal tract determined by a new technique. *Yale J. Biol. Med.* **28**, 457–464.

WALL, P. D. & TAUB, A. (1962). Four aspects of trigeminal nucleus and a paradox. *J. Neurophysiol.* **25**, 110–126.

THE MONOSYNAPTIC REFLEX

In 1897 Sherrington introduced the term *synapse*—from the Greek word meaning "to clasp"—for the functional connection between two nerve cells. At this time the concept of the neuron doctrine was still questioned by some prominent neuroanatomists, although rapid advances in unraveling the anatomy of the nervous system were being made.

Camillo Golgi (36), an Italian physician, published in 1873 the first adequate pictures of the general morphology of the whole nerve cell. The method which now bears his name did not become generally known until 1887. Cajal became extremely interested in the use of silver in studying nervous structures, and began work with Golgi's method in that year (37). In 1889, Cajal applied Golgi's method to the spinal cords of bird and mammalian embryos (38). Prior to this work Cajal stated: "In truth, the histology of this nervous organ (the spinal cord) presented only one important datum which was solidly established: the true origin of the anterior (i.e., ventral) roots" (37). In favorable Golgi preparations, Cajal was able to see collaterals from the dorsal root fibers making contact with motor horn cells (39). Thus the concept of a monosynaptic reflex has existed on an anatomic basis from about 1890, but it was not proved a functional entity until Renshaw's study of 1940.

The concept of a synapse was amplified by Sherrington and various estimates of synaptic delay times were made prior to Renshaw's study. By stimuli delivered through an electrode in the ventral horn of the cord, Renshaw was able to activate (1) presynaptic fibers and then, by increasing the strength of stimuli, (2) postsynaptic cells (motoneurons). The time difference between the arrival of the two discharges at the ventral root was therefore taken to indicate transmission across a single synapse.

Three years after Renshaw's paper, Lloyd published a paper in which he measured the various delay times in the different limbs of the myotatic reflex and conclusively demonstrated that the stretch reflex is indeed a monosynaptic reflex.

REFERENCES

36. Golgi, C. *Gass. Med. Ital. Lombarda.* **33:** 244–246 (1873).

37. Cajal, Ramón y, S. *Recollections of my life.* Philadelphia, American Philosophical Society, 1937.

38. Cajal, Ramón y, S. *Studies on Vertebrate Neurogenesis.* Charles C. Thomas, Springfield, Illinois, 1960.

39. Cajal, Ramón y, S. *Histologie du Système Nerveux de l'Homme et des Vertébrés.* Maloine, Paris, 1909.

SUGGESTED TEXTS

Ruch *et al.* Chapter 6.

Ochs, S. Chapters 13, 14, and 16.

Mountcastle, V. Chapter 75.

ACTIVITY IN THE SIMPLEST SPINAL REFLEX PATHWAYS

BIRDSEY RENSHAW*†

Laboratories of The Rockefeller Institute for Medical Research, New York

(Received for publication May 21, 1940)

ALTHOUGH Cajal (1890, 1894) demonstrated that collaterals of the dorsal root fibers extend through the cord to the anterior horn, there to make synaptic connections with motoneurons, and although reflex arcs of two neurons, *i.e.*, of one synaptic relay, have played a prominent role in schemata of cord activity (*cf.* Cajal, 1909), there has been little physiological evidence of activity in such direct pathways.

Most of the determinations of the central reflex time for homolateral responses in the cord have given minimal values of approximately 3 to 5 msec. (Jolly, 1911; Forbes and Gregg, 1915; Eccles and Sherrington, 1931a). Eccles and Sherrington, however, found that these values, determined by recording the activity of a flexor muscle, may be greatly reduced when the cord is conditioned by a previous volley arriving over the dorsal roots; and Eccles and Pritchard (1937), by applying strong electrical stimuli to dorsal roots, obtained from the unconditioned cord ventral root discharges with reduced latencies of 0.7 to 1.0 msec. Since, according to Lorente de Nó (1935a, c, d; 1938a), the synaptic delay at the motoneurons of the third cranial nucleus varies within the narrow limits of 0.5–0.6 to 0.8–0.9 msec., and since comparable delays have been observed in other pathways (Kemp, Coppée and Robinson, 1937; Bishop and O'Leary, 1938), it is likely, as Eccles (1939) points out, that these minimal central reflex times for the cord pertain to two-neuron pathways.

In the present work determinations of the synaptic delays at neurons in the spinal cord, in conjunction with measurements of central reflex times, demonstrate the validity of this interpretation. Under certain experimental conditions activity in arcs of two neurons is a prominent feature of cord activity. The facilitation and inhibition of activity in these direct pathways have been examined.

METHODS

Cats, either decerebrated or under light Dial anesthesia (Ciba, 0.4–0.6 cc/kg.) were used. The spinal cord was often transected at the lowest thoracic or the highest lumbar level. One or both dorsal roots and the ventral root on one side of either the seventh lumbar or the first sacral segment were prepared. Pairs of stimulating electrodes were applied to the dorsal roots. The proximal electrode in each case was 12 to 15 mm. from the cord. A second method of stimulation was through bipolar needle electrodes inserted into the gray matter. The discharge in ventral roots was led from electrodes placed sufficiently far from the cord to prevent appreciable complication of the record by the "electrotonic" ventral root potentials of Barron and Matthews (1936, 1938). The potential changes de-

---

* Fellow in Biology, 1938–1939, National Research Council.

† A preliminary report of these experiments was made at the meeting of the American Physiological Society, New Orleans, La., March 15, 1940.

Renshaw, B. Activity in the simplest spinal reflex pathways. *J. Neurophysiol.* **3**: 374–387, 1940.

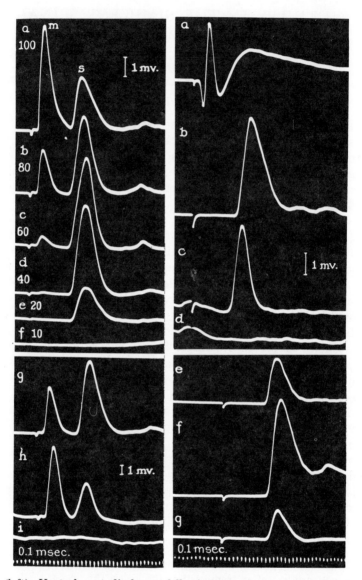

FIG. 1.(left). Ventral root discharge following stimulation by needle electrodes in the region of the intermediate gray matter. Decerebrated cat acutely spinal at the highest lumbar level. *a–f*, decreasing stimulus strengths, relative values indicated on the figure. *g–i*, the effect of conditioning the cord by a maximal dorsal root volley; *g*, needle stimulation; *h*, needle stimulation following a dorsal root volley by 3 msec.; *i*, end of response to dorsal root stimulation. Time, 0.1 msec.

FIG. 2 (right). *a*, cord potential, monopolar lead from the dorsum of the cord, stimulus a shock maximal for A fibers applied to the dorsal root. *b–g*, discharge in ventral root following stimulation of dorsal root. Same preparation as Fig. 1. *b*, discharge due to single maximal A volley. *c*, the same conditioned by a similar volley preceding by 3 msec. *d*, end of the response to the conditioning volley alone, showing baseline on which the response to the testing volley wrote. *e–f*, effect of DC polarization of the cord; current passed between the ventral root and muscles on the opposite side at the same level of the vertebral column. *e*, no current; *f*, 20 µA, root positive; *g*, 20 µA, root negative. Time, 0.1 msec.

274

veloped in the cord were recorded between an indifferently placed electrode and a small Ag-AgCl ball, 0.5 to 1.0 mm. in diameter, placed on the dorsum of the cord. For the determination of activity at points within the cord, the ball electrode was replaced by a micro-electrode which could be inserted into any desired position; use was made both of micropipettes and of fine steel needles insulated except near the tip. The customary stimulating apparatus and differential amplifier were used. The preparations were covered with paraffin oil to a depth of about one centimeter, in order to help maintain the cord and its roots at the proper temperature (*cf.* Table I) and otherwise in good condition for long periods of time.

RESULTS

1. *Synaptic delay at motoneurons.* The synaptic delay at the motoneurons in the cord has been determined by a method originally used for another system by Lorente de Nó (1935d, 1939). Small bipolar needle electrodes were inserted into the cord, in order both to stimulate some motoneurons directly and to activate fibers and collaterals making synaptic connections with additional motor cells. The discharge in an adjacent, homolateral ventral root following such stimulation produces the two prominent waves that have been labelled *m* and *s* in Fig. 1 and 3. The threshold of stimulation for the *m* wave is lower than that for the *s* wave when the stimulating electrodes are in ventral positions within the cord—at or below the ventral horn. It is lower for the *s* wave when the electrodes are located more dorsally. The *m* wave represents a practically synchronous volley of impulses in fibers of the ventral root, and its latency is approximately accounted for by conduction from the cord to the recording electrodes. It therefore arises from direct electrical stimulation of the motoneurons.

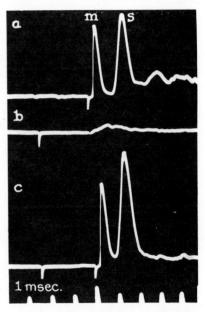

FIG. 3. Ventral root discharge following stimulation of the cord through needles in the central gray matter. Decerebrated cat, acutely spinal at the highest lumbar level. *a*, response to needle stimulation; *b*, to submaximal stimulation of the homolateral dorsal root; *c*, needle and root stimulation in combination. Time, 1 msec.

The *m* wave may be conditioned by the delivery of a previous shock to the dorsal root (Fig. 1*g–i*, 3). Since in the experiment from which the records of Fig. 1*g–i* are taken some motoneurons had responded to the conditioning shock, it might perhaps be thought that the increase in the *m* wave in record *h* is attributable to direct stimulation by the testing shock of additional motor fibers which were in a supernormal condition. This is scarcely possible, because the first motoneurons responded to the conditioning volley only 2.2 msec. (shock interval, 3.0 msec.) before the application of the test stimulus causing the *m* wave; and according to Gasser and Grundfest (1936) and Graham and

Lorente de Nó (1938) refractoriness gives way to supernormality in blood-perfused nerves only after 2 to 5 msec. Moreover, in the experiment of Fig. 3 facilitation of the m wave was observed without previous reflex discharge. Therefore, the facilitation of the m wave must be interpreted as due to a summation of the induction shock with subliminal synaptic stimuli (Lorente de Nó, 1935d; Lorente de Nó and Graham, 1938).

The s wave, which represents a somewhat asynchronous volley of impulses, follows the m at an interval of about 0.7 to 0.8 msec. As the stimulus is increased in strength from low values, both waves increase in size together until at high values the s wave decreases as the m wave continues to grow (Fig. 1f–a), obviously because motoneurons responding in the s group have

Table 1. *Central reflex times and synaptic delays at motoneurous, determined together in several preparations*

Experiment	Preparation	Rectal temperature	Cord temperature (Thermocouple)	Synaptic delay at motoneurons (msec.)		Central reflex time (msec.)	
				Unconditioned	Conditioned	Unconditioned	Conditioned
5/23/39	Decerebrated	38.0 – 38.4		0.7+	0.6	0.8–0.85	0.6–0.7
6/17/39	Decerebrated	36.8 – 37.8		0.9	0.65	0.9	0.7
6/27/39	Decerebrated	40.2 – 40.5	39.7 ± 0.2	0.8 –	0.6 –	0.65	0.5+
8/ 7/39	Decerebrated	40.0		0.9	0.7	0.85	0.7
10/10/39	Spinal	38.5		0.75	0.7	0.65	0.5

shifted to the m and become refractory. It is to be emphasized that the reduction of latency when motoneurons responding in s pass into m is not gradual but discontinuous. The interval between the two waves remains nearly constant over a considerable range of stimulus strengths and cannot be decreased by more than 0.1 to 0.3 msec., even when the cord has been conditioned by a maximal volley in the dorsal root (Fig. 1g–i). As a rule, the intervals between the feet of the m and s waves have ranged from 0.6 to about 1.0 msec. Since the conduction time for impulses exciting the motoneurons responding in the s wave must be small and since no procedures that have been tested reduce this interval significantly, it has been interpreted as representing the duration of one synaptic delay, i.e., that at the motoneurons. The values obtained in several experiments are presented in Table 1.

2. *Central reflex time for homolateral reflex.* A close parallel exists between the results reported in the preceding section and observations made on central reflex times (see Table 1). The discharge in a ventral root, due to a volley maximal for most of the A fibers other than the delta group in the cor-

responding homolateral dorsal root, is usually characterized by an early wave (Eccles and Pritchard, 1937), with an unreduced latency of 1.0 to 1.4 msec. (Fig. 2 and 4). The well-known discharges which last 8 to 10 msec. or more often follow. The first wave may be small compared with the later phases, but usually it is the conspicuous deflection of the reflex oscillogram. The size of the intramedullary spike of the cord potential may be used as a rough measure of the number of A fibers stimulated. Judging on this basis, the appearance of the early wave generally requires the stimulation of $\frac{1}{4}$ to $\frac{1}{2}$ of the A fibers of the dorsal root. With weaker stimuli, responses of longer latency appear, and by varying the strengths of the testing and conditioning shocks applied to the dorsal roots, a continuous series of reflex latencies, ranging upward from the minimum, may be obtained.

The central reflex time is the observed reflex latency, minus conduction time in the afferent and efferent nerves. Conduction time in the dorsal roots has been measured as the interval between the stimulus escape and, as a good approximation to the time of arrival of impulses at the cord, the time corresponding to half the descent into the first positive trough of the primary spike of the cord potential (Fig. 2a). The latency of the m wave in such records as a–c of Fig. 1 has been taken as the conduction time in the ventral root. Since this correction is small and little altered by a considerable increase in the strength of the stimulus (Fig. 1c–a), the use of the shock-response interval for the determination of conduction time is justified. Except for about 3 mm. of the relatively stout "collatérales réflexo-motrices" (Cajal, 1909),

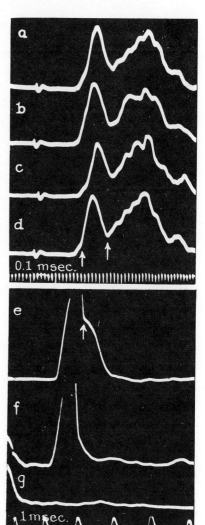

FIG. 4. Reflex discharges in ventral roots showing discontinuities in the populations of responding motoneurons. Discharges in ventral roots following the delivery of a single shock, maximal for A fibers, to the corresponding homolateral dorsal roots, a–d, decerebrated cat, acutely spinal at highest lumbar level. The corrections for conduction in the roots amounted to 0.4 msec. Discontinuities in the discharge occur at central reflex times of about 1.0 and 1.7 msec. Time, 0.1 msec. e–g, decerebrated cat. The corrections for conduction time in the roots amounted to 0.4 + msec. e, single testing volley; f, the same preceded by a similar volley; g, end of the response to the conditioning volley alone. Note the discontinuity in e at a central reflex time of about 1.7 msec. and its absence in f. Time, 1 msec.

which extend from the dorsum of the cord to the anterior horn, these corrections completely account for conduction time in the fast fibers of the direct reflex pathways.

In the experiment from which the records of Fig. 1 and 2 have been taken the corrections for root conduction are each about 0.2 msec. (Fig. 2a; 1a–c). The uncorrected latency of the first portion of the early wave of the discharge from the unconditioned cord is 1.05 msec. (Fig. 2b), giving a

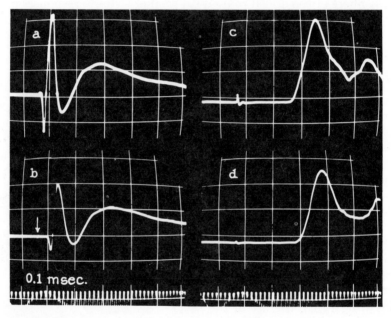

Fɪɢ. 5. a, b, cord potentials recorded from the dorsum of the cord; c, d, the corresponding reflex discharges in the ventral root. a and c, are responses to shocks applied to the dorsal root a few mm. from the cord; b and d are responses to stimuli applied 17 mm. more distally. All the shocks were 5 times the threshold for the intramedullary spike and the negative cord potential. Time, 0.1 msec.

central reflex time of 0.65 msec. As shown in Fig. 2c, this was reduced to about 0.5 msec. by a maximal conditioning volley preceding the testing in the same dorsal root by 3.8 msec. The data of several experiments are presented in Table 1.

The corrections for conduction time in the dorsal roots were based upon activity of the fastest fibers. The dorsal roots contain A fibers of a wide range of conduction velocities (Gasser and Grundfest, 1939), and the central reflex times as determined would be in error if activity in fibers conducting at significantly less than the maximum velocity were important for the reflex discharges. This possibility was tested in the following way (Fig. 5). Two pairs of stimulating electrodes were placed on a dorsal root, one pair near the cord and the other more distally. The distance between cathodes was 17 mm. The reflex discharges in the corresponding ventral root, and the potential changes at the dorsum of the cord, were recorded for graded series of stimuli applied through each pair of electrodes.

The shock-response intervals for various points on the first portion of the intramedullary spike which followed distal stimulation were greater than the corresponding intervals for proximal stimulation (Fig. 5a, b). The difference indicated a maximal conduction velocity in the dorsal root of about 80 m. per sec., which approximates the known value for the fastest sensory fibers. The latency of each point of the early part of the reflex discharge to stimulation via the distal electrodes was also greater than that to stimulation through the proximal electrodes (Fig. 5c, d), and by an interval equal to or only slightly longer than the conduction time between the cathodes for the fastest afferent fibers. If activity in fibers of significantly submaximal velocity were important for the earliest discharges, then parts or all of the first wave of the reflex to distal stimulation would have appeared only after a greater delay.

In view of these data it is conservative to state that the first portions of the reflex discharge are due to activity in A fibers conducting at velocities ranging between maximal and no less than two-thirds maximal. The corrections for conduction time in the dorsal roots, based upon activity in the fastest fibers, amounted to about 0.2 msec. For fibers conducting at two-thirds the maximal velocities the corrections are increased by only 0.1 msec. Accordingly, the corrections as used cannot be in serious error.

These observations incidentally provide conclusive evidence that the stimuli applied to the dorsal roots did not spread to cause direct excitation of central structures.

An attempt further to shorten the central reflex time by polarization of the cord with constant currents, has failed. Barron and Matthews (1936, 1938) and Matthews (1937) have shown that the passage of small currents from a motor root to an adjacent point on the spinal cord causes a rhythmic discharge in fibers of the ventral root at frequencies up to 70 per sec., depending upon the strength of the current. No discharge occurs when the current is passed in the opposite direction, *i.e.*, cathode on root. Figure 2e–g demonstrates that in fact very small direct currents, too weak to cause appreciable rhythmic discharge, nevertheless condition the cord. Figure 2e shows a central reflex discharge recorded with no current flowing, 2f the augmented response obtained when a current of 20 microamperes was passing from a point on the ventral root to an electrode placed on muscles of the contralateral side at the same level of the vertebral column, and 2g the reduced response seen during the passage of $20\mu A$ in the opposite direction. A current of $10\mu A$ was sufficient to produce smaller but definite effects of the same nature. Although in Fig. 2f the augmentation of the response is considerable, no appreciable decrease in latency occurred.

3. *Conditioning of first wave of homolateral reflex by single contralateral volley.* The data of the previous sections have been interpreted as demon-

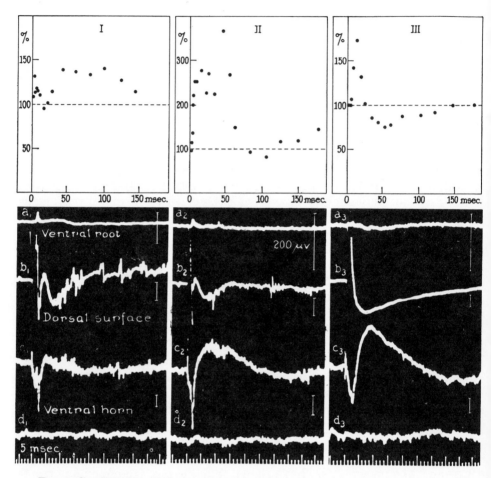

Fɪɢ. 6. Conditioning of the first wave of the dorsal-to-ventral root reflex by a single crossed volley. Data from three spinal cats, I and II decerebrated, III under light Dial narcosis. Abscissae of the graphs: intervals at which the homolateral stimulus followed the

contralateral. Ordinates $\dfrac{\text{height of conditioned first wave}}{\text{height of unconditioned first wave}}$ ×100. The oscillograms

show the responses to the crossed volley alone: a, reflex discharge in ventral root; b, potential changes recorded from the mid-dorsum of the cord; c, potential changes recorded by a micro-electrode in the ventral horn; d, as c but without the stimulus, to show the background of spontaneous activity. Voltage calibrations, 200 μV. Time, 5 and 20 msec.

strating that the early wave of the reflex discharge is a measure of activity in arcs of two neurons (see Discussion). Consequently there becomes available a convenient method for testing the average synaptic excitability of the motoneurons in the pool supplied by the stimulated dorsal root fibers; for these motoneurons may be directly stimulated at any chosen moment by a controlled afferent volley which produces a measurable submaximal discharge.

The conditioning of the first wave of the homolaterally evoked reflex by a single contralateral volley has been examined in a series of 23 spinal cats. Figure 6 presents data obtained from three of these. In addition to the conditioning curves, the figure includes oscillograms to show that a small reflex discharge is evoked by the contralateral volley. Also included, as indices of the internuncial activity induced by the contralateral volley, are records of the cord potentials produced by it on the mid-dorsum of the cord and in the ventral horn.

The conspicuous effect of a single crossed volley on the reflex activity of a flexor muscle is typically inhibition (Samojloff and Kisseleff, 1927; Eccles and Sherrington, 1931b; Hughes, McCouch and Stewart, 1937). Under the conditions of the present experiments, however, the early reflex discharges in the ventral roots of the majority of active, decerebrated preparations are facilitated by the contralateral volley. The facilitation may amount to several hundred per cent and last for 150–200 msec., as in curves I and II of Fig. 6. Other preparations, including nearly all animals under light Dial narcosis, yield conditioning curves in which facilitation gives way after 10–25 msec. to a more prolonged period of inhibition (curve III). The maximal inhibition occurs 30–50 msec. after the contralateral stimulus; at this time the height of the first wave of the conditioned testing volley is reduced to 50–80 per cent of its unconditioned size.

Discussion

The similarity of the values for the shortest central reflex time and the interval between the m and s waves (Table 1) demonstrates that the earliest reflex discharges represent activity in the direct pathways which have only a single synaptic relay; and the fact that it has not been possible to reduce either the central reflex time or the m–s interval below about 0.5 msec., suggests that this is a minimal value for the synaptic delay at the motoneurons.

The question that next arises, is, how *long* may be the synaptic delay? The central reflex times obtained for conditioned and unconditioned reflex responses to dorsal root volleys of varying size represent a series, continuous to the precision of the measurements, extending from 0.5 msec. to 2 msec. or more; and in many experiments in which the first motoneurons respond at the shortest central reflex times there is clear evidence that others become active at progressively longer intervals. The long latencies do not necessarily signify prolonged synaptic delays, however, and considerable evidence favors the alternative view that they represent activity in arcs containing interneurons (Lorente de Nó, 1938b). It is known that interneurons are present. They may be interpolated between the dorsal root fibers and the motoneurons to form reflex arcs of two, three and more synaptic relays; and they are activated by afferent impulses (Gasser and Graham, 1933; Hughes and Gasser, 1934a). A synaptic delay is properly measured from the time of arrival of the latest impulse which is effective in firing the post-synaptic neuron. Hence, because of the probability that motoneurons are effectively stimulated by the delayed internuncial impulses, it is difficult to determine the maximal central reflex times associated with activity in the direct pathways. It may only be stated that the range of latencies must extend from 0.5 msec. upward to at least the minimal central reflex time for activity in three-neuron arcs. This shortest central reflex time for pathways of three neurons can be no less than the sum of the minimal delay at a motoneuron and the minimal delay at an interneuron. The duration of the delay at interneurons thus becomes a matter of interest.

The available evidence suggests that 0.5 msec. is an approximate minimal value for the delay at interneurons, as well as at motoneurons. Inspection of Fig. 2a, which represents the potential changes produced at the dorsum of the cord by an afferent volley, shows that the curve crosses the baseline to rise into the negative cord potential (Gasser and Graham, 1933) only 0.6 msec. after the impulses in the dorsal root fibers have reached the cord. This suggests that 0.6 msec. is an upper limit for the synaptic delay at the earliest responding interneurons. Stewart, Hughes and McCouch (1940) report slightly longer latencies in the monkey. Similar short delays have been found in other parts of the nervous system. Lorente de Nó (1939) reports that in the internuncial nuclei associated with the oculomotor nucleus the synaptic delays correspond to those at the motoneurons; that is, they may be as short as 0.5 to 0.6 msec. The results of Bishop and O'Leary (1938) indicate a delay of 0.5 msec. for visual impulses relayed at the lateral geniculate body; and Kemp, Coppée and Robinson (1937) have calculated the slightly longer minimal value of 0.8 msec. for impulses relayed in the auditory pathways at the cochlear nucleus and the olivary complex.

The sum of the shortest synaptic delays that have been determined for interneurons and motoneurons, each 0.5 msec., is 1.0 msec. Accordingly, unless internuncial delays of unsuspected brevity occur in the cord, 1.0 msec. must be the minimal central reflex time for activity in three-neuron arcs. Therefore, all central reflex times of from 0.5 msec. to 1.0 msec. must pertain to arcs of two neurons. With one reservation, the synaptic delays at the motoneurons must extend over this range of values. The reservation arises from the fact that the time for conduction in the 2–3 mm. of collateral within the cord was not considered; and, of course, the corrections for conduction time in the dorsal roots were based upon activity in fibers conducting at maximal velocities. The early part of the reflex is mediated only by fibers conducting at velocities near the maximal; the stoutness of the collaterals of these large sensory fibers (cf. Cajal, 1909) justifies the assumption that they do not conduct at low velocities. Consequently these factors can contribute at most an additional 0.1 msec. to conduction time, and 0.9 msec. becomes a conservative *minimal* value for the longest synaptic delay at motoneurons of the cord. At present it is not possible to state whether still longer delays occur.

Little is known of the range of variation of the delays at interneurons, but if it be assumed that the interpolation of an interneuron into a reflex arc increases the central reflex time by an amount likewise varying between 0.5 and about 1.0 msec., then the central reflex times for three-neuron pathways can vary between 1.0 and 2.0 msec., for four-neuron pathways between 1.5 and 3.0 msec., and so forth. Motoneuron discharges, such as may be observed at all reflex times longer than the minimum, can therefore be accounted for. At the same time it becomes apparent that, except for the earliest discharges, the number of synaptic relays involved in the production of any reflex activity cannot be strictly calculated from the central delay. It is impossible, for example, to state whether motoneurons firing after a central time of 2.4 msec. represent activity in pathways of three synaptic relays with an average delay of 0.8 msec., or in arcs of an additional relay where the average delay amounts to only 0.6 msec., or in both.

Although some motoneurons may be fired at each moment during the period of reflex activity, the discharges do not give smooth curves. As reference to any actual record brings out, the synaptic delays gather about modes, and the motoneurons, especially in the early part of a discharge, tend to be fired in groups. Hence for the first portions of a discharge it is possible to make a fairly exact estimate of the number of synaptic relays involved.

The reflex discharges in the records of Fig. 4 exhibit typical grouping of the responding motoneurons and show the discontinuities which consequently appear at characteristic central reflex times. The discharges following four identical afferent volleys in a single experiment are shown in Fig. 4a–d. It is obvious that the grouping of responding units is relatively constant. At a central reflex time of 1.0 msec., as marked by the first arrow, the number of active units increases. Again at 1.7 msec., as indicated by the second arrow, the discharge is suddenly augmented. The second wave follows the first at an interval of 0.7–0.9 msec., the duration of an average synaptic delay. Figure 4e depicts the reflex discharge from another experiment. Activity begins after a central reflex time of 0.9 msec. and, as marked by the arrow, is also characterized by a discontinuity at about 1.7 msec. The activity following the discontinuity is largely abolished in the conditioned response shown in Fig. 4f, whereas the discharges at shorter reflex times behave as a homogeneous group and are somewhat increased.

In some experiments (Fig. 2b) the first wave of the reflex discharge is due almost entirely to activity of motoneurons which respond at central reflex times of 1.0 msec. and less. In the experiments of Fig. 4, however, the first wave represents the activity of motoneurons which fire at intervals ranging from 0.8 and 0.9 msec. to more than 1.0 msec., in fact to about 1.2 msec. The portion of the first wave which corresponds to central reflex times of 1.0 msec. and less must of course represent activity in arcs of two neurons. It cannot at present be stated with finality that the motoneurons which discharge in the later portion of the first wave have not been activated via an interpolated interneuron, rather than directly by the primary afferent fibers. At any rate, on conditioning the first wave behaves more or less as a unit in facilitation and inhibition. Hence, if an interneuron is interposed, it must be one which follows the activity in the afferent fibers very nearly in a 1:1 ratio under various conditions. This hypothetical behavior is in contrast with that of the spinal interneurons which have been studied, for it is well known that these respond subnormally after a conditioning volley (Hughes and Gasser, 1934b).

The possibility of exciting motoneurons directly by a controlled afferent volley, the size of which does not vary with the level of excitation in labile internuncial systems, provides an excellent method for testing the average synaptic excitability of the motoneurons in the pool supplied by the stimulated dorsal root fibers. Illustrative experiments, in which the synaptic excitability of the motoneurons was tested at various intervals after the delivery of a contralateral volley to the cord, reveal the action of mechanisms for facilitation and inhibition which have been described by Gasser (1937a, b), Hughes and Gasser (1934b), and by Lorente de Nó (1935c, 1936, 1938b, 1939).

Although the contralateral volley fires few motoneurons, it facilitates others, and the direct response to a homolateral volley is increased for a period of time, as in all three curves of Fig. 6. In most decerebrated preparations the facilitation is long continued, as in curves I and II, with at most only transitory intervention of slight inhibition. In other experiments, particularly when a light dose of Dial is given, the facilitation passes over into inhibition after 10–25 msec., as in curve III.

The potential changes produced in the ventral horn by the crossed volley reveal a mechanism for the facilitation. Although the significance of the envelope to the sequence of potential changes is not yet clear, the width and roughness of the baseline may be used as indices of the level of background activity. Comparison of records a with c and d (Fig. 6) reveals that even in the ventral root lead, where recording is more favorable than in the volume of the cord, the active motoneurons produce relatively small deflections compared to the changes observed in the ventral horn. Consequently most of the background activity of the ventral horn must be interneuronal. At least some of the internuncial impulses must ordinarily impinge upon the motoneurons. The periods during which the testing two-neuron discharge is facilitated are characterized by an increase of the background of internuncial activity above its resting level (records c, also b). Facilitation, therefore, is accomplished by convergence of internuncial impulses with the primary testing impulses.

During inhibition (curve III) the deficit in the response of the two-neuron arcs must be due, at least in part, to subnormality in the few motoneurons which were fired by the contralateral volley. Antidromic stimulation has revealed that, following activity, motoneurons exhibit a prolonged period of lowered synaptic excitability (Eccles, 1931; Lorente de Nó, 1935b, 1939; Gasser, 1939).

Subsequent experiments have shown that, although in spinal animals most of the unconditioned discharge of short central latency goes to flexor muscles, some impulses are in fibers to extensors. Also, in acutely spinal animals the contralaterally evoked impulses do not necessarily represent a discharge only of motoneurons associated with extensor muscles (McCouch, Snape and Stewart, 1935, McCouch, 1936).

For the sake of completeness it may be mentioned that the conditioning volleys must have evoked crossed dorsal root reflexes. The centrifugal impulses of these discharges may have interfered with and blocked centripetal impulses of the testing volleys. Any such modification of large testing volleys must be slight, for crossed dorsal root reflexes are small and dispersed discharges (Toennies, 1938).

The cord potentials produced by the contralateral volley in the ventral horn point to the existence of a second factor for inhibition. Subnormality in interneurons may be expected to follow the increased activity which characterizes the antecedent period of facilitation; and, in fact, during the period in which the testing two-neuron discharge shows a pronounced deficit (curve III), the background of internuncial activity is decreased below the resting level (record c_3). Withdrawal of the facilitating effect of these impulses may raise the threshold of the motoneurons and aid in the production of the observed deficit.

SUMMARY

A shock which excites $\frac{1}{4}$ to $\frac{1}{2}$ of the fibers of maximal and nearly maximal conduction velocity in the seventh lumbar or the first sacral dorsal root of the decerebrated cat typically produces in the corresponding homolateral ventral root a reflex discharge with a central delay varying between 0.65 and about 1.0 msec. Conditioning the cord by means of a previous dorsal root volley may decrease the central reflex time slightly, but no procedures have reduced it below about 0.5 msec. Ventral root discharges resulting from direct electrical stimulation of the central gray matter demonstrate that the synaptic delays at the motoneurons vary over a similar range of values. Consequently central reflex times of 0.5 to about 1.0 msec. represent activity in reflex arcs of two neurons (one synaptic relay). It is not possible to state whether or not longer synaptic delays sometimes occur, for central reflex times as short as about 1.0 msec. may conceivably pertain to activity in arcs of three neurons.

Motoneurons may respond at any or all central reflex times for several milliseconds after the first discharge to a dorsal root volley—a result to be expected even if the synaptic delays at interneurons as well as at motoneurons range between limits no wider than 0.5 to 1.0 msec. Nevertheless, the synapse times show modes, and large groups of motoneurons are typically discharged at particular central reflex times.

Direct excitation of motoneurons by the primary sensory fibers offers a method of testing the synaptic excitability of the motoneurons. The motoneurons are facilitated for some time after the arrival at the cord of a volley over a contralateral dorsal root. During the period of facilitation, as can be determined from cord leads, the motoneurons are receiving a barrage of impulses from interneurons. Facilitation, therefore, is accomplished by convergence of internuncial impulses with the impulses of the testing volley. A period of inhibition sometimes follows the facilitation. The inhibition must be attributable, at least in part, to subnormality in the few motoneurons which were fired by the crossed volley. An additional factor for inhibition may be subnormality in the neurons of internuncial systems which tonically barrage the motoneurons; for following the increased activity of the period of facilitation, the number of internuncial impulses impinging upon the motoneurons is reduced below the resting level.

It is a pleasure to express my appreciation to Dr. Herbert S. Gasser and to Dr. Rafael Lorente de Nó for their advice and helpful criticism during the course of this work.

REFERENCES

BARRON, D. H., and MATTHEWS, B. H. C.   Electrotonic conduction of the potentials of grey matter. *J. Physiol.*, 1936, *86*: 29p–31p.

BARRON, D. H., and MATTHEWS, B. H. C.   The interpretation of potential changes in the spinal cord. *J. Physiol.*, 1938, *92*: 276–321.

BISHOP, G. H., and O'LEARY, J.   Potential records from the optic cortex of the cat. *J. Neurophysiol.*, 1938, *1*: 391–404.

CAJAL, S. R.   Sur l'origine et les ramifications des fibres nerveuses de la moelle embryonaires. *Anat. Anz.*, 1890, *5*: 85–95.

CAJAL, S. R.   *Les nouvelles idées sur la structure du système nerveux chez l'homme et chez les vertébrés.* Paris, C. Reinwald et Cie., 1894, 200 pp.

CAJAL, S. R.   *Histologie du système nerveux de l'homme et des vertébrés.* Paris, Maloine, 1909.

ECCLES, J. C.   Studies on the flexor reflex. III. The central effects produced by an antidromic volley. *Proc. roy. Soc.*, 1931, *B107*: 557–585.

ECCLES, J. C.   The spinal cord and reflex action. *Ann. Rev. Physiol.*, 1939, *1*: 363–384.

ECCLES, J. C., and PRITCHARD, J. J.   The action potential of motoneurons. *J. Physiol.*, 1937, *89*: 43p–45p.

ECCLES, J. C., and SHERRINGTON, C. S.   Studies on the flexor reflex. I. Latent period. *Proc. roy. Soc.*, 1931a, *B107*: 511–534.

ECCLES, J. C., and SHERRINGTON, C. S.   Studies on the flexor reflex. VI. Inhibition. *Proc. roy. Soc.*, 1931b, *B109*: 91–113.

FORBES, A., and GREGG, A.   Electrical studies in mammalian reflexes. I. The flexion reflex. *Amer. J. Physiol.*, 1915, *37*: 118–176.

GASSER, H. S.   On control of excitation in the nervous system. *Harvey Lect.*, 1936–37, 169–193.

GASSER, H. S.   Sequence of potential changes, Chapt. IV; and, The excitability cycle, Chapt. V in: ERLANGER, and GASSER, *Electrical signs of nervous activity.* 1937b, Univ. Penn. Press, Phila., 221 pp.

GASSER, H. S.   Axons as samples of nervous tissue. *J. Neurophysiol.*, 1939, *2*: 361–369.

GASSER, H. S., and GRAHAM, H. T.   Potentials produced in the spinal cord by stimulation of dorsal roots. *Amer. J. Physiol.*, 1933, *103*: 303–320.

GASSER, H. S., and GRUNDFEST, H.   Action and excitability in mammalian A fibers. *Amer. J. Physiol.*, 1936, *117*: 113–133.

GASSER, H. S., and GRUNDFEST, H.   Axon diameters in relation to the spike dimensions and the conduction velocity in mammalian A fibers. *Amer. J. Physiol.*, 1939, *127*: 393–414.

GRAHAM, H. T., and LORENTE DE NÓ, R.   Recovery of blood-perfused mammalian nerves. *Amer. J. Physiol.*, 1938, *123*: 326–340.

HUGHES, J., and GASSER, H. S.   Some properties of the cord potentials evoked by a single afferent volley. *Amer. J. Physiol.*, 1934a, *108*: 295–306.

HUGHES, J., and GASSER, H. S.   The response of the spinal cord to two afferent volleys. *Amer. J. Physiol.*, 1934b, *108*: 307–321.

HUGHES, J., McCOUCH, G. P., and STEWART, W. B.   Cord potentials in the spinal cat. *Amer. J. Physiol.*, 1937, *118*: 411–421.

JOLLY, W. A.   On the time relations of the knee-jerk and simple reflexes. *Quart. J. exp. Physiol.*, 1911, *4*: 67–87.

KEMP, E. H., COPPÉE, G. E., and ROBINSON, E. H.   Electric responses of the brain stem to unilateral auditory stimulation. *Amer. J. Physiol.*, 1937, *120*: 304–315.

LORENTE DE NÓ, R.   The synaptic delay of the motoneurons. *Amer. J. Physiol.*, 1935a, *111*: 272–282.

LORENTE DE NÓ, R.   The effect of an antidromic impulse on the response of the motoneurone. *Amer. J. Physiol.*, 1935b, *112*: 595–609.

LORENTE DE NÓ, R.   Facilitation of motoneurones. *Amer. J. Physiol.*, 1935c, *113*: 505–523.

LORENTE DE NÓ, R.   The electrical excitability of the motoneurones. *J. cell. comp. Physiol.* 1935d, *7*: 47–71.

LORENTE DE NÓ, R.   Inhibition of motoneurones. pp. 231–247. in: *The problems of nervous physiology and of behavior. Symposium dedicated to Prof. J. S. Beritoff*, Tiflis, Georgian Branch, Acad. Sci., U.S.S.R., 1936.

LORENTE DE NÓ, R.   Limits of variation of the synaptic delay of motoneurons. *J. Neurophysiol.*, 1938a, *1*: 187–194.

LORENTE DE NÓ, R.   Analysis of the activity of the chains of internuncial neurons. *J. Neurophysiol.*, 1938b, *1*: 207–244.

LORENTE DE NÓ, R.   Transmission of impulses through cranial motor nuclei. *J. Neurophysiol.*, 1939, *2*: 402–464.

LORENTE DE NÓ, R., and GRAHAM, H. T.   Recovery cycle of motoneurons. *Amer. J. Physiol.*, 1938, *123*: 388–399.

MATTHEWS, B. H. C.   Do the rhythmic discharges of nerve organs and of motor neurones originate in the same way? *Proc. roy. Soc.*, 1937, *B123*: 416–418.

McCOUGH, G. P.   Note upon crossed reflexes in the acutely spinal cat. *Amer. J. Physiol.*, 1936, *115*: 78–81.

McCOUCH, G. P., SNAPE, W. J., and STEWART, W. B.   Note on reflex thresholds in the cat during spinal shock. *Amer. J. Physiol.*, 1935, *111*: 263–271.

SAMOJLOFF, A., and KISSELEFF, M.   Zur Charakteristik der zentralen Hemmungsprozesse. *Pflüg. Arch. ges. Physiol.*, 1927, *215*: 699–715.

STEWART, W. B., HUGHES, J., and McCOUCH, G. P.   Cord potentials in spinal shock. Single volleys. *J. Neurophysiol.*, 1940, *3*: 139–145.

TOENNIES, J. F.   Reflex discharge from the spinal cord over the dorsal roots. *J. Neurophysiol.*, 1938, *1*: 378–390.

CONDUCTION AND SYNAPTIC TRANSMISSION OF THE REFLEX RESPONSE TO STRETCH IN SPINAL CATS

DAVID P. C. LLOYD

Laboratories of The Rockefeller Institute for Medical Research,
New York, N. Y.

(Received for publication May 25, 1943)

IN THE PRECEDING PAPER (14) it was found that the reflex discharge provoked by stimulation of the large $(20-12\mu)$, low-threshold muscle afferent fibers, and transmitted through arcs of two neurons (12) possesses the characteristic and restricted distribution of the myotatic reflex (9). The identity of distribution was so rigidly maintained that it seemed justifiable to attribute to the two-neuron-arc pathways the mediation of myotatic reflexes. The concept, of course, is not new (8), but the older evidence in support of the concept lost weight with the advent of more precise measurements of the delay involved in synaptic transmission. Furthermore, one is constantly aware of the danger inherent in drawing conclusions as to natural reflex performance from experiments utilizing electrical stimulation of bare nerve trunks. Therefore, the conclusion derived from such experiments could be sustained and accepted only if the myotatic reflex evoked by the appropriate natural stimulus, *viz.*, stretch, were found, on reinvestigation, to have the same characteristics of conduction and synaptic transmission as the two-neuron-arc reflex discharge obtained by stimulation of muscle nerves. The present experiments were designed to examine the temporal course of the reflex response to phasic stretch. Some of the observations were mentioned briefly in a preliminary note (13).

The experiments were performed on cats made spinal by transection accomplished through the atlanto-occipital membrane. Following transection artificial respiration was instituted and the ether anaesthetic discontinued. The pelvis was fixed by heavy pins, the femur and tibia by drills. These were held by heavy standards which were firmly attached to the operating platform, of two-inch oak, supported by three-inch I-beams on a sand-filled oak table. Satisfactory fixation of the muscle origins was thus obtained. The stretching mechanism was similarly mounted on another sand-filled table. The use of two such tables separated by an air gap prevented the direct transmission of mechanical jar to the preparation. A hooked steel wire impaling the tendon of the gastrocnemius muscle served to connect it to the stretch mechanism, which consisted of a plunger operated by two solenoids arranged in opposition to each other. The solenoids were activated by condenser discharges timed by the usual stimulating circuit. One solenoid was arranged to pull, through the steel wire, on the freed tendon of the muscle. The other served to check the first so that the extent and duration of the stretch could be limited. In order to overcome inertia, the solenoid plunger was allowed to gain its momentum before acting upon the wire affixed to the tendon. A break contact on this wire fed an impulse to the amplifier to signal the onset

Lloyd, D. P. C. Conduction and synaptic transmission of reflex response to stretch in spinal cats. *J. Neurophysiol.* **6**: 317–326, 1943.

of stretch-movement. The time relations of the movement were recorded by the use of a photoelectric cell. Although the mechanism is not as flexible as one might desire, it behaved in a constant manner for any given setting of the controls, and served the immediate purpose of producing a brief stretch synchronized with the sweep of the cathode ray oscillograph.

The gastrocnemius muscle was employed for all the present observations. The tendon together with its insertion into the tuberosity of the calcaneus was fully isolated and freed from the insertion of the soleus muscle. Extensive denervation of the limb was regularly practised. Since the ventral roots were cut for the purpose of recording the reflex responses, the muscle itself was unable to participate in the reflex response. This arrangement is particularly useful, for the jerk reflex proper is divorced from all secondary phenomena such as the response to active tension, the myotatic appendage and incipient clonus.

Figure 1 illustrates stretch-evoked afferent discharges recorded from the nerve to the medial head of the gastrocnemius muscle. Records A, C, E show, by photoelectric recording, the extent and duration of the stretch-movement imparted to the gastrocnemius tendon to provoke the afferent discharges recorded in B, D, F respectively. The afferent discharge 1B is caused by a stretch of 1 mm. effected in 4.0 msec. It will be seen that the recognizable

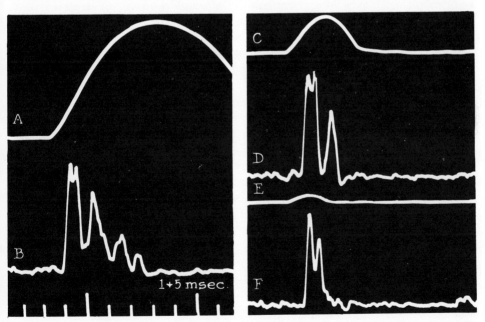

Fig. 1. Afferent responses to brief stretch of M. gastrocnemius recorded from the nerve to the medial head of that muscle. In A, C, E are recorded the extent and duration of the stretches employed to obtain the responses B, D, F respectively. The extent of stretch indicated in A is 1 mm.; in C, 0.3 mm.; in E, 0.05 mm. Most of the observations illustrated in this paper were obtained by the use of 0.2–0.3 mm. stretches. Time in 1 and 5 msec. intervals.

discharge occurs during the period of stretch-movement, and takes the form of a succession of imperfectly synchronized volleys. When the stretch is reduced to approximately 0.3 mm. effected in 1.7 msec., the afferent discharge, 1D, is correspondingly reduced in duration. The last two discharge peaks present in 1B are no longer realized, and the second peak is reduced in amplitude. The initial discharge peak, however, is intact. Further reduction of the stretch to approximately 0.05 mm. causes a further reduction in the afferent response, 1F, only the initial discharge remaining; this is decreased and further 'splintered.' The degree of stretch employed for response 1F is still well above threshold. It will be remembered that Denny-Brown and Liddell (3) obtained a jerk reflex in the decerebrate supraspinatus muscle with a stretch of approximately 8μ.

In the records illustrated in Fig. 1 there is a degree of diphasicity which results in emphasis of the relatively synchronous discharges of stretch-movement over the asynchronous activity apparently maintained throughout the period of muscle elongation. The latter discharges are seen to better advantage in Fig. 5B and 6B.

The latency of the afferent discharge as recorded in Fig. 1 approximates 0.7 msec., of which a considerable fraction is consumed in simple conduction. A number of attempts to obtain a valid estimate of 'end-organ delay' have been made. In a typical experiment the afferent response to stretch is first recorded. Then, with stimulating electrodes buried in the heart of the muscle belly, the preterminal nerve bundles are stimulated, the conducted action being recorded as before. The latency of the naturally evoked volley is longer than that of the electrically stimulated volley by as little as 0.2–0.3 msec. The electrically stimulated volley is conducted, of course, in both afferent and motor fibers, but this fact has no practical bearing on the outcome of the experiment for as will be seen in connection with Fig. 2 and 3, the afferent impulses provoked by sudden stretch travel in the forefront of the action potential of the mixed nerve. Values obtained by this method must be maximal rather than minimal values, for error due to possible spread of the stimulus or improper placement of the stimulating electrodes would decrease the apparent conduction time for the electrically stimulated volley, and by subtraction this would increase the apparent latency of the stretch response.

Some fraction of the 'excess latency' of the stretch-evoked response is needed for transmission of the tension wave from the free end of the tendon to the site of the first-responding receptors, wherever that may be. Another small fraction of time must be allocated for conduction from the point at which the end-organ excites the afferent fiber to the point at which the electrical stimulus excites the fiber. What little time is left probably may be accounted for in terms of a 'temps utile.' Altogether the evidence appears to militate against the view that a specific end-organ delay is involved in the stimulation by stretch of the particular end-organs mediating the initial afferent response. In essence, this is the conclusion reached by Forbes, Campbell and Williams (4), although Jolly's earlier measurements indicated the existence of a true end-organ delay (7).

Figure 2 presents an experiment designed to measure the conduction velocity of the afferent fibers mediating the response to stretch. The afferent discharge was first recorded from the first sacral (S1) dorsal root, severed from its connection with the spinal cord, and subsequently from the tibial nerve in the popliteal space. The conduction distance between the proximal (to the muscle) recording leads of the two pairs was 12 cm. The difference in latency of conduction is 1.025 msec., which yields a conduction rate of 117 M per sec.

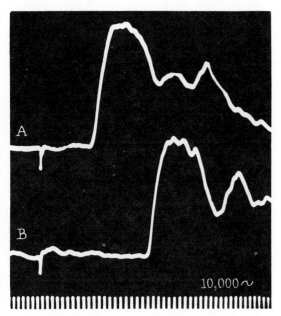

FIG. 2. Conduction of stretch-evoked afferent response. A—afferent response recorded from tibial nerve, B—from S1 dorsal root. Conduction distance—12 cm. Differential latency—1.025 msec. Conduction rate—117 M per sec. Time—10,000 cycles.

In the graph of Fig. 3 are plotted the results of five experiments such as that illustrated in Fig. 2. Each point on the graph represents an experiment, and relates the latency difference between the discharge recorded at two points along the afferent pathway to the conduction length of the pathway between the two recording stations. The observations at short conduction distances were made with both recording stations on the tibial nerve, or on one or both of the nerves to the gastrocnemius muscle. Those observations at long conduction distances were made with one of the electrode pairs on the dorsal root. In two experiments the conduction velocity of a volley evoked by electrical stimulation of the intramuscular branches of the nerve to the medial head of the gastrocnemius muscle was determined in addition. All of the observations from the various preparations fall about a straight-line plot having a slope of 116 M per sec. It follows that fibers mediating the afferent response to stretch fall among those of highest velocity in the muscle nerve. Within the limits of measurement the secondary peaks of the afferent discharge evoked by stretch represent activity in fibers of similar properties (cf. Fig. 2). Thus, one criterion for the identification of the myotatic reflex pathway with the two-neuron-arc pathway is satisfied.

Comparison of the afferent discharges encountered in the present experiments with those recorded by Matthews using single fiber preparations (15) suggests that the relatively synchronized volleys of stretch-movement have their origin in the A type receptors, by virtue of low threshold, rapid response and sudden cessation. This would indicate that the muscle spindles are the sensient organs originating these discharges.

The succession of afferent discharge peaks may represent the successive recruitment of end-organs to the active 'pool,' or the repetitive discharge of end-organs recruited at the onset of stretch movement. In the latter case the rate of firing would approach 1000/sec., if the discharge peaks represent the rate, and not a multiple of the rate, of the individual end-organ discharges. This figure seems high, but the nerve fibers are capable of responding at such rates, for a short time at least (6). Employing the single fiber technique, the highest discharge rate observed by Matthews (15) was 500/sec. during a stretch of 5 mm. at the rate of 25 cm./sec. The highest rate of stretch attained in the present experiments was approximately 35 cm./sec. over a shorter distance, so it is possible that a higher rate of firing was induced. Since the stretch-movement usually lasted 2–3 msec. some repetitive discharge certainly would have occurred, but successive recruitment is not thereby eliminated.

In order to examine the central latency of the reflex response to stretch

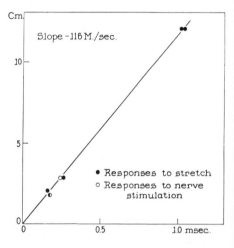

FIG. 3. Graph to show average conduction rate of afferent response to stretch in five experiments. Each point represents the difference in latency of the afferent response recorded at two points along the afferent pathway (as in Fig. 2) plotted against the conduction distance between the two points. For two of the experiments the conduction rate for an electrically stimulated volley is plotted. Average maximum conduction rate—116 M per sec.

the following procedure was adopted. The reflex was first recorded from the S1 ventral root. This appears in the inset of Fig. 4 and again in 4C. Only the initial volley is to be seen in Fig. 4C. The S1 dorsal root was then stimulated at a shock strength which yields a two-neuron-arc reflex discharge of approximately the same size as the initial stretch-evoked reflex volley. A record of the segmental two-neuron-arc reflex volley is found in 4B. The dorsal root was then severed at its junction with the spinal cord and equipped with recording leads. The proximal (to the muscle) recording lead was placed as close as possible to the point occupied by the cathode of the stimulating pair employed to obtain record 4B. With this disposition of leads the afferent response to the stretch was recorded; this is found in 4A. Now, if the initial volley of the stretch-evoked reflex is indeed transmitted through arcs of two neurons as predicted (14), the sum of the latencies in 4A and 4B should approximate the latency in 4C ,which it does to within 0.1–0.2 msec. The slight additional latency of the naturally evoked reflex is referable to the greater dispersion of the afferent volley caused by long afferent conduction and natural stimulation. The initial reflex discharge in response to stretch, then, is transmitted through arcs of two neurons.

The initial volley of the stretch-evoked reflex is followed at an interval of approximately 0.8 msec. by a second reflex volley, which is much larger than the first. The second volley like the first is transmitted through arcs of two neurons. Figure 5A, B, C illustrate in order the time relations of stretch, the afferent response recorded from the gastrocnemius nerves, and the reflex response recorded from the S1 ventral root in another preparation. The latency of the initial reflex volley is approximately 3.9 msec., that of the second reflex volley 0.8 msec. longer. Since there are two clearly defined successive afferent discharges impinging upon the spinal cord (5B), one would expect to realize two reflex volleys. Furthermore, the interval between the two reflex volleys is equal to or very slightly less than the interval between the two afferent volleys (compare 5B and 5C). This being so the central delay of the second reflex volley is of the same order of magnitude as that of the first reflex volley.

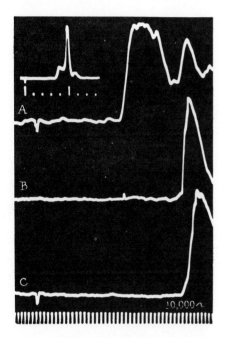

FIG. 4. Reflex latency of the response to brief stretch. A—afferent response recorded from the S1 dorsal root. B—segmental two-neuron-arc reflex (stimulus S1 dorsal root, recording S1 ventral root). C—reflex evoked by stretch. The sum of the latencies in A and B approximates that of C, showing that the initial reflex response to stretch is conducted through arcs of two neurons. Inset—the complete reflex response in this experiment consists of three successive volleys. Time for A, B, C—cycles. Time for inset in 1 and 5 msec. intervals.

The latency differential between the two successive reflex volleys is not sufficiently long to admit the possibility that the second reflex volley is evoked through three-neuron-arc pathways by the action of the afferent impulses set up at the very beginning of stretch. The three-neuron-arc reflex discharge results from the stimulation not of group I fibers, but of group II fibers (13). When the two groups of fibers are stimulated in the thigh, the group II volley reaches the spinal cord 0.4 msec. after the group I volley, the conduction distance being 12 cm. (14, Fig. 5). The pathway from the mid-belly of the gastrocnemius muscle to the spinal cord is 18–20 cm. in length. Assuming that group II fibers were to participate in the first afferent response to stretch, the resulting group II volley would reach the cord dorsum at least 0.6 msec. after the group I volley. To this must be addded another 0.6 msec. for the additional synaptic relay of a three-neuron-arc, to give a minimum of 1.2 msec. by which the second reflex volley should trail the initial reflex volley. This minimum value is considerably longer than the observed interval of 0.8 msec.

The discharges mediated through arcs of three neurons are directed into flexor channels (14). It is known from the experiments of Denny-Brown (2) that activity may appear in the tibialis anterior muscle as the result of sud-den stretch of the gastrocnemius muscle, but it does so during the heart of the silent period of the extensor muscles. According to Denny-Brown the latency for activity in the tibialis anterior muscle averaged 22.7 msec. compared with 8.6 msec. for the la-tency of the tendon-jerk reflex in the gastrocnemius muscle itself. The sec-ond reflex discharge in the present ex-periments, and the third when it is present (inset of Fig. 4), is obviously part of the tendon-jerk reflex proper, rather than a contribution to flexor ac-tivity associated with the silent period of the extensor muscles. In addition to these considerations there is the fact that the gastrocnemius nerves con-tain relatively few group II fibers. Group II reflexes of any order are not regularly produced by stimulation of the gastrocnemius nerves (14). For these various reasons it is concluded that the second reflex volley in response to brief stretch, like the initial volley, is con-ducted through arcs of two neurons.

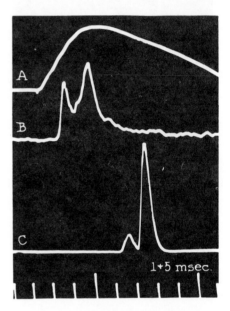

Fig. 5. Tendon-jerk reflex of M. gas-trocnemius. A—stretch imposed upon the gastrocnemius muscle. B—afferent re-sponse recorded from the gastrocnemius nerves in the thigh. C—reflex response re-corded from S1ventral root. Time in 1 and 5 msec. intervals.

When the stretch produced by the pulling solenoid used in these experi-ments is unchecked by the opposing solenoid, it may happen that a third reflex volley, of small size, is discharged (cf. inset of Fig. 4). This reflex volley occurs later rather than earlier than the hypothetical three-neuron-arc time discussed above, but the other arguments advanced in favor of the view that the second reflex discharge pertains to arcs of two neurons hold also for the third reflex volley when this is in evidence.

The initial afferent volley of the stretch response may prove subliminal for the motoneurons, in which case the reflex volley provoked by the second afferent volley may constitute the whole reflex response. Figure 6 presents an experiment in which this occurred. Records A, B, C show in order the stretch imposed upon the gastrocnemius muscle, the afferent response recorded from the S1 dorsal root, and the reflex response recorded from the S1 ventral root. Although the afferent response is dispersed over a period equal to that of the stretch, and contains two prominent discharge peaks, the reflex consists of a single volley, no more dispersed than is the response obtained by single shock stimulation of the gastrocnemius nerves (12, 14). The latency for this reflex is approximately 4.9 msec., which is almost identical to the latencies of the second reflex discharges in Fig. 4 and 5. The time relationship between the second afferent discharge peak (6B) and the reflex (6C), moreover, accords with the conclusion that the second afferent volley is the immediate provocative agent for the reflex recorded.

COMMENT

For the duration of stretch impulses are continually bombarding the motor nucleus at an intensity greater than that maintained during the 'resting posture' of the muscle. Signalling the onset of stretch-movement, and for the duration of stretch-movement, regularly spaced synchronized afferent volleys appear, as though superimposed on a continuum of activity. The first of these afferent volleys may (Fig. 4, 5) or may not (Fig. 6) provoke a discharge of motoneurons. By the time the second afferent volley reaches the motor nucleus conditions have changed. Depending upon the initial reflex discharge a few motoneurons may be refractory, but the greater part of the motor nucleus is more excitable than formerly by virtue of the continued impact of afferent activity. Motoneurons are more readily available to the second afferent volley and a large reflex volley results. The central latency of this volley may be even a little shorter than that of the initial reflex volley (temporal facilitation). Subsequent afferent impulses usually fail to reach motoneuron threshold, due possibly to the number of motoneurons already fired by the immediately preceding volleys. The end result is a reflex discharge of shorter total duration than that of the afferent influx. One must bear in mind the possibility that some of the afferent impulses may mediate direct inhibition (10) rather than excitation to the motor nucleus thus shutting off rather than aiding the reflex, or they may serve to feed ascending paths without concern for the local reflex mechanism. Undoubtedly the reflex picture would be different if the stretched muscle were allowed to participate in the reflex action, as was necessarily the case in earlier work on the tendon jerk which depended largely upon either the action potential of the muscle or upon mechanical registration for a means of recording.

The present experiments associate the large (group I) afferent fibers and two-neuron-arc connections with the mediation of the myotatic reflex. It is not known whether or not the smaller afferent fibers in the gastrocnemius nerves partake in the afferent response to stretch of the degree imposed in the present experiments. With greater extension of the muscle other than the large afferent fibers might be recruited into the response, possibly bringing into play the lengthening reaction. Of course afferent responses which depend upon active tension would not appear at all in these experiments. Since stimulation of some, at any rate, of the smaller fibers of the gastrocnemius nerve yields reflex discharges directed into flexor nerves (14, Fig. 7), it is a fair assumption that those fibers subserve nociception rather than proprioception. Certainly no responses resembling the group III reflex obtained by strong stimulation of the gastrocnemius nerves (14, **Fig.** 7) have been realized on the occasion of brief stretch in the present experiments.

The latency of the stretch-evoked reflex at the ventral root in the experiments of this series has varied between 3.6 and 3.9 msec. In order to estimate the minimum total reflex latency for the tendon-jerk of the gastrocnemius muscle it is necessary to add to the latency at the ventral root sufficient time for conduction to the muscle and for neuromuscular delay. The additional motor conduction time is approximately 1.8 msec.: neuromuscular delay is approximately 0.55 msec. (11). The minimum total latency from the onset of stretch to the onset of the muscle action potential *at the end plate zone* would approximate 5.95 msec. This is somewhat shorter than the value 8.6 msec. obtained by Denny-Brown (2). Since this value is based on the known transmission time through the minimum reflex arc, it is not expected that the minimum reflex time for the tendon-jerk can be further reduced, except inasmuch as some muscles are closer, anatomically speaking, to the spinal cord, and would involve less time in simple conduction. Other latency values for the most part have been obtained from the knee-jerk preparation rather than the ankle-jerk preparation (8, 5, 1, 2). The conduc-

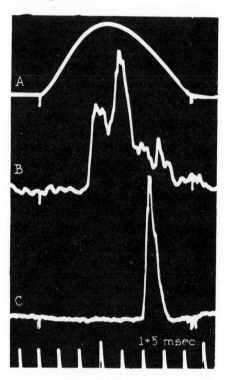

Fig. 6. Tendon-jerk reflex as in Fig. 5, but in another preparation. A—stretch imposed upon the gastrocnemius muscle. B—afferent response recorded from the S1 dorsal root. C—reflex response recorded from the S1 ventral root. The single reflex volley corresponds to the second reflex volley in the experiment of Fig. 5. The initial afferent volley is subliminal for the motoneurons. Time in 1 and 5 msec. intervals.

tion pathway for the knee-jerk is shorter and that reflex should appear with shorter latency. The shortest latency encountered by Jolly was 5.3 msec. (8).

Summary

The afferent response to brief stretch of the gastrocnemius muscle is mediated by large (group I) fibers at an average maximum velocity of 116 M per sec.

There is little if any true delay at the sensient organs responding to stretch.

The reflex response to brief stretch of the gastrocnemius muscle is transmitted through arcs of two neurons.

It was previously shown (14) that the distribution of two-neuron-arc discharges accords with that of the myotatic reflex. For these several reasons it appears that the two-neuron-arc pathways are reserved for the mediation of myotatic reflexes.

The calculated overall minimum latency for the tendon jerk reflex of the gastrocnemius muscle is approximately 5.95 msec.

REFERENCES

1. BALLIF, L., FULTON, J. F., and LIDDELL E. G. T Observations on spinal and decerebrate knee-jerks with special reference to their inhibition by single break-shocks. *Proc. roy. Soc.*, 1925, *B98:* 589–607.
2. DENNY-BROWN, D. On inhibition as a reflex accompaniment of the tendon-jerk and of other forms of active muscular response. *Proc. roy. Soc.*, 1928, *B103:* 321–336.
3. DENNY-BROWN, D. E., and LIDDELL, E. G. T. Observations on the motor twitch and of reflex inhibition of the tendon-jerk of M. supraspinatus. *J. Physiol.*, 1927, *63:* 70–80.
4. FORBES, A., CAMPBELL, C. J., and WILLIAMS, H. B. Electrical records of afferent nerve impulses from muscular receptors. *Amer.J. Physiol.*, 1924, *69:* 283–303.
5. FULTON, J. F., and LIDDELL, E. G. T. Electrical responses of extensor muscles during postural (myotatic) contraction. *Proc. roy. Soc.*, 1925, *B98:* 577–589.
6. GASSER, H. S., and GRUNDFEST, H. Action and excitability in mammalian A fibers. *Amer. J. Physiol.*, 1936, *117:* 113–133.
7. JOLLY, W. A. On the latency of sensory nerve endings to mechanical stimulation. *J. Physiol.*, 1910, *41:* xiv–xv.
8. JOLLY, W. A. On the time relations of the knee-jerk and simple reflexes. *Quart. J. exp. Physiol.*, 1911, *4:* 68–87.
9. LIDDELL, E. G. T., and SHERRINGTON, C. S. Reflexes in response to stretch (myotatic reflexes). *Proc. roy. Soc.*, 1925, *B96:* 212–242.
10. LLOYD, D. P. C. A direct inhibitory action of dromically conducted impulses. *J. Neurophysiol.*, 1941, *4:* 184–190.
11. LLOYD, D. P. C. Centripetal discharges in dorsal and ventral roots following stimulation of muscle by ventral root volleys. *Proc. Soc. exp. Biol., N. Y.*, 1941, *47:* 44–47.
12. LLOYD, D. P. C. Reflex action in relation to the pattern and peripheral source of afferent stimulation. *J. Neurophysiol.*, 1943, *6:* 111–119.
13. LLOYD, D. P. C. The afferent fibers mediating myotatic reflexes and their central connections. *Fed. Proc. Amer. Soc. exp. Biol.*, 1943, *2:* 29–30.
14. LLOYD, D. P. C. Neuron patterns controlling the transmission of ipsilateral hind limb reflexes in the cat. *J. Neurophysiol.*, 1943, *6:* 293–315.
15. MATTHEWS, B. H. C. Nerve endings in mammalian muscle. *J. Physiol.*, 1933, *78:* 1–53.

INFLUENCE OF AFFERENT INPUTS
ON THE MONOSYNAPTIC REFLEX

Few neurophysiologists would dispute Lloyd's contention (40) that "perhaps the thorniest of all problems connected with the study of nervous organization is that of clarifying the mechanisms of inhibition." The myotatic reflex was one of the first neural patterns for which the mechanism of inhibition was elucidated. In 1941 both Lloyd (41) and Renshaw (42) reported that convergence of dorsal root volleys resulted in direct inhibition of the stretch reflex. Lloyd found that when afferent volleys were simultaneously initiated in the sixth lumbar and first sacral dorsal roots, the monosynaptic discharge produced by the sacral root volley alone was diminished. Subsequently Bradley *et al.* (43) demonstrated that this inhibitory path was not monosynaptic but rather disynaptic, having an interposed inhibitory interneuron.

Work reported in the first Lloyd paper (1943) presented in this section (1) determined that the fibers responsible for the stretch reflex conducted at Group I fiber rates and (2) measured the times involved in the various components of the myotatic reflex. The importance of the paper derives from the fact that the work verified that the monosynaptic reflex elicited by dorsal root stimulation and muscle stretch are indeed the same process, clearly showing that the myotatic reflex and the monosynaptic reflex are identical.

In work reported in the second paper, Lloyd utilized stimulation of peripheral nerves rather than dorsal roots for conditioning and test volleys. This allowed restricting the excitation to the Group I fibers, which he had previously shown to be involved in the myotatic reflex. This also made initiation of conditioning and test volleys easier. With these methods, Lloyd clarified the basis of a concept first clearly stated by Sherrington: reciprocal innervation. Furthermore, he was able to define the time course of the facilitatory and inhibitory inputs.

The final Lloyd paper elucidates the specificity of the activity of the afferent fibers arising from synergistic and antagonistic muscle groups and demonstrates the essential components of the myotatic unit and its role in reciprocal innervation.

REFERENCES

40. Lloyd, D. P. C. Functional organization of the spinal cord. *Physiol. Rev.* 24: 1–17 (1944).

41. Lloyd, D. P. C. A direct inhibitory action of dromically conducted impulses. *J. Neurophysiol.* **4:** 184–190 (1941).

42. Renshaw, B. Influence of discharge of motoneurons upon excitation of neighboring moto-neurons. *J. Neurophysiol.* **4:** 167–183 (1941).

43. Bradley, K., D. M. Easton, and J. C. Eccles. An investigation of primary or direct inhibition. *J. Physiol.* **122:** 474–488 (1953).

BIBLIOGRAPHY

Granit, R. *Muscular Afferents, and Motor Control.* John Wiley & Sons, New York, 1966.

SUGGESTED TEXTS

Ruch *et al.* Chapter 7.

Ochs, S. Chapter 15.

Mountcastle, V. Chapters 74 and 75.

NEURON PATTERNS CONTROLLING TRANSMISSION OF IPSILATERAL HIND LIMB REFLEXES IN CAT

DAVID P. C. LLOYD

Laboratories of The Rockefeller Institute for Medical Research,
New York

(Received for publication May 25, 1943)

THE SEGMENTAL REFLEX discharge (7, 31, 21) must be considered of anatomical rather than functional significance in that it contains, in unnatural combination, those elements which constitute the several distinct ipsilateral reflexes. In the present paper are the results of experiments designed to resolve the segmental reflex into its functional components. The observation that a major division of the segmental reflex into its direct (two-neuron-arc) and indirect (multineuron-arc) components followed segregation of muscle afferent and cutaneous afferent fibers for afferent stimulation (21) provides the point of departure for the experiments to be described. Some of the present observations have been mentioned briefly in a preliminary note (23).

A general discussion of these and other results will be found in another paper (25).

The afferent fibers of the A group (14) exhibit a range of diameters extending from 20μ to 1.5μ (36). In a dorsal root the whole range of fibers is present, but in the peripheral nerves significant segregations are found (36, 8, 29, 14) which permit a degree of selective stimulation of the various components (21). For the purposes of the present discussion the afferent fibers will be classified into groups, each group being marked by a peak in the fiber distribution plots of one or another of the several peripheral nerves. Group I consists of the largest afferent fibers, which are to be found only among the afferent fibers arising from muscle. Approximately these fibers range from 20μ to 12μ in diameter (8, 29), with a distribution peak at 15 to 16μ. Group II contains fibers of approximately 12μ to 6μ in diameter, with a mode at 8 to 9μ. These fibers form a prominent peak in the fiber distribution plots of cutaneous nerves (8, 30, 14), but they are poorly represented among the muscles afferent fibers (8, 29). Group III consists of fibers gathered about a peak at 3 to 4μ (the delta pile). These last are to be found in both muscle and cutaneous nerves. Another category, to consist of the C fibers, the afferent and reflex function of which is proven (3, 2), should be included as group IV. These fibers have not been studied during the course of the present experiments.

Since group I and group II fibers are the lowest threshold fibers in muscle and cutaneous nerves respectively, they may be excited in isolation by the simple expedient of selecting the appropriate nerves for stimulation (21). There is no means at present of stimulating group III fibers in isolation but their contribution to reflex action, on stimulation, is easily recognizable as addition to the reflex discharges caused by stimulation of the larger, lower threshold fibers [after-discharge?.] (45)

Lloyd, D. P. C. Neuron patterns controlling transmission of ipsilateral hindlimb reflexes in cat. *J. Neurophysiol.* **6**: 293–315, 1943.

The experiments were performed on cats, made spinal by transection accomplished through the dorsal atlanto-occipital membrane under ether anaesthesia, after which artificial respiration was instituted and the anaesthetic discontinued.

Group I reflexes. The reflex discharge resulting from stimulation of group I afferent fibers has been studied chiefly, but not exclusively, in connection with the nerve supply to the gastrocnemius muscle. Several considerations prompted this choice, not the least among which is the fact that the afferent fibers from this muscle have been examined by histological means (8, 29). Moreover, the gastrocnemius muscle is supplied through the seventh lumbar (L7) and first sacral (S1) segments of the spinal cord, which provides a favorable site for study by virtue of the length of the nerve roots pertaining to those segments.

Figure 1A illustrates the reflex discharge, recorded from the S1 ventral root following stimulation of the nerves of the gastrocnemius muscle. The

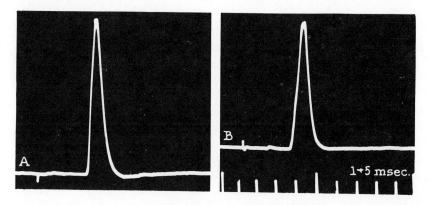

Fig. 1. Group I reflex. A—reflex discharge recorded from the S1 ventral root on stimulation of the gastrocnemius nerves. B—reflex discharge recorded from the gastrocnemius nerves on stimulating the S1 dorsal root. Time in 1 and 5 msec. intervals. In all figures where there are two time designations these are for the small and large divisions respectively.

ventral roots supplying the muscle were severed distally in order to record the reflex and to prevent the penetration of the inevitable antidromic volley into the spinal cord. Under these circumstances the gastrocnemius nerves are connected with the spinal cord only through the dorsal roots, and may be regarded therefore as 'afferent' nerves. Figure 1B presents the reflex discharge obtained by stimulating the S1 dorsal root while recording from the gastrocnemius nerves. The dorsal root was severed distally to prevent the dorsal root volley from coursing antidromically into the gastrocnemius nerves. Under these circumstances the gastrocnemius nerves may be regarded as 'purely efferent' in function. The reflex discharge from the dorsal root to the gastrocnemius motor fibers is essentially similar in latency and duration to that from the gastrocnemius afferent fibers to the ventral root. The conduction length of the reflex pathways is similar for the experiments illustrated in Fig. 1A and B, and so therefore are the central delays. The reflex discharges in Fig. 1 have a latency of approximately 2.6 msec., which is appropriate for reflexes transmitted through arcs of two neurons, considering the overall length of the pathways involved. Figure 2 presents an estimate in greater detail of the central delay of a reflex discharge comparable to that illustrated in Fig. 1A.

The gastrocnemius nerve to S1 ventral root reflex latency for the experiment illustrated in Fig. 2 is 2.5 msec. In the inset (B) of Fig. 2 the conduction time for the long afferent limb of the reflex is recorded by the use of leads, one placed on the dorsum of the spinal cord at the root entry zone of the (intact) S1 dorsal root, the other on nearby cut bone. By measurement, afferent conduction to the spinal cord requires 1.4 msec. By subtraction, 1.1 msec. is required for conduction in the intraspinal course of the dorsal root fibers, for synaptic delay, and for ventral root conduction. Of these events ventral root conduction accounts for approximately 0.3 msec. The remainder, 0.8 msec., may be designated as central delay, *i.e.* synaptic delay and central conduction. A central delay of this order of magnitude forces the opinion that arcs of two neurons are involved (27, 31). The total duration of the reflex spike-potential is 1.45 msec.; the total conduction distance approximately 19 cm.; the band of fibers active extends approximately from 20μ to 12μ. If the duration of the single axon spike is taken as 0.5 msec. (14), the total reflex

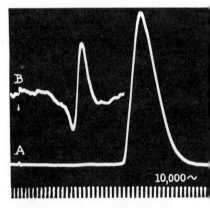

FIG. 2. Group I reflex. A—reflex discharge recorded on S1 ventral root on stimulation of the gastrocnemius nerves. B—afferent volley evoked by stimulation of the gastrocnemius nerves and recorded from the dorsum of the spinal cord at the root entry line. The difference in latency of A and B measures the sum of central latency and ventral root conduction time for the reflex discharge. Time 10,000 cycles.

has a dispersion of approximately 0.95 msec. Now, at 19 cm. conduction, a volley, initially synchronous, would have, on travelling in a group of fibers varying from 20μ to 12μ in diameter, a dispersion of 1.05 msec. calculated by using the conversion constant of 6 proposed by Hursh (17) to derive conduction velocity from diameter. Granting that some or all of these figures may be approximations, the dispersion encountered in experiment with the *reflex* discharge is within the limit calculated for simple transmission along an equivalent nerve bundle. There is, in consequence, reason to suppose that the reflex two-neuron-arc pathways alone can account for the group I reflex discharges that have been described.

The two-neuron-arc discharge reflects into the stimulated muscle nerve. When stimulating and recording leads are placed on the same nerve, with all central connections to the spinal cord intact, a two-neuron-arc discharge may be recorded, as illustrated in Fig. 3A. The stimulated volley courses centrally in both afferent and motor fibers, and since these fibers are in general similar in the case of the group I reflexes, the reflex afferent volley and the antidromic volley will reach the spinal cord essentially in simultaneous combination. Only a small fraction of the reflex volley under these circumstances (22), however, intermediate strengths of stimulation can be found which provide a sufficiently large afferent volley to produce a reflex without blocking too many of the reflex pathways by virtue of the antidromic volley The use of a large nerve trunk facilitates the adjustment of the stimulus to attain this end.

At this point a note relative to the dorsal root reflex is in order. In many of

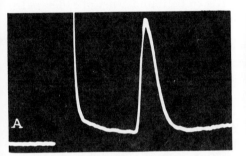
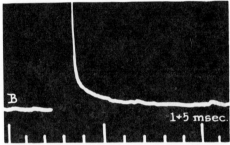

FIG. 3. Group I reflex. A—reflex volley stimulated and recorded on the tibial nerve. B—the same stimulation after transecting the L7 and S1 dorsal roots of the same side to confirm the reflex nature of the discharge. The 'tail' of the directly conducted volley is seen in both A and B. The time relations of the reflex volley show that it is transmitted through arcs of two neurons. Cf. also Fig. 9, 10 for other examples of two-neuron-arc reflex transmission into the stimulated nerve.

the present experiments afferent fiber pathways between the stimulating and recording leads exist to provide potential paths for the transmission of dorsal root reflexes to the recording leads. This is the case particularly when recording from the stimulated peripheral mixed nerve (44). As the central latency of the dorsal root reflex is 4 msec. (44), it does not interfere with the recording of group I reflexes, but it may appear in the nerve later to mimic other true reflex discharges. In practice, the temperature of the preparation is maintained as near normal as possible to minimize the dorsal root reflex.

In Fig. 3A is shown the reflex discharge through two-neuron-arc pathways as recorded on the tibial nerve on stimulation of that nerve. The reflex discharge follows by approximately 4.0 msec. the volley conducted directly from stimulating to recording electrodes. The added latency for this reflex over that found when the reflex is recorded on a ventral root (Fig. 1, 2) is approximately 1.5 msec., which is just sufficient to account for the added efferent conduction distance from the ventral root to the recording leads on the tibial nerve (cf. also Fig. 9A, G for a similar reflex discharge recorded from another preparation). Figure 3B shows that the two-neuron-arc discharge is removed by section of the appropriate dorsal roots. After section of the dorsal roots there may be a slight residual discharge, which is due in part to a recurrent or 'pseudo-reflex' volley from the central regions of the motoneurons as a result of the uncurtailed antidromic volley (32, 22), and in part probably to discharges arising in the manner of the Hering phenomenon at the cut ends of the dorsal roots (15, 34, 20), possibly by the action of negative after-potential. Whatever the residual discharges may represent, Fig. 3B provides the essential control to show that the centrifugal volley in Fig. 3A is a true reflex volley rather than a recurrent volley of similar time relationships (32, 22).

The two-neuron-arc reflex discharge does not reflect into muscle nerves other than the one stimulated. In Table 1 is to be found a list of reflex pathways from one nerve to another which have been searched for two-neuron-arc

Table 1. *Reflex pathways without two-neuron-arc reflex discharges*

Stimulated nerve	Recorded nerve	Remarks
Gastroc. lat.	Gastroc. med.	Fig. 4B and C
Gastroc. med.	Gastroc. lat.	Fig. 4E and F
Gastroc. (med. and lat.)	Tibial (less gastroc.)	Fig. 4H and I
		Fig. 8B and C
Tibial (less gastroc.)	Gastroc (med. and lat.)	Fig. 4K and L
Peroneal	Gastroc.	No reflex or very small delayed discharge, possibly a dorsal root reflex
Gastroc.	Peroneal	Fig. 7F, G, H, I. Group III reflex, sometimes group II reflex.
Sciatic (less gastroc.)	Gastroc.	No reflex discharge
Hamstring	Gastroc.	No reflex discharge
Tibial	Peroneal	Fig. 4M, 9. Group II and group III reflexes.
Peroneal	Tibial	Very small late discharge, possibly dorsal root reflex or residual ipsilateral extensor discharge.
Superficial peroneal	Deep peroneal	Late discharges.
Tibial	Tibialis anterior	Fig. 10. Late discharges.
Tibial	Deep peroneal	Fig. 11. Late discharges.
Peroneal (less tibialis anterior)	Tibialis anterior	Late discharges. Group II reflexes.

reflex discharges to no avail, together with references to the several figures containing illustrative records.

Figure 4 illustrates the absence of reflex discharges from one to another of the divisions of the tibial nerve, even at strengths of stimulation calculated to recruit all the A fibers of the stimulated nerve into the 'afferent' volley. Record M of Fig. 4, for which the tibial nerve was stimulated while recording from the peroneal nerve, serves as a control for the viability and patency of the central portions of the reflex system in the experiment illustrated. It will be noted that the discharge recorded in 4M has a latency of 5.8 msec., whereas the two-neuron-arc discharge should appear, as in Fig. 3, with a latency approximating 4.0 msec.

Particularly interesting among the observations of Fig. 4 is the fact that no reflex is obtained as between the nerves to the two heads of the gastrocnemius muscle. At this juncture one should recall the experiment originally performed by Sherrington (41, 42), and confirmed by Liddell and Sherrington (18) and again by O'Leary, Heinbecker and Bishop (29). In each case the effect of stimulating the central end of the severed nerve to one head or

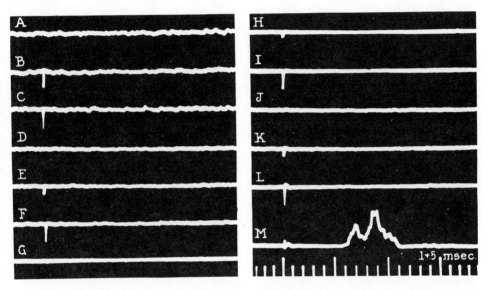

Fig. 4. The two-neuron-arc discharge is not transmitted to muscle nerves other than the one stimulated (cf. also Table I and Fig. 7, 8, 9, 10). Group II and group III reflexes are not recorded ordinarily from extensor nerves (cf. also Fig. 8). A, D, G, J—blank sweeps with recording leads on the gastroc. med., gastroc. lat., tibial, and gastroc. nerves respectively. B, C—weak and strong stimulation of gastroc. lat. N. recording gastroc. med. N. E. F.—Similar to B, C but stimulating and recording leads interchanged. H, I—stimulation of N. gastroc. recording on N. tibial (less its gastroc. branches). K, L—similar to H, I, but stimulating and recording leads interchanged. M—stimulation of tibial N. recording from peroneal N.—group II reflex.

fraction of a muscle (gastrocnemius or quadriceps) was inhibition of the innervated remainder of that muscle, gauged on a background of decerebrate rigidity or crossed extensor reflex. At the time these experiments were performed it was not realized that the antidromic volleys unavoidably transmitted centrally to the central portions of the motoneurons could effect the transmission of reflex effect through neighboring motoneurons not involved in the antidromic volley (32). The effect, usually inhibitory, is particularly potent as between motoneurons supplying parts of the same muscle. There can be little doubt that this action of antidromic volleys accounts, in good measure, for the observations of Sherrington, Liddell and Sherrington, and O'Leary, Heinbecker, and Bishop. Of course, the possibility of direct inhibition in the orthodromic sense (19, 21) cannot be neglected but the crucial experiment has not yet been devised to demonstrate direct orthodromic inhibition in this situation.

In spite of the known antagonism between the reflex arcs to the several heads of a muscle, and the fact that this antagonism is exerted when the interacting volleys arrive at the motoneurons in concert, the action cannot contribute significantly to the absence of two-neuron-arc discharges from one head to another within a muscle (Fig. 4B, C, E, F) or from one nerve to another (Fig. 4H, I, K, L, 7, 8, 9, 10, 11) for the depressent action of anti-dromic volleys is not great for the two-neuron-arc reflex at the time relation-ships which obtain in the present experiments, *i.e.* (virtually simultaneous combination of the afferent and antidromic volleys at the spinal cord).

From the experiments described it is possible to conclude that the afferent limb for the mediation of two-neuron-arc reflex discharge consists of the large, low threshold group I afferent fibers arising in muscle (*cf.* also 21), and that the two-neuron-arc discharge reflects only into the muscle group of muscles or head of a muscle, the afferent fibers of which are stim-ulated. Of course it is reasonable that, on the occasion of further sub-division of a muscle nerve twig, a stage might be reached, perhaps fortuitously, in which two-neuron-arc discharges could be obtained by stimulation of one subdivision while recording from another. The endeavor to achieve this state of subdivision has not been pursued.

One cannot escape the identity of distribution that obtains between the two-neuron-arc reflex discharge and the myotatic reflex (18). In effect the two-neuron-arc connections appear to constitute the pathway for mediation of the myotatic reflex. The relatively synchronous discharge evoked in this pathway by single shock stimulation would then imitate the phasic response to stretch (*i.e.*, the tendon-jerk) in its most brief, and possibly unattainable (*cf.* 12, 24) form. Further direct evidence for this position is to be found in another paper (24).

A comparison of group I and group II reflex effect. While the local reflex effect attending stimulation of group I fibers is confined to two-neuron-arc pathways, the reflex discharge following stimulation of a cutaneous nerve or of the medium threshold fibers (cutaneous for the most part) of a mixed nerve, has all the attributes of the multineuron-arc discharge as encountered in the segmental reflex (21). Furthermore, the distribution of the reflex evoked by stimulation of the cutaneous afferent fibers is quite different from that of the group I reflex.

In Fig. 5 are compared the effects of stimulating group I and group II fibers, as recorded from the dorsum of the spinal cord after the manner of Gasser and Graham (13) and of Hughes and Gasser (16). Figure 5A char-acterizes the events on stimulation of the nerve to the medial head of the gastrocnemius muscle, the appropriate ventral roots being severed. Re-corded with the same electrode positions, Fig. 5B illustrates the events on stimulation of the sural (external saphenous) nerve. Fig. 5C shows the recorded result of combined stimulation of the two nerves. The conduction distance from the stimulating electrodes to the spinal cord was so arranged as to be equal in the two nerves. Study of Fig. 5 reveals that the group I afferent volley is recorded from the dorsum of the spinal cord as a triphasic variation (*cf.* 13) practically devoid of an associated and ensuant negative intermediary potential, whereas, in contrast, the smaller group II spike potential is followed immediately by a prominent negative intermediary potential, signalling internuncial activity. In 5C, on the occasion of simultaneous stimulation of the two nerves, all the elements occurring severally in records A and B are present in approximate summation, which indicates a rather high degree of independence between the two reflexes under the conditions of the experiment (*i.e.*, with synchronous stimulation) and among the elements that contribute to the cord potential as recorded from the cord dorsum (but *cf.* Fig. 12 for interaction at another interval of shocks. Comparison of Fig. 5, 6 and 12 illustrates the fact that the reflex effect of the cutaneous nerve stimulation, the flexor reflex, is prepotent).

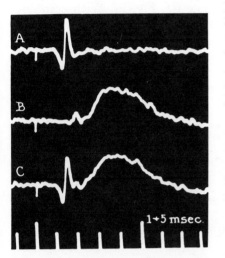

FIG. 5. Records from the dorsum of the spinal cord. A—the nerve to the medial head of the gastrocnemius muscle is stimulated. B—stimulation of the sural nerve. C—combined stimulation of the gastroc. med. N. and the sural N. Note longer conduction time for sural nerve volley than for gastroc. med. nerve volley, and negative intermediary potential evoked by sural nerve stimulation.

Figure 5 emphasizes the different conduction characteristics of the group I and group II afferent volleys. The difference in latency of conduction amounts to approximately 0.4 msec. with conduction distance of 12 cm. It is important, therefore, to make corrections for differential afferent conduction velocities when comparing the time relationships of group I and II reflexes, the correction value of course increasing as the afferent limb of the reflexes is increased in length.

The reflex discharges evoked by stimulation of group I and group II afferent fibers, and as recorded from a ventral root are quite different (21). Figure 6 shows such reflex discharges, both severally and in combination. Record A of Fig. 6 shows the group I reflex on stimulating the gastrocnemius nerves. Records B, D, F, H, illustrate the group II reflex similarly recorded in isolation, and resulting from stimulation of the sural nerve. There is random variation in the response from one observation to another. In records C, E, G, I the two reflexes are combined by synchronous stimulation of the gastrocnemius and sural nerves. The conduction distances are equal. Again, there is variation from one observation to another, but there is apparently no systematic change to suggest that the transmission of the gastrocnemius (*i.e.*, extensor) two-neuron-arc discharge has had any definite effect, one way or the other, on the succeeding discharges. The reflex evoked by sural nerve stimulation is directed into flexor channels (43). It is an important consideration that the extensor two-neuron-arc reflex and the flexor multineuron-arc reflex evoked by a single *synchronous* stimulation are virtually independent, for this combination will occur on stimulation of a mixed nerve such as the tibial nerve even though only the flexor discharges are recorded, as when the recording leads are directed to the peroneal nerve (*cf.* Fig. 9). With combined stimulation, the two-neuron arc discharge is unhindered for, travelling in afferent fibers of the highest velocity, it finds the spinal cord in the 'resting' state.

Observations made from the dorsum of the spinal cord (Fig. 5) and from a ventral root (Fig. 6) under similar circumstances invite comparison. It

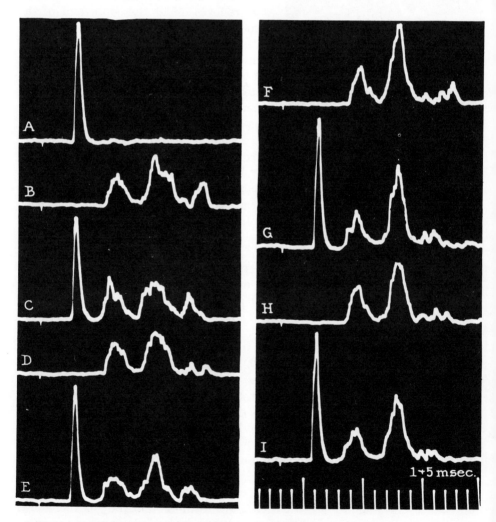

FIG. 6. Records from the S1 ventral root. A—stimulation of gastroc. nerves—group I reflex. B, D, F, H—stimulation of sural nerve—group II reflex. C, E, G, I—combined stimulation of gastroc. and sural nerves. The discharge of the group I reflex appears to have no systematic effect of the group II reflex which follows.

will be seen on comparing Fig. 5 and 6 that the group I reflex transmitted in its entirety is not accompanied by activation of the internuncial elements contributing to the cord potential (13, 16). On the contrary, the group II afferent fibers when stimulated yield intense activity among the interneurons of the dorsal regions of the spinal cord, which in turn causes the diffuse delayed discharges characterizing the group II reflex. Figures 7, 8, 9, 10, 11, 12 reveal that the group II multineuron-arc discharges are distributed overwhelmingly to the flexor musculature, as would be expected from the early observations of Sherrington (43). These facts provide ample confirmation for the association, developed by Hughes and Gasser (16), between the cord potentials and the flexor reflex.

The distribution of group II and group III reflexes. The peroneal nerve, considered as a 'motor' nerve, is distributed in the main to muscles of physiological flexion (43). In contrast, the tibial nerve contains motor fibers distributed to posterior tibial and plantar muscles, muscles of physiological extension. As an approximation these nerves may be considered as flexor and extensor nerves respectively, and in practice, no essential distinction, in terms of recorded reflex discharges, has been found between the parent trunk of the peroneal nerve and its constituent branch to the tibialis anterior muscle on the one hand, or between the parent trunk of the tibial nerve and its constituent branches to the gastrocnemius muscle on the other hand. With these considerations in mind, the distribution of activity engendered by stimulation of group II and group III afferent fibers has been examined.

Separation of the group II and group III fibers, the latter comprising essentially the delta fibers, depends primarily upon the strength of stimulation. Figure 7 illustrates the reflex responses recorded from the peroneal

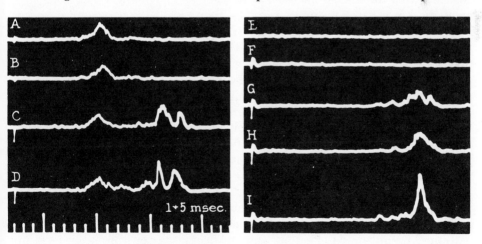

Fig. 7. A, B, C, D—stimulation of sural nerve. A, B—stimulation at group II strength. C, D—stimulation at group III strength. Recording leads on peroneal nerve. E—blank sweep. F, G, H, I—stimulation of gastroc. nerves recording leads to peroneal nerve. F—stimulation at group II strength—no reflex. G, H, I—stimulation at group III strength—group III reflex.

nerve as the result of stimulating the sural nerve (A to D) and the gastroc-nemius nerve (F to I). Record E shows the electrical base line in the absence of specific stimulation. The strength of stimulation will be referred to as weak (group II) or strong (group III).

Weak stimulation of the sural nerve (7A, B) results in a reflex discharge into the peroneal nerve with a total latency approximating 6 msec. With strong stimulation, this discharge grouping is present as before, but added thereto is another discharge grouping (7C, D). The latency of the sec-ond discharge (group III reflex) cannot be estimated with certainty, but approximates 11 msec. The situation is only slightly different when the gastrocnemius nerve is employed for afferent stimulation, for weak stimula-tion does not always result in any reflex discharge into the peroneal nerve (Fig. 7F). On strong stimulation of the gastrocnemius nerves, group III reflexes regularly appear in the peroneal nerve (7G, H, I) with the same time relationship as they exhibit on sural nerve stimulation (compare 7G, H, I with 7C, D). It will be remembered that flexor reflexes resulting from stimu-lation of the gastrocnemius nerves has been described by Sherrington (43) and Eccles and Sherrington (9). Presumably those reflexes frequently be-longed to group III of the present classification. The not infrequent absence of group II reflex discharge on stimulating the gastrocnemius nerves is re-lated to the poverty of medium sized afferent fibers (8, 29), but certainly there are sufficient to develop a subliminal field of excitation among the cen-tral neuron pools, and upon occasion to provoke a reflex discharge (cf. 21, Fig. 5A).

When the tibial nerve (less its branches to the gastrocnemius muscle) is substituted for the peroneal nerve to serve as an efferent reflex limb, little or no discharge attends stimulation of either sural or gastrocnemius nerves. Typically there is no reflex pathway from the gastrocnemius nerves to the (remainder of the) tibial nerve (Fig. 4H, I; Fig. 8B, C). A slight discharge may be found in the tibial nerve when stimulating the sural nerve; it is not increased apparently by strong stimulation (compare Fig. 8D, E). This last discharge is difficult to interpret; it might represent 'residual ipsilateral ex-tension' or specialized reflex activity directed to the small muscles of the foot through the plantar divisions of the tibial nerve. Since the residual ipsilateral extension reflex is usually a rebound following preliminary inhibition (4, p. 81, Fig. 43), this seems at the moment an unlikely explanation, for the la-tency would then be much greater.

Since the experiments of Fig. 7 and 8 are performed with the dorsal and ventral root systems of the spinal cord intact, antidromic volleys in the motoneurons ensue whenever a muscle nerve is utilized for 'afferent' stim-ulation. The untoward effects of the antidromic volleys probably need not be considered when the antidromically activated motoneurons and the reflexly tested motoneurons belong one to the peroneal nucleus, the other to the tibial nucleus (32), but as between the divisions of the tibial nerve care must be exercised in forming conclusions. It has been shown above that the antidromic volley would not seriously impede two-neuron-arc discharges coursing simultaneously through neighboring motoneurons, but this relative immunity need not extend to the group II and group III reflexes, for with their greater central latency they might find the motoneurons well advanced in the course of depression brought on by the antidromic volley in the neighboring motoneurons. The fact that little reflex effect is secured in the tibial nerve on stimulating the purely afferent sural nerve is a partial control, for in this case no antidromic volley is evoked. Furthermore, the number of group II fibers in the gastrocnemius nerves is small, making it unlikely that a substantial group II reflex would be found in the tibial nerve if a way were devised to avoid the antidromic volley. Finally the result of stimulation of cutaneous nerves on extensor muscles (*e.g.*, the vasti, crureus, semimem-

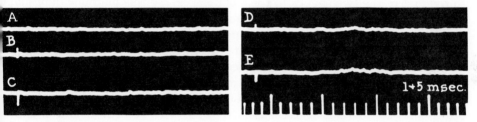

Fig. 8. A, B, C—records obtained from the tibial nerve (less its constituent branches to the gastrocnemius muscle). A—blank sweep. B, C—group II and group III strength stimulation respectively. D, E—stimulation of the sural nerve at group II and group III strength respectively. Note slight discharge in D and E.

branosus, anterior part of the biceps femoris, soleus, gastrocnemius) is inhibition (43) rather than excitation (*cf.* also Fig. 12A, B, C). There is reason to believe, however, that a group II or group III reflex would be realized among extensor motor nerves if the extensor inhibitory component of the flexor response evoked by stimulation of the plantar nerves were obviated by the use of natural stimulation (*cf.* discussion on the extensor thrust reflex in connection with Table 2).

The shortest reflex pathway from one peripheral nerve to another. The most powerful reflex discharges transmitted from one hind limb nerve to another are those to be recorded in the peroneal nerve, or a suitable branch thereof, following stimulation of the tibial nerve. Because of this fact the tibial nerve to peroneal nerve reflex has been chosen as the system in which to examine the simplest reflex link from one nerve to another. The simplest link from one nerve to itself is the two-neuron-arc pathway. In order to establish a time reference by which to gauge the minimum central delay of the tibial nerve to peroneal nerve reflex, the group I reflex from the tibial nerve back into itself has been examined. Stimulation and recording leads are arranged so that the conduction distance for the two reflexes is comparable. Figure 9 illustrates an experiment performed after this manner. In observations A and G of Fig. 9 are shown the reflex into the tibial nerve on stimulation of that nerve (compare with Fig. 3). The latency of the two-neuron-arc reflex is approximately 3.8 msec. Observations B and H illustrate the onset of reflex discharge into the peroneal nerve on stimulation of the tibial nerve. The latency of the first action is approximately 5.3 msec., *i.e.*, 1.5 msec. longer than that to be expected on transmission through two-neuron-arc pathways. It is obvious that the reflex discharge resulting from a single stimulation need not necessarily be transmitted through the shortest available pathway (*cf.* 10). Accordingly the discharge through the tibial nerve to peroneal nerve pathway has been examined under conditions of repeated stimulation calculated to yield the greatest facilitation of the response to the second of two successive shocks. A stimulation interval of 3.0 msec. was found to be most effective. In Fig. 9C,–F and I–L, the responses to single and double stimulation are presented in alternation, the single responses being those to the first of the two shocks to the tibial nerve. By this plan one may judge the approximate electrical base line upon which is written the facilitated responses to the second shock. A prominent peak appears in records D, F, J, L with a latency of 4.9 msec. as measured from the time of the second shock. Comparison of the facilitated responses D, F, J, L with the control responses B and H shows that the latency of the reflex into the peroneal nerve is reduced by 0.4 msec. due to the action of the antecedent stimulation. On the other hand comparison of records D, F, J, L with records A and G shows that the latency of the reflex into the peroneal nerve, in spite of powerful facilitation, is 1.1 msec. longer than that of the two-neuron-arc reflex back into the tibial nerve.

The latency differential between the two reflexes under consideration is not all referable to difference in central latency, for the reflex in the tibial nerve results from stimulation of group I afferent fibers, while the reflex in the peroneal nerve results from stimulation of group II afferent fibers. The proper correction for the differential afferent conduction under the conditions of the experiment illustrated in Fig. 9 amounts to 0.5 msec., or a little less (*cf.* also Fig. 5). Then, with allowance of 0.5 msec. for the slower afferent conduction of the reflex into the peroneal nerve, there remains a latency differential of 0.6 msec. between the two reflexes, all of which is attributable to excess central latency. Since this value is appropriate for the delay occasioned by a single synaptic relay (27), it appears that the minimum reflex pathway from the tibial nerve to the peroneal nerve contains one more neuron in series than does the reflex pathway back into the tibial nerve, and is, therefore, a three-neuron-arc pathway. Since the reflex pathway from the tibial nerve to the peroneal nerve contains all the paths pertaining to the classical reflex of the ankle flexor as studied by Eccles and Sherrington (10), it follows that the minimum pathway for this flexor reflex proper is one of three neurons.

Group I and group II reflex discharges into flexor nerves. Although the shortest pathway mediating the flexor reflex proper is one of three neurons (Fig. 9), the motoneurons of flexor muscles are supplied directly by primary afferent fibers´ and under the appropriate experimental conditions, two-

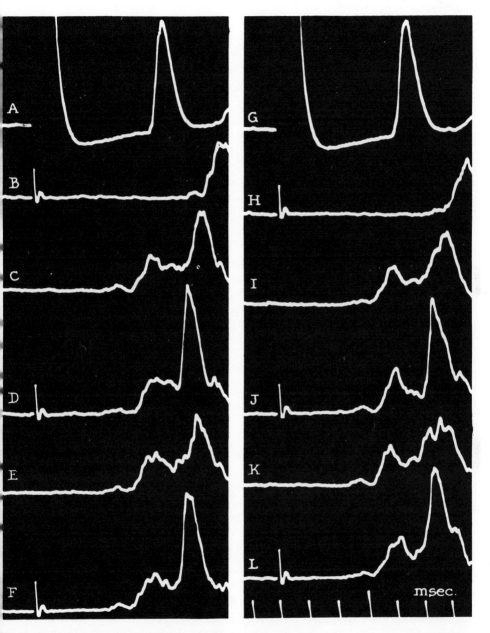

Fig. 9. Reflex discharges on stimulation of the tibial nerve. A, G—the group I reflex recorded on the tibial nerve as in Fig. 3. B, H—onset of group II reflex recorded on the peroneal nerve. In D, F, J, L the reflex into the peroneal nerve is facilitated by an antecedent shock to the tibial nerve, the reflex response to which is seen in C, E, I, K. Comparison of the latency of the facilitated reflex in the peroneal nerve with that of the reflex in the tibial nerve indicates that the minimum central pathway between the tibial nerve and the peroneal nerve contains an interneuron in series.

neuron-arc reflex discharges may be demonstrated in flexor nerves. The experimental conditions are those by which similar discharges may be recorded in the extensor paths (Fig. 1, 3, 9).

Figure 10 illustrates the reflex discharges to be found in the nerve to the tibialis anterior muscle on stimulation of the tibial nerve and the peroneal

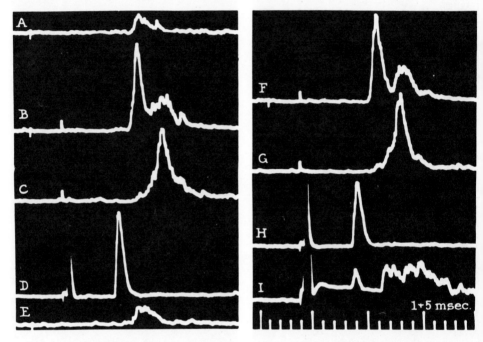

FIG. 10. Reflex discharges into the nerve to the tibialis anterior muscle (ankle flexor). A,E—submaximal group II reflex evoked by stimulation of tibial nerve. C, G—maximal group II reflex evoked by stimulation of the tibial nerve. B, F—facilitated reflex by combined stimulation of the tibial nerve. D, H—group I reflex evoked by stimulation of the parent trunk of the peroneal nerve at approximately half maximal group I strength. I— when the peroneal nerve shock is increased the group I reflex volley is diminished by the consequently greater antidromic volley and group II (and group III) reflex discharges appear *de novo*.

nerve (the latter being the parent trunk for the nerve to the tibialis anterior muscle). Observations A, C, E, G show the reflex discharges resulting from single shock stimulation of the tibial nerve, the shock being stronger for C and G than for A and E. Observations B and F present the result of combined stimulation of the tibial nerve, the stronger shock preceded at an interval of approximately 3.0 msec. by the weaker shock. Comparison of B and F with C and G shows that the latency of the response to the second tibial nerve shock is shortened by 0.8 msec. to a value of 5.8 msec. In contrast, stimulation of the parent trunk of the peroneal nerve results in a group I (two-neuron-arc) reflex into the nerve to the tibialis anterior muscle (Fig. 10D, H). The latency for this group I reflex is 4.6 msec. The reflex pathway from the stimulating electrodes through the spinal cord and back to the recording leads on the nerve to the tibialis anterior muscle approximates 38 cm., or 7 cm. longer than the total reflex pathway obtaining in the experiment illustrated in Fig. 3. The additional latency (0.6 msec.) of reflex 10D, H over that of reflex 3A is only sufficient to account for conduction through the additional 7 cm. length of pathway at a velocity of 117 M/sec. Again, the records 10D, H were obtained by the use of shocks submaximal for the group I fibers of the peroneal nerve. This is shown by the fact that the group I reflex is decreased on increasing the strength of stimulation, due to the increase in the antidromic volley, and consequent extension of central refractoriness (compare H with I in Fig. 10). Also, with the increase in strength of the peroneal nerve shock, group II reflex discharges appear in the nerve to the tibialis anterior muscle.

The peroneal nerve is a mixed nerve. The low threshold reflex appearing in the nerve to the tibialis anterior muscle on stimulation of the peroneal nerve does so by virtue of the stimulation of afferent fibers arising in the tibialis anterior muscle, for, stimulation of the peroneal nerve after segregation of the tibialis anterior nerve results only in delayed discharges into the latter (cf. Table 1). Conversely the late discharges seen in record I of Fig. 10 must be due largely, but not exclusively, to the stimulation of cutaneous afferent fibers reaching the peroneal nerve trunk through its superficial branch. Thus the initial discharge into the tibialis anterior muscle, on stimulating the parent peroneal trunk has the latency, threshold, and distribution features to be expected of a group I reflex. In this connection it will be noted that Sherrington (38), Asayama (1) and Denny-Brown (5) have described the tendon-jerk, or 'pluck' reflex in flexor muscles, and that Forbes Campbell and Williams (11) and Matthews (28) have demonstrated afferent responses to stretch of flexor muscles. Since the two-neuron-arc reflex does not appear in the pathway of the flexor reflex, there is ample reason to regard the two-neuron-arc connections of flexor muscles as devoted to the mediation of the tendon-jerk or 'pluck' reflex exhibited by those muscles.

In connection with Fig. 9 and 10 it has been seen that the latency of the group II reflex discharges is shortened by antecedent stimulation, as would be expected from the experiments of Eccles and Sherrington (10). In the absence of antecedent stimulation discharges through the three-neuron-arc pathway of the group II flexor reflex are almost (Fig. 9B, H) or quite absent (Fig. 4M, 7, 10) i.e., subliminal, when the afferent stimulation is applied to a peripheral nerve, even though this stimulation be powerful, But, just as flexor reflex activity is shunted into the shorter available paths by facilitation (Fig. 9, 10), so is it similarly advanced by shifting the site of afferent stimulation from a peripheral nerve to a dorsal root.

Figure 11 presents an experiment in which are compared the reflex discharges into the deep peroneal nerve by stimulation of the tibial nerve, the S1 dorsal root and the L7 dorsal root. The deep peroneal nerve supplies the tibialis anterior, extensor longus digitorum and extensor brevis digitorum, all three of which respond in the great flexion reflex (43). It is a convenient nerve

structure for the recording of flexor activity. As a preface to the consideration of Fig. 11, one should bear in mind the differences between the L7 and
S1 spinal segments in relation to the three muscles served through the deep
peroneal nerve. The L7 segment regularly supplies the muscles mentioned
(35, 10). The S1 segment may contribute a small twig to the peroneal nerve
when the arrangement of the plexus is of the postfixed type. One would ex-

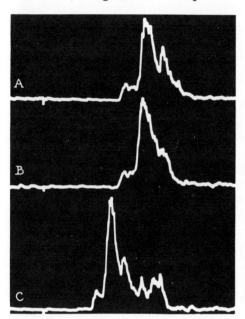
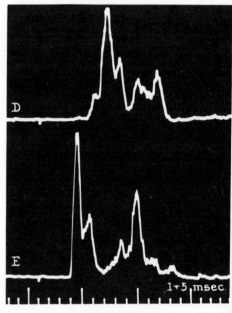

FIG. 11. Reflex discharges into the deep peroneal nerve (supplying MM. tibialis anterior, extensores longus et brevis digitorum). A, B—reflex discharge on stimulation of the
tibial nerve, C, D—reflex discharges on stimulation of the S1 dorsal root. E—reflex discharge on stimulation of the L7 dorsal root. Note 'synapse skipping' and concentration of
activity through shorter reflex chains when stimulation is advanced from peripheral nerve
to dorsal root, also threshold two-neuron-arc discharge when stimulating S1 dorsal root
compared with powerful two-neuron-arc discharge when stimulating L7 dorsal root.

pect to find, therefore, little (postfixed preparation) or no (prefixed preparation) two-neuron-arc reflex discharge from the S1 dorsal root to the deep
peroneal nerve, but a not inconsiderable two-neuron-arc discharge from the
L7 dorsal root to the deep peroneal nerve.

Figure 11A and B illustrates the reflex discharge recorded from the deep
peroneal nerve on stimulating the tibial nerve. The latency of this discharge
is approximately 7 msec. Observations C and D illustrate the reflex discharge
similarly recorded, on stimulating the S1 dorsal root. As might be expected
there is a small, but quite regular two-neuron-arc discharge appearing after
a latency of 3.2 msec. (compare C and D with E, obtained by stimulation of
the L7 dorsal root, and which contains a powerful two-neuron-arc discharge).
The arrangement of the plexus in this preparation was postfixed, and direct
fiber connection between the deep peroneal nerve and both the S1 dorsal root

and S1 ventral root was proved by the recording of directly conducted alpha spike potentials between the nerve and the roots. Disregarding the two-neuron-arc discharge in C and D for the moment, for this represents reflex activity arising from the deep peroneal nerve rather than the tibial nerve, the latency of the next discharge in order is 4.4–4.6 msec., encompassing some slight variation from one observation to another. On advancing the site of stimulation from the tibial nerve to the dorsal root, therefore, the latency of the flexor reflex proper is reduced from 7 msec. to approximately 4.5 msec. Some fraction of this latency differential is referable to the shortening of the afferent limb of the reflex. Since the tibial nerve contains group I fibers in addition to the group II fibers mediating the reflex in question, the exact allowance for afferent conduction cannot be measured. Assuming that as much as 1.7 msec. afferent conduction time is involved (this would represent 12 cm. conduction at 70 M/sec.) there is still a shortening of central latency amounting to 0.8 msec., which occurs by virtue of 'skipping a synapse' (26).

The most prominent discharge peak in C and D of Fig. 11 has a latency of 5.6 msec., which is shorter than that of the initial discharge in A and B only by the equivalent time for conduction from the tibial nerve to the S1 dorsal root. It would seem that this peak in C and D represents the same 'order' of reflex discharge as the initial discharge in A and B, but it has gained greatly in potency.

The effect of advancing the site of stimulation from the peripheral nerve to the dorsal root, then, is an intensification of the discharge through the shorter available paths at the expense of discharge through the longer paths, in addition to the simple shortening of latency due to shortening the afferent limb of the reflex pathway. It seems probable that a decrease in central latency brought about in this manner accounts for the apparent long afferent conduction time and correspondingly short minimum central reflex time calculated for the flexor reflex by Eccles and Sherrington (10), for they measured the afferent time by the difference in reflex latency when stimulating the tibial (popliteal) nerve and the S1 (8th post-thoracic) dorsal root.

On the conditioning of two-neuron-arc reflexes. According to the evidence of the present experiments, the segmental reflex discharge is constituted of two-neuron-arc discharge directed in varying ratio, depending upon the segment employed and other considerations, to muscles of flexor and extensor action, together with multineuron-arc discharges almost exclusively directed to muscles of physiological flexion, irrespective of the segment employed. Some of the vagaries of conditioning experiments in which segmental two-neuron-arc reflex discharges are employed as test volleys are undoubtedly due to the dual nature of those discharges. It is frequently found, on causing a two-neuron-arc volley to fall during the multineuron-arc discharge in response to an antecedent shock, that the two-neuron-arc volley is subjected simultaneously to temporal facilitation and spatial inhibition. The explanation for this anomalous behavior becomes clear when the components of the segmental reflex are segregated as in the experiment presented in Fig. 12. The extensor two-neuron-arc component is obtained by stimulating the nerves to the gastrocnemius muscle, the flexor two-neuron-arc component by stimulating the deep peroneal nerve, and the multineuron-arc component by stimulating the sural nerve. Records are obtained from the L7 or S1 ventral root.

Record A of Fig. 12 shows the extensor two-neuron-arc reflex recorded from the S1 ventral root following stimulation of the gastrocnemius nerves.

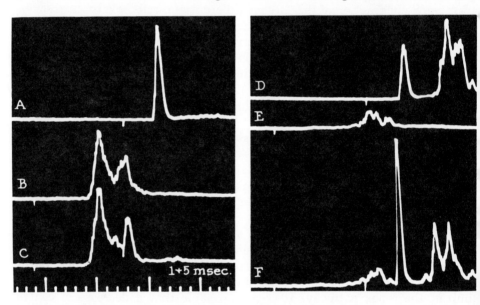

FIG. 12. Conditioning of extensor two-neuron-arc and flexor two-neuron-arc reflexes by stimulation of a cutaneous nerve (sural). A, B, C recorded from the S1 ventral root. A—gastroc. nerves stimulated. B—sural nerve stimulated. C—combined stimulation of sural and gastroc. nerve at interval of 8.5 msec. The gastroc. two-neuron-arc is inhibited, D, E, F—recorded from the L7 ventral root. D—deep peroneal nerve stimulated—note two-neuron-arc and later discharges. E—sural nerve stimulated. F—combined stimulation of sural nerve and deep peroneal nerve. The two-neuron-arc reflex is facilitated both spatially and temporally by the action of the sural nerve volley.

Record B shows the multineuron-arc discharge resulting from stimulation of the sural nerve. On combining these two stimulations (record C) at an interval of 8.5 msec. the extensor two-neuron-arc reflex is inhibited, although few if any extensor motoneurons could have discharged in the earlier reflex. Record D illustrates the response recorded from the L7 ventral root on stimulation of the deep peroneal nerve. The two-neuron-arc discharge is here followed after an interval by multineuron-arc discharges. Record E shows the response evoked by stimulation of the sural nerve. In record F, sural and deep peroneal nerve stimulation are combined as were the sural and gastrocnemius nerve stimulations in 12C. In this case, however, the flexor two-neuron-arc discharge is facilitated, both temporally and spatially.

Similar results can be obtained when stimulating dorsal roots while seg-regating the extensor and flexor components on the motor side (*cf.* also 33), but the method here illustrated seems preferable in theory for the input to the spinal cord is restricted so that only the flexor or the extensor testing two-neuron-arc discharges are elicited, depending upon choice. On the con-trary, when segregation is effected on the motor side, stimulation of dorsal roots will cause activation of both flexor and extensor two-neuron-arcs in parallel, and although only one or the other is recorded, the way is open for undesirable interaction, and the possibility of confusion phenomena within the testing system remains.

The classification of ipsilateral hind limb reflexes. Throughout most of the present paper the reflex discharges described have been classified according to the arbitrary groups outlined in the introduction, but certain obvious correlations with hind limb reflexes as they are known on the basis of motor performance have emerged. Table 2 forms a summary of these correlations and of the foregoing experiments.

Table 2. The classification of ipsilateral hind limb reflexes

Group	Approximate afferent fiber range	Central connections	Origin	Destination	Type of reflex
I	$20–12\mu$	Direct, or two-neuron-arc reflexes	(a) extensor muscles	The extensor muscle from which it arises	Myotatic reflex (the tendon-jerk)
			(b) flexor muscles	The flexor muscle from which it arises	Flexor tendon-jerk (the pluck reflex)
II	$12–6\mu$	Multineuron-arc reflexes. Three-neuron-arc minimum	(a) skin	flexor muscles	The flexion reflex
				extensor muscles (slight)	Residual ipsilateral extension ?
			(b) muscle (slight)	flexor muscles	The flexion reflex
III	$6–1\mu$	Multineuron-arc reflexes. ? minimum	(a) skin	flexor muscles	'Delta' flexion reflex
			(b) muscle	flexor muscles	'Delta' flexion reflex
IV	unmyelinated (C) fibers				(*cf.* 3, 2)

It will be seen at once that the outstanding omission from Table 2 is the ipsilateral reflex of extension known as the extensor thrust (40). This reflex is elicited by pressure or 'deep touch' on the planta (37, 39), whereas nocuous stimulation of the same area elicits flexion of the limb. The plantar nerves are essential to the transmission of the extensor thrust reflex (39), and hence mediate the afferent limb of this reflex. Yet stimulation of these nerves themselves yields flexion (42), accompanied by relaxation of extensors. The extensor reflex is presumably inhibited by the concomitant and prepotent flexor reflex. The extensor thrust seems, therefore, not to be a group I reflex, for with simultaneous combination a group I reflex would outstrip the flexion reflex and thereby escape inhibition. One would expect the extensor thrust to belong in group II. Undoubtedly more prominent group II discharges to extensor muscles would be found in the fore limb, in which the stimulation of digital nerves promotes ipsilateral extension (6). Considerations such as these invoke again the problem to which there is still no decisive answer: it is not yet known to what extent fractionation of spinal centers is determined by anatomical limitation of neuron connections, or to what extent it is attained primarily by functional means, with direct inhibition possibly playing a dominant role.

SUMMARY

The reflex function within the hind limb of myelinated afferent fibers has been examined. Three sub-groups of these fibers are recognizable. The large fibers form direct connections with the motoneurons, the medium and small fibers connect with interneurons.

Reflex discharge mediated through the direct (two-neuron-arc) connections reflects only into the muscle, head of a muscle, or combination of muscles, the large afferent fibers of which are subjected to stimulation. Because of the identity of distribution holding for the two-neuron-arc discharge and the myotatic reflex, it is concluded that the two-neuron-arc pathways are reserved for mediation of the myotatic reflex.

Multineuron-arc discharges, evoked by stimulation of medium and small afferent fibers, are directed for the most part into the nerves of flexor muscles, and represent the flexor reflex proper. The minimum central pathway devoted to this reflex is one of three neurons.

Under appropriate conditions the flexor muscles receive excitation through arcs of two neurons as well as through the multineuron reflex arcs. The conditions are exactly those governing the transmission of two-neuron-arc excitation to extensor muscles. It is concluded that the flexor two-neuron-arc reflex represents the flexor tendon-jerk, or 'pluck' reflex in contradistinction to the flexor reflex proper.

The segmental reflex discharge recorded from a ventral root on stimulation of the dorsal root of the same segment contains three major elements, an extensor two-neuron-arc, a flexor two-neuron-arc and flexor multineuron-arc discharges. Reflex activity through extensor two-neuron-arcs is inhibited, that through flexor two-neuron-arcs facilitated by the transmission of multi-neuron-arc reflex action.

REFERENCES

1. ASAYAMA, C.   The proprioceptive reflex of a flexor muscle. *Quart. J. exp. Physiol.*, 1915, *9*: 265–279.
2. BISHOP, G. H., and HEINBECKER, P.   The afferent functions of non-myelinated or C fibers. *Amer. J. Physiol.*, 1935, *114*: 179–193.
3. CLARK, D., HUGHES, J., and GASSER, H. S.   Afferent function in the group of nerve fibers of slowest conduction velocity. *Amer. J. Physiol.*, 1935, *114*: 69–76.
4. CREED, R. S., DENNY-BROWN, D., ECCLES, J. C., LIDDELL, E. G. T., and SHERRINGTON C. S.   *Reflex activity of the spinal cord.* Oxford, Clarendon Press, 1932, 183 pp.
5. DENNY-BROWN, D. E.   On the nature of postural reflexes. *Proc. roy. Soc.*, 1929, *B104*: 252–301.
6. DENNY-BROWN, D. E., and LIDDELL, E. G. T.   Extensor reflexes in the forelimb. *J. Physiol.*, 1928, *65*: 305–325.
7. ECCLES, J. C., and PRITCHARD, J. J.   The action potential of motoneurones. *J. Physiol*, 1937, *89*: 43P–45P.
8. ECCLES, J. C., and SHERRINGTON, C. S.   Numbers and contraction-values of individual motor-units examined in some muscles of the limb. *Proc. roy. Soc.*, 1930, *B106*: 326–357.
9. ECCLES, J. C., and SHERRINGTON, C. S.   Reflex summation in the ipsilateral spinal flexion reflex. *J. Physiol.*, 1930, *69*: 1–28.
10. ECCLES, J. C., and SHERRINGTON, C. S.   Studies on the flexor reflex. I. Latent period. *Proc. roy. Soc.*, 1931, *B107*: 511–534.
11. FORBES, A., CAMPBELL, C. J., and WILLIAMS, H. B.   Electrical records of afferent nerve impulses from muscular receptors. *Amer. J. Physiol.*, 1924, *69*: 283–303.
12. FULTON, J. F., and LIDDELL, E. G. T.   Electrical responses of extensor muscles during postural (myotatic) contraction. *Proc. roy. Soc.*, 1925, *B98*: 577–589.
13. GASSER, H. S., and GRAHAM, H. T.   Potentials produced in the spinal cord by stimulation of dorsal roots. *Amer. J. Physiol.*, 1933, *103*: 303–320.
14. GASSER, H. S., and GRUNDFEST, H.   Axon diameters in relation to the spike dimensions and the conduction velocity in mammalian A fibers. *Amer. J. Physiol.*, 1939, *127*: 393–414.
15. HERING, E.   Beitrage zur allgemeinen Nerven und Muskel-Physiologie. IX. Über Nervenreizung durch den Nervenstrom. *S. B. Akad. Wiss. Wien.*, 1882, *85*: 237–275.
16. HUGHES, J., and GASSER, H. S.   Some properties of the cord potentials evoked by a single afferent volley. *Am. J. Physiol.*, 1934, *108*: 295–306.
17. HURSH, J. B.   Conduction velocity and diameter of nerve fibers. *Amer. J. Physiol.*, 1939, *127*: 131–139.
18. LIDDELL, E. G. T., and SHERRINGTON, C. S.   Reflexes in response to stretch (Myotatic reflexes). *Proc. roy. Soc.*, 1925, *B96*: 212–242.
19. LLOYD, D. P. C.   A direct central inhibitory action of dromically conducted impulses. *J. Neurophysiol.*, 1941, *4*: 184–190.
20. LLOYD, D. P. C.   Stimulation of peripheral nerve terminations by active muscle. *J. Neurophysiol.*, 1942, *5*: 153–165.
21. LLOYD, D. P. C.   Reflex action in relation to the pattern and peripheral source of afferent stimulation. *J. Neurophysiol.*, 1943, *6*: 111–119.
22. LLOYD, D. P. C.   The interaction of antidromic and orthodromic volleys in a segmental spinal motor nucleus. *J. Neurophysiol.*, 1943, *7*: 143–151.
23. LLOYD, D. P. C.   The afferent fibers mediating myotatic reflexes and their central connections. *Fed. Proc. Amer. Soc. exp. Biol.*, 1943, *2*: 29–30.
24. LLOYD, D. P. C.   Conduction and synaptic transmission of the reflex response to stretch in spinal cats. *J. Neurophysiol.*, 1943, *6*: 317–326.
25. LLOYD, D. P. C.   Functional organization of the spinal cord. *Physiol. Rev.* (in preparation).
26. LORENTE DE NÓ, R.   Facilitation of motoneurones. *Amer. J. Physiol.*, 1935, *113*: 505–523.

27. LORENTE DE NÓ, R.   Limits of variation of the synaptic delay of motoneurons. *J. Neurophysiol.*, 1938, *1*: 187–194.
28. MATTHEWS, B. H. C.   Nerve endings in mammalian muscle. *J. Physiol.*, 1933, *78*: 1–53.
29. O'LEARY, J., HEINBECKER, P., and BISHOP, G. H.   Analysis of function of a nerve to muscle. *Amer. J. Physiol.*, 1935, *110*: 636–658.
30. RANSON, S. W., DROEGEMUELLER, W. H., DAVENPORT, H. K., and FISHER, C.   Number, size and myelination of the sensory fibers in the cerebrospinal nerves. *Res. Publ. Ass. nerv. ment. Dis.*, 1935, *15*: 3–34.
31. RENSHAW, B.   Activity in the simplest spinal reflex pathways. *J. Neurophysiol.*, 1940, *3*: 373–387.
32. RENSHAW, B.   Influence of discharge of motoneurons upon excitation of neighboring motoneurons. *J. Neurophysiol.*, 1941, *4*: 167–183.
33. RENSHAW, B.   Reflex discharges in branches of the crural nerve. *J. Neurophysiol.*, 1942, *5*: 487–498.
34. RENSHAW, B., and THERMAN, P. O.   Excitation of intraspinal mammalian axons by nerve impulses in adjacent axons. *Amer. J. Physiol.*, 1941, *133*: 96–105.
35. SHERRINGTON, C. S.   Notes on the arrangement of some motor fibers in the lumbosacral plexus. *J. Physiol.*, 1892, *13*: 621–772.
36. SHERRINGTON, C. S.   On the anatomical constitution of nerves to skeletal muscles, with remarks on recurrent fibers in the ventral spinal nerve-root. *J. Physiol.*, 1894, *17*: 211–258.
37. SHERRINGTON, C. S.   On the innervation of antagonistic muscles. Sixth note. *Proc. roy. Soc.*, 1900, *66*: 66–67.
38. SHERRINGTON, C. S.   The muscular sense. *Schäfer's Textbook of Physiology*, 1900, *2*: 1002–1025.
39. SHERRINGTON, C. S.   Qualitative difference of spinal reflex corresponding with qualitative difference of cutaneous stimulus. *J. Physiol.*, 1904, *30*: 39–46.
40. SHERRINGTON, C. S.   *The integrative action of the nervous system.* New York, Scribner's, 1906, 411 pp.
41. SHERRINGTON, C. S.   On innervation of antagonistic muscles. Ninth note, Successive spinal induction. *Proc. roy Soc.*, 1906, *B77*: 478–497.
42. SHERRINGTON, C. S.   On reciprocal innervation of antagonistic muscles. Tenth note. *Proc. roy. Soc.*, 1907, *B79*: 337–349.
43. SHERRINGTON, C. S.   Flexion-reflex of the limb, crossed extension-reflex, and reflex stepping and standing. *J. Physiol.*, 1910, *40*: 28–121.
44. TOENNIES, J. F.   Reflex discharge from the spinal cord over the dorsal roots. *J. Neurophysiol.*, 1938, *1*: 378–390.
45. TUREEN, L. L.   Form of the reflex response in relation to the pattern of afferent stimulation. *Proc. Soc. exp. Biol., N. Y.*, 1941, *46*: 543–544.

FACILITATION AND INHIBITION OF
SPINAL MOTONEURONS

DAVID P. C. LLOYD

Laboratories of The Rockefeller Institute for Medical Research, New York

(Received for publication June 18, 1946)

STUDIES ON the duration of excitation and inhibition resulting at the motoneurons from the arrival of a single volley of impulses have suffered from the defect that such a volley seemingly was unattainable due to the intervention of internuncial bombardment. Clearly it is important to examine facilitation in circumstances that minimize, or preferably eliminate, internuncial activity as a factor in the conditioning of motoneurons. The description of experiments which follows is designed to show to what extent the attempt has been successful, and the results that have been obtained.

CONDITIONS OF EXPERIMENT

The decapitate cat preparation has been employed, spinal section being accomplished through the dorsal atlanto-occipital membrane during ether anaesthesia, after which artificial respiration was commenced and the anaesthetic discontinued. Laminectomy was performed and the ventral roots of the lumbar enlargement sectioned, those of the seventh and eighth post-thoracic segments being prepared for the recording of reflex discharges. In the hind limb various combinations of muscle nerves belonging to the femoral, hamstring or sciatic groups were prepared for afferent stimulation. In this fashion, activity through two-neuron-arc reflex systems has been obtained, with functional selection made on the afferent limbs of the reflex pathways (cf. 12).

It has been found convenient to classify the afferent fibers of the A group (myelinated fibers of the somatic nerves) into three subdivisions (12). Group I, according to this classification, consists of the largest (20μ to 12μ approximately) afferent fibers found in the nerves of muscle. Group II includes the medium sized fibers (12μ to 6μ approximately)—many in number in cutaneous nerves, sparsely present in muscle nerves. Group III coincides with the delta group. It is the group I fibers that form direct connections with motoneurons (11, 12, 13).

Dorsal roots are not satisfactory for afferent "conditioning" stimulation. Two-neuron-arc reflexes belonging to specific muscles or muscle groups may be obtained by stimulating appropriate dorsal roots and recording from the nerve to the muscle or muscles in question (22), or by stimulating a selected muscle nerve while recording from an appropriate ventral root (11, 12). Serious objections to the use of the former technique arise if the object is the conditioning of motoneurons. These are: (i) the afferent fibers of muscles of many actions, allied an d antagonistic, are stimulated indiscriminately, and unavoidably so; and (ii) it is virtual y impossible, in a dorsal root, to stimulate group I afferent fibers without the participation of group II afferent fibers in the stimulated fraction. For instance, Gasser and Graham (7) on stimulating dorsal roots found the negative intermediary potential appearing in threshold responses of the spinal cord. Again (11), discharges through multineuron reflex arcs have been seen when a dorsal root is stimulated at a strength just sufficient to evoke a two-neuron-arc discharge. Recently Eccles, too (5), has reported encountering this same difficulty.

Muscle nerves as sources of afferent conditioning activity. The chances of obtaining afferent volleys confined to group I fibers are increased if muscle nerves rather than dorsal roots are employed for afferent stimulation. Even so, certain precautions must be observed. It is important to stimulate with near-threshold shocks, otherwise indisputable evidence of internuncial activity frequently is encountered. In fact, analysis of the conditioning action of group I impulses may be furthered by observing the effect of deliberate, slight increase in the strength of the conditioning shocks (cf. Figs. 4, 5, 8, 9, 10). The fact that internuncial

Lloyd, D. P. C. Facilitation and inhibition of spinal motoneurons. *J. Neurophysiol.* **9:** 421–438, 1946.

activity of ipsilateral origin is predominantly excitatory to flexors and inhibitory to extensors (12) is an aid to identification.

The use of near-threshold shocks introduces some difficulty attending threshold "play." This is most serious in testing the early course of conditioning action in motor nuclei. However, since internuncial actions are delayed by slower afferent conduction in group II fibers and added synaptic time, the early course (but not the later course) of conditioning as revealed by weak shocks may be confirmed by the use of stronger shocks (15).

A group I volley stimulated in a muscle nerve possesses functional homogeneity, a most important factor in the present experiments.

Test volleys. From present knowledge there would appear to be no serious objection to the use of dorsal root volleys while recording from specific muscle nerves as two-neuron-arc test reflexes. In the experiments discussed here, this would be plausible only in certain situations dependent upon anatomy, as a result of the necessity for cutting ventral roots and preserving dorsal roots to provide for the conditioning activity. Therefore the practice of employing volleys selected on the afferent limb has been followed for the test system as

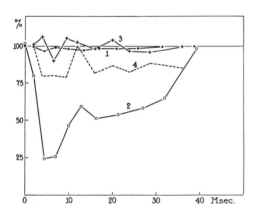

Fig. 1. Influence on reflex discharge of antidromic volleys in neighboring motoneurons. Gastrocnemius, nucleus. Curve 1: Antidromic volley maximal, reflex afferent volley maximal. Curve 2: Antidromic volley maximal, reflex afferent volley 12 per cent maximal. Curve 3: Antidromic volley 50 per cent maximal, reflex afferent volley 50 per cent maximal. Curve 4: Antidromic volley maximal, reflex afferent volley 50 per cent maximal. A strong antidromic volley coupled with a weak reflex volley is the requirement for significant depression of reflex discharge.

well as for the conditioning system. Strong stimulation of the test nerve, producing the maximum two-neuron-arc reflex attainable by stimulation of that nerve in isolation, has been used routinely. The occurrence of multineuron-arc reflex activity following the test two-neuron-arc response is of no consequence, and the advantage is gained that random variability is less than it is with submaximal reflexes.

Minimizing random variation. Spontaneous fluctuation in the excitability of the preparation has proved something of a difficulty. The use of strong test shocks is of some benefit, but it has been found advisable, for each point on the experimental curves—examples of which are illustrated—to record a number of observations, with conditioned and control records obtained in alternation. The average is struck for conditioned and control values and the two compared.

Influence of motoneuron discharge upon the excitability of neighboring motoneurons. Since Renshaw (21) demonstrated that antidromic volleys occupying some motoneurons can, in some circumstances, alter the excitability of neighboring motoneurons either in the direction of enhancement or depression, it is of obvious importance to assess the possible influence of comparable effects in the present experiments. Since the ventral roots have been severed, one does not have to consider the action of antidromic volleys as such, but, embracing for the moment the assumption that firing motoneurons would have comparable actions whether fired antidromically or orthodromically, the possibility of interaction exists. Accordingly, some of Renshaw's experiments have been repeated with general conditions, such as the type of preparation, absence of anaesthesia and site of stimulation, adjusted to conform more closely with those obtaining in the experiments to be described. Illustrative interaction curves are presented in Figure 1, in which is examined the effect upon a reflex discharge into the nerve of one head of gastrocnemius of an antidromic volley from the nerve to the other head of gastrocnemius. The curve represented by dots was obtained by employing maximal antidromic volleys and maximal reflex volleys. It should be emphasized that the reflex was maximal in the sense that increased stimulation of the dorsal root did not further increase the test reflex, not in the sense that the reflex did not increase by virtue of facilitation by convergent activity of similar origin. A slight depression is noted, the maximum amounting to 3.5 per cent at 4.5 msec. separation of antidromic and orthodromic volleys.

Reduction of the test reflex to approximately 12 per cent of its former size, the antidromic volley remaining maximal, resulted in a change in the interaction curve to that designated by circles. At maximum a depression of reflex response amounting to 75 per cent is realized. The third curve of Figure 1, that indicated by crosses, was obtained by a combination of antidromic and orthodromic volleys, both types being about 50 per cent of maximum. The deviation of the points, insofar as it may be significant, is about equally in the direction of enhancement and depression. The third curve may be compared with the fourth, represented by a broken line, to obtain which the antidromic volley was increased to maximum, the orthodormic volley being retained at the same size, to yield a half-maximum reflex.

It is concluded from the data presented in Figure 1 that the conditions for significant interaction between motoneurons, even those pertaining to the nucleus of a single muscle, are: (i) powerful activation, in terms of numbers, of the motoneurons acting together as the agent; and (ii) feeble activation of the responding test reflex system. Since, in the experiments to be considered in this paper, the discharge of motoneurons by the conditioning volley is at most very small compared with that realized by antidromic activation, and since the test reflexes are strong by comparison with those that are significantly altered by antidromic volleys in nearby motoneurons, further consideration of motoneuron interaction is unnecessary for the purpose at hand.

Results

I. Facilitation of motoneurons by the direct action of primary afferent impulses. Although reflex discharges through arcs of two neurons return only to the muscle nerve from which they arise (12), it has been found that mutual facilitation obtains between closely allied two-neuron-arc pathways. For example, group I volleys arising in the nerves to different parts of biceps femoris posterior interact at the biceps motor nucleus. Similar facilitatory interaction occurs between the two heads of gastrocnemius (also noted by Eccles (5), to whom credit is due for the prior demonstration of this interaction), and even between semitendinosus and biceps femoris posterior, two distinct although synergic muscles. The fact of such interaction provides the required situation for a study of the summation period at the motoneurons.

Figure 2 presents records obtained from an experiment in which two nerve branches to biceps were employed for stimulation by single shocks, reflex discharge being recorded from the eighth post-thoracic ventral root. The branches were of unequal size, and the shock to the smaller, called here the conditioning shock, evoked an afferent volley that was insufficient to secure a reflex discharge. The shock to the larger branch, here called the test shock, resulted in the two-neuron-arc reflex discharge to be seen, in isolation, in records A and O of Figure 2. The two afferent paths were of equal length so that, with synchronous shocks, the two afferent volleys reached the spinal cord in concert. Record B illustrates the result of such synchronous stimulation of the two branches. The reflex response is increased three-fold. As the test shock falls increasingly later with respect to the conditioning shock

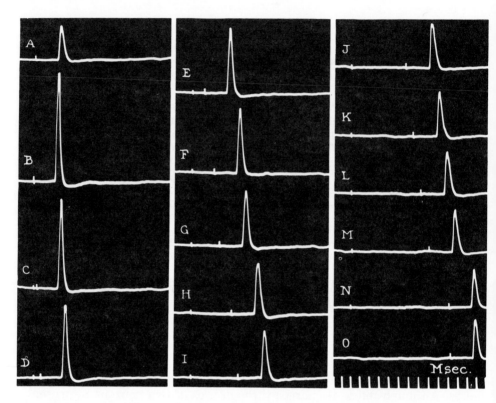

FIG. 2. Facilitation of biceps reflex by afferent volley from another branch of biceps nerve. A, O: biceps reflex in isolation. B–N: Biceps reflex tests effect in the biceps nucleus of the afferent conditioning volley, coincident with (B), and at various intervals after arrival of the conditioning volley. The conditioning volley evokes no reflex response. Time: msec.

(Records C to N of Fig. 2), facilitation of the test reflex declines progressively, at first rapidly and then more slowly, over a time course extending in the figure to 10 msec.

A better indication of the time course of facilitation in motor nuclei may be found in Figure 3, in which are plotted the results obtained in seven individual experiments on as many preparations. In four of the experiments facilitation in flexor nuclei was examined, either by fractionating the afferent inflow from biceps or by causing interaction between volleys arising in the nerves of semitendinosus and biceps. The three other experiments, performed in examination of facilitation in extensor nuclei, record the interaction at the motoneurons of volleys arising in the nerves to the two heads of gastrocnemius. Naturally the intensity of facilitation varies from one experiment to another, hence the points from the individual experiments have been scaled so that they concide at the time of maximum facilitation.

It will be seen from Figure 3 that facilitation is maximal if the two volleys arrive simultaneously at the motoneurons, and that it decays over a relatively prolonged time course that can be represented by an exponential curve, as drawn, having a value for $1/e$ of approximately 4 msec. Furthermore, there are no apparent discontinuities in the curve of facilitation to suggest the intervention of relayed activity in the conditioning of the test reflexes, and finally, the points obtained by experiment on flexor and extensor nuclei show satisfactory correspondence. From the evidence presented it appears

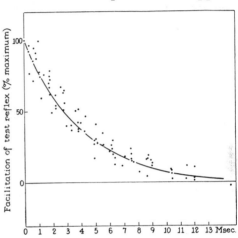

FIG. 3. Facilitation of motoneurons by impulses in primary afferent fibers. Points from seven experiments, scaled on the ordinates to coincide at the time of maximum facilitation. Relative facilitation, expressed in per cent maximum, is plotted as a function of time. The plotted curve is an exponential regression having successive half-values at 2.8, 5.6, 8.4, 11.2 and 14 msec. In four experiments facilitation in flexor nuclei was examined; the remaining three were concerned with extensor nuclei. Individual experiments on facilitation in flexor and extensor nuclei are to be found in Figs. 4 and 5 respectively.

that the facilitation curves, and hence the summation periods at the motoneurons, are similar whether the motoneurons belong to a flexor or to an extensor nucleus. The summation period defined by the curve in Figure 3, therefore, would seem to be a general property of the synapses of two-neuron-arc systems of the spinal cord. It may be noted that the curve of Figure 3 is drawn according to a regression having successive half-values at 2.8, 5.6, 8.4, 11.2, and 14 msec. In all of the succeeding figures the same curve has been drawn. Divergences from reasonable agreement with the function and curves representing the conditioning of motoneurons by internuncial activity have been plotted by simple joining of the experimentally determined points. All solid line plots represent experimental observations, broken line curves being extrapolations according to expectation.

II. Effect in a flexor nucleus of increasing the conditioning volley. One naturally is reluctant to accept prolonged excitatory action such as that described in connection with Figures 2 and 3 as resulting from single synchronous volleys of impulses unaided by the reverberant activity of parallel chains of interneurons. A way to assess the "purity" of the action is to observe the effect within a motor nucleus of deliberate addition, into the conditioning volleys, of some group II impulses; and by this means, adding known internuncial activity to the total conditioning agent at the motoneurons tested. Figure 4 illustrates the result of an experiment dealing with a flexor nucleus, in which are compared the conditioning effects of afferent volleys of two strengths. The conditioning stimulation was applied to the nerve of semitendinosus, the test stimulation to a branch supplying biceps. The experimental points, indicated by dots in Figure 4, were obtained by the use of a shock 1.1 threshold for the (inconstant) appearance of reflex response in the conditioning system. The test stimulus was strong. The experimentally determined points are represented satisfactorily by the regression curve as drawn. In order to obtain the curve represented in Figure 4 by the crosses, the conditioning shocks were increased to 1.4 threshold, the test shocks remaining at the same strength. One will notice that no appreciable change in the course of facilitation has taken place in the first 1.5 msec. However, at about this stimulus interval a sharp break in the curve occurs

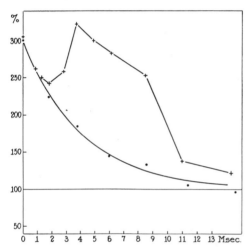

FIG. 4. Facilitation of biceps reflex by afferent volleys in semitendinosus nerve. Amplitude of the test reflex, expressed as per cent of control amplitude, is plotted as function of the time interval between conditioning and test volleys. To obtain the curve represented by dots, conditioning volleys of near reflex threshold strength were used. Stronger conditioning volleys caused the appearance of a second period of facilitation (crosses).

and thereafter a second period of facilitation supervenes. Since the test object is in this instance a flexor nucleus, and since the action of interneurons in an ipsilateral system is predominantly excitatory to flexors (12), the observed result of increasing in strength the conditioning volleys is entirely in accord with expectation on the proposition that conditioning by internuncial activity has been added to conditioning by the primary afferent fibers that course directly to the motoneurons. The latency for the internuncial action, measured approximately by the time to the break between the two curves, is accounted for by additional afferent conduction time required for group II fibers (12) and additional synaptic delay.

III. Effect in an extensor nucleus of increasing the conditioning volley. It is appropriate to investigate the effect of slight increase in the size of conditioning volleys where the object of study is an extensor rather than a flexor nucleus. Figure 5 presents results that have been obtained in experiment designed for this purpose. Conditioning shocks were applied to the nerve of one head of gastrocnemius, test shocks to the other. The points indicated by dots were obtained with the use of weak conditioning volleys, and may be represented by the usual regression curve as drawn. The points indicated by crosses were obtained by repeating the experiment utilizing somewhat stronger conditioning volleys. It is obvious, by comparison of the earliest points of the two curves, that the weaker of the two strengths of conditioning shock was submaximal for the direct fibers of the nerve. Accordingly, we find the curve obtained by the use of the stronger shocks beginning higher. The broken line, then, is an extrapolation indicating the curve of facilitation to be expected as a result of the stronger conditioning volleys, provided no change other than increase in the group I afferent volleys took place. In actual fact this curve is representative of the experimental points during the

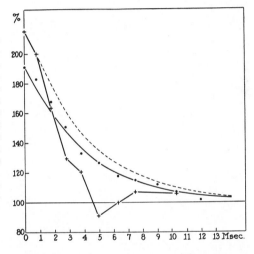

FIG. 5. Facilitation of reflex pertaining to one head of gastrocnemius by afferent volleys in nerve to the other head. Ordinates and abscissae as in Fig. 4. The dots represent points obtained by the use of weak conditioning volleys. On strengthening the conditioning volleys slightly, the points identified by crosses were obtained. Initially, by use of the stronger conditioning volleys, facilitation is increased but the subsequent course is interrupted by secondary inhibition. Broken line: extrapolation to show expected course of facilitation if not so interrupted.

first msec., but, thereafter, the experimental points diverge in the direction of inhibition. Since the object of study is an extensor nucleus and since ipsilateral internuncial activity is predominantly inhibitory to extensor neurons, the conditioning curve obtained by the use of the stronger conditioning shocks is interpreted as the resultant of a combination of excitation by direct action of primary afferent fibers and inhibition by the action of interneurons.

IV. Inhibition of motoneurons. Afferent fibers that yield inhibition of motoneurons by direct action (10) are known to be indistinguishable, on the basis of elementary properties, from those that yield excitation (11). Therefore they too are large afferent fibers of muscle origin. Inasmuch as afferent fibers of this group arising in heads of a single muscle, or in closely allied synergists, mutually facilitate the excitatory actions of each other, one might reasonably expect inhibitory interaction to result between volleys arising in the afferent fibers of antagonists. The expectation is based on the supposition that direct inhibition by primary afferent fibers represents the stretch-evoked inhibition of antagonists described by Sherrington (24) and by Liddell and Sherrington (9). Experimental result is in accord with this expectation.

Figure 6 presents records from an experiment in which a shock for conditioning, small in size, was applied to the deep peroneal nerve, and a strong test shock was applied to the combined gastrocnemius nerves. Recordings were made from the eighth post-thoracic ventral root. The afferent paths were of unequal length, that for the conditioning volleys being the longer.

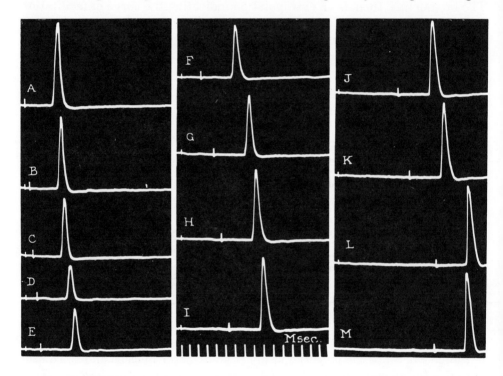

Fig. 6. Inhibition of gastrocnemius two-neuron-arc reflex by weak afferent volleys in deep peroneal nerve. A, M: control records of gastrocnemius reflex in isolation. B–L: conditioning effects when conditioning and test shocks are separated by various intervals. Since the afferent paths were of unequal length shock interval does not give volley interval. The necessary correction is given in the text. Time: msec.

For this reason a correction must be made to the shock interval to allow for differential conduction time. It was found that the conditioning and test volleys arrived at the spinal cord simultaneously when the test shock followed the conditioning shock by approximately 0.4 msec. The conditioning shock evoked no reflex response in the eighth post-thoracic ventral root, whereas the test shock evoked, in that root, the two-neuron-arc reflex response to be seen in observations A and M of Figure 6. For observation B the two volleys (but not the shocks) were separated by an interval of approximately 0.2 msec. Inhibition is well established. As the test shock falls progressively later with respect to the conditioning shock (C to L of Fig. 6), inhibition of the test response increases rapidly to a maximum and then regresses slowly over a prolonged time course.

A more complete representation of the course of inhibition may be obtained by inspection of Figure 7, in which are plotted the results of four experiments dealing with inhibitory interaction. In three of the experiments inhibition in a flexor nucleus was measured; in the fourth, the reverse situation was examined. Since the degree of inhibition varied from experiment to experiment, the experimental points have been scaled to coincide at 0.5 msec. on the abcissa. This point for coincidence was chosen for two reasons:

FIG. 7. Inhibition of motoneurons by impulses in primary afferent fibers. Experimental points from four experiments are included; the points are scaled to coincide at a conditioning volley-test volley interval of 0.5 msec. The ordinates therefore relate the degree of inhibition, in per cent of maximum, to the time interval between volleys (on the abscissae). Three experiments were concerned with flexor nuclei, the remaining with an extensor nucleus. Curves obtained in individual experiments may be found in Figs. 8 and 9.

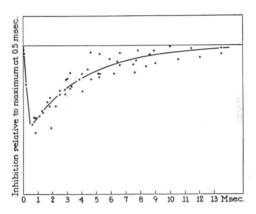

inhibition is maximal at approximately this time and internuncial activity, if such were present, would not influence the scaling of the points. The regression curve that has been drawn through the points in Figure 7 is the same as that drawn for facilitation in Figure 3: it decays to successive half-values of 2.8, 5.6, 8.4, 11.2 and 14 msec.

The plotted curve in Figure 7 is a fair representation of the experimental points: it shows that inhibition begins with synchronous arrival of the interacting volleys at the spinal cord (9), that there is an incremental phase of approximately 0.5 msec. duration, and that inhibition regresses over a prolonged time course that may be represented by an exponential curve having a value for $1/e$ of approximately 4 msec. The inhibitory period is similar whether examined in flexor or in extensor nuclei, and therefore would seem to be a general property of the inhibitory junctions in the motor nuclei.

V. Effect in a flexor nucleus of increasing conditioning volley. As in the study of facilitation, it is possible to demonstrate that sharp departures from the simple inhibitory curve result from the deliberate instigation of internuncial activity by increased conditioning volleys. Figure 8 presents an experiment in which a flexor two-neuron-arc reflex was conditioned by volleys arising in the nerves to the antagonist extensor. The influence on the test reflex of two strengths of afferent conditioning volleys is compared. The conditioning stimulation was applied to the nerves of gastrocnemius, the test stimulation to the nerve of tibialis anterior. Records were obtained from the seventh post-thoracic ventral root. The experimental points indicated by dots were obtained by the use of the weaker conditioning volleys. These points are represented satisfactorily by the solid line regression curve as drawn. The experimental points indicated by crosses resulted from conditioning with the slightly stronger afferent volleys. It is apparent from a consideration of Figure 8 that the weaker conditioning shocks were not maximal

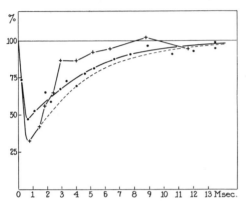

FIG. 8. Inhibition in a flexor nucleus, and interruption of inhibition by excitation of internuncial origin. To obtain the points identified by dots, weak gastrocnemius nerve afferent volleys were used to condition the reflex of tibialis anterior. On strengthening the conditioning volleys (crosses) the primary inhibition was increased, but after a brief interval is interrupted by facilitation of flexor reflex origin. Broken line: extrapolation to show inhibitory curve to be expected if stronger conditioning volleys had had no effect other than increasing primary inhibition.

for the group I afferent fibers of the gastrocnemius nerve since on increasing those shocks the inhibition in the nucleus of tibialis anterior, at the shortest shock intervals, was increased. The broken line regression curve is drawn by extrapolation from the first two points represented by crosses, in order to indicate the curve of inhibition to be expected if, as a result of the increased conditioning shocks, no change other than increase in the number of group I fibers stimulated took place. The experimentally determined points diverge from this curve at an interval of approximately 1.5 msec. between volleys, and do so in the direction of facilitation. The latency for the beginning of divergence and the direction of the divergence—since the test system was a flexor two-neuron-arc reflex—are consistent with the view that internuncial activity was added by the stronger conditioning shocks to the direct action of the primary afferent fibers, and that the internuncial activity was responsible for the break in the resulting conditioning curve.

VI. Effect in an extensor nucleus of increasing conditioning volley. Conditioning effects in the gastrocnemius (extensor) nucleus evoked by afferent volleys arising in the deep peroneal (flexor) nerve reveal a more complex situation than has yet been encountered, but one that is entirely consistent with the known reflex behaviour of gastrocnemius muscle. One will recall the study made by Denny-Brown (cf. 1, p. 73) of the comparative behaviour of gastrocnemius and soleus in response to stimulation of afferent nerves. Particularly noteworthy is the fact that stimulation by weak shocks of the peroneal nerve, acting on a background of stretch reflex in gastrocnemius and soleus, results in an increased contraction of the former coincident with relaxation, from the stretch reflex plateau, of the latter. Stronger stimulation of the peroneal nerve caused both muscles to relax. The experiments illustrated in Figures 9 and 10 should be interpreted in the light of those findings.

The experimental points (identified by dots in Fig. 9) were obtained by the use of weak shocks to the deep peroneal nerve delivered for the purpose

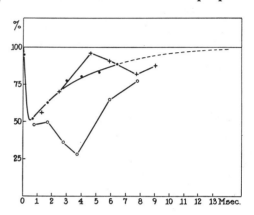

FIG. 9. Inhibition in an extensor (gastrocnemius) nucleus resulting from afferent volleys in deep peroneal nerve. The curves indicate various admixtures of primary inhibition by the direct action of primary afferent fibers, secondary facilitation and secondary inhibition, resulting from internuncial action. Further details in text.

of conditioning a gastrocnemius two-neuron-arc reflex. The points were obtained in the order of increasing shock interval, and may be represented by the usual regression curve. Next in order the points indicated by crosses were obtained, without deliberately increasing the conditioning volleys. These points indicate a good correspondence at short intervals, but a degree of divergence thereafter, first in the direction of facilitation, subsequently in the direction of inhibition. Deliberate slight increase in the conditioning volleys then resulted in the points identified by circles. These last points reveal the appearance of a second phase of inhibition. The curves represented in Figure 9 by crosses and circles are interpreted as indicating the conditioning of gastrocnemius motor nucleus by a combination of direct inhibitory action of primary afferent fibers, together with varying admixtures of excitatory and inhibitory internuncial activity.

Figure 10 illustrates another experiment in which the conditioning effect on gastrocnemius nucleus of volleys in the deep peroneal nerve was examined. The first curve (indicated by dots) was obtained by the use of conditioning shocks obviously submaximal for the initial inhibition, since this inhibition was increased by increasing the conditioning shocks. The shocks, therefore, were submaximal for the group I fibers of the deep peroneal nerve; and yet the curve shows, after the first 1.5 msec., a distinct deviation in the direction of facilitation. Slightly stronger conditioning stimulation increased the direct inhibitory action to maximum (curve indicated by crosses), and the later deviation is somewhat less in the direction of facilitation. Finally (curve indicated by circles), by virtue of further increase in the conditioning stimulation, the secondary deviation is strongly in the direction of inhibition, there being no further intensification of the primary inhibitory action.

Consider now, in connection with Figures 9 and 10, the three effects in gastrocnemius nucleus resulting from afferent volleys in the deep peroneal nerve: primary inhibition, secondary facilitation and secondary inhibition. A distinct threshold difference distinguishes the afferent fibers responsible for the first two effects and those responsible for the last mentioned. It seems quite clear, therefore, that secondary inhibition results from the stimulation of group II fibers, that it represents the extensor-inhibitory component of the flexor reflex and that it is the result of internuncial activity. The origin of secondary facilitation is less certain, not in the sense that there is any reason to suppose that it does not result from internuncial activity, but in the sense that experiment has not indicated clearly the classification to which the executant afferent fibers belong. Bearing in mind the vagaries of stimulation, the overlapping thresholds for primary inhibition and secondary facilitation in the reflex system being considered may not indicate overlapping properties of the afferent fibers giving rise to the two effects. On the other hand, it is so difficult to extricate the primary inhibition in gastrocnemius nucleus from the secondary facilitation that one must entertain the possibility that secondary facilitation in this nucleus represents the activity of certain interneurons stimulated into activity by collaterals of the group I afferent fibers of the deep peroneal nerve. For that matter, if one considers the weak afferent stimulation that is necessary in order to realize simple conditioning curves in the light of Cajal's demonstration of collaterals given off to the internuncial regions by the "reflexo-motor collaterals," it may be that isolated direct action at the motoneurons appears only when the supposed volleys entering the internuncial pools by way of these collaterals are of intensity insufficient to discharge interneurons. This possibility does not modify the main conclusions that the simple conditioning curves represent the unaided conditioning activity—excitatory and inhibitory at proper loci—of primary afferent fibers, and that the bulk of the secondary conditioning effects, following strictly the reciprocal pattern of the flexor reflex, results from the stimulation of group II afferent fibers that are known to mediate the flexor reflex (12).

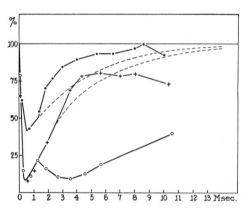

FIG. 10. As in Fig. 9, from another experiment. Full description in text.

COMMENT

VII. Considerations relating to excitation of motoneurons. The "*synaptic potential.*" With synaptic transmission in the spinal cord blocked completely by deep anaesthesia, Eccles (5) has shown that an afferent volley evokes in an appropriate ventral root a potential change that has negative direction at the recording lead adjacent to the spinal cord. As recorded, this "synaptic potential" has a rising phase of 2.5 msec. duration, followed by an approximately exponential regression falling to $1/e$ in 7.5 msec. Assuming that the site of origin of the synaptic potential is central to the point of electrode contact, allowance should be made for changes suffered in the course of electrotonic spread to the ventral root from the presumed site of origin. This having been done, it is likely that a reasonable degree of agreement would obtain between the decay of facilitation at the motoneurons and the decay of the synaptic potential. One may assume a correlation between the two phenomena.

It is of interest that Eccles finds the exponential regression of the synaptic potential interrupted by a "hump" if the anaesthesia is not sufficiently deep to block all internuncial discharge. This effect is comparable to the break from exponential regression in the facilitation curve if a test reflex in the unanaesthetized preparation is conditioned by afferent volleys slightly larger than critical size (*e.g.*, Fig. 4). Thus Eccles has achieved by deep anaesthesia and strong volleys what is achieved here by the use of feeble volleys in muscle nerves: the avoidance of internuncial activity. Obviously the latter method would not be very satisfactory for study of the synaptic potential, which, because of the necessary condition, would be impractically small.

On the course of excitation at the motoneuron. Focussing one's attention solely upon the action at the motoneurons of a single synchronous "excitatory" volley, uncomplicated by the restimulating action of interneurons, it appears necessary now squarely to face the question of whether or not the excitatory event at the synapse contains two (at least) components: one brief, powerful, and capable of adequate stimulation of the motoneurons; the other of longer duration, not so powerful, capable of facilitating the action of the first mentioned component, but not of itself capable of discharging motoneurons. The first component would be identified as the detonator action (2, 3, 18); the latter, for reasons that will become apparent as the argument develops, may be called "residual facilitation."

The train of evidence that led to the concept of a brief excitatory or detonator action is well known and has been summarized extensively (2, 18); it need not be reiterated here. The existence, at least in significant measure, of a second excitatory component of synaptic excitation in the central nervous system has remained problematical until the recent demonstrations by Eccles, and in the present paper. Before the demonstration of a prolonged summation period of significant proportions it was unnecessary, as Lorente de Nó stated (18), to assume excitatory actions other than detonator action in theoretical discussion of the then known properties of synaptic transmission. At the present time the alternatives are to assume two components in synaptic excitation, or to reject the concept of detonator action (4, 5). For a number of reasons the latter course seems precipitate, if not unjustified.

The postulation of two components of synaptic excitation does not demand the assumption of elementary properties that have no analogues in peripheral nerve. There are in published form at least three lines of evidence to support the assertion: (i) impulses arriving at a block in peripheral nerve establish two gradients of negativity at the margin of the block, one of spike-like dimensions, the other (called residual negativity) having a more enduring character (18). Facilitation across the block reflects faithfully the potential sequence, and so too exhibits two components. (ii) Lorente de Nó and Davis (19) have described two components of electrotonus in nerve, one fast, the other slow. (iii) Marrazzi and Lorente de Nó (20) have shown two components in the membrane potential change of fibers influenced by the passage of impulses in neighboring fibers. One important consideration in each of these three situations in peripheral nerve is the fact that the fast components exhibit a sharp spatial decrement, whereas the slow components spread for considerable distance. The first of the three situations is particularly important for present considerations, for Lorente de Nó (18) has employed the block in nerve as a model of synaptic transmission that makes adequate provision for the assumption of two successive gradients of negativity at the synaptic knobs: detonator negativity and residual negativity. Detonator negativity would be characterized by brief duration, powerful action and sharp spatial decrement. Residual negativity would be more prolonged, less powerful and more widespread. Indeed, it seems likely that the known differential decrement of fast and slow components, when applied to synaptic events, might be a partial explanation for the fact that the synaptic potential recorded at the ventral root does not indicate the presence of a detonator negativity. Clearly then, one should not preclude the existence of detonator negativity or detonator action from considerations of the synaptic potential as recorded.

Problem of facilitation without discharge. One observation of particular concern in this paper is well accommodated by the assumption of two components in synaptic excitation. Afferent volleys in group I fibers arising in one fraction of a muscle give rise to two-neuron-arc discharges reflecting into the motor fibers of that fraction of the muscle but not elsewhere (12), yet the motoneurons pertaining to the rest of the muscle and its immediate synergists are facilitated for a considerable period of time. Admitting the assumption of the first component of excitation, it is a sufficient explanation for the absence of "cross discharge" to suppose that the afferent fibers from one fraction of a muscle have synaptic knobs on the motoneuron somata of the other fractions, but not at any point in dense clusters (17, 14). A second component would account for "cross facilitation" having the properties described. Rejection of the assumption of the first component of excitation, because of the nature of the second component, would remove the anatomical and functional bases for an understanding of the absence of "cross discharge."

In view of these considerations and others, such as the brief, relatively fixed duration of synaptic delay (16) that are not of immediate concern here, it is concluded that the present experiments demonstrate, and descr be some of the properties of, a second phase of summation at synapses in the central nervous system.

VIII. Considerations relative to inhibition. The experiments described in this paper indicate the existence of an unitary inhibitory process set into operation by ordinary nerve impulses travelling in afferent nerve fibers that are indistinguishable from those that excite motoneurons (10, 11). The inhibitory process as revealed at the motoneurons is characterized by an incremental phase of some 0.5 msec. duration followed by an essentially exponential regression falling to $1/e$ in approximately 4 msec. The continued influence of the inhibitory action evoked by a synchronous volley is recognizable in experiment for 14 to 15 msec. The inhibitory process is active in the sense that afferent impulses, of inhibitory effect at a given locus, exert their action directly upon the structures, the excitability of which is depressed—the effect not depending in any way upon refractoriness anywhere in the system. The inhibitory process does not depend upon prior activity other than the conducted impulse that sets it in operation. It may properly be said that the operation of the inhibitory process is revealed only by its contrary influence on excitation, for there is as yet no known potential sign that may be correlated with the threshold change evoked by the inhibitory process.

By virtue of their similarity of regression (compare Figs. 3 and 6) it seems that the inhibitory process should be identified as the functional opposite of residual facilitation. As yet there is no indication in experiment of an inhibitory counterpart of detonator action and, although this fact may indicate merely that the experimental conditions for its demonstration have not been satisfied, it is certainly unnecessary to assume such a counterpart in discussion of the known properties of inhibition.

Inhibition in two-neuron-arc systems is distributed strictly in accord with the requirements of reciprocal innervation (15), regardless of the anatomical location of the nuclei of the antagonist systems. Anatomical proximity of the nuclei belonging to the conditioning and testing systems, therefore, is not a factor in the production of inhibition. For example, direct inhibitory interaction obtains between the reflex pathways of quadriceps and biceps, muscles whose motor nuclei possess little segmental, or axial, overlap; whereas gastrocnemius and biceps, segmentally identical, and with their nuclei in close proximity in cross section, possess entirely independent two-neuron-arc reflex pathways (15). On any thinkable schema of inhibition it would appear that the group I afferent fibers of quadriceps must approximate the reflex path of biceps, which they inhibit, more closely than do the comparable afferent fibers of gastrocnemius which are without action on the reflex path of biceps. Accordingly it is not reasonable to suppose that inhibitory interaction takes place outside the confines of motor nucleus of the inhibited muscle. It follows that there are two reasonable hypotheses: either inhibition results from the action of impulses in the terminal regions of some fibers upon the impulses in the terminal regions of other fibers, the net result being a decrease in the potency of the excitation delivered by the latter to the motoneurons (23), or inhibition results from the action of impulses in the terminal regions of fibers upon the somata of motoneurons. Since it is difficult to conceive of impulses affecting the terminations of fibers in a motor nucleus without at the same time influencing the motoneurons, the latter possibility merits the most careful and serious consideration; indeed, the two possibilities are not mutually exclusive.

IX. Possible origin of brief summation periods. Conditioning curves obtained by stimulation of dorsal roots, in contrast with those illustrated here, quite regularly and reproducibly exhibit brief initial periods of summation comparable to those described by Lorente de Nó (18). The only essential distinction between the two types of experiment, each involving stimulation of group I afferent fibers, lies in anatomical rather than functional selection of the afferent fibers for conditioning stimulation. Dorsal root stimulation of necessity produces volleys in antagonistic as well as allied reflex arcs. As a result of dorsal root stimulation, motoneurons are presented indiscriminately with the conditioning influences: detonator action, residual facilitation and inhibition. One may suppose that the latter two processes, being largely comparable except in direction and developing pari passu with strength of stimulation (11), would cancel each other, leaving detonator actions alone to determine the form of the interaction curve. On this interpretation, the brief facilitation periods obtained by the use of mixed volleys in dorsal roots —and presumably in tracts as well—define the summation period of the detonator process.

Conclusions and Summary

Facilitation and inhibition, by the direct actions of primary afferent fibers, of two-neuron-arc reflexes has been examined by experiment.

An afferent volley, in group I fibers arising in one head of a muscle, facilitates the action of its synergists and inhibits the action of its antagonists. Details of the distribution of these actions are presented elsewhere (15).

The temporal characteristics of facilitation and inhibition have been defined. Facilitation is maximal on the occasion of synchronous convergence of "conditioning" and "test" volleys, and decays exponentially along a curve falling to $1/e$ in approximately 4.0 msec. Inhibition displays an incremental phase of approximately 0.5 msec. duration, thereafter decaying in the same manner as facilitation.

Reasons are given for supposing that the facilitation described here is the expression of a process additional to the detonator action of earlier descriptions. Accordingly it may be called "residual facilitation."

The assumption of two excitatory events, detonator action and residual facilitation, makes no demand for elementary processes unknown in peripheral nerve. Their existence is predicted by the nerve-block model of synaptic transmission (18), only the significance of the latter, as far as the central nervous system is concerned, having remained in doubt in the absence of demonstration. The functional importance of residual facilitation now has been established.

According to present evidence, it is permissible to assume a correlation between residual facilitation and the "synaptic potential" of Eccles.

Residual facilitation and inhibition are regarded as functional opposites, they being similar in all known characteristics excepting direction.

Of many possible factors, three: detonator action, residual facilitation and inhibition, have received sufficient documentation to necessitate inclusion in theoretical consideration of the known properties of synaptic transmission.

Reason is given for supposing that the brief facilitation periods evident in appropriately designed experiments do, as had been supposed, measure the effective duration of the detonator action.

REFERENCES

1. CREED, R. S., DENNY-BROWN, D. E., ECCLES, J. C., LIDDELL, E. G. T., and SHERRINGTON, C. S.   Reflex activity of the spinal cord. Oxford, Clarendon Press, 1932, vii, 183 pp.
2. ECCLES, J. C.   Synaptic and neuromuscular transmission. Ergebn. Physiol., 1936, 38: 393–444.
3. ECCLES, J. C.   The discharge of impulses from ganglion cells. J. Physiol., 1937, 91: 1–22.
4. ECCLES, J. C.   Synaptic potentials and transmission in sympathetic ganglion. J. Physiol., 1943, 101: 465–483.
5. ECCLES, J. C.   Synaptic potentials of motoneurones. J. Neurophysiol., 1946, 9: 87–120.
6. ECCLES, J. C. and SHERRINGTON, C. S.   Numbers and contraction values of individual motor-units examined in some muscles of the limb. Proc. roy. Soc., 1930, B106: 326–357.
7. GASSER, H. S. and GRAHAM, H. T.   Potentials produced in the spinal cord by stimulation of dorsal roots. Amer. J. Physiol., 1933, 103: 303–320.
8. LIDDELL, E. G. T. and SHERRINGTON, C. S.   Reflexes in response to stretch (Myotatic reflexes). Proc. roy. Soc., 1924, B96: 212–242.
9. LIDDELL, E. G. T. and SHERRINGTON, C. S.   Further observations on myotatic reflexes. Proc. roy. Soc., 1925, B97: 267–283.
10. LLOYD, D. P. C.   A direct central inhibitory action of dromically conducted impulses. J. Neurophysiol., 1941, 4: 184–190.
11. LLOYD, D. P. C.   Reflex action in relation to pattern and peripheral source of afferent stimulation. J. Neurophysiol., 1943, 6: 111–120.
12. LLOYD, D. P. C.   Neuron patterns controlling transmission of ipsilateral hind limb reflexes in cat. J. Neurophysiol., 1943, 6: 293–315.
13. LLOYD, D. P. C.   Conduction and synaptic transmission of reflex response to stretch in spinal cats. J. Neurophysiol., 1943, 6: 317–326.
14. LLOYD, D. P. C.   On the relation between discharge zone and subliminal fringe in a motoneuron pool supplied by a homogeneous presynaptic pathway. Yale J. Biol. Med., 1945, 18: 117–121.
15. LLOYD, D. P. C.   Integrative pattern of excitation and inhibition in two-neuron reflex arcs. J. Neurophysiol., 1946, 9: 439–444.

16. LORENTE DE NÓ, R.   Limits of variation of the synaptic delay of motoneurons. *J. Neurophysiol.*, 1938, *1*: 187–193.
17. LORENTE DE NÓ, R.   Synaptic stimulation as a local process. *J. Neurophysiol.*, 1938, *1*: 194–207.
18. LORENTE DE NÓ, R.   Transmission of impulses through cranial motor nuclei. *J. Neurophysiol.*, 1939, *2*: 402–464.
19. LORENTE DE NÓ, R. and DAVIS, L.   Electrotonus produced by direct current pulses in frog nerve. *Amer. J. Physiol.*, 1941, *133*: P366.
20. MARRAZZI, A. S. and LORENTE DE NÓ, R.   Interaction of neighboring fibres in myelinated nerve. *J. Neurophysiol.*, 1944, *7*: 83–102.
21. RENSHAW, B.   Influence of discharge of motoneurons upon excitation of neighboring motoneurons. *J. Neurophysiol.*, 1941, *4*: 167–183.
22. RENSHAW, B.   Reflex discharges in branches of the crural nerve. *J. Neurophysiol.*, 1942, *5*: 487–498.
23. RENSHAW, B.   Interaction of nerve impulses in the gray matter as a mechanism of central inhibition. *Fed. Proc. Amer. Soc. exp. Biol.*, 1946, *5*, *II*: 86.
24. SHERRINGTON, C. S.   Note on the knee-jerk and the correlation of action of antagonistic muscles. *Proc. roy. Soc.*, 1893, *52*: 556–564.

INTEGRATIVE PATTERN OF EXCITATION AND INHIBITION IN TWO-NEURON REFLEX ARCS

DAVID P. C. LLOYD

Laboratories of The Rockefeller Institute for Medical Research, New York

(Received for publication June 18, 1946)

THE PRECEDING paper presents an investigation of the elementary properties of the excitatory and inhibitory processes at the junctions of primary afferent fibers with the motor nuclei (9). Included are descriptions of residual facilitation and inhibition as events at such junctions additional to the earlier described detonator action (2, 10). The occurrence of inhibition, as a direct action, has been documented since 1941 (5); residual facilitation only now (3, 9) has proved to be quantitatively significant, although for some time the possibility of its existence has been considered (10). In the case of both actions it remains to demonstrate that the phenomena have significant relation to the integrative pattern of the spinal cord. The importance of such a demonstration can hardly be overemphasized, for in its absence an observed phenomenon may or may not have significance in reflex performance. A positive demonstration of lack of relation to integrative pattern, on the other hand, would indicate very strongly the essentially artifactual nature of an observed phenomenon. A fruitful technique for examining the functional significance of observed actions in the spinal cord (in this instance, residual facilitation and inhibition) is to determine their distribution among the several motor nuclei, when evoked by specified afferent volleys. This has been done, and the experiments to be described are representative of the results obtained.

The preparation used and the experimental arrangements were similar to those outlined in the preceding paper (9), with the exception that conditioning shocks sufficient to stimulate group I and group II afferent fibers were employed routinely. This was done in order to uncover the conditioning potentialities of the muscle afferent fibers. Eight combinations of conditioning and test volleys are to be considered.

RESULTS

I. Volleys in nerves of flexor muscles acting at the same joint. Curve 1 of Figure 1 illustrates the conditioning effect upon a two-neuron-arc reflex, pertaining to biceps femoris posterior, of an afferent volley arising in the nerve to semitendinosus. These muscles are synergic flexors of the knee. It will be seen that facilitation of the test reflex begins with synchronous arrival of the conditioning and test volleys, and for brief intervals between the two volleys may be described by the curve typical of primary facilitation (9). The course of primary facilitation is interrupted by secondary facilitation, resulting from the stimulation of group II fibers, and representing flexor reflex activity.

II. Volleys in nerves of flexor muscles acting at different joints. Curve 2 of Figure 1 illustrates the result of conditioning the two-neuron-arc reflex

Lloyd, D. P. C. Integrative pattern of excitation and inhibition in two-neuron reflex arcs. *J. Neurophysiol.* **9**: 439–444, 1946.

of a flexor muscle by afferent volleys deriving from flexor muscles of other nearby joints. The test stimulations were applied to the flexor fraction of the hamstring nerve (representing biceps femoris and semitendinosus, flexors of the knee), and conditioning stimulations were applied to the deep peroneal nerve (representing flexors of the foot). One notes in curve 2 of Figure 1 the absence of any interaction between the systems until the conditioning volleys antecede the test volleys, at the spinal cord, by an interval of approximately 1.5 msec. Thereafter a period of facilitation obtains. This period of facilitation is comparable to the second period of facilitation in curve 1 of Figure 1 and, like it, is referable to the action through interneurons of group II impulses. The distinction between the two curves of Figure 1 lies in the presence (curve 1) or absence (curve 2) of facilitation attributable to the direct action of primary afferent fibers.

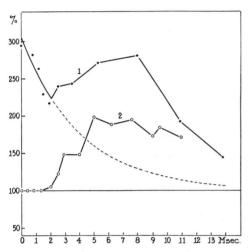

FIG. 1. Conditioning of two-neuron-arc reflexes by afferent volleys in group I and group II fibers of muscle nerves. In this and subsequent figures the conditioning effect on the test reflexes is expressed, on the ordinates, as the per cent of control amplitude achieved by the reflexes when conditioned. This is plotted as a function of time expressed on the abscissae, in msec. Solid line curves represent experimental points. The expected contribution to conditioning by the continued action of direct impulses (cf. 9) is expressed by the broken line extrapolations according to the exponential function proposed in the previous paper. In each case the interaction of afferent volleys arising in the nerves of muscles serving the same joint is indicated by dots, that of afferent volleys arising in the nerves of muscles serving neighboring joints is indicated by circles. Curve 1: Semitendinosus volleys conditioning biceps reflex. Curve 2: Deep peroneal volleys conditioning combined biceps-semitendinosus reflex.

III. Volleys in nerves of extensor muscles that act together at a joint. Figure 2 illustrates (curve 1) the conditioning effect, upon the two-neuron-arc reflex of one head of gastrocnemius, of volleys arising in the nerve to the other head. The two heads of gastrocnemius naturally are synergic at one and the same joint. By the use of synchronous volleys the test reflex was increased to 485 per cent of its control amplitude, the experimental point not being indicated in the figure. The facilitation occurring at brief shock intervals, at greater intervals, is superseded by inhibition, the latter representing the inhibitory aspect of the flexor reflex. Analysis with the aid of the facilitation curve to be expected if group I fibers alone had been active (broken line) places the onset of inhibitory action within the second msec.

IV. Volleys in nerves of extensor muscles that act at adjacent joints. Curve 2 of Figure 2 charts the conditioning effect, upon the two-neuron-arc reflex of gastrocnemius (ankle extensor), of volleys arising among the afferent fibers of quadriceps (knee extensor). Inhibition, beginning at an interval of approximately 1.5 msec. separation of conditioning and test volleys at the cord, is quite evident, but there is no indication of interaction between the pathways of quadriceps and gastrocnemius at shorter intervals. Therefore the interaction of afferent volleys from extensor muscles, like those from flexor muscles, is characterized by the presence of direct effects—afferent fiber to motoneuron—if the muscles act as a common joint, or by the absence of direct effects if the muscles do not so act.

At this juncture it is well to correct an error made in 1944 (8, p. 12) while endeavoring to interpret direct inhibition on the basis of the information then available. It was thought, in view of the known interaction of group I afferent volleys stimulated in dorsal roots of various segments (5), that direct inhibition would account for the silent period shown by Denny-Brown (1) to occur in gastrocnemius as the reflex accompaniment of a tendon jerk in quadriceps. Experiment does not support the supposed relation since (i) there is no direct connection between quadriceps afferent fibers and gastrocnemius motor nucleus and (ii) the threshold for inhibition of gastrocnemius by stimulation of afferent fibers from quadriceps (as seen in Fig. 2, curve 2) accords with that of group II fibers.

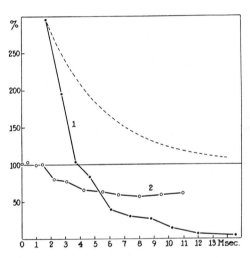

FIG. 2. Curve 1: Gastrocnemius afferent volleys conditioning gastrocnemius reflex. Curve 2: Quadriceps afferent volleys conditioning gastrocnemius reflex.

V. *Volleys in extensor nerve-flexor nerve sequence, the muscles of origin being antagonists at a given joint.* Curve 1 of Figure 3 illustrates the conditioning effect, on a two-neuron-arc reflex arising in the combined nerves of semitendinosus and biceps, and hence of knee-flexor origin, of volleys stimulated in the nerve of quadriceps (knee extensor). The initial effect of the conditioning volleys in this arrangement is inhibitory, the primary inhibition, after approximately 1.5 msec., being abrogated by facilitation of internuncial and flexor reflex origin.

VI. *Volleys in extensor nerve-flexor nerve sequence, the muscles of origin serving neighboring joints.* By way of contrast with the preceding situation, it will be seen from Figure 3, curve 2 that afferent volleys arising in the nerves to gastrocnemius (ankle extensor) have no conditioning effect upon a two-neuron-arc reflex of biceps (knee flexor) origin unless the respective afferent volleys are separated by an interval of more than 1.5 msec. Prominent, however, is the secondary facilitation representing flexor reflex activity.

VII. Volleys in flexor nerve-extensor nerve sequence, the muscles of origin being antagonists at a given joint. Figure 4, curve 1 illustrates the conditioning of a two-neuron-arc reflex obtained by stimulation of the tibial nerve, by volleys arising in the deep peroneal nerve. The nerves stimulated represent muscles of extension and flexion of the foot respectively. Two successive periods of inhibition are apparent, the first beginning with synchronous arrival of the conditioning and test volleys, the second beginning when the test volleys follow the conditioning volleys by an interval slightly greater than 1.0 msec. The first period of inhibition represents direct action of primary afferent fibers, the second period representing the action of interneurons.

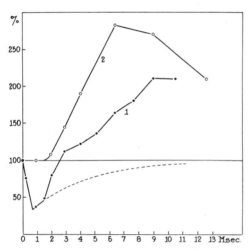

FIG. 3. Curve 1: Quadriceps afferent volleys conditioning biceps-semitendinosus combined reflex. Curve 2: Gastrocnemius afferent volleys conditioning biceps reflex.

VIII. Volleys in flexor nerve-extensor nerve sequence, the muscles of origin serving adjacent joints. If the test reflex pertains to the ankle extensor, gastrocnemius, and the conditioning volleys have their origin in the knee flexor, biceps femoris, then but a single period of inhibition is realized (Fig. 4, curve 2). This period of inhibition is comparable to the second period of inhibition evidence in curve 1 of Figure 4, and is the result of internuncial action at the motoneurons.

Conclusions relative to the distribution in motor nuclei of the direct actions of primary afferent fibers. Considering together the experiments illustrated, it follows that the group I afferent fibers of one fraction of a muscle or muscle group, in addition to their powerful connections to the motoneurons of that fraction (6, 7), have direct excitatory connection with the remainder of the muscle or muscle group but not with muscles of like action serving neighboring joints, either proximally or distally situated in the limb. To parallel the excitatory connections, the group I afferent fibers of a given muscle group have direct inhibitory connection to the motor nuclei of antagonists that act as the same joint but not to the motor nuclei of functional opposites that serve neighboring joints. Thus a muscle, through two-neuron-arc reflex connections, is controlled by itself, its immediate synergists and its immediate antagonists. In turn, through like central connection, that muscle influences its immediate neighbors, synergists and antagonists.

Two-neuron-arc discharges are known to represent the myotatic reflexes (6, 7). In origin and distribution, inhibition by the direct action of primary afferent collaterals now is found to possess the characteristics of stretch-evoked inhibition of antagonists (4, 11). Direct facilitation of allied muscle fractions is newly discovered (3, 9), but is seen to be distributed in strict accord with the requirements of reciprocal innervation. The absence of direct action on motoneurons pertaining to muscles of neighboring joints is consonant with the nature of myotatic reflex activity. In every instance the described actions of primary afferent fibers are expressions of reciprocal innervation. For these several reasons it is concluded that the actions described are of functional significance in the integrative pattern of the spinal cord and that they are concerned with the mediation of stretch-evoked, or myo-

tatic, reflex performance. The muscles of a given joint being by direct reflex interconnection mutually dependent, and yet independent of other muscles at the myotatic level of postural performance, together constitute—along with the direct reflex paths that bind them—what may be called a myotatic unit.

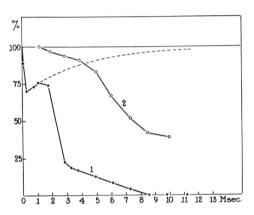

Without the necessity of other than direct reflex connections, the myotatic unit exhibits within itself in full measure the elementary mechanism of reciprocal innervation. In the circumstances of the present experiments—that is, with the preparation in the spinal state —utilizing synchronous stimula-

FIG. 4. Curve 1: Deep peroneal afferent volleys conditioning tibial nerve reflex. Curve 2: Biceps afferent volleys conditioning gastrocnemius reflex.

tions so that the reflex discharges mimic phasic rather than static stretch responses, and with the possibility of feedback eliminated as the result of "opening" the reflex arcs for study, the flexor and extensor moieties of the myotatic unit possess essentially equal potentialities for reflex discharge, facilitation and inhibition. Therefore, it would seem that dominance of one moiety by the other arises largely as an expression of influences external to the myotatic unit. The reflex taxis of decerebrate rigidity provides the most obvious example.

Although the myotatic units are independent one from another in the central courses, it is possible for one unit to influence the next by action at the periphery. To cite a familiar example: quadriceps in active contraction acts to increase the distance between the origins and insertion of the two-joint gastrocnemius, and so subjects it to stretch. All things being equal, activity within the myotatic unit containing gastrocnemius would result. The same would not be true of quadriceps in relation to the single-joint soleus. Two-joint muscles, therefore, may be considered as bridges between individual myotatic units.

Before the distribution of inhibition within the myotatic unit was understood it was necessary to consider alternative possibilities: that it represented the silent period that appears in neighboring myotatic units (1, 8); that it represented the autogenous inhibition of the lengthening reaction;

that it was an artifact. It is now clear that the silent period of Denny-Brown and autogenous inhibition are mediated by interneurons. Likewise, in view of its functional affinities, the possibility of direct inhibition, mediated by orthodromic volleys (5), being an artifact is very remote indeed.

SUMMARY

An afferent volley arising in the nerve of a given muscle or muscle fraction has, by direct impingement upon motor nuclei, the following actions:—

1. If above threshold, it discharges motoneurons that supply that muscle or muscle fraction; otherwise, excitation is subliminal.

2. It facilitates the action of motoneurons that supply the muscle remainder, or synergists, at the same joint.

3. It inhibits the action of motoneurons that supply antagonists at the same joint.

The afferent volley in question, by direct action, neither excites nor inhibits motoneurons of muscles, flexor or extensor, that act at neighboring joints.

In every instance the actions described are in strict accord with the requirements of reciprocal innervation.

The origin and distribution of excitation and inhibition so evoked indicate the role they play in myotatic reflex performance.

The mutually dependent muscles of a joint, together with the direct reflex paths that bind them, may be considered as constituting a myotatic unit.

The myotatic units in the first instance are independent one from another. Two-joint muscles form peripheral bridges between adjacent myotatic units.

Without the necessity for other than direct reflex connections, the myotatic unit exhibits, complete within itself, the elementary mechanism of reciprocal innervation.

REFERENCES

1. DENNY-BROWN, D. E.   On inhibition as a reflex accompaniment of the tendon-jerk and of other forms of active muscular response. *Proc. roy. Soc.*, 1928, *B103:* 321–336.
2. ECCLES, J. C.   The discharge of impulses from ganglion cells. *J. Physiol.*, 1937, *91:* 1–22.
3. ECCLES, J. C.   Synaptic potentials of motoneurones. *J. Neurophysiol.*, 1946, *9:* 87–120.
4. LIDDELL, E. G. T. and SHERRINGTON, C. S.   Further observations on myotatic reflexes. *Proc. roy. Soc.*, 1925, *B97:* 267–283.
5. LLOYD, D. P. C.   A direct central inhibitory action of dromically conducted impulses. *J. Neurophysiol.*, 1941, *4:* 184–190.
6. LLOYD, D. P. C.   Reflex action in relation to pattern and peripheral source of afferent stimulation. *J. Neurophysiol.*, 1943, *6:* 111–120.
7. LLOYD, D. P. C.   Neuron patterns controlling transmission of ipsilateral hind limb reflexes in cat. *J. Neurophysiol.*, 1943, *6:* 293–315.
8. LLOYD, D. P. C.   Functional organization of the spinal cord. *Physiol. Rev.*, 1944, *24:* 1–17.
9. LLOYD, D. P. C.   Facilitation and inhibition of spinal motoneurons. *J. Neurophysiol.*, 1946, *9:* 421–438.
10. LORENTE DE NÓ, R.   Transmission of impulses through cranial motor nuclei. *J. Neurophysiol.*, 1939, *2:* 402–464.
11. SHERRINGTON, C. S.   Note on the knee-jerk and the correlation of action of antagonistic muscles. *Proc. roy. Soc.*, 1893, *52:* 556–564.

RECURRENT INHIBITION

The Golgi preparations of Cajal (44,45) had shown that some spinal motoneurons possessed recurrent collaterals which arose from the axon before it exited from the ventral horn gray matter. The question was posed as to whether these collaterals were excitatory or inhibitory on the cells they synapsed with. However, stimulated cut ventral roots failed to produce an efferent discharge in the roots, thus suggesting that the collaterals might be inhibitory to motoneurons (46).

Renshaw had in 1941 shown that antidromic stimulation of the ventral roots often inhibited the monosynaptic reflex elicited by a simultaneous dorsal root volley. Renshaw's reports were followed by studies in Eccles' laboratory which implied a negative feedback on the output side of the reflex arc at the final common path (motoneuron). As the motoneurons whose axons are antidromically stimulated inhibit adjacent motoneurons, those neurons receiving sufficient orthodromic excitation can over-ride the recurrent inhibition while those in the subliminal fringe are inhibited; thus the specificity of the efferent discharge (myotatic reflex) is assured.

Eccles named the interneurons involved *Renshaw cells*, and demonstrated that these cells received their innervation from motoneuron collaterals and produced inhibitory postsynaptic potentials in the other motoneurons in the area. Dale (47) had suggested that a fiber will liberate only one kind of transmitter at all of its terminations, a proposal which has come to be known as Dale's Law. Therefore, Eccles reasoned that since it had been fairly conclusively demonstrated that the axons of motoneurons liberate acetylcholine at the myoneural junction, their recurrent collaterals must release the same transmitter at the motoneuron collateral–Renshaw cell junction.

A large number of papers issuing from V. J. Wilson's laboratory at the Rockefeller Institute through the early 1960's (48–52) did much to elaborate the many connections made with Renshaw cells, both inhibitory and facilitatory. These workers demonstrated that the Renshaw cells could be inhibited by many kinds of afferent input but that those normally associated with noxious stimulation usually resulted in more powerful inhibition. From these findings it was concluded that the afferent part of the inhibitory pathway consists of Group II and Group III fibers from muscles and alpha (and some delta) fibers from the skin. It was also demonstrated that the recurrent facilitation which had been originally reported by Renshaw was indeed not true facilitation but rather disinhibition by Renshaw cells of tonically discharging, inhibitory interneurons in the reflex path.

REFERENCES

44. Cajal, Ramón y, S. *Textura del Sistema Nervioso del Hombre y de los Vertebrados.* Moya, Madrid, 1899.

45. Cajal, Ramón y, S. *Histologie du Système Nerveux de l'Homme et de Vertébrés.* Maloine, Paris, 1909.

46. Gesell, R. A neurophysiological interpretation of the respiratory act. *Ergeb. Physiol.* **43:** 477–639 (1940).

47. Dale, H. H. Pharmacology and nerve endings. *Proc. Roy. Soc. Med.* **28:** 319–332 (1935).

48. Wilson, V. J. Recurrent facilitation of spinal reflexes. *J. Gen. Physiol.* **42:** 703–713 (1959).

49. Brooks, V. B., and V. J. Wilson. Recurrent inhibition in the cat's spinal cord. *J. Physiol.* **146:** 380–391 (1959).

50. Wilson, V. J., W. H. Talbot, and F. P. J. Diecke. Distribution of recurrent facilitation and inhibition in cat spinal cord. *J. Neurophysiol.* **23:** 144–153 (1960).

51. Wilson, V. J., and P. R. Burgess. Disinhibition in the cat spinal cord. *J. Neurophysiol.* **25:** 392–404 (1962).

52. Wilson, V. J., W. H. Talbot, and M. Kato. Inhibitory convergence upon Renshaw cells. *J. Neurophysiol.* **27:** 1063–1079 (1964).

BIBLIOGRAPHY

Scheibel, M. E., and A. B. Scheibel. Spinal motoneurons, interneurons and Renshaw cells. *Arch. Ital. Biol.* **104:** 328–353 (1966).

SUGGESTED TEXTS

Ruch *et al.* Chapter 7.

Ochs, S. Chapters 16 and 17.

Mountcastle, V. Chapter 72.

CHOLINERGIC AND INHIBITORY SYNAPSES IN A PATHWAY FROM MOTOR-AXON COLLATERALS TO MOTONEURONES

By J. C. ECCLES, P. FATT and K. KOKETSU

Department of Physiology, The Australian National University, Canberra, Australia

(*Received* 22 *June* 1954)

Although a central inhibitory action of antidromic impulses in motor-nerve fibres had been postulated or sought for on several occasions (Brown, 1914; Eccles & Sherrington, 1931; Forbes, Smith, Lambert, Caveness & Derbyshire, 1933), it was first demonstrated by the refined experiments of Renshaw (1941), and has since been investigated by Lloyd (1946, 1951*b*). There is general agreement that the antidromic inhibitory action resembles direct inhibition in the brevity of its latent period, but differs in its relatively long duration, 40–50 msec, as against about 15 msec for direct inhibition. There is also general agreement that the antidromic inhibitory action is exerted preponderantly on motoneurones, the somas of which are located close to the somas of those being activated, while functional relationship is not an essential factor.

The classical neurohistological investigations employing the Golgi technique revealed that the axons of nerve cells often gave off collateral branches soon after their origin, and there are extensive accounts of axon collaterals in the older literature (Kölliker, 1891; Lenhossek, 1893; Cajal, 1909). However, the precise mode of termination of these axon collaterals has remained obscure. Most of the axon collaterals of motoneurones are shown terminating in the ventral horn, but whether they establish synaptic connexions with motoneurones or with interneurones is an open question. Nevertheless, neurophysiologists have not hesitated to postulate functional connexions by which these axon collaterals would exert inhibitory or excitatory actions on motoneurones (Brown, 1914; Gesell, 1940; Renshaw, 1941; Holmgren & Merton, 1954). In particular, Renshaw (1941, Fig. 6D) depicted a motor-axon collateral with postulated connexions either directly to a neighbouring motoneurone, or indirectly through an interneurone, but he regarded such explanations of the antidromic inhibitory action as purely speculative. As an alternative explanation he proposed that the inhibition was caused by the polarizing effects of

Eccles, J. C., P. Fatt, and K. Koketsu. Cholinergic and inhibitory synapses in a pathway from motor-axon collaterals to motoneurones. *J. Physiol.* **126**: 524–562, 1954.

electric currents generated by the responses of motoneurones. This explanation has been further developed by Brooks, Downman & Eccles (1950) and by Lloyd (1951 b), who have shown that the positive after-potential generated by the antidromic invasion of a motoneurone would produce currents which would depress adjacent motoneurones for approximately the duration of the observed antidromic inhibition. However, it must be questioned if such currents are of sufficient intensity to cause the observed inhibition (cf. Renshaw, 1941).

In a later investigation Renshaw (1946) discovered that interneurones in the ventral horn discharged repetitively at high frequency in response to an antidromic volley in motor axons. He did not attempt to relate rigorously the operation of these interneurones to the above-described inhibition, but considered that the establishment of a causal relationship would have to await anatomical evidence. The relationship is established in the present paper by recording electric potential changes in the cell bodies of individual motoneurones and by demonstrating the parallel effects of different chemical substances on the potential changes in the motoneurones on the one hand and on the discharges of the interneurones on the other.

Questions of some general interest are raised by this investigation. It is shown that, in the inhibition of neighbouring motoneurones, electric fields need not be postulated to play a significant part, but instead all intercellular effects can be accounted for satisfactorily by synaptic processes which have specific chemical sensitivity. With this case eliminated as a possible instance of the interaction of neurones by electric fields, the probability that such fields might be important in the functioning of the central nervous system is lessened. Another point which is raised concerns the specific type of transmission occurring in the synapses of this pathway. Strong evidence is produced indicating that at the synapses formed by the collaterals of motor axons on the interneurones transmission is mediated by acetylcholine.

A preliminary report of this investigation has been published (Eccles, Fatt & Koketsu, 1953).

METHOD

The experiments have been performed on the sixth and seventh lumbar segments of the spinal cord of cats under light pentobarbital anaesthesia.

The microelectrode techniques for the intracellular recording of electric potentials from motoneurones and for the exploration of extracellular potential fields among groups of neurones have been described in recent papers (Brock, Coombs & Eccles, 1952; Eccles, Fatt, Landgren & Winsbury, 1954).

The technique for administering solutions of drugs to the lower lumbar region of the spinal cord by injection into its arterial blood supply resembles that used by Holmstedt & Skoglund (1953). Injections were made into the lower part of the aorta. All the main vessels below the renal arteries were ligated, except the lumbar arteries which supply the spinal cord.

A. *Antidromic inhibitory post-synaptic potential*

When the central end of the severed motor nerve to a muscle is stimulated and the appropriate dorsal roots are cut, only the antidromic volley in the motor-nerve fibres is able to enter the spinal cord. The most obvious effect of this volley is to generate action potentials in the central parts of those moto-neurones whose axons are excited. In addition to this antidromic activation, the volley has another effect on motoneurones. By testing the electric potentials occurring in a number of motoneurones, it is revealed that this volley increases the membrane potential in a large proportion of those located at the segmental levels at which the antidromic volley enters the spinal cord. For example, in Fig. 1A–F an antidromic volley in the biceps-semitendinosus motor axons caused a microelectrode placed within motoneurones belonging to several different muscles to become more negative relative to an indifferent lead. When it was extracellular, virtually no potential change of this form was observed (cf. Figs. 1M, N and 3A–D); hence the potential change represents entirely a hyperpolarization of the motoneuronal membrane, and the electrical processes producing it must be intrinsic to this membrane.

When the motoneurone belonged to the muscle whose motor nerve was stimulated, its response to the antidromic invasion would be superimposed on any hyperpolarizing response. However, by combining several procedures it has been possible to discriminate between, on the one hand, the various potential changes evoked in a motoneurone when it was antidromically invaded (Brock, *et al.* 1952, 1953), and, on the other hand, the potential change indentifiable with the hyperpolarizing response described above. For example, in Fig. 2A the stimulus to the motor nerve was adjusted so that it was just-threshold for the motor axon belonging to the motoneurone that was impaled by the microelectrode (cf. also Fig. 1A). About one-third of the stimuli excited this axon (response a) and two-thirds failed (response b). The difference between responses a and b may be assumed to give the response which is generated in a motoneurone by an impulse in its axon. The response so calculated is seen in Fig. 2D (continuous line) to have the characteristic features of the after-potentials of a motoneurone. Fig. 2B (response c) further shows that, on strengthening the stimulus to maximum for the motor nerve, there was an additional hyperpolarization above that observed for the just-threshold response. As a first approximation it may be assumed that the difference between response c and that attributable to antidromic invasion of the moto-neurone $(a-b)$, i.e. $(c-(a-b))$, gives the total hyperpolarizing response of the type observed when stimulating motor nerves other than that nerve containing the axon of the cell under observation (dotted line, Fig. 2D). The steep

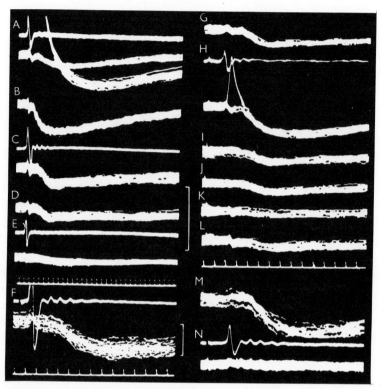

Fig. 1. Potentials generated in a motoneurone by an antidromic volley in motor-nerve fibres and recorded between an intracellular electrode and an indifferent electrode. Downward deflexions signal increasing intracellular negativity. Each record is made by the superposition of about forty faint traces so as to reject random noise as far as possible. This procedure has been adopted for all the illustrated recordings from motoneurones except Fig. 4 D–H and Fig. 17 F. In A, C, E, F, H and N accompanying records show spike potentials recorded simultaneously from the dorso-lateral surface of the spinal cord. Negativity relative to the indifferent electrode is downwards. A to F show responses evoked in six motoneurones of different function by a maximum antidromic volley in biceps-semitendinosus motor axons. The motoneurones are those supplying biceps-semitendinosus, semimembranosus, plantaris, flexor digitorum longus, deep peroneal, and gastrocnemius muscles respectively. Time scale below E gives msec for A, C, D and E; time scale below F gives msec for F. For G–L microelectrode was in a biceps-semitendinosus motoneurone and antidromic volleys were in motor fibres of semimembranosus, biceps-semitendinosus, gastrocnemius, plantaris, flexor digitorum longus and deep peroneal nerves respectively. For M and N the antidromic volley was in gastrocnemius motor fibres and the microelectrode in a flexor digitorum longus motoneurone, M, and immediately outside it, N. Time scale below L gives msec for G–N. In A and H the stimulus applied to the motor nerve was at threshold strength for exciting the axon of the motoneurone under observation. The shorter perpendicular line gives 1 mV potential scale for C, F, M and N; the longer line gives 5 mV for the remaining records.

spike potential curves of the a and c responses make the calculated curve indeterminate for the first 3 msec.

Since it cannot be assumed that the hyperpolarization is accurately summed with the after-potentials following antidromic invasion of a motoneurone, it was fortunate that in some motoneurones the antidromic impulse was blocked downstream from the motoneurone, probably at the medullated-non-medullated junction (cf. Brock *et al.* 1953). Under such conditions only a small

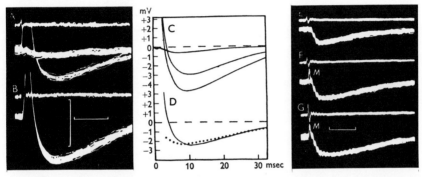

Fig. 2. Motoneurone potentials and accompanying surface potentials evoked and recorded as in Fig. 1. A and B show potentials recorded in a biceps-semitendinosus motoneurone by an antidromic volley set up in biceps-semitendinosus motor fibres (A) by a stimulus which is just-threshold for the axon of the motoneurone and (B) by a maximum stimulus. Plotted responses of A and B are drawn in C and the subtracted curves in D (see text). Zero time signals the arrival of the antidromic volley at the spinal cord. E to G are the responses of a semimembranosus motoneurone to an antidromic volley in semimembranosus axons. For F the stimulus was just-threshold for the axon of that motoneurone, while in E it was below threshold and in G the stimulus was maximum for all motor fibres. Small spike evoked by the antidromic impulse is labelled M in F and G. Time scale in 10 msec is drawn for each series; potential scale is 5 mV.

spike with no detectable after-potential was recorded by a microelectrode in the motoneurone whose axon was stimulated. For example, in Fig. 2F a stimulus strength was chosen so that the motor axon was not excited at every trial. The only indication that the axon was excited is the small spike (M) that was evoked in about half the superimposed responses. Following this spike there was accurate superimposition of all the responses with no trace of the two distinct types of responses a and b as seen in Figs. 1A and 2A. Thus in the three records (Fig. 2E, F, G), the hyperpolarization was recorded free from complication by after-potentials. Our many series of observation of this type (cf. Figs. 1H, 3H and I, 4A, 17A) have served to establish that, apart from the response caused by antidromic invasion of a motoneurone, the impulse in a motor axon has no special hyperpolarizing action on the motoneurone to which this axon belongs.

Fig. 1G–L shows typically that a hyperpolarization is usually evoked in

any one motoneurone by antidromic volleys in the motor axons supplying
several different muscles of diverse functions. The complete results of our investigations on motoneurones in the seventh lumbar segment have been
assembled in Table 1. Usually large hyperpolarizations have been evoked by
volleys in the motor nerve containing the axon of the motoneurone being
studied, e.g. from semimembranosus to semimembranosus in Table 1. Closely
allied groups of motoneurones such as plantaris and gastrocnemius-soleus
have exhibited similarity both in respect of the hyperpolarizing actions of
antidromic volleys (columns 4 and 5) and the responses of motoneurones (rows
4 and 5). However, reciprocity between the action of the antidromic volley

TABLE 1. Mean values in mV of inhibitory post-synaptic potentials evoked in various types of
motoneurones by antidromic volleys in various motor-nerve fibres. The neuronal types are
arranged in rows (numbers in brackets giving numbers of the type), the nerve types in
columns, both sets having the same identifying symbols: BST = biceps-semitendinosus
(excluding anterior biceps); AB = anterior biceps; SM = semimembranosus; GS = gastrocnemius-soleus; P = plantaris; FDL = flexor digitorum longus; DP = deep peroneal;
Q = quadriceps; CVR = contralateral L_7 ventral root.

Neuronal type	Nerve volley types								
	BST	AB	SM	GS	P	FDL	DP	Q	CVR
BST (13)	0·55	—	0·32	0·18	0·03	0·03	0·16	0	0
AB (3)	0·15	—	2·37	0·42	0·12	0	0·02	0	0
SM (4)	1·26	—	1·44	0·62	0·28	0·05	0·21	0	0
GS (2)	0·30	—	0	0·50	0·43	0·17	0	0	0
P (5)	0·62	—	0·04	1·31	0·54	0·29	0·08	0	0
FDL (5)	0·52	—	0·15	1·26	0·55	0·18	0	0	0
DP (4)	0·19	—	1·36	0	0	0·09	2·27	0·22	0

and the motoneuronal response was not a general rule, as, for example, may
be seen with the gastrocnemius-soleus antidromic volley effectively hyperpolarizing semimembranosus motoneurones, while gastrocnemius-soleus
motoneurones were unaffected by a semimembranosus antidromic volley. A
failure of reciprocity is also seen in Table 1 with plantaris and biceps-semitendinosus. It is certainly established that the hyperpolarizing action of an
antidromic volley in a muscle nerve is exerted on motoneurones of diverse
function—flexors or extensors at the various joints of a limb. No meaningful
co-ordination pattern can be detected, the only determining factor appearing
to be proximity in the spinal cord (cf. Renshaw, 1941). When the antidromic
volley entered the spinal cord about one segment more rostral than the motoneurones, as with a quadriceps antidromic volley, Table 1 reveals that the only
hyperpolarization that was observed in the motoneurones of the L_7 segment
occurred with two deep peroneal motoneurones in the extreme rostral part of
L_7 segment. Probably the hyperpolarizing action of an antidromic volley
extends along the spinal cord for no more than half a segment from the zone
of entry of the volley, while large hyperpolarizing actions are exerted only on
motoneurones at the same segmental level. No hyperpolarization has ever

been observed when the antidromic volley was in a contralateral ventral root, i.e. the effect is strictly ipsilateral.

In measuring the latent period of the hyperpolarization it was important to withdraw the microelectrode from the motoneurone and take an extracellular record immediately after the intracellular record. Two such series are shown

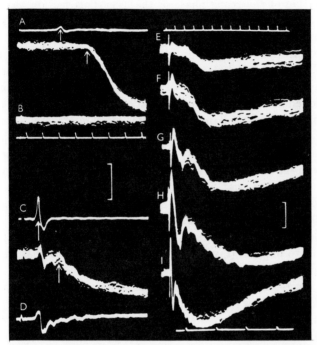

Fig. 3. Motoneurone potentials and accompanying surface potentials evoked and recorded as in Fig. 1. A was obtained with the microelectrode in a deep peroneal motoneurone, and in B after having withdrawn the microelectrode to an extracellular position. The first arrow marks the time of entry of the antidromic volley into the spinal cord, while the second gives the onset of the hyperpolarization. C and D were recorded as in A and B, but from a semimembranosus motoneurone. E–H are from an unidentified motoneurone showing the potentials generated by antidromic volleys of progressively increasing size in the seventh lumbar ventral root, H being maximum. I is the same as H, but at slower sweep speed. Time scale below B is in msec for A–D; above E in msec for E–H, and below I in 10 msec for I. Perpendicular scales give 1 mV for corresponding records.

in Fig. 3 A, B and C, D respectively. In the A, B series the extracellular record shows very little potential change and the onset of the hyperpolarization is easily determinable (second arrow), while the time of entry of the antidromic volley into the spinal cord is given by the crest of the positive (upward) spike as recorded by the surface electrode (first arrow). The latent period as measured between the two arrows was about 1·6 msec. In the C, D series the extracellular record shows an initial series of waves resembling those recorded intracellularly, and the two records must be carefully compared in order to determine where they start to diverge (second arrow). The latent period so measured between the two arrows was 1·25 msec. In our experiments the extreme range of measured latent periods for the hyperpolarization was 1·1–1·8 msec, but probably still longer values would obtain for very small hyperpolarizations.

The duration of the rising phase of the hyperpolarization has varied considerably, from 3 to almost 10 msec, according as the hyperpolarization was small or large respectively. This effect is best seen in series such as Fig. 3E, F, G, H, where the size of the antidromic volley has been progressively increased (cf. also Fig. 2E, F, G). On careful examination of the rising phases of the large hyperpolarizations it is seen to be formed by superposition of a series of wave-like additions at a frequency of about 1000/sec (cf. Figs. 2G, 3H and 4A). Towards and beyond the summit this rhythmic composition gradually became obscured. The origin of this repetitive wave, together with the alteration of latency with response size, will be considered in a later section.

It has been shown that a direct inhibitory volley generates a hyperpolarization of motoneurones that has a latent period sufficiently short and a time course sufficiently long for it to be causally related to the direct inhibition (Eccles, 1953, p. 158; Eccles, Fatt & Landgren, 1954); hence this hyperpolarization has been called the inhibitory post-synaptic potential (IPSP). It remains now to inquire: (i) whether the hyperpolarization that an antidromic volley produces in motoneurones has the latent period and time course that would be expected if it were causally related to the antidromic inhibitory action discovered by Renshaw (1941); and (ii) whether the antidromic hyperpolarization is generated by a process similar to that which generates the IPSP of direct inhibition. The general time course of large antidromic hyperpolarizations as, for example, in Figs. 2G and 3I, corresponds closely to the antidromic inhibitory curves of Renshaw (1941) and Lloyd (1946, 1951b) with summits at about 10 msec and total durations usually of about 40–50 msec. Comparison of the respective latent periods is complicated on account of the fairly wide range of synaptic delays for responses of the various motoneurones giving the testing monosynaptic reflex discharge. Renshaw (1941) concluded that inhibition was first induced when an antidromic volley arrived at the motoneurones approximately simultaneously with the afferent impulses that were evoking the testing monosynaptic reflex. Since the longest latent period for the reflex discharge was considerably greater than 1 msec, it may be concluded that the observed latent period for the hyperpolarization (1·1–1·8 msec) is just brief enough to account for the observed latent period of the inhibition. The relative timing is best appreciated if attention is focused on the time of the testing reflex discharge, for inhibition can occur so long as the reflex discharge of longest latency is not antecedent to the onset of the hyperpolarization (Eccles, 1953; Eccles, Fatt & Landgren, 1954).

Various experimental procedures have established that an identical process gives the antidromic hyperpolarization and the other inhibitory post-synaptic potentials. Two simple tests are illustrated in Fig. 4. Exactly as would be expected for an IPSP (Coombs, Eccles & Fatt, 1953), introducing chloride ions into a motoneurone causes the antidromic hyperpolarization (Fig. 4A) to be converted to a depolarization (Fig. 4B), which may become very large. This

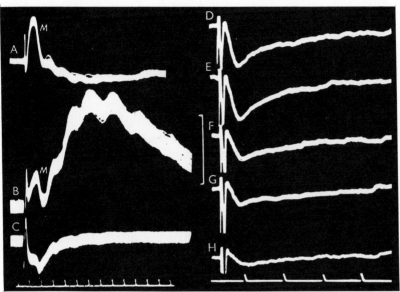

Fig. 4 A to C. Potentials generated in biceps-semitendinosus motoneurone by an antidromic volley in the seventh lumbar ventral root. Note initial M spike. Chloride is injected into the motoneurone by passing $2 \cdot 5 \times 10^{-8}$ A for 120 sec through the microelectrode, thereby changing the hyperpolarization of A to the depolarization of B. C shows extracellular potential recorded on withdrawal of microelectrode from the motoneurone. Time is in msec. Potential scale gives 5 mV.

Fig. 4 D to H. The effect of strychnine in depressing a potential which had been previously shortened by the injection of dihydro-β-erythroidine hydrobromide (cf. Fig. 17C, D). Single traces only are recorded. The potentials are generated in a quadriceps motoneurone by an antidromic volley in the sixth lumbar ventral root. 0·1 mg strychnine hydrochloride/kg body weight was injected intravenously between D and E. E to G were recorded at 10, 20 and 30 sec after the injection. Maximum depression was attained at G. H shows the maximum depression after a further 0·1 mg/kg. Time is in 10 msec. Potential scale is the same as for A–C.

large inverted potential shows very well the constituent rhythm on its rising phase and summit. Further evidence relating to the synaptic origin of the antidromic inhibitory potential is given by the depressant action of strychnine. For example, intravenous injection of 0·1 mg strychnine hydrochloride per kg caused the antidromic hyperpolarization rapidly to decrease from the initial size (Fig. 4D) to about half (Fig. 4G), while an additional similar dose caused a further diminution (Fig. 4H). The same relative diminution is observed with the direct IPSP, and provides a satisfactory explanation of the depression of inhibitory action by strychnine (Bradley, Easton & Eccles, 1953). The identity of the antidromic hyperpolarization and an IPSP is also indicated by the similar changes produced in them when the membrane potential of the motoneurone has been changed over a wide range by extrinsic currents (Coombs *et al.* 1953).

These investigations lead to the conclusion that the antidromic hyperpolarization is produced by ionic movements across the motoneuronal membrane which are identical with those giving the IPSP of direct inhibition. It is probable that strychnine depresses direct inhibition by blocking the postsynaptic receptors for the inhibitory transmitting substance (Bradley *et al.* 1953); hence the similar depressant action of strychnine on antidromic hyperpolarization indicates that it is caused by mediation of the same transmitting substance. It is therefore justifiable to identify the antidromic hyperpolarization as a true IPSP and to attribute it to the action of a synaptic mechanism similar to that giving the direct IPSP. It remains now to determine the pathway by which antidromic impulses activate inhibitory synapses on motoneurones.

B. *Interneuronal discharges*

On account of the paucity of experimental evidence Renshaw (1946) refrained from concluding that the antidromic inhibitory action was mediated by the repetitive interneuronal discharges which he found to be evoked in the ventral horn by a volley in motor axons. Important additional evidence for this causal relationship is provided by the rhythmic steps on the rising phase of large antidromic IPSP's (cf. Figs. 2G, 3H and 4A, B), which suggests that the antidromic IPSP is produced by a repetitive synaptic bombardment. The frequency of this wave is approximately the same as the interneuronal discharges observed by Renshaw. In addition to confirming almost all of Renshaw's findings, a detailed study of the interneuronal discharges has established that these interneurones form a specialized group mediating the inhibitory path from motor axons. They may appropriately be given the distinguishing title of 'Renshaw cells'.

Convergence of motor impulses on to Renshaw cells. Usually antidromic impulses in axons of several motor nerves exert an excitatory action on any one Renshaw cell. For example in Fig. 5A–E maximum volleys in bicepssemitendinosus, gastrocnemius, flexor digitorum longus, plantaris and superficial peroneal nerves evoked respectively 14, 5, 3, 2 and 1 discharges from the same Renshaw cell (note characteristic shape of spike), while in Fig. 5F–H volleys in semimembranosus, tibialis posterior and deep peroneal nerves were ineffective. The slower record (Fig. 5I) shows that the BST volley actually evoked 22 discharges from the Renshaw cell over a total duration of about

40 msec. It has invariably been observed that the frequency of discharge is highest for the first impulses and progressively falls thereafter. Fig. 5 K–Q shows the responses of another Renshaw cell to various sizes of an antidromic volley. These sample records illustrate seven distinct gradations of response

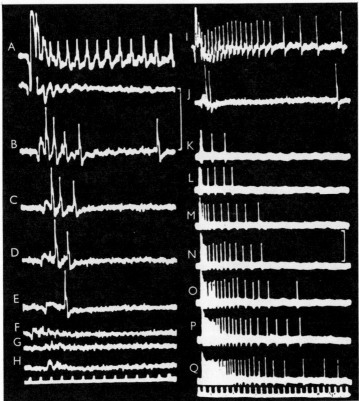

Fig. 5 A to E show discharges of a Renshaw cell generated by antidromic volleys in various motor nerves as described in text. The surface responses are also shown in A with the exception of the initial diphasic spike. F–H show the failure of antidromic volleys in three other motor nerves. Usually the diphasic antidromic response of the motoneurones can be seen preceding the first Renshaw cell spike. Time is in msec. Potential scale gives 1·0 mV. I and J show responses to the same volley as A and D respectively, but at one third the sweep speed. K–Q give specimen records of seven different intensities of response evoked in another Renshaw cell by a progressively increasing antidromic volley. The initial high frequency response cannot be resolved at the sweep speed employed. Time is in 10 msec. Potential scale gives 1·0 mV.

that were revealed by some 90 records with gradually increasing volley size. Several such gradations were always observable with intense Renshaw cell responses. Thus it may be concluded that the Renshaw cell illustrated in Fig. 5A–J was converged upon by impulses in probably as many as ten different axons distributed over at least five motor nerves. It was always possible to demonstrate the convergence of impulses in several different motor axons upon any Renshaw cell.

Latent period, frequency and duration of discharge. The Renshaw cell discharge illustrated in Fig. 6A is shown at higher amplification and faster speed in Fig. 6E in order to allow accurate measurement of latent period and initial frequency. When measured from the arrival of the antidromic volley at the

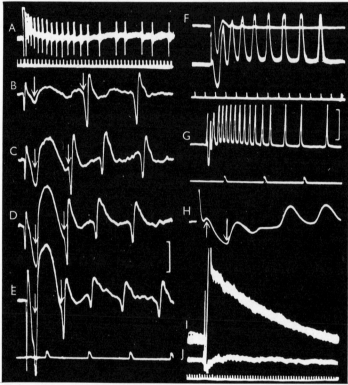

Fig. 6. B–E show responses evoked in a Renshaw cell by antidromic volleys of progressively increasing sizes in the seventh lumbar ventral root and recorded at a fast sweep speed. A is at a much slower speed. Note the diphasic motoneuronal response preceding the first Renshaw cell spike. Latent periods are measured between the two arrows. With A and E the motor axon volley is maximum. Time is in msec. Potential scale gives 1 mV. F–H are the responses evoked in another Renshaw cell by a maximum volley in seventh lumbar ventral root and recorded intracellularly, upward deflexion indicating positivity of microelectrode relative to the indifferent electrode, i.e. it is the reverse of other figures in which the Renshaw cell discharges have been recorded extracellularly. With F the surface response is also shown inverted. Three different sweep speeds are used as shown by the msec time scales for F and H, G scale being as for A. Smaller responses in H are due to progressive failure of cell. Latent period is measured between the two arrows, the initial motoneuronal response appearing inverted. Note that the second of the four Renshaw cell responses is so early that it is greatly reduced in size. Potential scale gives 5 mV. I and J show potentials recorded inside (cf. F–H) and just outside another Renshaw cell at much slower sweep speed (see time scale in msec). Potential scale is the same as for A–E. Further description is given in the text.

spinal cord (first arrow), the latent period of onset of the first discharge was 0·62 msec, while the subsequent intervals between discharges were 0·62, 0·76 and 0·88 msec respectively. Progressive diminution of the antidromic volley size in Fig. 6 E–B lengthened both the latent period and the intervals between discharges. The latent period in Fig. 6 B was 1·16 msec. Still longer latent periods have been observed with antidromic volleys that just evoked a discharge. For example, in Fig. 5 D it was 1·4 msec for the first plantaris response and it was almost 1·9 msec for the single response evoked by the superficial peroneal volley (Fig. 5 E), which is one of the longest latent periods that we have observed, and considerably longer than the longest value illustrated by Renshaw (about 1·5 msec). In general, when an antidromic volley evoked a fast repetitive response of Renshaw cells, the latent period of the first response was between 0·6 and 0·7 msec, values which are in precise agreement with those reported by Renshaw (1946). An exceptionally brief latent period of 0·54 msec was observed with a Renshaw cell into which a microelectrode had been inserted (Fig. 6 H), an effect which presumably is attributable to the depolarizing influence of the injury. Usually the latent period was so brief that the first Renshaw cell spike arose during the declining phase of the soma spike potential (cf. Figs. 5 A, 11 F).

Likewise the highest frequencies that we have observed are in good agreement with Renshaw's value of about 1500/sec. It was invariably observed that the shortest interval was between the first two responses, there being a progressive lengthening of interval with each successive response (Figs. 5 A, I, 6 A, G, 11 A, F, '13 A, B), so that after ten responses the frequency was always well below 1000/sec. At such high initial frequencies the successive spikes were, as expected, subnormal in size (cf. Figs. 5 A, I, 11 A, F, 13 A, B). Usually the decline in frequency was fairly regular, but there was often wide variation in the intervals between the last few responses, as, for example, may be seen in the last response to the gastrocnemius volley in Fig. 5 B occurring after an interval of 7·5 msec, and occasionally intervals longer than 20 msec were observed in later observations on this same Renshaw cell, as is illustrated in Fig. 5 J, where a third response occurred more than 30 msec after the first two. There has been great variability in the total duration of the Renshaw cell discharge generated by a single antidromic volley. However, after a powerful excitatory action generating a high-frequency discharge, the discharge usually continued for 30–50 msec, but exceptionally durations in excess of 100 msec have been observed (Fig. 5 Q).

Usually a penetrating microelectrode kills a Renshaw cell almost instantaneously, there being a brief high-frequency response at the instant of penetration. Exceptionally it has been possible to record intracellularly from Renshaw cells for a brief period as in Fig. 6 F–I. However, there was always evidence of severe injury of such Renshaw cells as revealed both by the very low voltage of the responses and by their rapid deterioration. Such recording has been of interest solely because it gives the time courses of the background synaptic depolarization and of the spike responses generated thereby. In Fig. 6F, G the spikes are seen to arise from a background depolarization of rather less than 1 mV. However, the intracellular recording was very imperfect as the spike potentials were less than 10 mV. On a few rare occasions the potential wave form illustrated in Fig. 6I has been generated by an antidromic volley immediately after penetration of a Renshaw cell. Apparently, after an initial spike discharge, a large depolarizing potential gradually decays over more than 40 msec. This is precisely the time course of the depolarization that would be expected to evoke the repetitive Renshaw cell discharges with their progressive decline from a high initial frequency.

Anatomical pathway for Renshaw cell activation. It has been suggested by Toennies & Jung (1948), Toennies (1949) and Jung (1953) that Renshaw cells are activated by the reversed synaptic action of antidromic impulses that propagate to the terminals of the dendrites of the motoneurones. On the contrary, Renshaw (1946) suggested as a possibility that the antidromic impulses would invade the motor-axon collaterals and so might excite the Renshaw cells synaptically. He suggested, alternatively, synaptic excitation by 'hypothetical afferent fibres in the ventral roots'. Actually his own observations would exclude this last suggestion, for he observed that the same interneurone could be activated secondarily to a reflex discharge as well as by an antidromic volley, an observation which has repeatedly been confirmed in our experiments. Furthermore, the range of stimulus thresholds of the fibres activating Renshaw cells has conformed precisely with the thresholds for large motor axons (cf. Figs. 5K–Q, 6B–E). No additional excitatory effect on Renshaw cells has been detectable with stimuli strengthened sufficiently to excite the small motor axons.

It is possible to distinguish experimentally between the two remaining alternative mechanisms for activation of Renshaw cells. Normally only a fraction of the dendrites of a population of motoneurones is invaded by an antidromic volley, and this invaded fraction can be greatly increased by the depolarization produced by excitatory synaptic action (Renshaw, 1942, Lloyd, 1943; Brooks & Eccles, 1947; Brock et al. 1953). Thus, if Renshaw cells are activated by impulses in the motoneuronal dendrites, facilitation of the antidromic invasion of the dendrites by a suitably timed monosynaptic excitatory volley should effectively increase the Renshaw cell response to a given antidromic volley. On the other hand, the antidromic invasion of motor-axon collaterals should not be appreciably enhanced by a monosynaptic excitatory volley, and hence this volley should cause no modification of the Renshaw cell discharge. It was important to avoid a complication that occurred when the monosynaptic excitatory volley itself caused a discharge of the Renshaw cell as a consequence of the reflex discharge which it evoked. Fig. 7 illustrates two of the nine series of investigations, all of which showed that facilitation of the antidromic invasion by a monosynaptic excitatory volley (upper graph) had no effect on the activation of Renshaw cells by that antidromic volley (open and filled circles in lower graph). The control observations were provided by the Renshaw cell discharges set up by the antidromic

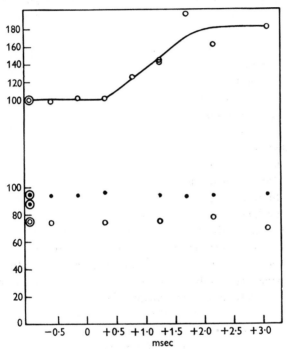

Fig. 7. Abscissae give intervals between the arrival times at the spinal cord of an afferent volley travelling via the dorsal roots from gastrocnemius and biceps-semitendinosus nerves and of an antidromic volley in the seventh lumbar ventral root. The upper curve shows the time course of facilitation of antidromic invasion of motoneuronal somas and dendrites, the ordinates being sizes of the antidromic soma spike potentials as percentages of control size in the absence of a conditioning afferent volley. Each filled and open circle below plots the total number of impulses discharged by a Renshaw cell in response to six separate tests at the plotted interval between arrival of the afferent and the antidromic volleys. Control numbers for antidromic volleys alone are indicated by ringed values. Further description is given in the text.

volley alone and by the antidromic volley when it was too early for its invasion to be facilitated by the monosynaptic excitatory volley (intervals of −0·61 to +0·31 msec in Fig. 7). Each point plotted in Fig. 7 represents the aggregate number of Renshaw cell discharges generated in six successive tests by the antidromic volley either alone or in the indicated time relationship to the monosynaptic excitatory volley.

The uniformly negative results of our experiments lead to the conclusion that Renshaw cells are activated by antidromic impulses spreading up the motor-axon collaterals to terminals that make synaptic contacts with Renshaw cells. It may be assumed that reflexly discharged impulses from motoneurones would also spread along these axon collaterals, hence an explanation is available for the generation of Renshaw cell discharges by afferent volleys entering the spinal cord through dorsal roots. As expected, such volleys in group I afferent fibres are effective only when they evoke a considerable reflex discharge.

Further physiological experiments on Renshaw cells. In his investigation on the interaction of two antidromic volleys, Renshaw (1946) described both summation and inhibition. Summation has been a regular finding in our experiments, and has been demonstrated with two volleys neither of which produced a discharge. The summation interval has been as long as 50 msec. When each volley alone produced a repetitive discharge, the discharge evoked by both volleys together was larger than either of the two individual responses, but less than their sum, i.e. occlusion was regularly observed. We have never observed that, on simultaneous combination of two antidromic volleys, one caused a diminution of the discharge produced by the other, i.e. we have never observed the inhibitory action described by Renshaw. However, a preceding antidromic volley has always diminished the discharge evoked by a subsequent volley over intervals as long as 100 msec (cf. Renshaw, 1946, Fig. 5), whether the two volleys were in the same or in different nerves.

It is a fairly general finding that, following a period of intense repetitive bombardment, synapses exhibit a prolonged increase in effectiveness, which has been called post-tetanic potentiation (Lloyd, 1949, 1952; Hagbarth & Naess, 1951; Eccles & Rall, 1951; Ström, 1951). Fig. 8 shows that there is also post-tetanic potentiation for the antidromic activation of Renshaw cells. Following an antidromic tetanus at 660/sec for 10 sec there is seen to be an increase both in the frequency and duration of the Renshaw cell discharge evoked by another antidromic volley in the same motor axons (Fig. 8, inset). The time course of the effect is plotted in Fig. 8, where the test volley was applied initially at about 2·5 sec intervals and later at about 4 sec intervals, and the total number of discharges is plotted for each test interval. The time course of the rise and decay of the post-tetanic potentiation resembles that observed for monosynaptic reflexes after a comparable conditioning tetanus (Lloyd, 1949; Eccles & Rall, 1951). One experimental series departed from the usual type illustrated in Fig. 8, the potentiation being maximum as early as 3 sec after the end of the tetanus, after which the potentiation declined much more rapidly than in Fig. 8 and after 30 sec was succeeded by a prolonged depression.

Location and orientation of Renshaw cells. Usually the first few spike potentials generated by discharges of Renshaw cells were superimposed on irregular waves of negativity having approximately the same frequency (cf. Figs. 5A, 10A, lower record). In fact the proximity of the microelectrode to Renshaw cells was signalled by the prominence of this characteristic rhythmic wave-form that followed immediately after the negative spike generated by anti-dromic invasion of the motoneurone. This decrementing rhythmic wave at about 1000/sec (cf. Fig. 10A, lower record) was first reported by Barakan, Downman & Eccles (1949) as an almost invariable sequel to the antidromic spike potential, and Lloyd (1951 a) has also illustrated 'wavelets' following the antidromic spike potential.

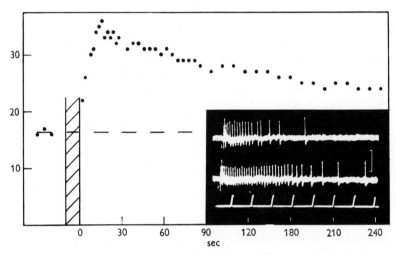

Fig. 8. The inset figure gives specimen records of Renshaw cell discharges evoked by an anti-dromic volley in the seventh lumbar ventral root before and during the post-tetanic potentia-tion that follows conditioning by an antidromic tetanus at 660/sec for 10 sec. Time is in 10 msec. Potential scale gives 0·5 mV. [In the main figure the time course of the post-tetanic potentiation is plotted. Each point gives the number of Renshaw cell discharges evoked by the antidromic volley at the indicated interval after the cessation of the conditioning tetanus. Initial control values are plotted at the extreme left, the mean level being given by the broken line. The tetanic period is shown by the hatched area.

As the microelectrode was slowly inserted through a region of the ventral horn rich in Renshaw cells, its passage in close proximity to several cells was signalled as one cell after another was seen to generate a characteristic sharp spike potential which rose above the background rhythmic wave as illustrated in Fig. 10A. Repeated observations of this nature provide convincing evidence that the background rhythmic wave is generated by the cumulative effects of discharges in a population of Renshaw cells, none of which lies sufficiently close to the microelectrode to contribute an independently recognizable spike. As indicated in Figs. 5A, 6E, 11F and 13B, Renshaw cells that were intensely excited had almost identical values for the latent period of the first discharge and for the intervals between the first few discharges; hence the approximate superposition of these first discharges to give the composite wave-form. The progressive decrease in amplitude of the successive waves to eventual extinction (cf. Fig. 10A) would be expected to occur as the successive discharges of the various Renshaw cells gradually became more and more out of phase.

When this Renshaw cell wave-form was systematically recorded at 0·2 mm intervals along a series of parallel microelectrode tracks lying 0·2 mm apart in the transverse plane, it was possible to construct a map (Fig. 9B) showing the focus for maximum response, exactly as has been done for other potential waves (Eccles, Fatt, Landgren & Winsbury, 1954). But, in addition, such systematic investigations revealed a remarkable feature, a reversal of the phase of the rhythmic wave. As illustrated by records along one such microelectrode track (Fig. 9A), in the lateral and dorso-lateral regions of the spinal cord the rhythmic wave is of the same frequency but of reversed polarity to the rhythmic wave that is recorded in close proximity to the Renshaw cell focus (cf. Fig. 10A) and generally in the ventro-medial regions. The dotted line in the map illustrated in Fig. 9B indicates the boundary between these two inverse phases, i.e. it is the line of phase-reversal. The seventh record of Fig. 9A was recorded at such a region of phase-reversal, while the ninth record was close to the maximum for Renshaw cell activity. Lines of phase-reversal for the rhythmic waves have been previously plotted and closely resemble the line of Fig. 9B (cf. Barakan et al. 1949; Figs. 1 and 10, the lines formed by large dots). The rhythmic wave of inverted phase is particularly large on the dorso-lateral surface of the spinal cord, an observation which enables investigations to be conducted on Renshaw cell discharges without the complications of microelectrode technique. For example, a platinum wire electrode led the large potentials of Figs. 10A (upper record) and 15A, C from the dorso-lateral surface of the spinal cord.

The phase-reversal of the rhythmic wave from the ventro-medial to the dorso-lateral aspect of the spinal cord gives the general orientation of the extracellular currents that occur during the discharges of impulses by Renshaw cells. It has already been seen that the discrete negative spikes generated by discharges from individual Renshaw cells are synchronous with the negative phases of the waves recorded ventro-medially, and hence with the positive phases of the waves recorded dorso-laterally. Thus, when Renshaw cells generate impulses, current flows into them from sources situated dorso-laterally. Presumably this current in the external circuit is flowing from the axons into the bodies of the Renshaw cells, i.e. the axons run dorso-laterally from the bodies.

The great majority of the individually recognizable Renshaw cells have been situated close to the focus in the ventro-medial region of the ventral horn in close proximity to the paths of the emerging motor axons (cf. Balthasar, 1952).

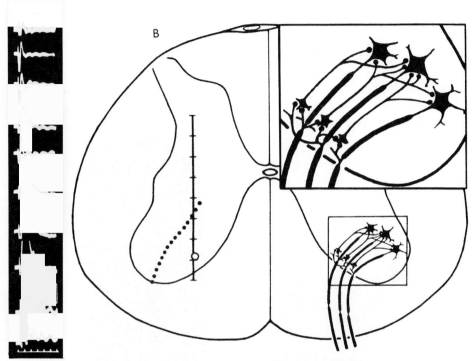

Fig. 9 A. Potentials recorded from the seventh lumbar segment of the spinal cord in response to a maximum antidromic volley in the seventh lumbar ventral root. Each record is formed by, the superposition of about 40 faint traces. The uppermost record is by a surface lead from the dorso-lateral surface. The remaining records are obtained at the depths indicated by short transverse lines along the track shown by the continuous line running dorso-ventrally in Fig. 9 B. Time is in msec. Potential scale gives 0·5 mV for all but the uppermost record, where it gives 0·05 mV. Upward deflexions signal negativity of recording electrode relative to the indifferent lead.

Fig. 9 B. Drawing of a transverse section of the spinal cord. In the left half the open circle indicates the maximum focus of Renshaw cell activity as detected by the systematic exploration described in the text. Also shown is the electrode track along which records of Fig. 9 A were recorded. The dotted line separates the ventro-medial zone of Renshaw cell negativity from the dorso-lateral zone of Renshaw cell positivity (see text). On the right half is shown in schematic form the proposed nervous pathways (see details in inset) consisting of motor-axon collaterals, Renshaw cells and motoneurones. The Renshaw cells are located in the region from which most recordings from individual cells are obtained and their axons course therefrom in the direction that accounts for the phase-reversal of the rhythmic wave generated by their discharges (see text).

However, some have been observed more dorsally, even at the extreme dorsal limits of the motoneuronal area.

When Renshaw cells gave large spike potentials, it has been possible to keep the same potentials under observation even when the microelectrode was moved over a considerable distance. For example, in the series of Fig. 10 B the microelectrode was moved inwards 25μ between each successive record. Actually the successive movements were only $12 \cdot 5\mu$, but it is sufficient for illustration to show only alternate records. The largest spike response is seen

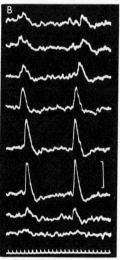

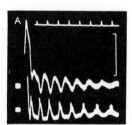

Fig. 10 A. Simultaneous records (superposition of about forty faint traces) of potential waves evoked by an antidromic volley in the seventh lumbar ventral root and recorded from the dorso-lateral surface of the cord (upper record) and in close proximity to a Renshaw cell (lower record). Upward deflexions signal negativity of the recording electrodes relative to the in-different lead. Note that on the lower record a small Renshaw cell spike is superimposed on each rhythmic wave, but there is a progressive increase in the variability of timing of this spike. Time is in msec. Same potential scale gives 1 mV for lower record and $0 \cdot 1$ mV for upper record.

Fig. 10 B. Series of records from a single Renshaw cell recorded by a microelectrode during a series of successive inward moves of 25μ. Each record shows two spike responses at approximately the same position. Time scale in $0 \cdot 1$ msec. Potential scale gives $0 \cdot 5$ mV.

in the sixth record as a diphasic wave with an initial negative phase of about $0 \cdot 2$ msec followed by a small but longer positive phase. Despite the background noise, it can be seen in all but the deepest record that there was no significant change in this time course over the whole range of depths, i.e. there was an initial sink even 125μ more superficial than the point in closest proximity to the Renshaw cell. With rare exceptions the time courses of the Renshaw cell spikes were similar to those of Fig. 10 B (cf. Renshaw, 1946). However, this extracellular recording in a volume conductor gives merely the time courses of the external currents that flow during the discharge of impulses. For example, Fig. 10 B shows that there was a current into the body and dendrites of the Renshaw cell for about 0·2 msec, and then there was a small reverse current for about 0·6 msec. On the other hand, the intracellular recording of Fig. 6F–H gives a reliable measure of the time course of the spike potential, which is seen to have a total duration of about 0·7 msec, a value rather shorter than that for the motoneurone (Brock *et al.* 1952) Presumably in Fig. 10B the initial inward current ceased when the discharged impulse invaded the whole cell including the axon, and the subsequent outward current is attributable to the more delayed re-polarization of the axon. The large Renshaw cell spikes of Fig. 6A–E have the unusual feature of an initial positivity, which is possibly attributable to a small injury due to the very close proximity of the microelectrode. Exceptionally, also, an initial positive phase has been recorded about 100μ dorso-laterally to the zone of largest potentials. Presumably the microelectrode was then close to the axon of the Renshaw cell and so recorded the initial outward currents present at that site.

It is probable that the corresponding positive spike potentials around the ramifying axons of Renshaw cells were usually so small that they were lost in the background noise. However, as we have seen, summation of such potentials for the whole population of Renshaw cells may be assumed to give the rhythmic wave of inverted phase in the dorso-lateral region of the spinal cord. The much smaller voltage of this inverted wave-form (compare fifth and ninth records of Fig. 9A and the ten-fold difference between the voltages of two records of Fig. 10A) is in accord with this explanation.

C. *Pharmacological studies on Renshaw cells*

Investigations on chemical transmission at peripheral neuro-effector junctions have led to the postulate that the same chemical transmitting substance is employed at all junctions operated by a particular cell (Dale, 1934, 1952; Feldberg, 1950, 1952). This postulate has been employed in an attempt to discover the central synaptic transmitter for those dorsal root fibres that by an axon-reflex mechanism are responsible for peripheral vasodilatation (Hellauer & Umrath, 1948; Holton & Holton, 1952), but no satisfactory identification has yet been achieved. This same postulate leads to the expectation that the synaptic transmitter by which motor-axon collaterals activate Renshaw cells is identical with that by which, at their peripheral terminals, the same motor-nerve fibres activate muscle fibres, i.e. even as the peripheral transmitter is acetylcholine, so is the central transmitter. This expectation has been tested pharmacologically by three classes of drugs: those that depress cholinergic transmission; those that prolong it by acting as anticholinesterases; and the suspected transmitter, acetylcholine. The present account will be restricted to those pharmacological observations that are of significance in establishing the cholinergic activation of Renshaw cells by motor-axon collaterals. Further pharmacological investigation will be described in a later paper (from this laboratory).

Depressants of cholinergic transmission. By far the most intense depression has been produced by dihydro-β-erythroidine. Intravenous injection of a very small dose (0·1 mg dihydro-β-erythroidine hydrobromide/kg) has invariably

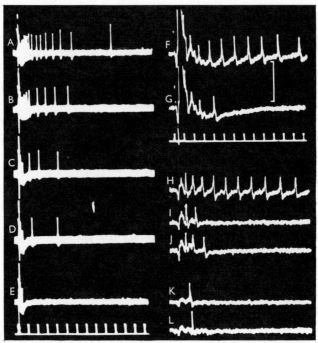

Fig. 11. A shows a Renshaw cell response to a maximum antidromic volley in the seventh lumbar ventral root. B–E show the development, as described in the text, of depression following the intravenous injection of 0·1 mg dihydro-β-erythroidine hydrobromide/kg body weight. Time scale is in 10 msec. F and G are the same series, but at a faster sweep speed, and correspond to A and E respectively. Note the first Renshaw cell spike on the declining phase of the soma spike potential. Time scale is in msec. H–L show the depression of the response of another Renshaw cell produced by the intravenous injection of a ten-fold larger dose (1 mg/kg). Before the injection H and K are the responses of the same cell to maximum antidromic volleys in biceps-semitendinosus and in semimembranosus motor axons respectively, while I and L show the responses to these volleys obtained during maximum depression. J is recorded 1 hr later than I to show the small degree of recovery of the response. Time is the same as for G. Potential scale gives 1 mV for all records.

had a depressant action which has reached a maximum within a few seconds and has persisted for hours. For example, very little depression had occurred in Fig. 11 B 10 sec after the injection, but Fig. 11 C and D at about 15 and 20 sec after injection show the rapid onset and by 30 sec the maximum depression was attained (Fig. 11 E). Actually, as shown in the faster record (Fig. 11 G), the Renshaw cell still gave four early discharges. Careful comparison with the initial control at the same sweep speed (Fig. 11 F) reveals typically that this small dosage of dihydro-β-erythroidine had produced absolutely no change in the timing of the first three responses. As illustrated in Fig. 11 H and I, even a ten-fold larger dosage regularly failed to suppress the first two discharges of an intensely activated Renshaw cell, and furthermore it also failed to suppress the single discharge produced by a much less effective anti-

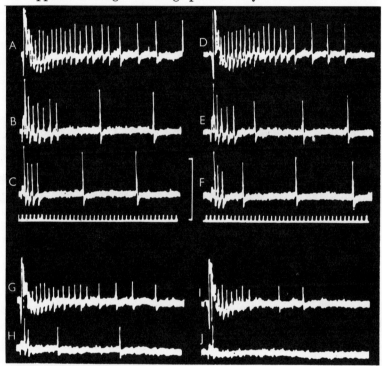

Fig. 12. A, B and C show spike responses of a Renshaw cell to maximum antidromic volleys in motor fibres of biceps-semitendinosus, gastrocnemius and flexor digitorum longus nerves respectively. D, E, F are the corresponding responses at 2 min after intravenous injection of 1 mg D-tubocurarine chloride/kg body weight. Similarly G–J show the action of the intravenous injection of 2 mg atropine sulphate/kg body weight. G and H are the responses to biceps-semitendinosus and gastrocnemius volleys before, and I and J after the injection. Time is in msec for all of the figure. Potential scale gives 1·0 mV.

dromic volley (Fig. 11 K, L). Thus it has been an invariable finding that the low-frequency later discharges are very sensitive to depressant drugs, while the initial discharges are very insensitive. The very slow recovery from such a large dosage is seen in Fig. 11 J, where the number of discharges had increased only from 2 to 3 at 1 hr after the injection.

The much less potent action of atropine even in very large doses (2 mg atropine sulphate/kg body weight) and the ineffectiveness of D-tubocurarine (1·0 mg D-tubocurarine chloride/kg body weight) are illustrated in Fig. 12.

Anticholinesterase drugs. When given by intravenous injection, eserine has greatly prolonged the repetitive discharges evoked by an antidromic volley, but has had no appreciable action on the initial period of high-frequency discharge. For example, the lengthening is shown in Fig. 13 A and C, while the initial discharges were not significantly altered (Fig. 13 B and D). The action of eserine has the slow onset characteristic of anticholinesterase effects. In Fig. 13 C, 100 sec after injection of 0·2 mg eserine sulphate/kg, the discharge was less than 200 msec in duration, while 400 sec later (Fig. 13 E) the discharge was almost 600 msec in duration. However, at 1000 sec after the injection the duration had shortened to about 450 msec. A further injection of 0·5 mg eserine sulphate/kg then caused the much longer and more intense discharge of Fig. 13 F, which by slower recording was found to persist for at least 2 sec. Still

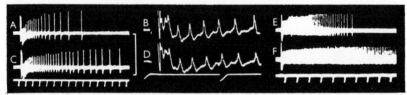

Fig. 13. A and B show Renshaw cell response to a maximum antidromic volley in the seventh lumbar ventral root at slow and fast sweep speeds, while C and D show the respective responses 100 sec after the intravenous injection of 0·2 mg eserine sulphate/kg body weight. Time scales are in 10 msec. E shows the full development of the prolonged discharge due to this injection, and F the further prolongation due to the injection of an additional 0·5 mg/kg. Time scale is in 100 msec. Potential scale gives 1·0 mV for all of the figure.

larger doses of eserine, e.g. 1·0 mg/kg, caused a spontaneous background discharge of Renshaw cells, so it was then impossible to assess the duration of the discharge evoked by a single antidromic volley. In contrast to prolonging the response of Renshaw cells to a single volley, eserine suppressed the response to successive volleys in a repetitive series (cf. section *D*).

Tetraethylpyrophosphate (TEPP) and the dimethylcarbamate of 3-hydroxy-2-dimethylaminomethylpyridine dihydrochloride (Roche, NU 2126) were equally as effective as eserine. Prostigmine, however, was virtually ineffective even in high doses (1·0 mg prostigmine bromide/kg body weight).

Acetylcholine. Acetylcholine has been injected into the spinal cord by employing the intra-arterial technique (cf. Holmstedt & Skoglund, 1953) when the microelectrode had been inserted close to a Renshaw cell which was indicated by the rhythmic spike potentials evoked by an antidromic volley. As illustrated in Fig. 14 A some Renshaw cells were readily excited by relatively small injections of acetylcholine. Identification was established by the similarity of the spike potentials, when observed in detail at fast sweep speeds (Fig. 14 G, H), to those generated by an antidromic volley (Fig. 14 F). The double discharges seen in Fig. 14 A, B, G were an unusual feature. The threshold for the cell illustrated in Fig. 14 A was $8\mu g$ acetylcholine chloride. Larger injections of acetylcholine gave higher frequencies and longer durations of the discharge. Frequencies as high as 100/sec have been evoked by relatively large injections (100 μg), and the duration of the discharge was then as long as 10 sec. The upper row of Table 2 gives the total number of impulses discharged by a Renshaw cell in response to graded dosage with acetylcholine.

Approximately half the Renshaw cells that we have tested have been caused to discharge by injections of not more than 20 μg acetylcholine chloride. Some of the remainder have failed to respond even to $200\mu g$. Larger doses could not be given because contractions of the lumbar musculature produced troublesome artifacts and movements. Hence we have the surprising observation that, as judged by the action of injected acetylcholine, there was a great variability between different Renshaw cells, and yet all behaved identically when their responses to antidromic volleys were subjected to the actions both of drugs which block cholinergic transmission and of anticholinesterases which prolong cholinergic action.

As would be expected, the effectiveness of a given injection of acetylcholine was always greatly increased by prior intravenous injection of eserine. For example, comparison of Fig. 14 B, C with Fig. 14 A shows the increased frequency of response evoked by injection of $30\mu g$ acetylcholine chloride after injection of 0·2 mg eserine sulphate/kg. A further injection of 0·5 mg eserine sulphate/kg increased the frequency still further to almost 100/sec (Fig. 14 D). The second row of Table 2 shows the great increase in the total number of impulses generated by a given dosage of acetylcholine, and it also shows the lowering of threshold, $2\mu g$ being as effective as $8\mu g$ before the eserine injection.

Fig. 14 E and Table 2 further illustrate the depressant action which a small dose of dihydro-β-erythroidine hydrobromide (0·1 mg/kg) exerts on the response to injected acetylcholine. The frequency of discharge suffered a five-fold diminution, and was greatly curtailed in duration, resembling a just-threshold response. Comparison of the third with the second rows of Table 2 shows that there has been approximately a ten-fold diminution in sensitivity to injected acetylcholine, e.g. $30\mu g$ then gives a response of about the same order as $3\mu g$ beforehand.

D. *Pharmacological investigations on the inhibitory pathway*

The pharmacological investigations of the preceding section were specifically designed to test the postulated cholinergic transmission at the synapses on Renshaw cells. Related investigations aid in establishing other features of the inhibitory pathway.

It has already been seen that the rhythmic wave recorded from the dorso-lateral regions of the spinal cord is of the same frequency but of inverted

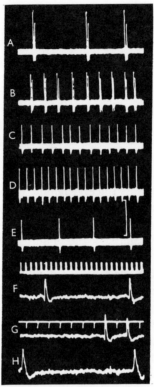

Fig. 14. A–E and G, H are records of Renshaw cell discharges evoked by intra-arterial injections of 30μg acetylcholine chloride as described in the text. Each record is a brief excerpt from the most intense part of a discharge that persisted for several seconds. B and C show responses at 10 and 18 min after the intravenous injection of 0·2 mg eserine sulphate/kg, while D is the response 10 min after a further injection of 0·5 mg eserine sulphate/kg. Between D and E 0·1 mg dihydro-β-erythroidine hydrobromide/kg body weight was injected intravenously. Time scale is in 10 msec. F–H are much faster records, showing in F the later part of a Renshaw cell response evoked by an antidromic volley. In G one of the double discharges is evoked as in A, and in H two of the rhythmic discharges are evoked as in D. Time scale is in msec. Potential scale gives 0·5 mV.

TABLE 2. Numbers of impulses evoked in a quiescent Renshaw cell by intra-arterial injection of acetylcholine

| | Amounts of acetylcholine chloride injected in μg | | | | | | | | |
	2	3	5	8	10	20	30	60	90
Initial response	—	—	—	12	43	118 100	126	233	—
After injection 0·7 mg eserine sulphate/kg	12 14	31	75	—	172 229	573	790	—	—
After further injection 0·1 mg dihydro-β-erythroidine hydrobromide/kg	—	—	—	—	—	—	20	173	249

374

polarity to the larger rhythmic wave in the ventro-medial regions (cf. Fig. 9 A), which is itself synchronized with the initial discharges of the Renshaw cells (cf. Fig. 10 A). It was postulated that the rhythmic discharges of the whole population of Renshaw cells produced a current from the axons to the cell bodies lying ventro-medially, the discharges initially being sufficiently synchronized to give the rhythmic wave whose decrementing amplitude would be largely attributable to increasing asynchronism of the individual components. This postulate receives further support from pharmacological investigations. Comparison of Fig. 15 C with A shows that intravenous injection

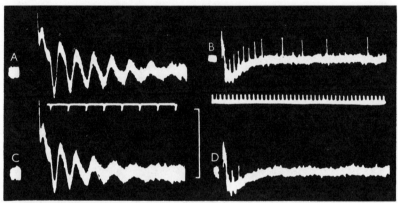

Fig. 15. A and B give the potentials evoked by a single antidromic volley (in the seventh lumbar ventral root) and recorded respectively on the dorso-lateral surface of the spinal cord and in proximity to a Renshaw cell in the ventral horn. C and D give corresponding potential records after the injection of 0·2 mg dihydro-β-erythroidine hydrobromide/kg body weight. Both time scales are in msec. The same potential scale gives 0·1 mV for A and C and 1·0 mV for B and D. A and C are formed by the superposition of about 40 faint traces.

of 0·2 mg of dihydro-β-erythroidine hydrobromide/kg depressed the later stages of the rhythmic wave, while correspondingly the much slower records of a Renshaw cell discharge showed the usual suppression of the later discharges (Fig. 15 B, D). The relatively small diminution of the earlier stages of the rhythmic wave corresponds with the resistance of the initial Renshaw cell discharges to the depressant action (cf. Fig. 11).

That a relation exists between the surface oscillatory wave and the repetitive discharge of Renshaw cells is confirmed by the modification produced in both by anticholinesterases during repetitive motor-axon stimulation. In the records illustrated in Figs. 5, 6, 11, 12, 13 there has been an interval of 3·5 sec between each successive antidromic volley, and with such an interval the responses of Renshaw cells to successive volleys have been well maintained even when under the influence of heavy anticholinesterase dosage. In Fig. 16 much faster repetition rates have been employed, 2, 8 and 27/sec respectively for the records in the three columns. Before dosage with the anticholin-esterase TEPP (Fig. 16A to E), the first three discharges of the Renshaw cell correspond as usual with the first three downward deflexions of the surface record, which is shown below the simultaneously recorded Renshaw cell response. Responses at 2 and 8/sec are virtually identical (cf. Fig. 16A and C, B and D), but at 27/sec (Fig. 16E) the first discharge has a longer latent period and the frequency is lower. Moreover, the rhythmic wave is not so well main-tained with the surface record in Fig. 16F, as compared with Fig. 16B and D. Comparison of Fig. 16G, H with A, B reveals that, even with repetitive

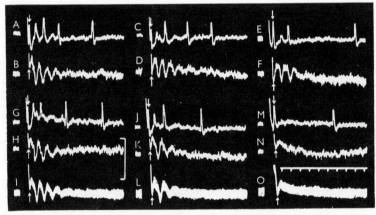

Fig. 16. A and B give simultaneously recorded potentials evoked by a single antidromic volley (in seventh lumbar ventral root) during a repetitive series at 2/sec, A showing a Renshaw cell response and B potential waves led from the dorso-lateral surface of the spinal cord. C, D and E, F are similar, but the repetitive series are at 8/sec and 27/sec respectively. G and H are similar to A and B respectively, but after the injection of 0·2 mg TEPP/kg. I is similar to H, but is formed by 40 superimposed faint traces in order to smooth out noise. J, K and L likewise correspond to C and D; and M, N and O to E and F. The first spikes discharged by the Renshaw cell and the corresponding initial positive waves in the surface records are marked by arrows in all records. The second spikes are usually much smaller. In all records a gap occurs during the large initial motoneuronal spike potentials. Further description is in text. Time scale is in msec. Potential scale gives 1·0 mV for Renshaw cell records and 0·1 mV for surface records.

stimulation as fast as 2/sec, there was after TEPP dosage very little depression in the Renshaw cell response, as shown both by direct recording from one and by recording the inverted surface wave that was generated by the whole population of Renshaw cells. This surface response is better seen in the super-imposed traces of Fig. 16I, L and O. However, comparisons of Fig. 16J with C and K or L with D reveal that at the repetition rate of 8/sec the Renshaw cell response was considerably depressed by the TEPP, being comparable with the normal responses at 27/sec (Fig. 16E, F). A much greater depression after the TEPP dosage occurred with the repetition rate of 27/sec (Fig. 16M, N, O), there being only one initial discharge both in the Renshaw cell response and in the surface response. Intermediate levels of response were observed with repetition rates of 4 and 12/sec.

It may be concluded that the surface oscillatory wave is produced by repetitive Renshaw cell activity. It should also be pointed out that the depressant effect of an anticholinesterase is a well-known phenomenon with repetitive activation of the neuro-muscular junction (Bacq & Brown, 1937; Cowan, 1938), where it is largely attributable to the accumulation of acetylcholine at the junctional region; hence the observations illustrated in Fig. 16 further support the postulate that Renshaw cells are activated by cholinergic synapses.

It remains to remove the possibility that the surface wave might be due to the repetitive wave component of the hyperpolarization produced in motoneurones (cf. Figs. 2G, 3H, 4A). Strychnine adequately differentiates the two phenomena. As noted earlier strychnine reduces the hyperpolarization in the motoneurone (Fig. 4D–H). At the same time the Renshaw cell discharge was slightly increased and the surface wave showed no significant change.

If the impulses discharged by Renshaw cells are responsible for generating the antidromic IPSP of motoneurones, it would be expected that modification of the Renshaw cell discharge by pharmacological agents would be associated with corresponding alterations in the time course of the antidromic IPSP. The predicted effects are illustrated in Fig. 17. Intravenous injection of 0·1 mg dihydro-β-erythroidine hydrobromide/kg caused little depression in the initial rate of development of the IPSP, but the summit was earlier and lower and the recovery therefrom much more rapid (cf. Fig. 17A with C and B with D). This is precisely the effect that would be expected on account of its depressant action on the later rather than the earlier Renshaw cell discharges (cf. Fig. 11). Since dihydro-β-erythroidine has been observed to have no action on direct IPSP's, it may be presumed that the whole effect seen in Fig. 17C and D is attributable to its depressant action on Renshaw cell discharges. As would be expected from the effect on Renshaw cell discharge (Fig. 13), the anticholinesterase, eserine, had the opposite action on the antidromic IPSP. The rising phase to the summit was not appreciably altered, but thereafter the time course was greatly slowed (Fig. 17E, F), as may be seen in the slower recording of Fig. 17G, where the time from the summit of the IPSP to half decay was a three-fold lengthening from the corresponding value for Fig. 17E. Such a change may be satisfactorily attributed to the large increase which eserine brings about in the later stages of a Renshaw cell discharge, the initial discharges being virtually unaltered (Fig. 13).

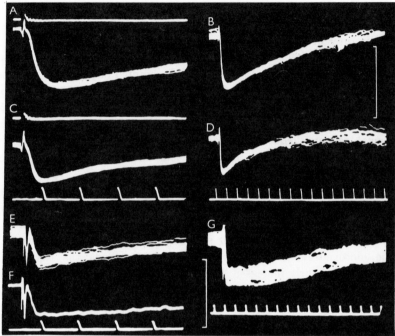

Fig. 17. Intracellularly recorded inhibitory post-synaptic potentials evoked in a motoneurone by a single antidromic volley in the seventh lumbar ventral root. A, B are before and C, D after the injection of 0·1 mg dihydro-β-erythroidine hydrobromide/kg body weight. Time scales in 10 msec are shown below the corresponding records. Potential scale gives 10 mV. E and F show IPSP's similarly evoked in another experiment, E before and F 5 min after the injection of 0·3 mg eserine sulphate/kg body weight. G is the same as F but at a slower sweep speed. Time scales are in 10 msec. Potential scale gives 5 mV. All records except F are formed by the superposition of about 40 faint traces.

DISCUSSION

The anatomical pathway

In our usual experiments Renshaw cells have been excited to discharge by stimuli applied either to ventral roots or to motor nerves, the appropriate precautions being taken to prevent impulses in afferent fibres from entering the spinal cord. By graduating the strength of stimulation it has been shown that activation of Renshaw cells is caused solely by impulses in nerve fibres whose range of thresholds corresponds to the large motor-nerve fibres (cf., for example, Fig. 6 B–E). However, nerve volleys entering the spinal cord via the dorsal roots frequently evoke discharges of Renshaw cells (Renshaw, 1946). Discharges occurring after a short latent period have been observed to be associated with large reflex discharges from motoneurones, and the depression of this reflex by deeper anaesthesia has abolished the Renshaw cell response. Such Renshaw cell activation may therefore be assumed to be secondary to the reflex discharge of impulses outwards along the motor-nerve fibres, the impulses having presumably the same action as impulses propagating anti-dromically up these fibres. However, volleys in the small group III afferent fibres often evoke discharges of Renshaw cells which have a much longer latent period and which are not secondary to the discharge of impulses from moto-neurones. While this aspect of Renshaw cell activity has not been fully explored, it does indicate that motor-axon collaterals do not provide the only excitatory pathway to Renshaw cells. In addition, Renshaw (1946) reported a slight inhibitory action of antidromic volleys on Renshaw cells, but this report requires confirmation.

The negative results of the facilitation experiments illustrated in Fig. 7 have been taken to exclude the possibility that Renshaw cells are activated by the antidromic volley after it has traversed the cell body and invaded the dendrites of the motoneurones. On neuro-histological grounds the only alternative would appear to be activation by means of the axon collaterals. However, this postulate is made without any histological evidence that these collaterals end synaptically on special interneurones in the ventral horn. The usual electro-physiological location of Renshaw cells in the ventro-medial zone of the ventral horn may be taken as additional evidence supporting their synaptic stimulation by means of motor-axon collaterals; for it is in this zone that these collaterals arise from the motor axons and terminate by extensive ramification (Cajal, 1909, Fig. 133).

Though interneurones are relatively numerous in the ventral horn, out-numbering motoneurones by three to one (Balthasar, 1952), it has been possible to find only one account in the literature which may relate specifically to Renshaw cells. After section of the ventral roots, Sprague (1951, Figs. 5, 10) found that the chromatolytic reaction occurred not only in large cells which undoubtedly are motoneurones but also to a variable degree in many small cells which, in the lower lumbar region, were concentrated in the extreme ventro-medial zone of the ventral horn. This is precisely the focal region for Renshaw cells (cf. Fig. 9B). He suggested that these cells (designated Type II cells) were small motoneurones, i.e. the motoneurones of small motor fibres innervating muscle spindles. However by antidromic activation it has been shown that the small motoneurones of a muscle are located in proximity to the large motoneurones and not in the ventro-medial zone. It therefore seems probable that the Type II cells are Renshaw cells. Sprague himself states that the atypical chromatolytic changes do not provide conclusive evidence that the Type II cells are motoneurones.

The present experiments confirm Renshaw's (1946) conclusion that impulses in many motor fibres activate any one Renshaw cell. This has been shown both by the effects of varying the size of the antidromic volley in any one motor nerve and by the excitatory action of volleys in many different motor nerves

(Fig. 6). Since the latent period of activation (0·6–0·7 msec) is about the minimum duration for a single synaptic relay in the central nervous system, there can be no interpolated neurones. As judged by the steady decline in the rate of discharge of a Renshaw cell, the activating transmitter substance reaches a maximum within 1 msec of the invasion of the terminals of the motor-axon collaterals, and thereafter it steadily declines along a time course which is indicated in Fig. 6 I. There is no need to postulate that the prolonged discharge is due to delay-paths from motor-axon collaterals through chains of interneurones to Renshaw cells.

It has already been pointed out that the antidromic IPSP has precisely the latency and time course that would be predicted if it were generated by the discharges of Renshaw cells. It has further been observed that impulses in many motor-nerve fibres sum in producing the IPSP of a motoneurone. Undoubtedly this convergence on to a motoneurone is largely attributable to the convergence on to individual Renshaw cells. However it is also necessary to postulate that several Renshaw cells contribute to the IPSP of a motoneurone. The rhythmic discharges of Renshaw cells undoubtedly give the rhythmic wave-form seen on the rising phase and summit of the IPSP (Figs. 2 G, 3 H, 4 A, B). If this rhythmic wave-form were due to the rhythmic discharges of a single Renshaw cell, it should become accentuated as the frequency declines, but the reverse occurs. It is therefore necessary to assume that the rhythm is smoothed out because it is generated by the discharges of many Renshaw cells which progressively become out of phase, exactly as occurs with the rhythmic waves recorded on the surface and in the spinal cord (cf. Figs. 9 A, 10 A).

The antidromic IPSP may begin after a central delay as brief as 1·1 msec, which is only 0·5 msec after the initiation of the earliest spike in a Renshaw cell discharge. However by recording the negative spike of a Renshaw cell extracellularly (Fig. 10 B), it is seen that about 0·2 msec is required for the invasion of the whole cell. Hence 0·3 msec remains between the invasion of the Renshaw cell terminals and the commencement of the IPSP, which agrees closely with the value determined for the direct inhibitory pathway (Eccles, Fatt & Landgren, 1954). Even when the central delay for the antidromic IPSP is as long as 1·8 msec, there is no time for the interpolation of a neurone between Renshaw cells and motoneurones, for with weak activation of Renshaw cells the latent period for their discharge may be longer than 1 msec (Fig. 5 C, D, E; Fig. 6 B, C). The prolonged time course of the antidromic IPSP is sufficiently explained by the prolonged repetitive Renshaw cell discharge.

Thus the anatomical pathway may be drawn as on the right side of the transverse section shown in Fig. 9 B. Motor-axon collaterals converge on to Renshaw cells and have an excitatory action thereon. Renshaw cells in turn converge on to motoneurones on which they have an inhibitory action.

The synaptic events

The fact that motor-nerve fibres produce and liberate acetylcholine at their peripheral contacts with muscle fibres makes it probable that acetylcholine is also the transmitter substance at the synapses which motor-axon collaterals make with Renshaw cells (Dale, 1934, 1952; Feldberg, 1950, 1952). The pharmacological investigations illustrated in Figs. 11–17 give strong confirmation to this postulate. Furthermore the investigations illustrated by Fig. 17 demonstrate that antidromic volleys in motor axons generate IPSP's in motonerones exclusively through the mediation of Renshaw cells, for the changes produced in the antidromic IPSP by dihydro-β-erythroidine and by eserine correspond precisely to the changes which these drugs produce in the discharge of Renshaw cells (Figs. 11, 13, 14, 15).

Various experimental procedures have indicated that the inhibitory synapses which Renshaw cells make with motoneurones resemble the synapses made by other inhibitory pathways to motoneurones. All the synapses are similarly affected by strychnine. Furthermore the potentials are similarly affected by the injection of ions into the cell and by the passage of currents across the surface membrane (cf. Coombs *et al.* 1953).

Conclusions

The conclusions derived from these experimental observations are illustrated in Fig. 18 which gives the successive physiological events and relates them to a diagrammatic representation of the anatomical pathway. The single impulse in the motor-axon collateral (Fig. 18A) causes the liberation of acetylcholine at synapses on Renshaw cells. The persistence of this acetylcholine (Fig. 18B) effects a prolonged depolarizing action on the Renshaw cell (cf. Fig. 6I) with the consequent generation of a repetitive discharge of impulses (Fig. 18C; cf. Fig. 6G) that gradually slows from a very high initial frequency. The latent period for the first discharge (0·6 to 0·7 msec) is in good agreement with the shortest values obtaining for other types of monosynaptic transmission. At the inhibitory synapse on the motoneurone each impulse from a Renshaw cell is shown in Fig. 18D liberating, after a delay of about 0·4 msec, the inhibitory transmitter substance, which has a characteristic brief duration of about 2 msec (Eccles, Fatt & Landgren, unpublished observations), and which in turn generates after a very brief delay the IPSP that has much the same time course as the IPSP observed with direct inhibition (Brock *et al.* 1952; Coombs *et al.* 1953). At the high initial frequencies there is fusion of the successive responses to give a considerable summation of the IPSP's, but for any one synapse this fusion will decrease as the frequency declines (Fig. 18E). However, as already suggested, the smooth contour of the IPSP beyond its summit (Figs. 2G, 3H, I) indicates that the discharges of several

Renshaw cells are responsible for generating the IPSP on any motoneurone, the asynchronism of the various discharges effecting a smoothing of the wave-form as indicated in Fig. 18F. The sites of action of the blocking agents dihydro-β-erythroidine and strychnine are also indicated in Fig. 18 between B and C and between D and E respectively, i.e. it is postulated that blockage occurs by interference with the action of the respective synaptic transmitters.

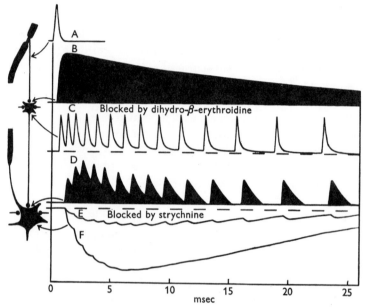

Fig. 18. Diagram summarizing the postulated sequence of events from an impulse in a motor axon to the inhibition of a motoneurone. All events are plotted on the time scale shown below and the corresponding histological structures (cf. Fig. 9B) are shown diagrammatically to the left (note indicator arrows). The six plotted time courses are for the following events: A, the electrical response of impulse in motor-axon collateral; B, the effective concentration of the acetylcholine which it liberates at a synaptic terminal; C, the electrical response evoked in a Renshaw cell by the cumulative effect of acetylcholine at many synapses, showing impulses superimposed on a background depolarization (cf. Fig. 6G); D, the effective concentration of inhibitory transmitter substance which these impulses liberate at a synaptic terminal of the Renshaw cell, showing summation at the high initial frequency; E, the IPSP generated in the motoneurone by the Renshaw cell discharge and the inhibitory transmitter shown in C and D, respectively; F, the aggregate IPSP evoked in a motoneurone that is repetitively bombarded by many Renshaw cells which progressively become more asynchronous so smoothing the latter part of the ripple shown in E. The morphological diagram to the left shows converging synapses both on the Renshaw cell and on the motoneurone (cf. Fig. 9B).

The inhibitory action which an antidromic volley exerts on motoneurones is sufficiently explained by the synaptic inhibitory pathway through Renshaw cells. Certainly the electric field explanation of Brooks *et al.* (1950) and Lloyd (1951*b*) is in good agreement with the temporal course of the inhibition. But its quantitative aspect has been in doubt, and the present experiments establish that at best it is of secondary significance. For example in Figs. 1 N and 3 B, D no positivity is detectable when the electrode is withdrawn to a just-extracellular position. No voltage scale is given for the electric field potentials recorded by Lloyd (1951 b), but the background noise level indicates a magnitude measurable in hundredths of mV, which is the magnitude recorded by Brooks et al. (1950). Only a fraction of this voltage drop would appear across the motoneuronal membrane to produce a hyperpolarization and consequent inhibition by field action. On the other hand the inhibitory synaptic potentials generated by a maximum antidromic volley in a ventral root usually attain several millivolts, i.e. the synaptic mechanism would be as much as one hundred times as effective as the field effect. Thus the electric field theory can be discounted on quantitative grounds until experimental investigation has established that an effective inhibition is thereby produced in addition to that arising from the synaptic mechanism demonstrated in this paper. It is further suggested that a search for synaptic mechanisms should be made in other instances in which neuronal interactions in the central nervous system have been attributed to the action of electrical fields.

The functional significance of this inhibitory pathway from motor axons to motoneurones remains obscure. As judged by the size of the IPSP, the intensity of the inhibition is often relatively high, being with many motoneurones larger than the direct IPSP. But on the other hand no antidromic IPSP has been detectable with about one-fifth of the motoneurones that we have investigated. We would agree with Renshaw that no functional meaning can yet be given to this potent and widely distributed inhibitory action, except in so far as it would exercise a generalized suppressor function (cf. Holmgren & Merton, 1954), which would be of importance in the limitation of such widely distributed and intense motoneuronal activity as, for example, occurs in convulsions. The long duration of the synaptic excitatory action on Renshaw cells (cf. Fig. 18 B) would fit them particularly well for summing the individual excitatory actions of impulses which are discharged at the relatively low frequencies characteristic of motoneurones.

In addition Renshaw cells may also lie in other inhibitory pathways to motoneurones. This has been shown to obtain for impulses arising in group III afferent fibres. Possibly, too, Renshaw cells may be activated by descending pathways that have an inhibitory action on motoneurones, e.g. from inhibitory areas of the bulbar reticular formation (Magoun & Rhines, 1946; Niemer & Magoun, 1947). It is further possible that Renshaw cells may make synaptic contact with other neurones as well as with motoneurones.

SUMMARY

1. Intracellular recording from motoneurones in the lumbar region of the cat's spinal cord has revealed that volleys of impulses in motor axons generate a hyperpolarization of the motoneuronal membrane which has all the features of an inhibitory post-synaptic potential. A particular motoneurone is affected by impulses in many different axons supplying different muscles, but its own axon has no special action in this regard. Both the distribution of the axons which effect a hyperpolarization of the motoneurones supplying a given muscle and the time course of the hyperpolarization show that a satisfactory explanation is hereby provided for the antidromic inhibitory effect discovered by Renshaw (1941).

2. In addition to generating this inhibitory post-synpatic potential, impulses in motor axons set up a prolonged repetitive discharge of special interneurones in the ventral horn, which was first described by Renshaw (1946). The activation of these interneurones (designated Renshaw cells) is not caused by impulses propagating over the somas and dendrites of motoneurones; it is therefore postulated that their activation takes place via the collaterals of motor axons.

3. In conformity with Dale's principle (1934, 1952) that the same chemical transmitter is released from all the synaptic terminals of a neurone, pharmacological investigation has indicated that acetylcholine mediates the excitation of Renshaw cells by impulses in the collaterals of motor axons just as it mediates the excitation of muscle fibres at the peripheral terminals of the same axons. For example the transmission to Renshaw cells is readily depressed by dihydro-β-erythroidine and to a lesser extent by atropine and is greatly prolonged by such anticholinesterases as eserine and TEPP. However, transmission is not affected by either D-tubocurarine or prostigmine. Further evidence relating to the transmission is that Renshaw cells are caused to fire repetitively by the administration of acetylcholine via the arterial blood supply of the spinal cord. There is however a wide range of variability of Renshaw cells in their response to acetylcholine thus applied. As would be expected the sensitivity of Renshaw cells to injected acetylcholine is greatly increased by eserine and depressed by dihydro-β-erythroidine.

4. Experimental investigation establishes that the antidromic inhibitory potential of motoneurones is produced through the mediation of Renshaw cells. The latent period and time course of the inhibitory potential are in precise accord with this explanation. Furthermore depression and shortening of the Renshaw cell discharge by dihydro-β-erythroidine and its prolongation by anticholinesterases are accompanied by corresponding changes in the inhibitory potential.

5. The proposed anatomical pathway is shown in Fig. 9B. Motor-axon collaterals converge on to and make synaptic contacts with Renshaw cells whose

axons in turn converge on to and make synaptic contacts with motoneurones at the same segmental level. Systematic mapping of electric potential fields in the spinal cord reveals that Renshaw cells are concentrated in the ventro-medial zone of the ventral horn and send their axons dorso-laterally towards the motoneurones. The repetitive spikes which an antidromic volley generates in Renshaw cells are initially so well synchronized that they fuse to give a rhythmic potential wave at about 1000/sec. When recorded dorso-laterally in the spinal cord this wave has a polarity which is the inverse of the polarity in the ventro-medial zone where it arises from the repetitive discharges of Renshaw cells.

6. The physiological events in the pathway from motor-axon collaterals to motoneurones are summarized in diagrammatic form in Fig. 18.

7. The functional significance of this inhibitory pathway and of Renshaw cells is briefly discussed. A sufficient explanation is thereby provided for the inhibitory action of antidromic volleys on motoneurones. The previously postulated interaction by the electric fields which are set up by currents around active cells appears to be insignificant.

The authors wish to express grateful acknowledgement to Hoffmann-La Roche Inc. for the prostigmine bromide, acetylcholine chloride and NU 2126; to Eli Lilly and Co. for the TEPP; to Merck and Co. for the dihydro-β-erythroidine hydrobromide; and to Elliotts and Australian Drug Pty. Ltd. for the D-tubocurarine chloride.

REFERENCES

BACQ, Z. M. & BROWN, G. L. (1937). Pharmacological experiments on mammalian voluntary muscle, in relation to the theory of chemical transmission. *J. Physiol.* **89**, 45–60.

BALTHASAR, K. (1952). Morphologie der spinalen Tibialis- und Peronaeus-Kerne bei der Katze. *Arch. Psychiat. Nervenkr.* **188**, 345–378.

BARAKAN, T. H., DOWNMAN, C. B. B. & ECCLES, J. C. (1949). Electric potentials generated by antidromic volleys in quadriceps and hamstring motoneurones. *J. Neurophysiol.* **12**, 393–424.

BRADLEY, K., EASTON, D. M. & ECCLES, J. C. (1953). An investigation of primary or direct inhibition. *J. Physiol.* **122**, 474–488.

BROCK, L. G., COOMBS, J. S. & ECCLES, J. C. (1952). The recording of potentials from motoneurones with an intracellular electrode. *J. Physiol.* **117**, 431–462.

BROCK, L. G., COOMBS, J. S. & ECCLES, J. C. (1953). Intracellular recording from antidromically activated motoneurones. *J. Physiol.* **122**, 429–461.

BROOKS, C. McC., DOWNMAN, C. B. B. & ECCLES, J. C. (1950). After-potentials and excitability of spinal motoneurones following antidromic activation. *J. Neurophysiol.* **13**, 9–38.

BROOKS, C. McC. & ECCLES, J. C. (1947). Electrical investigation of the monosynaptic pathway through the spinal cord. *J. Neurophysiol.* **10**, 251–274.

BROWN, T. G. (1914). On the nature of the fundamental activity of the nervous centres; together with an analysis of the conditioning of rhythmic activity in progression, and a theory of the evolution of function in the nervous system. *J. Physiol.* **48**, 18–46.

CAJAL, S. R. (1909). *Histologie du Système nerveux de l'Homme et des Vertébrés*, vol. **1**. Paris: Maloine.

COOMBS, J. S., ECCLES, J. C. & FATT, P. (1953). The action of the inhibitory synaptic transmitter. *Aust. J. Sci.* **16**, 1–5.

COWAN, S. L. (1938). The action of eserine-like and curare-like substances on the responses of frog nerve-muscle preparations to repetitive stimulation. *J. Physiol.* **93**, 215–262.

DALE, H. H. (1934). Pharmacology and nerve endings. *Proc. R. Soc. Med.* **28**, 319–332.

DALE, H. H. (1952). *Transmission of effects from nerve-endings.* (Lecture) Oxford University Press.

ECCLES, J. C. (1953). *The Neurophysiological Basis of Mind: the Principles of Neurophysiology.* Oxford: Clarendon Press.

ECCLES, J. C., FATT, P. & KOKETSU, K. (1953). Cholinergic and inhibitory synapses in a central inhibitory pathway. *Aust. J. Sci.* **16**, 50–54.

ECCLES, J. C., FATT, P. & LANDGREN, S. (1954). The 'direct' inhibitory pathway in the spinal cord. *Aust. J. Sci.* **16**, 130–134.

ECCLES, J. C., FATT, P., LANDGREN, S. & WINSBURY, G. J. (1954). Spinal cord potentials generated by volleys in the large muscle afferents. *J. Physiol.* **125**, 590–606.

ECCLES, J. C. & RALL, W. (1951). Effects induced in a monosynaptic reflex path by its activation. *J. Neurophysiol.* **14**, 353–376.

ECCLES, J. C. & SHERRINGTON, C. S. (1931). Studies on the flexor reflex. VI. Inhibition. *Proc. Roy. Soc.* B, **109**, 91–113.

FELDBERG, W. (1950). The role of acetylcholine in the central nervous system. *Brit. med. Bull.* **6**, 312–321.

FELDBERG, W. (1952). Central excitation and inhibition. *Proc. Roy. Soc.* B, **140**, 199–202.

FORBES, A., SMITH, O. C., LAMBERT, E. F., CAVENESS, W. F. & DERBYSHIRE, A. J. (1933). The central inhibitory mechanism investigated by means of antidromic impulses. *Amer. J. Physiol.* **103**, 131–142.

GESELL, R. (1940). Forces driving the respiratory act. *Science,* **91**, 229–233.

HAGBARTH, K. E. & NAESS, K. (1951). Reflex effects of tetanic stimulation of different afferent fibre-systems in the hind limb of the cat. *Acta physiol. scand.* **21**, 336–361.

HELLAUER, H. F. & UMRATH, K. (1948). Über die Aktionssubstanz der sensiblen Nerven. *Pflüg. Arch. ges. Physiol.* **249**, 619–630.

HOLMGREN, B. & MERTON, P. A. (1954). Local feedback control of motoneurones. *J. Physiol.* **123**, 47–48P.

HOLMSTEDT, B. & SKOGLUND, C. R. (1953). The action on spinal reflexes of dimethyl-amido-ethoxyphosphoryl cyanide, 'Tabun', a cholinesterase inhibitor. *Acta physiol. scand.* **29**, suppl. 106, pp. 410–427.

HOLTON, F. A. & HOLTON, P. (1952). The vasodilator activity of spinal roots. *J. Physiol.* **118**, 310–327.

JUNG, R. (1953). *The Spinal Cord, Ciba Foundation Symposium,* p. 130. London: Churchill.

KÖLLIKER, A. (1891). Zur feineren Anatomie des centralen Nervensystems. Zweiter Beitrag. Das Rückenmark. *Z. wiss. Zool.* **51**, 1–54.

LENHOSSEK, M. (1893). *Das feinere Bau des Nervensystems im Lichte neuester Forschungen.* Berlin: Kornfeld.

LLOYD, D. P. C. (1943). The interaction of antidromic and orthodromic volleys in a segmental spinal motor nucleus. *J. Neurophysiol.* **6**, 143–151.

LLOYD, D. P. C. (1946). Facilitation and inhibition of spinal motoneurones. *J. Neurophysiol.* **9**, 421–438.

LLOYD, D. P. C. (1949). Post-tetanic potentiation of response in monosynaptic reflex pathways of the spinal cord. *J. gen. Physiol.* **33**, 147–170.

LLOYD, D. P. C. (1951a). Electrical signs of impulse conduction in spinal motoneurons. *J. gen. Physiol.* **35**, 255–288.

LLOYD, D. P. C. (1951b). After-currents, after-potentials, excitability, and ventral root electrotonus in spinal motoneurons. *J. gen. Physiol.* **35**, 289–321.

LLOYD, D. P. C. (1952). Electrotonus in dorsal nerve roots. *Cold Spr. Harb. Symp. quant. Biol.* **17**, 203–219.

MAGOUN, H. W. & RHINES, R. (1946). An inhibitory mechanism in the bulbar reticular formation. *J. Neurophysiol.* **9**, 165–171.

NIEMER, W. T. & MAGOUN, H. W. (1947). Reticulo-spinal tracts influencing motor activity. *J. comp. Neurol.* **87**, 367–379.

RENSHAW, B. (1941). Influence of discharge of motoneurons upon excitation of neighbouring motoneurons. *J. Neurophysiol.* **4**, 167–183.

RENSHAW, B. (1942). Effects of presynaptic volleys on spread of impulses over the soma of the motoneuron. *J. Neurophysiol.* **5**, 235–243.

RENSHAW, B. (1946). Central effects of centripetal impulses in axons of spinal ventral roots. *J. Neurophysiol.* **9**, 191–204.

SPRAGUE, J. M. (1951). Motor and propriospinal cells in the thoracic and lumbar ventral horn of the rhesus-monkey. *J. comp. Neurol.* **95**, 103–124.

STRÖM, G. (1951). Physiological significance of post-tetanic potentiation of the spinal mono-synaptic reflex. *Acta physiol. scand.* **24**, 61–83.

TOENNIES, J. F. (1949). Die Erregungssteuerung im Zentralnervensystem. *Arch. Psychiat. Nervenkr.* **182**, 478–535.

TOENNIES, J. F. & JUNG, R. (1948). Über rasch wiederholte Entladungen der Motoneurone und die Hemmungsphase des Beugereflexes. *Pflüg. Arch. ges. Physiol.* **250**, 667–693.

THE GAMMA EFFERENTS

One of the landmarks in the field of the regulation of muscle tonus was the 1945 monograph by Leksell (53), working in Granit's laboratory. He showed that the stimulation of the smaller-diameter ventral root fibers did not result in contraction of the extrafusal fibers, but rather produced changes in the afferent discharge from the muscle. In 1930, Eccles and Sherrington (54) had investigated the histological characteristics and the fiber size of deafferented motor nerves, and had found a bimodal distribution. The small-diameter fibers, grouped about 5 μ, accounted for about one-third of the total. Leksell recorded the action potential of these small-diameter fibers, and because they conducted at rates similar to the gamma component of Gasser and Erlanger, he named them *gamma efferent fibers*. In 1947, Kuffler and Gerard studied the small ventral root fibers in the frog and observed muscle effects different from those produced by stimulation of the large-diameter fibers.

Work reported in the paper by Kuffler, Hunt, and Quilliam studied the effect of gamma-efferent stimulation on muscle activity. It was found that gamma efferents did not produce extrafusal fiber contration, but resulted in changes in the intrafusal fibers—secondarily increasing discharges in the IA afferents arising in the spindle. The use of the dorsal root afferent responses as an indicator of spindle activity was introduced by these authors and has become a standard technique for the study of spindle activity.

REFERENCES

53. Leksell, L. The action potential and excitatory effects of the small ventral root fibres to skeletal muscle. *Acta Physiol. Scand.* **10**: (Suppl. 31) (1945).

54. Eccles, J. C., and C. S. Sherrington. Numbers and contraction-values of individual motor-units examined in some muscles of the limb. *Proc. Roy. Soc. (London)* **106B**: 326–357 (1930).

55. Kuffler, S. W., and R. W. Gerard. The small-nerve motor system to skeletal muscle. *J. Neurophysiol.* **10**: 383–394 (1947).

BIBLIOGRAPHY

Hunt, C. C. The effect of stretch receptors from muscle on the discharge of motoneurones. *J. Physiol.* **117:** 359–379 (1952).

Eldred, E., R. Granit, and P. A. Merton. Supraspinal control of the muscle spindles and its significance. *J. Physiol.* **122:** 498–523 (1953).

Granit, R. *Receptors and Sensory Perception.* Yale University Press, New Haven, Connecticut, 1955.

Matthews, P. B. C. Muscle spindles and their motor control. *Physiol. Rev.* **44:** 219–288 (1964).

Granit, R., J. -O. Kellerth, and A. J. Szumski. Intracellular recording from extensor motoneurons activated across the gamma loop. *J. Neurophysiol.* **29:** 530–544 (1966).

Granit, R. *Muscular Afferents and Motor Control.* John Wiley & Sons, New York, 1966.

SUGGESTED TEXTS

Ruch *et al.* Chapter 7.

Ochs, S. Chapter 17.

Mountcastle, V. Chapters 72 and 73.

FUNCTION OF MEDULLATED SMALL-NERVE FIBERS IN MAMMALIAN VENTRAL ROOTS: EFFERENT MUSCLE SPINDLE INNERVATION*

STEPHEN W. KUFFLER, CARLTON C. HUNT† AND JUAN P. QUILLIAM‡

Wilmer Institute, Johns Hopkins Hospital and University, Baltimore, Maryland

(Received for publication February 17, 1950)

MEDULLATED fibers of varying diameter pass from the ventral roots to vertebrate skeletal muscle. In mammals such as cat about one-third of this efferent innervation to muscle may consist of small diameter $(3-8\,\mu)$ nerve fibers. This paper is concerned with the function of such fibers in cat; the studies follow on investigations of similar ventral root components of the "small-nerve system" in frog. A preliminary report appeared some time ago (28).

The small-nerve fibers in frog innervate many muscles to a varying degree and produce contractile effects which are distinct from twitch responses. On stimulation, small-nerve fibers produce local, graded, non-propagated contractions of muscle about the nerve endings, accompanied by focal potential changes (27). This efferent system also shows a specific reflex pattern (29) and is probably concerned with the maintenance of a certain type of "tone." The small-nerve fibers can produce considerable tension when stimulated repetitively, and they innervate muscle fibers which show a number of specific properties.

Physiological interest in the mammalian small diameter ventral root fibers to muscle dates from the work of Eccles and Sherrington (11). They found that deafferented nerves to the muscles of the hind limb of cat contain medullated fibers which show a diameter spectrum with two distinct peaks. About 30 per cent of the fibers were grouped about a maximum of $4-6\mu$, the remainder about $12-15\mu$. On the basis of evidence then available it was concluded that the small diameter fibers had a similar function to the large motor fibers but supplied smaller groups of muscle fibers. Analysis of fiber size of various motor nerves in different species has been undertaken by several workers. (See Rexed, 35, for references.) Such diameter spectra show considerable species variation as well as differences between nerves of the same animal. While the two-peak distribution is common, as in cat, dog, and rabbit, some species, including man, may show considerable numbers of small fibers in the lumbosacral ventral root outflow without a distinct grouping being present. Physiological investigations of these small-nerve fibers have produced two divergent views as to their function.

O'Leary *et al.* (33) investigated the small diameter efferent fibers inner-

---

* Supported by a grant from the Rockefeller Foundation.

† Senior Fellow of the National Research Council; aided by a grant from the National Foundation for Infantile Paralysis, Inc.

‡ University of London Travelling Fellow; King's College.

Kuffler, S. W., C. C. Hunt, and J. P. Quilliam. Function of medullated small-nerve fibers in mammalian ventral roots: Efferent muscle spindle innervation. *J. Neurophysiol.* **14**: 29–54, 1951.

vating the cat gastrocnemius and concluded that these nerve fibers caused little or no contractile response in the muscle. They suggested that the large fiber group accounted for the contractile response of muscle, while the small diameter fibers innervated muscle spindles. Later Leksell (30), in an outstanding investigation, considered this problem in the same muscle. He was able to block most of the large nerve fibers by pressure or by constant current and found that stimulation of the small fibers then caused little or no contractile response but did increase the afferent discharge from the muscle.

Häggquist (17), using a different approach, caused selective degeneration of large efferent fibers to muscle by cord hypoxia, after which the small diameter fibers remained practically intact. On the basis of the spasticity which followed, he concluded that the small diameter fibers were concerned with the maintenance of muscle tone. A similar conclusion has been reached by Tasaki and Tsukagoshi (37). In this paper they report that the cat's small-nerve system is similar to that in frog, subserving the maintenance of tone and causing considerable muscle tension.

The present report deals with an extensive study of the innervation of the soleus and tenuissimus muscles of the cat, although in addition the small-nerve contribution to numerous other leg muscles was investigated. The approach has been developed and modified during the past two years. It will be demonstrated that the stimulation of efferent small diameter fibers to muscle, whenever effective, activates the intrafusal muscle fibers of the spindles. Such stimulation can set up discharges when the stretch receptor is "at rest," or it can increase an existing discharge rate.

METHOD

Cats were anesthetized with 0.5 ml./kg. of Dial (Ciba) intraperitoneally. In some experiments decerebrate preparations were used but, since the results reported here were not appreciably altered by the anesthetic, Dial was usually employed. Various hind limb muscles were used, principally the soleus and tenuissimus. The dissection was carried out under warm paraffin oil, retained by skin flaps, to prevent drying and cooling. The muscle was exposed and the nerve was freed for a length of several cm., separated from branches to other muscles, and cleaned of surrounding tissue under a dissecting microscope. This reduced shunting and facilitated the recording of impulses in small-nerve fibers. The tenuissimus, which has been fully described by Adrian (1), was often less than 1 mm. in thickness while 10–14 cm. in length, and was found to survive when suspended in paraffin oil or Ringer-Locke solution without circulation. Its nerve arises from the sciatic about 1 cm. before entering the muscle and divides into two or three main branches. The ends of the tenuissimus were gripped with two forceps and lifted into paraffin oil, only its nerve connecting it to the animal. Electrodes could then be placed on any point along the muscle or on the nerve or its branches. The tenuissimus was often thin enough to permit recording of sensory impulses travelling in intramuscular nerves (Figs. 5 and 6 below). Other muscles were left with their circulation intact, the tendon freed and attached to a myograph.

The spinal cord was exposed, the dura opened, and the dorsal and ventral roots in the lumbosacral region were cut near their insertion into the cord. The cord itself was then removed from about L6 downwards. This procedure again was carried out with the tissues covered by warm paraffin oil. The nerves in the hip and hind limb not innervating the muscle under study were cut; damage to the blood supply of the sciatic nerve was carefully avoided. The leg was then fixed and skin flaps elevated so as to retain a deep pool of paraffin oil above the spinal cord and around the exposed portion of the leg. The oil was maintained at 37°–39°C. by an infra-red lamp placed above the preparation.

The experimental set-up is diagrammatically shown in Figure 1. The dorsal and ventral roots could be subdivided with fine forceps and occasionally with steel needles, using a dissecting microscope. The rootlets lay on a dark-background glass plate and were directly illuminated. The relative lack of connective tissue made these operations simple. By this technique single or groups of nerve fibers to individual muscles could be isolated in the ventral or dorsal roots. They could be lifted into the paraffin oil and placed on stimulating or recording electrodes. The intact nerve, before entering the muscle, could also be raised on electrodes for stimulating or recording (Fig. 1). Considerable care was necessary to maintain the preparation in good condition, since many experiments lasted 10–19 hours. The spinal roots, although deprived of their circulation, continued to conduct for the duration of the experiments.

Capacity-coupled amplifiers were used in conjunction with a two-beam cathode-ray oscilloscope. Continuous records were photographed on moving film with the beam sweeping at relatively slow speeds. Contractions were measured with a torsion wire myograph with optical recording, or by a strain gauge set-up.

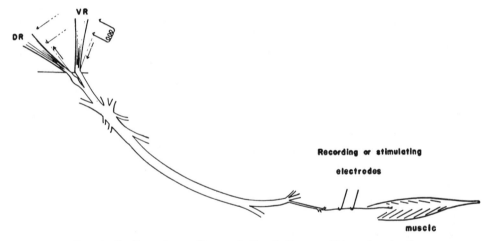

Fig. 1. Outline of recording and stimulating conditions (see text).

Results—Section A

1. Nerve fibers from lumbosacral ventral roots to muscle

The efferent fibers to the hind limb muscles of cat consist of two distinct diameter groups. This is evident from Figure 2 which shows the potential recorded from the nerve to the soleus when the second sacral ventral root was stimulated. In A the stimulus strength was just sufficient to excite the fast-conducting, low-threshold group, while in B the current strength was increased, resulting in the excitation of the slower conducting group of fibers. The relative sizes of the potentials from the fast and slow fiber groups in this figure are not representative of the whole efferent outflow, since this particular ventral root contained an unusually large proportion of small-nerve fibers. However, it shows clearly the two distinct groups of fibers with peak conduction velocities of 76 and 27 m./sec. This is in agreement with the distribution of fiber diameters as determined histologically in the deafferented nerve to the soleus by Eccles and Sherrington (11; see Fig. 3 below).

2. *Selective stimulation of small-nerve fibers*

It was difficult to evaluate the effects of stimulation of small-nerve fibers when contraction of the muscle was produced by simultaneous excitation of the larger efferent fibers. In the frog the large diameter fibers could be successfully blocked by pressure or electric current while conduction in the small fibers was maintained (27). Similar techniques were never completely satisfactory in the cat because: (i) the block could not be main-

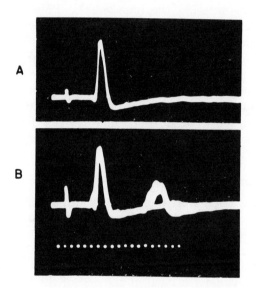

A

B

FIG. 2. Recording from central end of cut nerve to soleus. Stimulation of ventral root S_2. Multiple sweeps. A: Stimulus strength just maximal for fast conducting fibers. B: Stimulus strength increased during exposure. A high threshold, relatively slow conducting nerve component appears while large spike height remains unchanged. Entire potential complex shifts slightly due to latency shortening during increase in stimulus strength. Time base 2000 c.p.s. Conduction distance 14.5 cm.

tained constant, (ii) repetitive firing from some regions of the block was frequent, and (iii) although such blocking procedures preferentially affected the larger fibers, a residue of fast-conducting, low-threshold fibers usually persisted until the block was sufficient to halt conduction in the small diameter fibers as well. In order to excite the small-nerve fibers exclusively, individual efferent fibers were stimulated in filaments of the ventral roots. The potentials from these fibers could be recorded from the intact muscle nerve and, since the conduction distance was long, the fast and slow conducting fibers could easily be differentiated. Even when the intact nerve to the muscle was carefully cleaned so as to reduce shunting, the potentials from the small-nerve fibers were only 20–40 μV. These were often obscured by the larger potentials from afferent fibers although the latter were reduced in number by keeping the muscle slack. An alternative method of detecting small-nerve fibers was to stimulate the muscle nerve while recording from filaments of the ventral roots. Under these conditions it was found that the stimulus strength required to excite the small-nerve fibers was from two to four times maximal for large fiber excitation when a short condensor discharge (falling to half in 0.1 msec.) was used.

In many experiments on the soleus 20 or more small-nerve fibers were isolated, while five or six could often be separated to the tenuissimus. According to the estimate of Eccles and Sherrington (11) and Clark (8), the soleus receives about 200–250 efferent fibers, the small-nerve group comprising 65–75 of that number. About 20–30 per cent of the small-nerve fibers to these muscles could be isolated by the present technique.

Some observations have been made on the distribution of small-nerve fibers reaching the muscle. It is well known from histological studies that motor fibers branch extensively before entering the muscle (11). Physiological confirmation in this respect was provided by stimulation in the ventral roots of single small-nerve fibers which produced impulses in both branches of the nerve to the tenuissimus. Thus, in one case, of six fibers isolated, five went through the upper branch and all six through the lower branch. Furthermore, there are other indications of small efferent fibers dividing and innervating more than one spindle (see below, multiple spindle potentials). These observations also agree with Adrian's findings (1) that the sum of the medullated nerve fibers in the two branches was much larger (45–65 per cent) than in the nerve trunk to the tenuissimus.

3. Conduction velocities of individual small-nerve fibers

The conduction velocities of efferent fibers were measured by stimulating individual fibers in the ventral root filaments and recording their nerve impulses in the muscle nerve. The velocity was derived from the interval between shock artifact and the onset of the nerve action potential and the conduction distance. This introduces a number of possible errors, not the least being the measurement of the nerve length itself at the end of the experiment. Further, this method gives only the average conduction velocity over this distance, since tapering may occur. From the artifact-nerve impulse interval, 0.1 msec. was deducted for the time of setting up the nerve impulse at the stimulating cathode. This was determined in several experiments when recording from the site of the stimulating cathode (see also 5). Figure 3 shows the conduction velocities of over 100 individual small-nerve fibers to the soleus and about 75 to the tenuissimus. These fibers were selected at random although the larger potentials may have favored the detection of larger fibers. Also shown is the diameter spectrum of the deafferented nerve to the soleus from the data of Eccles and Sherrington (11). Since the conduction velocity and fiber diameter are directly related (15, 23), the scales have been made comparable. The small-nerve fibers to the soleus showed conduction velocities ranging between 15 and 50 m./sec. with a peak at about 30 m./sec. This clearly corresponds to the small diameter group as determined histologically and the selection of the small fibers appears representative of this group. The similar group of fibers to the tenuissimus conducted at slightly faster rates. The fastest fibers to the soleus conducted at 90–95 m./sec. with a peak between 70 and 80 m./sec.

Figure 4 illustrates the potentials recorded from the intact nerve to the tenuissimus when individual small-nerve fibers were excited in the ventral roots. In A, a fiber was stimulated which conducted at 36 m./sec. and in B one which had a velocity of 18 m./sec. C illustrates the potentials of five small-nerve fibers stimulated simultaneously.

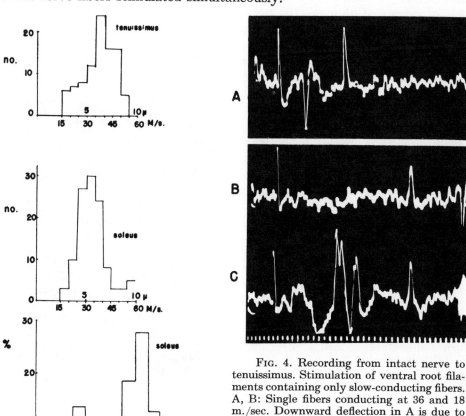

FIG. 4. Recording from intact nerve to tenuissimus. Stimulation of ventral root filaments containing only slow-conducting fibers. A, B: Single fibers conducting at 36 and 18 m./sec. Downward deflection in A is due to a sensory nerve impulse. First upward deflection is stimulus artefact. C: Collection of 5 slow-conducting fibers including A and B (40–18 m./sec.). Small-nerve impulses 20–30 μV. Time base 5000 c.p.s. Conduction distance 9.0 cm.

FIG. 3. Upper two figures: Conduction velocities plotted against numbers of individual small-nerve fibers from ventral roots to tenuissimus and soleus. Conversion to fiber diameters indicated (see text). Lower figure: Diameter spectrum of deafferented nerve to soleus of cat determined histologically, showing two distinct groups. Taken from Eccles and Sherrington (11).

4. *Effect of stimulation of different diameter ventral root fibers on muscle contraction and potentials*

Stimulation of fibers which conducted at speeds greater than 55 m./sec. always evoked a detectable contraction of the muscle and produced propagated muscle impulses. These were easily seen when a single large motor fiber was stimulated. In striking contrast, when fibers conducting at speeds of less than 50 m./sec. were stimulated, this twitch response was never detected. Since a small potential or contractile change might not be seen in the soleus because of its mass, the tenuissimus was used for these experiments. Under these conditions no propagated muscle potentials could be detected on small-nerve stimulation (see, however, below); and further, when as many as six small-nerve fibers to this muscle were stimulated together at frequencies as high as 120/sec., no contractile effect could be detected with

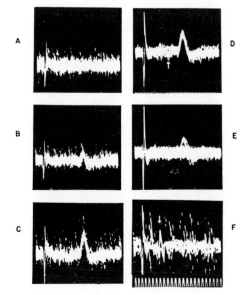

FIG. 5. *Spindle potentials recorded from a thin tenuissimus.* Stimulation of single efferent small-nerve fiber; multiple sweeps superimposed. First electrode on pelvic end of muscle (zero mm.), second moved to different positions. A: Second electrode 14 mm. from pelvic end, no muscle potential; only sensory impulses from intramuscular nerves appear on sweep. This is representative of all positions between 0 and 17 mm. B: 18 mm., first appearance of potential. C: 20 mm., potential has reached maximal size; no change in size or latency as electrode is shifted over remainder of muscle. D: Second electrode at 25 mm., potential recorded after muscle was crushed at 8 mm. Note potential as in C, but reduced number of sensory impulses. Arrow indicates estimated time of arrival of small-nerve impulse at spindle. E: Muscle crushed at 13 mm., spindle potential smaller and intermittent. F: Recording from nerve near its entry into tenuissimus, stimulation as above. Impulse of small-nerve fiber marked by arrow. Large and numerous sensory nerve impulses recorded. Here and in other records many of the afferent discharge deflexions are too faint for reproduction. Time base 2000 c.p.s., spindle potentials about 30 μV (see text).

a myographic recording system, which was sufficiently sensitive to record about 50 mg. tension changes.

Potentials set up by small-nerve impulses. Small-nerve stimulation did not elicit detectable potential changes in a muscle like the soleus, even with the highest available amplification. Recordings from the tenuissimus were similarly unsuccessful unless very thin muscles (about 1 mm. or less) were used. In the latter, potential changes were finally detected when single small-nerve fibers in the ventral roots were excited, while recording from the muscle surrounded by paraffin oil. A full investigation of the small-nerve-produced muscle potentials is made difficult, since in most cats the tenuissimus proved too large.

Figure 5 shows representative changes which were recorded in a thin tenuissimus muscle suspended in paraffin oil, when a single small-nerve fiber was stimulated in the ventral root. Potentials could be recorded over a considerable length of the muscle *without* significant decrement in size or change in latency. In spite of this "anomalous" recording situation, it could be demonstrated that the potential originated in a small circumscribed region of the muscle. When the electrodes were both on one or the other side of this region no potential appeared. For instance, in Figure 5 one electrode was kept stationary at the pelvic end of the muscle while the other was progressively moved toward the tibial end. Between zero and 16 mm. from the pelvic end no potential was seen, A, but at 18 mm. a potential was recorded, B, which reached its maximal size with a further electrode shift of 2 mm., C. As the electrode was moved over the remaining muscle length of about 10 cm., the potential maintained the same size and latency as in C. However, with increasing interelectrode distance more and more impulses, conducted in intramuscular sensory fibers, were seen (see later).

The muscle was then progressively crushed beginning at the pelvic end at 1 mm. intervals, using fine forceps, while recording from this end and from a point distally towards the nerve entry. The potential initially was similar to C and remained unchanged until the crushing had progressed to 13 mm. Figure 5D represents these records taken when the crushing had reached 8 mm. The only noticeable difference from C is the diminished number of sensory discharges, on the recurring sweeps, which had originated in the first 8 mm. stretch of the muscle. When the muscle was crushed at 13 mm., the potential became intermittent and somewhat smaller, E. Further crushing only 1 mm. distally abolished the muscle potential, although the downcoming small-nerve impulse could still be detected in the nerve, F.

In view of all subsequent findings (below) the potentials of Figure 5 are interpreted to originate in the intrafusal muscle fibers of a muscle spindle innervated by a small-nerve fiber. In the same preparation, for instance, four nerve fibers gave such potentials in several regions of the muscle, out of a total of six which were isolated and examined. While the site of the potential origin was determined to be confined to a few mm. of muscle length, the absence of electrotonic decay and the lack of change in latency of the potentials with shift of the mobile electrode could not be explained in spite of the apparently simple leading conditions (see Method). Although similar "false" or "extended" leads arise fairly frequently in nerve-muscle recording techniques, the explanation for such situations is not clear. The intermittent appearance and diminution of the focal potential E in Figure 5 seemed to be caused by some incomplete damage of the spindle mechanism due to the crushing of the muscle.

An estimate of times involved between small-nerve impulses arriving at the spindle and the potentials which they set up could be readily obtained. In Figure 5 the small-nerve impulse, F, is shown arriving in the nerve near its entry into the muscle about 3 cm. from the region where it subsequently set up the "spindle potential." Assuming a similar conduction velocity over the latter distance as between root and muscle (31 m./sec.), the small-nerve impulse reached the spindle about 1.0 msec. prior to setting up the potential. Most of this time is presumably concerned with the neuromuscular delay which is of a similar order in transmission processes between large-nerve fibers and extrafusal muscle fibers (10). The true size and time course of the spindle potentials could not be determined in these experiments. It is not possible to decide from the records whether potentials are caused by propagated or local impulses in intrafusal fibers. The latency changes with electrode shifts were not appreciable. If the spindle intrafusal fibers lie within a fluid-filled sack as described by many histologists, the effective leading conditions may be complex.

The spindle potentials showed no increment (facilitation) during repeated excitation. If the interval between two successive small-nerve impulses was shortened to about 2 msec., the second potential was reduced. Also, continued stimulation at high frequencies (100–130/sec.) eventually reduced the spindle potential. An analysis with microelectrodes may yield more information relating to potential changes in intrafusal muscle fibers.

Individual small-nerve fibers could set up potentials in widely separated muscle regions, for instance in the pelvic and tibial half of the muscle. Cutting the nerve branch to one muscle half then abolished the potential in the corresponding end. This is in line with the observations that small-nerve fibers frequently divide, sending nerve impulses into both main branches innervating the tenuissimus (see above).

Section B—Effect of Small-Nerve Stimulation on Afferent Discharges from Muscle

1. *Recording from nerve to muscle*

In the absence of detectable contractile effects, the action of small-nerve stimulation on the sensory discharge from muscle was investigated. When the muscle was subjected to even a slight stretch (resting tension of a few grams) the afferent discharges in the muscle nerve were so numerous that stimulation of several small-nerve fibers caused no clearly detectable change. With the muscle completely relaxed, however, the discharge rate was occasionally not too great for observation of a modification in the afferent impulse flow. Such an effect is seen in Figure 6 where A shows the baseline recording from the soleus nerve and B the effect produced by a train of seven stimuli at 9 msec. intervals to several small-nerve fibers to this muscle. A clear increase in the afferent discharge is seen, although there was no detectable contractile response of the muscle.

In some thin tenuissimus muscles, which may be only 1 mm. or even less in thickness, discharges from receptors which respond to stretch can be recorded with both electrodes placed on the muscle surface. With one lead on the end of the muscle more and more afferent units appear as the other electrode is moved progressively towards the nerve entry (see Fig. 5). Such impulses in intramuscular nerve fibers originate from discrete foci throughout the length of the muscle. Figure 6D-E shows the effect of small-nerve stimulation while thus recording from the muscle. In D, four stimuli at 9 msec. intervals to two small-nerve fibers in the ventral root caused a discharge from a receptor which had previously been quiescent at this muscle tension (Fig. 6C). When the number of small-nerve stimuli was increased to nine, the afferent discharge rate of the same unit was greater, E. The shunting effect of the muscle fibers allowed the recording of relatively large potentials only so that downcoming small-nerve impulses could not be detected with this amplification.

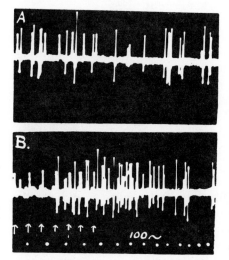
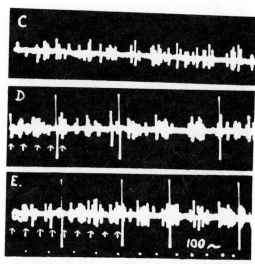

FIG. 6. A, B: Recording from nerve to soleus. Muscle tension zero g. A: Baseline. B: Stimulation of 2 small ventral root fibers, 7 stimuli at 9 msec. interval. Artefacts are marked by arrows. Note increase in afferent discharge. Potentials 50–100 μV. C, D, E: Recording from tenuissimus, leading from muscle. Initial tension of about 1 g. C: Baseline. D: Stimulation of 2 small efferent fibers, 5 stimuli at 9 msec. interval. An afferent discharge appears which was not in baseline. E: Same as D but 9 stimuli which set up an increased discharge rate of same unit. Largest potential 30 μV.

With such a technique it was established that the small-nerve fibers could cause to discharge the same receptors which responded to muscle stretch, thus confirming Leksell's earlier conclusions (30). However, this whole approach was limited by the large number of sensory units present, and the resultant need to keep the muscle slack. This presented a serious obstacle since it was found that the small-nerve effect on the afferent discharge was dependent on the muscle tension and was often absent when no external stretch to the muscle was applied (see below).

2. Recording from dorsal roots

More satisfactory information on the small-nerve effect was obtained by recording from single sensory elements in the dorsal roots. The usefulness of such single unit analyses is well known, and many of the basic features of muscle receptors have been studied by this technique (2, 6, 32).

By subdividing the dorsal roots containing the afferent flow from a muscle it was possible to record single fiber discharges from stretch receptors. In some experiments as many as 20–30 single fibers were studied. Barron and Matthews (4) had already noted that single fiber activity could be recorded in this way. Each stretch receptor was tested for its response to stimulation of all the previously isolated ventral root small-nerve fibers.* Afterwards the "active" small-nerve fiber was selected by stimulating each one separately. This procedure provided for study an arc involving a single efferent fiber, the elements of a muscle spindle, and a single afferent fiber.

Besides the response to small-nerve excitation and muscle stretch, each isolated receptor was tested for its behaviour during active muscle contraction and its conduction velocity was determined. In general, the outstanding results of Matthews (32) on stretch receptors in cat muscle were confirmed. In addition to stretch afferents, other nerve fibers have been found going from the muscle to the dorsal roots. Their locus of termination and their function is not known. These studies will be reported later. The only type of stretch afferent which responded to small-nerve stimulation was that considered to arise from muscle spindles, namely, the A type of Matthews (see Discussion).

It may be stated at the outset that the discharge from the muscle spindle can be regulated by two factors: (i) the tension of the muscle, and (ii) efferent discharges to the intrafusal fibers of the muscle spindle. While the effect of stretch on the muscle spindle discharge can be studied on its own, small-nerve actions cannot usually be investigated without subjecting the muscle to some tension (see below). When both factors are involved they modify each other's effect, since they act on the same end organ. Furthermore, the spindle discharge rate and its modification by stretch and small-nerve excitation is far from uniform in different units, although certain basic features are common to all. It must be emphasized that it was not possible to fit small-nerve effects on spindle discharges into rigid categories. The illustrations will show some of the response patterns which have been found more frequently.

The principal variants under which small-nerve excitation was studied were changes in resting tension (stretch) of the muscle, and changes in the frequency and duration of small-nerve stimulation. The small-nerve effect showed a striking dependence on all of these factors. Such tests on one unit often took an hour while responses remained remarkably constant.

3. Characteristics of excitation

A. *Effect of tension.* Figure 7 shows the response of a single spindle afferent to stimulation of a single small-nerve fiber under three different tensions to the muscle, while the number of stimuli at a constant frequency of 100/sec. was varied. The responses are grouped in this illustration according

---

* In later studies the selection of small-nerve fibers to spindles was considerably simplified (Hunt and Kuffler, *J. Physiol.*, in press.)

to the tension and number of stimuli and the effects of comparable small-nerve stimulation (B, C, D) can be seen. It is evident that approximately the same number of stimuli produce a greater response as the external stretch is increased. Also, at a given tension the response increases with the number of stimuli. For instance, at 20 g. tension, 10 small-nerve stimuli, C, set up 10

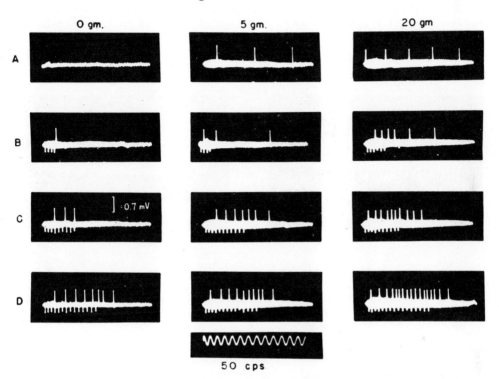

FIG. 7. Recording of single afferent discharges in dorsal root S_1 from soleus on sweep of 260 msec. duration. External stretch on muscle of 0, 5, and 20 g. Stimulation of single small efferent fiber to soleus in S_2 at 100/sec. Artifacts indicated by small downward deflexions. A: No stimulation; B: 4–6 stimuli; C: 9–11 stimuli; D. 14–16 stimuli. Note change in baseline discharge rate at different tensions. Effectiveness of small-nerve stimulation is greater at higher tensions and increases with number of stimuli. In this unit continued excitation at 100/sec. eventually established, after period of facilitation, response rate which was same as stimulus frequency ("driving"), even at zero tension (see text and Fig. 8).

afferent discharges, while a similar stimulation at zero g., C, caused only three discharges. However, if 14 stimuli were given at zero g. tension, D, eight afferent discharges resulted. Figure 7 also shows several phenomena, which will be discussed in detail later, such as the early facilitation—namely, the increasing effectiveness of successive stimuli. The depression of baseline afferent discharge which may follow cessation of small-nerve excitation is also seen (20 g., C). The unit of Figure 7 shows the interrelationship generally found between tension and number of small-nerve stimuli which governs the afferent response. The decrease in effectiveness of small-nerve stimulation caused by lowering the external tension can be compensated for, not only by increasing the number as shown above, but also the frequency of stimulation. Naturally, both factors may be combined. Phases of these phenomena are also well shown in subsequent illustrations.

B. *Facilitation*. The increase in the afferent discharge produced by small-nerve stimulation always showed a phenomenon of facilitation. The small-nerve effect increased gradually so that successive stimuli produced a progressively greater response until a maximum was reached. This facilitation period, before the ceiling effect was attained, depended on the stimulation

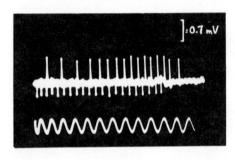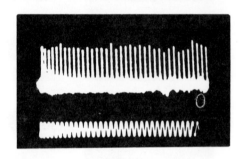

A   B

FIG. 8. Recording from single spindle afferent from soleus. A: Stimulation of single small-nerve fiber in ventral root at 100/sec. Note "driving" after period of initial facilitation. Muscle tension 5 g. Time base 50 c.p.s. B: Tuning fork vibrating at 116/sec. applied to tendon of muscle. Muscle tension 14 g. Time base 116/sec. Note that response frequency is identical to vibrating frequency.

frequency and the external tension on the muscle. It also varied with different afferent units. The facilitation can be seen in Figure 7. At zero g. tension nine stimuli, C, set up three discharges in the afferent fiber, while 14 stimuli, D, caused eight discharges, with the afferent discharge frequency gradually increasing. At higher muscle tensions the maximal discharge rate was often attained after only three to five stimuli at high frequency (Fig. 13). Low frequency of stimulation to a small-nerve fiber often produced a gradual increase in the discharge rate over a period of seconds (Fig. 10A).

The facilitation in the afferent response to small-nerve stimulation probably indicates that the intrafusal muscle elements can give graded contractions. This suggests a local non-propagated response of the intrafusal muscle fibers to small-nerve excitation (see Discussion).

C. *"Driving" of spindle discharge*. When a single small-nerve fiber was stimulated at frequencies of 50–180/sec., the receptor responding to this excitation often showed a discharge rate identical to the stimulation frequency. This "driving" of the sensory discharge usually required a certain amount of external stretch on the muscle, although different units varied considerably. In Figure 8A the discharge in the sensory fiber showed, after a

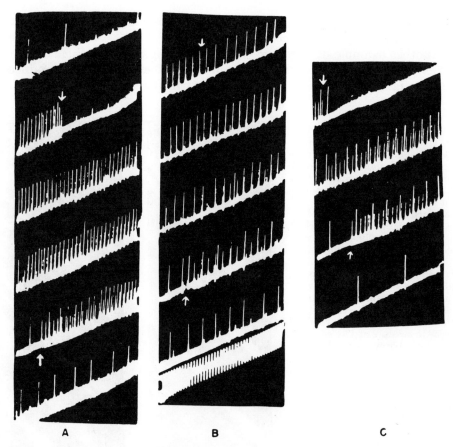

A   B   C

Fɪɢ. 9. Recording of single spindle afferent from soleus. Stimulation of small efferent fiber. Continuous records read from left to right. A: Resting tension 70 g. Baseline discharge rate 25/sec. Stimulation at 112/sec. between arrows (artifacts smaller upward deflexions). Note early facilitation after which response rate becomes same as stimulation frequency. In 3rd sweep a slight phase shift occurs between stimulus and response. Precise "driving" reappears in sweep 4. On cessation of stimulation, discharge rate shows a depression relative to baseline in first sweep. B: Same muscle tension and duration of stimulation as A, but at 56/sec. Note "driving" occurs after a much longer period of facilitation. On cessation of stimulation discharge rate shows no depression and is actually higher than baseline. C: Resting tension lowered (25 g.). Stimulation at 112/sec. between arrows. "Driving" is not established but after a facilitation period stimulus and response established a 2:1 relationship. Depression is seen after cessation of stimulation. Note second sensory discharge at similar rate, of smaller potential, in A and B which is not affected by stimulation of these particular small-nerve fibers. It ceases to discharge at lowered tension in C. Time base 130 c.p.s.

period of facilitation, the same rate as the small-nerve stimulation (100/sec.). In B, a mechanical vibration was applied to the tendon of the muscle with a frequency indicated by the sine wave in the lower trace (116/sec.). The receptor was also "driven" by this mechanical stimulus. These findings suggest that on small-nerve stimulation the intrafusal muscle fibers may produce "driving" by causing discrete contractile oscillations and thus excite the sensory endings (see Discussion).

Another example of "driving" is shown in Figure 9. In A, at a muscle tension of 70 g., stimulation of a small-nerve fiber at 112/sec. produced, after the facilitation period, a discharge rate which was identical to the stim-

FIG. 10. Recording of single muscle spindle afferent from soleus. Continuous records read from left to right. A: Stimulation of small-nerve fiber in ventral root at 10/sec. beginning in 1 and continued through record. Muscle tension 50 g. Stimuli marked with dots. Baseline rate was 15/sweep. Maximal response rate of 24/sweep was gradually reached and then maintained for duration of stimulation. Between 2 and 3, 2 sweeps were omitted (see "facilitation" section). B: Stimulation of small-nerve fiber begins in sweep 2 at 112/sec. and in 3 (at arrow) stimulus frequency was suddenly lowered to 56/sec. and discontinued in 4 (arrow). Muscle tension 42 g. Note facilitation at onset of stimulation, then "driving" at stimulation of 112/sec.; this unit also follows stimulation rate at 56/sec., rate changing abruptly in 3. There is marked depression of response following cessation of stimulation as compared with baseline rate of 29/sec. in 1. Between 2 and 3 and between 3 and 4 several sweeps were omitted. Others are consecutive in this and subsequent illustrations.

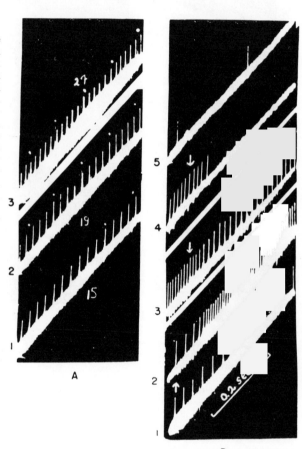

ulation frequency. In B, at the same muscle tension, stimulation at 56/sec. also produced a 1:1 ratio between stimulus and response, although the facilitation period, before driving was established, was longer. In C, the muscle tension was reduced to 25 g. and now stimulation at 112/sec. failed to produce "driving." Another example of driving at different frequencies is provided in Figure 10B. In this unit "driving" was established with a stimulation frequency of 112/sec.; decreasing the stimulus frequency to 56/sec. caused the discharge rate to fall to an equal extent, i.e., the receptor followed the pace set by the small-nerve excitation.

Additional observations have been made on the response of muscle receptors to mechanical vibration. When recording from the whole muscle nerve, the application of a vibrating tuning fork to the tendon of the muscle produced large synchronized afferent discharges recurring at the frequency of the mechanical oscillation. This response, like the small-nerve effect, de-

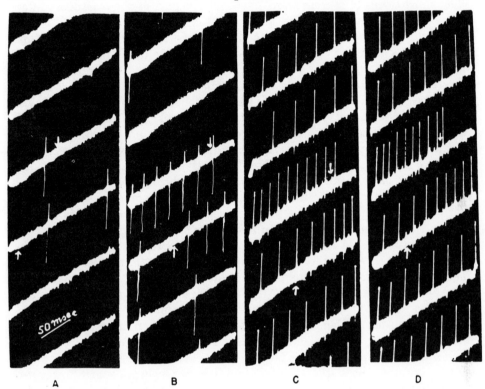

A   B   C   D

FIG. 11. *Effect of muscle tension on post-excitatory depression.* Recording from single spindle afferent from soleus in dorsal root. Continuous records read from left to right. In each case 32 stimuli at 112/sec., between arrows, were given to small efferent fiber. Muscle tensions: A: 5 g.; B: 25 g.; C: 50 g.; D: 75 g. Note increase in baseline rate and afferent response as tension is raised. Post-stimulation depression seen in B is progressively reduced with higher tensions, C and D. Electrode shifts between B and C caused potential reversal.

pended on the presence of external muscle stretch. These experiments show that the majority of stretch receptors readily follow high frequencies (several hundred per sec.) of mechanical stimuli. Similar findings have already been reported by Echlin and Fessard (12). Other sensory endings have also been shown to discharge at the frequency of an intermittent stimulus. Thus, certain receptors in the skin of frog can follow, at a high rate, an interrupted blast of air (7). Also sensory endings in the teeth can be made to discharge at the same frequency as an applied tuning fork (34).

D. *Excitability changes after cessation of small-nerve stimulation.* The pattern of afferent discharge which followed small-nerve stimulation showed marked variation between different units and was dependent on the number and frequency of preceding small-nerve stimuli and the external muscle stretch. In most preparations there was a tendency for the discharge set up by small-nerve stimulation to continue after cessation of that stimulation. When short trains of stimuli were given, a large part of the excitatory effect often occurred after the period of stimulation, and in some units the discharge rate gradually tapered off to the baseline level. On other occasions, at frequencies of 50–120/sec. the increased discharge rate continued beyond the period of stimulation ("overshoot"), so that two to six additional discharges often resulted at nearly the maximal response rate which had previously been reached (*e.g.*, Fig. 7). The "overshoot" was frequently followed by abrupt cessation of discharges. The cycle of changes in discharge rate which followed small-nerve excitation was subject to an interplay between facilitation and depression phenomena as illustrated below. For the present, they have to be discussed in a rather descriptive manner.

When the stimulation frequency was relatively high (100–120/sec.) and sufficiently prolonged, all units showed a period of depressed response rate after stimulation as compared to the baseline rate. However, this was extremely variable among different units and in some it required only a brief train of stimuli (3–4 at 10 msec. interval in Fig. 7) to show this phenomenon, while in others it was necessary to stimulate for more than one second. In a given unit the duration of this post-excitatory depression was varied by altering either the resting tension or the duration and/or frequency of stimulation. Thus Figure 11 illustrates the response obtained by identical stimulation to a small-nerve fiber, with the muscle at four different resting tensions. Since in A, at 5 g. tension, no baseline discharge was present, no index of post-excitatory depression can be seen. However, at a higher tension in B, when a baseline discharge of two impulses per sweep occurred, a post-stimulation depression lasting for at least the duration of one sweep (200 msec.) became apparent. When the tension was further increased (50 g.) in C, although more responses resulted from small-nerve stimulation, the duration of "silence" was shorter but some depression was still noticeable for two sweeps. In D, at the highest tension of 75 g. the resting discharge rate was not greatly increased by stimulation, but the post-excitatory depression was further diminished and was hardly noticeable 80 msec. after cessation of stimulation. Figure 12 illustrates the effect of changes in the duration of stimulation with the same unit at a constant resting tension of 40 g. The post-stimulation depression was greatly prolonged with increased duration of small-nerve stimulation at the same frequency. The effect of stimulation frequency on this phenomena of depression has already been strikingly demonstrated in Figure 9. In A there was a pronounced depression following stimulation at 112/sec. In B, however, under identical stretch and with the same duration of stimulation but at half the frequency, no depression at all was observed; rather a residual facilitation resulted (see below).

The post-stimulation depression may well find an explanation in some properties of the stretch receptor terminals rather than in other parts of the spindle complex, since similar depressions may be elicited in stretch receptors

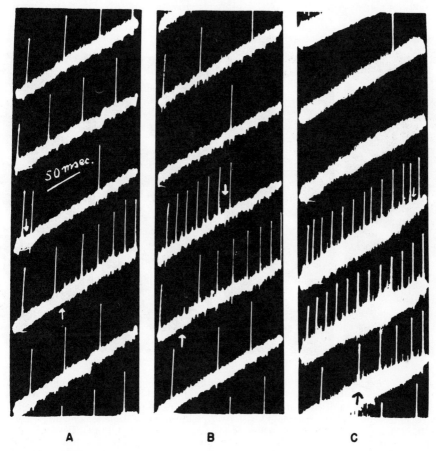

           A   B   C

Fig. 12. *Effect of duration of excitation on post-excitatory depression.* Same unit as Fig. 11. Muscle tension is now constant at 40 g. while duration of stimulation at 112/sec. is varied (between arrows). A: 16 stimuli; B: 31 stimuli; C: 57 stimuli. Note increased afferent response rate as stimulation is prolonged. Post-stimulation depression shows a progressive increase. (See Fig. 9 for effect of frequency on post-excitatory changes.)

without small-nerve excitation. For instance, when the resting muscle tension is abruptly reduced to a new steady level, the receptor discharge falls well below the baseline rate which will be established at the new tension. Matthews (32) found that it may take 2–4 seconds to attain this new "resting" discharge rate.*

---

   * A localization of such depressions in nerve terminals seems further indicated by the recent work of Katz who recorded positive potential changes in the terminals on release from stretch. (*J. Physiol.*, 1950, *111*: 248–260; 261–282.)

Apart from the "overshoot" immediately after stimulation, also a late facilitation was frequently observed. This is shown in Figure 13B, where the baseline discharge was zero. Small-nerve stimulation caused a train of responses followed by a period of quiescence and subsequently 12 impulses appeared at low frequency. At a slightly lower tension, A, these impulses

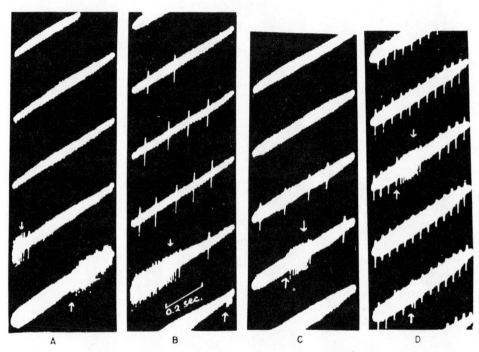

A   B   C   D

FIG. 13. *Post-excitatory facilitation*. Recording from single spindle afferent from soleus in dorsal root filament. Stimulation of small-nerve efferent fibers in ventral root. A: Muscle tension slightly less than 10 g., about 30 stimuli. B: Muscle tension 15 g., about 30 stimuli. C: Muscle tension slightly greater than 10 g., 13 stimuli. D: Muscle tension 20 g., 2 and 13 stimuli. Note prolonged discharge which follows stimulation in B and C. Lowering tension slightly, A, abolished this response. When tension was increased to 20 g. in D, this facilitation was no longer evident after stimulation, and only a brief post-excitatory depression is seen. In this unit maximal discharge rate was established after only 3 small-nerve stimuli. See also effect of 2 stimuli in sweep 1 of D.

disappeared. In C a briefer stimulation caused five delayed responses, but when the tension was further increased in D, no obvious facilitation was detected following identical stimulation. In the latter only post-stimulation depression is seen and following this the baseline rate was resumed. One has the impression that both facilitation and depression of the sensory discharge are always present after small-nerve stimulation, but that either of these may predominate depending on several variables.

Figure 14 shows a facilitation effect which may be important in the functioning of the small-nerve system. The response to a train of small-nerve stimuli at 112/sec. in A2 is followed by a new "resting" discharge rate which is more than double the baseline rate. When the stimulation was repeated in sweep 5, it evoked a greater afferent response and, in fact, became similar to the response which occurred at a subsequent higher resting tension, B. Thus, after small-nerve stimulation, prolonged effects may be seen which affect the spindle in a manner similar to raising the external tension.

The post-excitatory facilitation phenomena, in contrast to depression, may possibly be attributed to some lag in the contractile changes in the

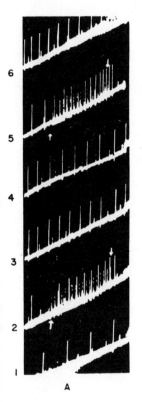

FIG. 14. Recording single afferent discharge from soleus in dorsal root. A: Muscle tension 50 g. Identical short bursts of stimulation at 112/sec. to small-nerve efferent fiber in sweeps 2 and 5. Baseline discharge rate of 12/sec. is increased, after stimulation in 2, to about 30/sec. in 3 and 4. Stimulation in 5 causes a greater afferent response than that in 2 and resembles response at higher muscle tension in B. B: Muscle tension 70 g. Stimulation as in A. Note slight post-stimulation facilitation at this tension. "Driving" occurs in B and in A5. Time base 130 c.p.s. (see text).

A   B

muscle spindles, in which the intrafusal muscle fibers may return only slowly to their original position owing to their viscosity or some "holding" action. This could also explain the tendency of some units to maintain for short periods an established frequency after cessation of stimulation ("overshoot"). On the other hand, post-excitatory facilitation and depression appear to be more general phenomena and also occur for instance in isolated nerves, or in the eye after illumination (13, 16, 19).

It is evident, then, that our technique gives only a rough qualitative indication of excitability fluctuations. Perhaps accurate recording methods from spindles would furnish better data.

Discussion

It is clear that in cat the small diameter ventral root fibers to muscle subserve a different function from the larger motor fibers in that they fail to evoke detectable contraction of the extrafusal muscle fibers. The present experiments indicate that a large proportion, if not all, of the small-nerve outflow to muscle in the cat is concerned with the motor innervation of the muscle spindles. This is somewhat surprising since one is not accustomed to consider an extensive efferent spindle innervation such as 30 per cent of the total ventral root outflow in the lumbosacral region.* The small-nerve fibers produce no detectable mechanical or potential changes in extrafusal muscle fibers. It is therefore necessary to revise the earlier calculations of motor unit tensions which were derived by dividing the maximal contractile response of a muscle by the number of motor nerve fibers (8, 11, 18).

It is generally agreed that mammalian muscle spindles are supplied with two types of sensory endings: the primary about the central portion of the spindle, and the secondary endings located more towards the poles. The configuration of these nerve endings differs among different muscle spindles, and there may be considerable variation in the number and location of sensory endings. (For more extensive information on spindle histology, consult 3, 21, and 22.) The striated intrafusal muscle fibers receive "large" (6–7 μ) and "small" (3–4 μ) medullated nerve fibers from the ventral roots which terminate in motor endplates lying towards the poles on both sides of the central region (3). The diameters of these efferent nerves are generally determined in or near the spindle. They may not be representative of the average diameter of these fibers in their course from the ventral root downwards. The "small" fibers, however, certainly correspond to those with which this study has been concerned. The "large" fibers probably also fit into the small-nerve spectrum of Figure 3, but may possibly belong to the lower end of the distinct second fiber group which sets up propagated muscle impulses in extrafusal fibers.† These may correspond to larger diameter motor fibers in *frog* which innervate both intra- and extrafusal muscle fibers as shown by Katz (25). He further found that in frog the small-nerve innervation caused local contractile responses which were not specifically connected with spindle discharge, although branches of these fibers may also innervate intrafusal muscle fibers. The mammalian intrafusal muscle fibers vary in number between different spindles (usually 4–8) and differ from the extrafusal fibers, among other respects, in their coarser striation, smaller diameter and centrally placed nuclei. The failure of the intrafusal muscle fibers to degenerate for long periods (36), when deprived of their motor

---

* The innervation of spindles is actually even more dense than indicated by the number of small-nerve fibers, since extensive branching occurs. Thus, later studies have shown that while each small-nerve fiber may innervate several spindles, each spindle also receives several small efferent fibers.

† Later evidence (Hunt and Kuffler, *J. Physiol.*, in press) indicates that all the efferent fibers to the spindles belong to the small-nerve group.

innervation, is an additional difference between extra- and intrafusal muscle elements.

A detailed study of stretch receptor behavior in single fiber preparations from cat was first made by Matthews (32). He found three major types of discharge patterns. The A_1 and A_2, apparently from muscle spindles, showed a low threshold to stretch and during submaximal contraction they ceased to discharge. When the stimulus was about maximal or slightly stronger (100–130 per cent of maximal), the A_2 type showed a series of discharges during contraction, while the A_1 remained silent. A third type, B, was considered to arise from tendon organs, and its response depended on tension development, applied either as external stretch, or by contraction. Thus the muscle spindles act as if they were "in parallel" to the contracting muscle elements, while the tendon organs behave as if they were located "in series" (14). Small-nerve stimulation affected only the A discharge type. Matthews considered the A_2 response to result from contraction of the intrafusal muscle fibers of the spindle. In that case different efferent fibers from the small-nerve group, as discussed here, were involved, since the latter are activated at two to four times the strength for maximal contraction, if short stimuli are used. Further, the character of the A_2 discharge differs from that obtained after excitation of small-nerve fibers, which do not produce a burst of afferent discharges with a single stimulus. In a subsequent detailed study it will be shown that many discharge types similar to the A_2 response of Matthews are caused by tension changes within the muscles, without specific efferent spindle activation.

The small-nerve impulses reach the spindle region about 1 msec. before setting up the potential in the intrafusal muscle fibers, much in line with other known phenomena where nerve-muscle transmission is involved (10). Certain features of the afferent discharge pattern suggest that the excitation of the intrafusal muscle fibers may be accompanied by only local changes about the small-nerve motor endings. These features include the facilitation mechanism, which is responsible for the graded afferent response pattern on small-nerve stimulation, and the resistance to fatigue. A good analogy to the frog's small-nerve system exists in this respect, although there the mechanism is used to exert appreciable direct muscle tension. The spindle potentials, owing to existing leading conditions, have not decided this question.

When studying spindle activation the excitation characteristics of the sensory endings have to be considered. Katz investigated the effect of stretch on the spindle receptor and recorded potential changes from the sensory fibers close to their terminations in the muscle spindles (26). During muscle stretch the terminals show a depolarization which was found to be a function of the velocity as well as the amplitude of stretching. For the present we may assume that small-nerve stimulation sets up contractile changes in the intrafusal muscle fibers which in turn act on the afferent terminals by their stretch-deformation effects. The synergistic effect of external stretch and small-nerve excitation also supports such an assumption. Thus, the small-nerve impulses are more effective at higher tensions, and the background excitation by stretch also counteracts the depression on sensory discharges which follows small-nerve excitation (Fig. 11). There are, however, aspects of the spindle discharge behavior during small-nerve stimulation which differ from the responses during muscle stretch. The afferent discharge to stretch depends on the rate of change as well as the amount of tension applied to the muscle. The characteristic response to a sudden increment of stretch is an increase in the discharge rate which gradually falls to a new, still-increased, steady level. Also, Matthews (32) found that when stretch was applied at a constant rate for rather long periods, the discharge rate first increased and then fell even during the period of extension. Since the intrafusal muscle elements presumably affect the sensory terminals by stretching them, one might expect the afferent response to small-nerve stimulation to show some diminution in discharge rate as stimulation is continued. However, the response to long-continued small-nerve stimulation shows no such change but is maintained at the maximal rate which has been attained. In all these events it is difficult to evaluate the effects contributed by mechanical factors such as visco-elastic properties, and by characteristics of the sensory endings themselves, like adaptation. Certainly many similar features are seen in the responses of retinal elements to excitation by light (16, 19) where no mechanical changes are involved.

The "driving" of the afferent discharge by small-nerve stimulation and the similar effect produced by a mechanical oscillation suggest that the intrafusal muscle fibers can give discrete contractile fluctuations at frequencies as high as 180/sec. and thus excite the sensory ending by intermittent stretch. When the mechanical response is recorded from the tendon of the soleus, complete fusion of the tension record occurs when the stimulation frequency is above 30/sec. On the other hand, from Hill's (20) and Katz's (24) studies it appears that the tension in muscle elements rises well before it is registered by conventional recording systems. The slowing is due to shortening of the contractile links against the series-elastic portions of the muscle and tendon. Therefore, mechanical changes may possibly be transmitted at a high rate to stretch receptors which lie in close proximity to the small-nerve endings. In cases where "driving" is established, one may imagine that during the early facilitation "slack" is taken up, perhaps by local contractile summation. Subsequent to this, each small-nerve impulse may set up a quick contractile change which provides a stimulus well above threshold for the receptor terminals. In such cases accommodation and viscous effects may not become apparent (see above).

Apart from factors such as tension, number of small-nerve stimuli, etc., causing a variable discharge pattern of a given spindle, further variables are introduced by anatomical differences between spindles. The effect of small-nerve excitation would almost certainly be modified by varying relationships of the terminals to the intrafusal fibers, especially if a local contractile process were involved. An appreciable distance between small-nerve end-plates and sensory endings would also interpose a visco-elastic tissue which could affect the rate at which the small-nerve effect develops and is maintained.

There is no information available about the role of the small-nerve system in reflex function, its central connections, or the anatomical distribution of cell bodies giving rise to the small diameter nerve fibers. However, if the small-nerve system is reflexly active, it would seem well-suited to modify or adjust the response rate and threshold to stretch of the spindle receptor when slow changes in muscle tension or length are involved. In these experiments only individual small-nerve fibers to a spindle were excited. However, if during actual function impulses in more small-nerve fibers should simultaneously reach the same spindle, the spindle output could be greatly increased, particularly at low frequencies.* Proprioceptive impulses from spindle receptors play an important role in the reflex control of posture and coordinated movement (9). Under these conditions the spindle mechanism is called upon to function at considerably different initial lengths or during maintained contraction. Since the small-nerve effect acts synergistically with externally applied tension, its activity would enable the same muscle stretch to cause a similar increment of sensory discharge at different initial tensions, thus providing a peripheral adjustment for maintaining the constancy of the reflex arc in the face of different conditions. Therefore, no fixed threshold values or response rates need to exist for a given spindle receptor during normal activity in the intact animal. The general principles of spindle excitation seem fairly clear and uncomplicated at present. However, the interplay between a number of factors such as tension, stimulation frequencies, and subsequent excitability cycles make the system appear more complex.

SUMMARY

The lumbosacral ventral root outflow in the cat contains about 30 per cent myelinated nerve fibers of 3–8 μ in diameter. The function of these fibers was investigated in several muscles, in particular the soleus and tenuissimus.

1. Nerve fibers of varying diameters were isolated and stimulated in the ventral roots. It was found that small diameter fibers conducting at 15–55 m./sec. did not cause a detectable muscle contraction nor set up propagated muscle impulses in ordinary muscle fibers. Fibers conducting at a faster rate always caused the well-known motor unit twitch response, accompanied by propagated muscle impulses.

2. Small-nerve stimulation caused small potential changes which could be detected in thin tenuissimus muscles. It is concluded that these potentials originate in the intrafusal muscle fibers of spindles. Small-nerve fibers tend to divide and innervate several muscle spindles.

---

* This, in fact, has now been demonstrated (Hunt and Kuffler, *J. Physiol.*, in press).

3. Small-nerve stimulation increases the existing afferent discharge rate of stretch receptors or causes discharges in receptors which are "quiescent." These effects can best be detected by recording discharges in the dorsal roots from single spindle afferents, while stimulating single efferent small-nerve fibers.

4. The effectiveness of small-nerve stimulation is greatly modified by various degrees of muscle stretch, being increased by higher muscle tensions and decreased by lower tensions. The effect of tension variations on the receptor discharge can be compensated for over a wide range by altering the number and/or frequency of small-nerve stimuli.

5. The excitatory effect of small-nerve stimulation on the spindle discharge shows a phenomenon of facilitation; the number of afferent discharges increases progressively during continued stimulation until a steady discharge rate is established. At a given muscle tension the facilitation period is shorter with higher frequencies of stimulation, and the maximal spindle discharge rate is also higher.

6. The discharge rates of some spindle receptors, after a period of facilitation, can become identical to the frequency of small-nerve stimulation. This "driving" effect, like all spindle discharge patterns, is influenced by muscle tension; it can be duplicated by applying mechanical oscillations to the tendon or muscle.

7. Small-nerve stimulation is followed by excitability fluctuations as indicated by the spindle discharge. It is thought that the period of depression originates mainly in the sensory nerve terminals.

8. All the evidence indicates that small-nerve excitation acts by causing contractile changes in the intrafusal muscle fibers which then excite the sensory endings by stretch-deformation effects.

9. The possible role of small-nerve activity in reflex function is briefly discussed. This efferent system appears well suited to act as a peripheral regulator of the proprioceptive spindle mechanism.

ACKNOWLEDGMENT

We are greatly indebted to Dr. S. A. Talbot for much valuable help, particularly in the design and development of most of the equipment.

REFERENCES

1. ADRIAN, E. D.   The spread of activity in the tenuissimus muscle of the cat and in other complex muscles. *J. Physiol.*, 1925, *60*: 301–315.
2. ADRIAN, E. D. AND ZOTTERMAN, Y.   The impulses produced by sensory nerve-endings. Part 2. The response of a single nerve-organ. *J. Physiol.*, 1926, *61*: 151–171.
3. BARKER, D.   The innervation of the muscle-spindle. *Quart. J. micr. Sci.*, 1948, *89*: 143–186.
4. BARRON, D. H. AND MATTHEWS, B. H. C.   Intermittent conduction in the spinal cord. *J. Physiol.*, 1935, *85*: 73–103.
5. BLAIR, E. A. AND ERLANGER, J.   On the process of excitation by brief shocks in axons. *Amer. J. Physiol.*, 1936, *114*: 309–316.
6. BRONK, D. W.   Fatigue of the sense organs in muscle. *J. Physiol.*, 1929, *67*: 270–281.
7. CATTELL, M. AND HOAGLAND, H.   Response of tactile receptors to intermittent stimulation. *J. Physiol.*, 1931, *72*: 392–403.

8. CLARK, A. D.   Muscle counts of motor units. *Amer. J. Physiol.*, 1931, *96*: 296–304.

9. DENNY-BROWN, D.   On the nature of postural reflexes. *Proc. roy. Soc.*, 1928, *104B*: 252–301.

10. ECCLES, J. C., KATZ, B., AND KUFFLER, S. W.   Nature of the "endplate potential" in curarized muscle. *J. Neurophysiol.*, 1941, *4*: 362–387.

11. ECCLES, J. C. AND SHERRINGTON, C. S.   Numbers and contraction-values of individual motor units examined in some muscles of the limb. *Proc. roy. Soc.*, 1930, *106B*: 326–357.

12. ECHLIN, F. AND FESSARD, A.   Synchronized impulse discharges from receptors in the deep tissues in response to a vibrating stimulus. *J. Physiol.*, 1938, *93*: 312–334.

13. ERLANGER, J. AND GASSER, H. S.   *Electrical signs of nervous activity*. Philadelphia, Univ. of Pennsylvania Press, 1937, 221 pp.

14. FULTON, J. F. AND PÍ-SUÑER, J.   A note concerning the probable function of various efferent end organs in skeletal muscle. *J. Physiol.*, 1928, *83*: 554–562.

15. GASSER, H. S. AND GRUNDFEST, H.   Axon diameters in relation to the spike dimensions and the conduction velocity in mammalian A fibers. *Amer. J. Physiol.*, 1939, *127*: 393–414.

16. GRANIT, R.   *Sensory mechanisms of the retina*. London, Oxford Univ. Press, 1947, 412 pp.

17. HÄGGQUIST, G.   A contribution to the question of the nervous and muscular substratum of the muscle tone. *Acta med. scand.*, 1940, *104*: 8–20.

18. HARREVELD, A. VAN.   On the force and size of motor units in the rabbit's sartorius muscle. *Amer. J. Physiol.*, 1947, *151*: 96–106.

19. HARTLINE, H. K. AND GRAHAM, C. H.   Nerve impulses from single receptors in the eye. *J. cell. comp. Physiol.*, 1932, *1*: 277–295.

20. HILL, A. V.   The "fundamental" mechanical change in muscle. *J. Physiol.*, 1949, *108*: 43P.

21. HINES, M. AND TOWER, S. S.   Studies on the innervation of skeletal muscles. *Bull. Johns Hopk. Hosp.*, 1928, *42*: 264–317.

22. HINSEY, J. C.   The innervation of skeletal muscle. *Physiol. Rev.*, 1934, *14*: 514–585.

23. HURSH, J. B.   Conduction velocity and diameter of nerve fibers. *Amer. J. Physiol.*, 1939, *127*: 131–139.

24. KATZ, B.   The relation between force and speed in muscular contraction. *J. Physiol.*, 1939, *96*: 45–64.

25. KATZ, B.   The efferent regulation of the muscle spindle in the frog. *J. exp. Biol.*, 1949, *26*: 201–217.

26. KATZ, B.   The electric response at a sensory nerve ending. *J. Physiol.*, 1949, *109*: 9P.

27. KUFFLER, S. W. AND GERARD, R. W.   The small-nerve motor system to skeletal muscle. *J. Neurophysiol.*, 1947, *10*: 383–394.

28. KUFFLER, S. W. AND HUNT, C. C.   Small-nerve fibers in mammalian ventral roots. *Proc. Soc. exp. Biol., N. Y.*, 1949, *71*: 256–257.

29. KUFFLER, S. W., LAPORTE, Y., AND RANSMEIER, R. E.   The function of the frog's small-nerve motor system. *J. Neurophysiol.*, 1947, *10*: 395–408.

30. LEKSELL, L.   The action potential and excitatory effects of the small ventral root fibers to skeletal muscle. *Acta physiol. scand.*, 1945, *10*: Suppl. 31, 84 pp.

31. LORENTE DE NÓ, R.   A study of nerve physiology, part 2. *Stud. Rockefeller Inst. med. Res.*, 1947, *132*: 1–548.

32. MATTHEWS, B. H. C.   Nerve endings in mammalian muscles. *J. Physicl.*, 1933, *78*: 1–53.

33. O'LEARY, J., HEINBECKER, P., AND BISHOP, G. H.   Analysis of function of a nerve to muscle. *Amer. J. Physiol.*, 1934, *110*: 636–658.

34. PFAFFMAN, C.   Afferent impulses from the teeth resulting from a vibratory stimulus. *J. Physiol.*, 1929, *67*: 270–281.

35. REXED, B.   Contributions to the knowledge of the post-natal development of the peripheral nervous system in man. *Acta Psychiat., Kbh.*, 1944, Suppl. 33: 206 pp.

36. SHERRINGTON, C. S.   On the anatomical constitution of nerves of skeletal muscles; with remarks on recurrent fibers in the ventral spinal nerve-root. *J. Physiol.*, 1894–1895, *17*: 211–258.

37. TASAKI, I. AND TSUKAGOSHI, H.   Comparative studies on the activities of the muscle evoked by two kinds of motor nerve fibers. *Jap. J. med. Sci.*, 1944, *10*: Part II, 245–251.

MYONEURAL JUNCTION

The discovery of acetylcholine in ganglia by Kibjakow (56), along with the observations of Loewi (57), Dale (58), and others, suggested that acetylcholine acted as the synaptic chemical mediator between parasympathetic postganglionic nerve endings and the effector cell. In 1934 Dale and Feldberg extended this hypothesis to transmission of nerve impulses across neuromuscular junctions (59).

At the end of the 1930's, it was discovered that a nerve impulse produces at the end-plate a prolonged external negative potential that is not propagated but is localized at the myoneural junction. In 1942 Kuffler (60) demonstrated the dual nature of the potential measured at the end-plates. With progressively increased application of curare, the local end-plate potential became smaller whereas the spike potential portion remained unaltered. When the end-plate potential was reduced to about one-third of the voltage on the noncurarized preparation, the spike potential was no longer elicited.

The two papers in this section can rightfully be considered classic for a number of reasons. The Fatt and Katz work provided a detailed analysis of the end-plate potential by using intracellular glass microelectrodes in an attempt to determine which ionic species crossed the end-plate membrane during the generation of the end-plate potential. Although later studies by the Takeuchis' (61) have modified the conclusions of this paper as to the ions involved, the Fatt and Katz paper still provides much basic information on the events that occur at the end-plate. Their work stimulated additional experiments seeking to define the nature of synaptic transmitter agents.

The del Castillo and Katz paper describes the phenomenon of minature end-plate potentials; this work gave rise to the concept that the transmitter was released in packets or quanta. The advent of electronmicroscopy and the discovery of synaptic vesicles prompted the suggestion that the vesicles contained the packets of transmitter. The quantal-release theory was tested by Liley (62) and others, by recording miniature end-plate potentials while varying the amount of depolarization of the muscle nerve. Results served to entrench the concept of quantal release, which has been extended to synapses of the central nervous system by the more recent work of Katz and Miledi (63).

REFERENCES

56. Kibjakow, A. W. Über humorale Übertragung der Erregung von einem Neuron auf das andere. *Pfluger's Arch.* **232:** 432–443 (1933).

57. Loewi, O. Über humorale Ubertragbarkeit der Herznervenwirkung. *Pfluger's Arch.* **189:** 239–42 (1921).

58. Dale, H. H. The action of certain esters and ethers of choline and their relations to muscarine. *J. Pharmacol.,* **6:** 147–190 (1914).

59. Dale, H. H., and W. Feldberg. Chemical transmission of motor nerve endings in voluntary muscle? *J. Physiol.* **81:** 39P–40P (1934).

60. Kuffler, S. W. Electric potential changes at an isolated nerve-muscle junction. *J. Neurophysiol.* **5:** 18–26 (1942).

61. Takeuchi, A., and N. Takeuchi. On the permeability of end-plate membrane during the action of transmitter. *J. Physiol.* **154:** 52–67 (1960).

62. Liley, A. W. The effects of presynaptic polarization on the spontaneous activity at the mammalian neuromuscular junction. *J. Physiol.* **134:** 427–443 (1956).

63. Katz, B., and R. Miledi. A study of spontaneous miniature potentials in spinal motoneurones. *J. Physiol.* **168:** 389–422 (1963).

BIBLIOGRAPHY

Dale, H. H., W. Feldberg, and M. Vogt. Release of acetylcholine at voluntary motor nerve endings. *J. Physiol.* **86:** 353–380 1936.

Eccles, J. C., B. Katz, and S. W. Kuffler. Nature of the "endplate potential" in curarized muscle. *J. Neurophysiol.* **4:** 362–387 (1941).

Krnjević, K., and J. F. Mitchell. The release of acetylcholine in the isolated rat diaphragm. *J. Physiol.* **155:** 246–262 (1961).

Katz, B., and R. Miledi. The measurement of synaptic delay, and the time course of acetylcholine release at the neuromuscular junction. *Proc. Roy. Soc.* **161B:** 483–495 (1965).

Csillik, B. *Functional Structure of the Post-Synaptic Membrane in the Myoneural Junction.* Akadémiai Kiadó, Budapest 1965.

SUGGESTED TEXTS

Ruch *et al.* Chapter 5.

Ochs, S. Chapter 9.

Mountcastle, V. Chapter 57.

AN ANALYSIS OF THE END-PLATE POTENTIAL RECORDED WITH AN INTRA-CELLULAR ELECTRODE

By P. FATT and B. KATZ

From the Physiology Department and Biophysics Research Unit, University College London

(*Received* 28 *May* 1951)

According to present knowledge, the process of neuromuscular transmission can be described by the following scheme: nerve impulse → acetylcholine → end-plate potential → muscle impulse → contraction. The evidence for this chain has been summarized by Eccles (1948), Hunt & Kuffler (1950) and Rosenblueth (1950), whose reviews may be consulted for further references. While there is little doubt that acetylcholine is released by the nerve impulse and depolarizes the end-plate, the mechanism of these two actions is at present unknown and requires further investigation. The most immediate electrical sign of neuromuscular transmission is the end-plate potential, a local depolarization of the muscle fibre which is presumably due to the direct action of the neuromuscular transmitter. By measuring this electrical change under suitable conditions, some light can be thrown on the preceding steps of the transmission process. The object of this paper is to investigate the properties of the end-plate potential even more closely than has previously been attempted, making use of the method of intra-cellular recording which has been developed by Graham & Gerard (1946), Ling & Gerard (1949) and Nastuk & Hodgkin (1950). This method offers several advantages: resting and action potentials at individual junctions can be recorded in whole muscles, without microdissection or even removing the muscle from a Ringer bath, and the measurements do not suffer from uncertainties which are usually associated with the shunting effect of the interstitial fluid.

The immediate concern of the present work is to determine the electric charge which passes through the end-plate membrane during the transmission of one impulse and to throw some light on the mechanism by which the transfer of ions across the end-plate is brought about.

METHODS

The method of intracellular recording was similar to that described by Ling & Gerard (1949) and Nastuk & Hodgkin (1950) except that the same muscle fibre, and often the same spot of the fibre, was used for a series of measurements and thus subjected to repeated insertions and withdrawals

Fatt, P., and B. Katz. An analysis of the end-plate potential recorded with an intra-cellular electrode. *J. Physiol.* **115:** 320–370, 1951.

of the microelectrode. This introduced an extra risk, for after a number of insertions local damage eventually resulted causing resting and action potentials to decline. It was, therefore, not always possible to complete a set of measurements and, in the non-curarized preparation, active movement of the muscle greatly increased the hazards of the experiment. But in spite of these inherent difficulties the method of repeated local insertions was satisfactory in many cases and gave consistent results which we could not have obtained by other means. For example, a quantitative study of the end-plate potential (e.p.p.) requires that the electric response in the same fibre should be measured at various distances from the junction. Furthermore, the size of the e.p.p. varies in individual muscle fibres much more than their resting potentials or spikes, and it was therefore desirable to compare measurements on the same junction when examining the effect of ions or drugs on the transmission process. Finally, it was only by successive insertion of the electrode at different points along a muscle fibre and so finding the position of maximum e.p.p. (cf. Fatt & Katz, 1950 a, b), that we could be certain of having located an end-plate accurately. (The term 'end-plate' is used here to describe the post-synaptic area of a muscle fibre which is in contact with the motor nerve endings, ignoring the fact that in frog muscle the shape of the junction resembles a 'bush' rather than a 'plate'.)

Preparation. The nerve-sartorius preparation of the frog (*Rana temporaria*) was used and mounted in the chamber shown in Fig. 1. The chamber was moulded from paraffin wax set in a Petri dish and was so arranged that it could be completely drained of fluid from a depression at one side of the

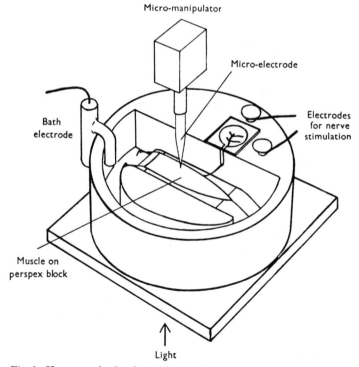

Fig. 1. Nerve-muscle chamber with stimulating and recording electrodes.

central trough. The muscle lay flat, deep surface uppermost, on a transparent Perspex block forming the floor of the central part of the chamber. It was held in this position by threads tied at each end which were looped under silver wire hooks embedded in the paraffin wax. The electrodes for nerve stimulation were situated in a separate moist compartment which was reached by the nerve via a narrow groove. The Petri dish was fixed to a glass plate which was itself carried by a mechanical stage on another large plate. Illumination was provided by light passing up through both glass plates and through the Perspex block. The preparation was viewed with a binocular dissecting microscope of magnification × 39. An eyepiece micrometer served for measurement of short distances along the muscle fibres, while coarser movements were obtained with the mechanical stage and read on the attached vernier.

The depth of fluid in the bath above the muscle was about 3 mm. It was kept at this low value in order to minimize the capacity to earth across the glass wall of the microelectrode.

The bath electrode was in the form of an agar-Ringer solution bridge connecting to a chlorided silver spiral. This led to earth via small series resistances through which steady calibration voltages and square pulses could be applied.

The microelectrode was held by a short piece of rubber tubing which led through an agar-Ringer solution bridge to a chlorided silver ribbon. The microelectrode assembly was carried on a de Fonbrune micromanipulator, the controls for which were placed outside the shielding metal box containing the preparation.

Microelectrode and amplifier. Capillary microelectrodes of external tip diameter less than 0·5 μ. and filled with 3 M-KCl were used. The wire connecting the micro-electrode to the amplifier was shielded, and the shield connected to the cathode of the first valve (RCA 954). A balanced d.c. amplifier with input cathode followers of low grid current and reduced grid-to-earth capacity was

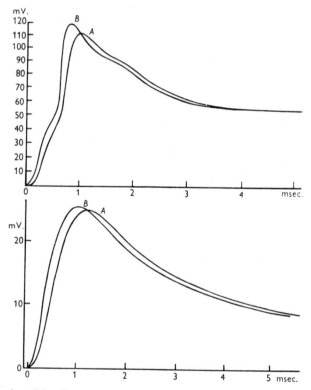

Fig. 2. Effect of amplifier distortion. Curves A are tracings of oscillograph records, curves B are corrected for high-frequency attenuation. Upper part: end-plate response during normal transmission (the muscle was treated with prostigmine, hence the large residual potential change). Lower part: curarized preparation, showing a pure e.p.p.

used, similar to those described by Nastuk & Hodgkin (1950) and Huxley & Stämfli (1949). The amplifier was calibrated by applying voltages in steps of 10 and 1 mV., and this procedure was also used to balance and measure resting potentials. In addition, a square pulse generator was used to test the time constant of the recording apparatus. This time constant varied with the resistance of the microelectrode which was apt to increase in the process of penetrating a muscle fibre. In some experiments a shielded junction box was inserted between microelectrode and amplifier. The box contained a micro-switch and 20 MΩ. shunt which could be placed across the input when a square pulse signal was applied. In this way it was possible to measure the resistance of the electrode when it was in the recording position. In other experiments a check was kept on the temporal distortion of a square pulse. The voltage wave-form at the amplifier input differed from the square pulse applied between bath and earth, in that it showed two distinct components, an instantaneously rising fraction which can be attributed to the initial displacement of charge at the glass wall of the immersed microelectrode and an exponentially rising portion which gives an indication of the time constant of the recording system. This time constant was usually between 50 and 200 μsec., and in some cases caused appreciable distortion in certain details of the electric response. In Fig. 2 a tracing is shown, together with a correction obtained by 'subtangent analysis' (cf. Rushton, 1937). The difference is rather more pronounced in this than in other experiments. On the whole, it was felt preferable to present the results without such correction, but it should be remembered that most time measurements given below are a little too large, exceeding the true value by about 0·1 msec.

Experimental procedure. In measuring membrane potentials the reference level was the potential of the bath on the surface of the fibres. As the tip of the microelectrode was moved from the bath into the interior of the fibre, the potential of the tip suddenly dropped by about 90 mV., and this drop was measured by compensating the deflexion of the cathode ray with a calibrated voltage input. The electric response, spike or end-plate potential, to a single stimulus.was then recorded, the electrode withdrawn, and the return of its potential to the original level was checked, the whole process taking usually about 15 sec. During successive insertions, apart from random variations of a few per cent, there was usually a slight progressive decline of the membrane potential, and as a rule the experiment on an individual fibre was discontinued when the resting potential fell below 80 mV. In curarized muscles, it was sometimes possible to make more than twenty successive measurements on the same fibre before excessive injury occurred, and even in normal twitching muscle twelve to fifteen successive electrode insertions could, on some occasions, be carried out without serious injury. We presume that in these cases a fortunate combination of circumstances allowed the muscle to withdraw from the impaled electrode at the beginning of the twitch without damaging either the electrode or itself. On some occasions, an unusual sign of injury was observed which appeared to be due to damage of fine nerve branches rather than muscle fibres: in these cases, the resting potential of the muscle was undiminished, but its end-plate response suddenly failed, and it was sometimes observed that nearby end-plates in adjacent muscle fibres had also failed, indicating that some damage had been inflicted to the common nerve axon. The important fact was that the continued observations of resting potential and electric response in any given fibre provided by themselves an adequate check of the state of the preparation.

Localization of end-plates. Fig. 5 shows a series of records obtained by recording at different points inside a curarized muscle fibre. As the micro-electrode approaches the end-plate the first sign is always a small and slow end-plate potential. With the electrode closer, there is a characteristic change in the amplitude and especially in the time course of the e.p.p. and it is possible, with some experience, to estimate the residual distance of the end-plate from observations of the shape of the response. In this way, the focal point can be approached quickly, with two or three insertions, and its position is then found more accurately by moving the electrode in 100 or 200 μ. steps. In Figs. 6 and 7 the changes in amplitude and time of rise with distance are shown in two experiments. It was unusual to find fibres which could be followed over long distances along the surface of the sartorius muscle: the outlines of individual fibres often become obscured by adjacent fibres and by nerve branches, blood vessels and connective tissue which tend to run across the surface, especially near the end-plate foci. If a part of the fibre is not perfectly clear in its outlines, there is a risk that the electrode tip might slip unnoticed into an overlapping neighbour, and we presume that the dotted curve in Fig. 6 arose from such an accident. In the experiment of Fig. 7 no such difficulty was experienced, and there was satisfactory agreement at every observed point between two series of measurements. In the great majority of the experiments, it was not necessary to follow individual fibres for any great length, but it was essential to be certain of the positions of individual end-plates throughout the experiment. For this purpose, the muscle was curarized at the beginning of the experiment, and a suitable number of points of maximum e.p.p. (i.e. 'end-plates') were located in the manner already described. By carefully mapping the microscopic field, noting all outstanding landmarks, it was possible to identify the fibre, and return to the same spot within 50 μ. The reliability of this procedure could be judged only from results; but the electric response at an end-plate differs so much from that of the immediate surroundings that no ambiguities arose, and it was clear that the proportion of failures in identifying previously located end-plates was minute.

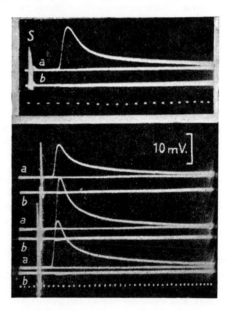

Fig. 3. End-plate potential in curarized muscle. Examples of focal recording, with the micro-electrode (a) inside the fibre, (b) on the surface of the fibre. S: stimulus artifact. Time marks: msec.

Extra-cellular potential changes. The error introduced into measurements of end-plate and action potentials by the existence of a small potential difference outside the fibre had to be considered. The magnitude of the external electric field is proportional to the radial current density at the surface of the fibre and to the specific resistance of the external solution, and it leads to a slight reduction and distortion of the observed membrane potential change. The size of the external potential change was checked in a number of experiments. After recording an end-plate or action potential with the electrode inside the fibre, another record was obtained when the electrode tip had just been withdrawn from the fibre. Examples are shown in Fig. 3. The external potential change varied a good deal: values between less than 1% and 5% of the internal action potential were obtained. Even in low-sodium solutions (4/5 of sodium chloride replaced by osmotically equivalent sucrose), where the effect of external potentials would be greatest, the amplitude of the external potential did not exceed 8% of the internal one, so that only a small correction was required when measurements made in solutions of different conductivities had to be compared. In most experiments of the present paper the conductivity of the bath remained constant (about 90 Ω. cm. at 20° C.), and no correction for external potentials was applied.

Direct stimulation. In some experiments an electric current was sent through the fibre in order to stimulate it directly or to determine its electrotonic 'cable constants' (cf. Hodgkin & Rushton, 1946; Katz, 1948). For this purpose another microelectrode was attached to a second micromanipulator which consisted of a combination of adjustable Palmer blocks and a vertical micrometer drive. The arrangement of stimulating and recording electrodes is shown in the diagram of Fig. 4. The procedure was to insert the recording electrode first, and then to introduce the stimulating microelectrode into the same fibre, either very nearby (at a distance of 20–50 μ.) or 1–2 mm. away. Repetitive subthreshold current pulses were used to indicate the moment when the stimulating electrode penetrated the required fibre, as this coincided with the sudden appearance of an electrotonic potential on the screen of the cathode-ray tube. There was usually also a drop of the resting potential by a few millivolts (cf. Nastuk & Hodgkin, 1950). In some of these experiments, a double-beam tube was used, the membrane potential being recorded by the first, and the current monitored by the second channel (see Fig. 4).

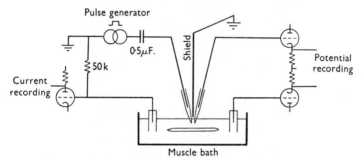

Fig. 4. Arrangement for measuring current and potential across the fibre membrane with two internal electrodes. Note: shield to reduce artifact.

The current passing through electrode and muscle membrane was usually a few tenths of a microampere. This required that several volts be applied to the electrode and gave rise to a high voltage gradient across the wall of the microelectrode tip. Not every electrode was suitable for these experiments, and with some there was evidence of dielectric breakdown occurring at the electrode tip: as the impressed voltage was increased, the current through the electrode would then suddenly rise and by-pass the muscle fibre, failing to produce or maintain a potential change across the membrane.

Temperature. Room temperature was recorded during the experiments, but checks made with a thermocouple indicated that the termperature of the preparation was about 1-1·5° C. lower, evidently because of evaporation occurring from the surface of the shallow portion of the chamber (Fig. 1). To avoid osmotic disturbance of the muscle, the bath was changed at intervals of less than 1 hr.

Solutions. In many experiments, a modified Ringer's solution was used with the composition: 113 mM. sodium, 2·0 mM. potassium, 3·6 mM. calcium, 1 mM. phosphate, 121 mM. chloride. The phosphate buffer maintained the pH at 6·8. This differed from normal Ringer mainly by its higher calcium content (3·6 mM. instead of 1·8 mM.). The advantage of this solution was that it raised the threshold of the muscle fibre, relative to the e.p.p., by about 25 % and therefore caused the e.p.p., both in curarized and normal preparations, to become somewhat more conspicuous. In other experiments, normal Ringer was used, either buffered by the addition of 1·0 mM. phosphate or unbuffered. Other solutions containing D-tubocurarine chloride (Burroughs Wellcome), or prostigmine bromide (Roche) were made up as described in the experimental section.

A. *End-plate potential in curarized muscle*

The electric response of the end-plate becomes relatively simple when neuro-muscular transmission is blocked by curarine (Eccles, Katz & Kuffler, 1941; Kuffler, 1942a). The effect of this drug is to reduce the amplitude of the e.p.p. below the threshold of the muscle fibre, so that no impulse arises and a local subthreshold potential change remains. Its general characteristics have previously been worked out on the whole muscle (Eccles *et al.* 1941). By

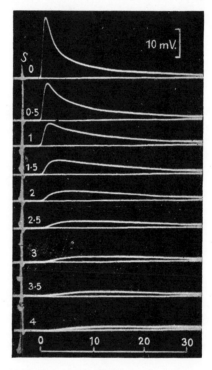

Fig. 5. End-plate potential in a single curarized muscle fibre. The position of the micro-electrode was altered in successive ½ mm. steps. The numbers give the distance from the end-plate focus, in mm. × 0·97. *S*: stimulus artifact. Time in msec.

placing a microelectrode into a curarized muscle fibre the situation becomes further simplified, for the observed response is now confined to that of a single end-plate. The method which was used in approaching the end-plate region of an individual fibre has been described above, and the results of an experiment are illustrated in Fig. 5. The e.p.p. consists of a single monophasic wave, which is rapidly attenuated as it spreads along the fibre. At the centre of the junctional region, the e.p.p. in a completely curarized muscle attains an amplitude of as much as 20–30 mV., but there are large variations of size in different fibres of the same muscle, the observed range of e.p.p. amplitudes with a given dose of curarine being greater than 10-fold. As the e.p.p. represents a graded subthreshold response, there is of course no reason to expect constancy of its amplitude, but it is remarkable that under given experimental conditions a 10- or even 20-fold variation should be found in the size of the end-plate response of different fibres. One may suspect that there are corresponding variations in the size of the junctional contact areas, or in the quantities of acetylcholine ejected from individual nerve endings.

When the e.p.p. is recorded at a 'focal' point, as in Fig. 3, it is found to rise suddenly, reaching its peak in little more than 1 msec. and declining to one-half in another 2 msec. The characteristic features of the 'focal' e.p.p. are listed in Table 1, which again shows that there is large variation in amplitude, but relatively little variation in time course.

TABLE 1. End-plate potential in curarized muscle

(These figures were obtained from ninety-four end-plates with focal recording. Most of these were selected end-plates giving e.p.p.'s of at least 10 mV. in a completely blocked muscle. Figures marked with asterisk*: these are uncorrected figures. To allow for the sytematic errors mentioned in 'Methods', subtract about 1° C. from temperature readings, and 0·1 msec. from time measurements, in this and all subsequent results. Temperature, 20° C. (16–24° C.)*. Calcium concentration, in most cases 3·6 mM. Curarine concentration, 3–5 × 10⁻⁶ D-tubocurarine chloride (Burroughs Wellcome).)

Resting potential (mV.)	E.p.p. amplitude (mV.)	Time from onset to peak (msec.) (mean and S.E. of mean)	Time from onset to half-decline (msec.)
90 (75–107)	2·5–29 (usually 10–20)	1·3±0·02 (1·0–1·6)*	3·9±0·08 (2·4–6·0)*

A more complicated picture is sometimes obtained when the electrode is inside a fibre which has a small e.p.p., but next to one with a very large e.p.p. In this case the record becomes seriously distorted by the external field due to the adjacent 'sink', and a combination is recorded of (i) a small true change of membrane potential and (ii) an external p.d. due to the neighbouring fibre. The two changes are of opposite electric sign, and may give rise to a diphasic potential change, starting with a brief downward deflexion (the micro-electrode becoming at first more negative). The diphasic response was seen only under these special conditions, and it should be realized that the initial phase is *not* a 'membrane potential', for it can be seen when the microelectrode is in the bath on the surface of the adjacent fibre. A similar explanation applies to the small diphasic or polyphasic disturbances which were observed in non-curarized muscle (cf. Nastuk & Hodgkin, 1950), and which are due to the external fields of impulses travelling in adjacent fibres.

Effect of curarine concentration on end-plate potential and resting potential

With an increased dose of curarine, the e.p.p. becomes further reduced in size without any other obvious changes. Conversely, it will be seen that the removal of curarine is associated with a large increase in the rate of rise of the e.p.p., but its peak amplitude then becomes obscured by the intervention of the muscle spike. The effect of curarine on the size of the e.p.p. is summarized in Table 2. It is noteworthy that the resting potential of the end-plate membrane is not significantly altered by curarine, the mean values being 90.5 ± 0.5 mV. (s.e. of mean, 176 measurements) for the non-curarized end-plates and 90 ± 0.6 mV. (94) for curarized end-plates. The differences of resting potential

TABLE 2. Effect of curarine on size of end-plate potential

A. Completely blocked muscle. Comparing the peak amplitudes at eight end-plates, with 5×10^{-6} and 2.5×10^{-5} D-tubocurarine chloride. Temperature, 21° C.

	5×10^{-6} curarine (mV.)		2.5×10^{-5} (mV.)		
Fibre	Resting potential	E.p.p.	Resting potential	E.p.p.	E.p.p. reduction
I	93	7.8	90	0.6	0.077
II	93	9.8	92	0.95	0.097
III	86	7.0	90	0.7	0.1
IV	80	6.5	86	0.95	0.146
V	83	6.9	91	0.55	0.08
VI	85	6.6	85	0.8	0.121
VII	83	17.4	81	2.5	0.144
VIII	86	20.7	90	2.7	0.13
Mean	86	10.3	88	1.22	0.112

B. Comparing normal and curarized muscle (4×10^{-6} D-tubocurarine chloride). The e.p.p. was measured at a fixed point of its rising phase, 0.44 msec. after its onset.)

	4×10^{-6} curarine (mV.)		Normal (mV.)		
Fibre	Resting potential	E.p.p. at 0.44 msec.	Resting potential	E.p.p. at 0.44 msec.	E.p.p. reduction
I	95	4.5	96	24.6	0.18
II	89	4.7	94	22.7	0.21
III	90	12.1	97	36.4	0.33
IV	82	8.8	98	34.8	0.25
V	96	6.4	100	32	0.2
VI	89	9.9	97	40	0.25
VII	86	5.4	86	28.4	0.19
VIII	88	12.2	84	36	0.34
IX	86	6.1	84	19.7	0.31
Mean	89	7.8	93	30.5	0.25

in the paired observations of Table 2 are also not significant. In Table 2 A, the mean difference is -2 ± 1.4 mV., the more deeply curarized end-plates having a slightly larger resting potential, while in Table 2 B, the mean difference is $+4 \pm 2$ mV.

An analysis of the spatial spread and decay of the end-plate potential

In two experiments, illustrated in Figs. 6 and 7, a fairly complete series of records was obtained at various distances from the focal point. In Fig. 8 several tracings are superimposed which show the characteristic decline and temporal spreading of the wave-form as the electrode is moved outward from the end-plate. It has been shown by several authors (Eccles *et al.* 1941; Kuffler, 1942*b*; Katz, 1948) that the e.p.p. arises from a rapid initial displacement of electric charge by the neuromuscular transmitter: this active phase appears to subside within a few milliseconds, and thereafter the time course of the e.p.p. is determined by the rate at which the charge spreads along, and leaks across, the muscle membrane. There are certain consequences of this hypothesis which can be subjected to a quantitative test.

The distribution of charge in a resting muscle fibre is described by the classical cable theory (see Hodgkin & Rushton, 1946). According to this theory, the total charge which the transmitter has placed on, or displaced from, the

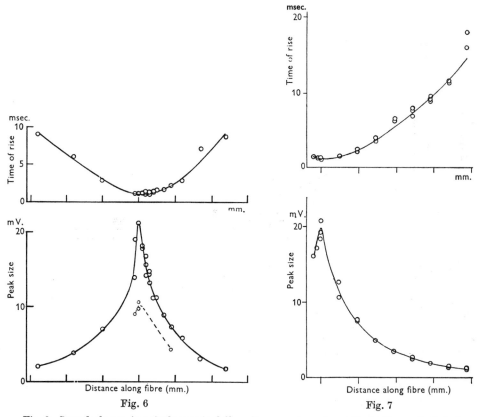

Fig. 6. Spread of e.p.p. in a single curarized fibre. Lower part: peak amplitude of e.p.p. is plotted against distance along the fibre (small circles: see text, p. 324). Upper part: time of rise of the e.p.p. is plotted against distance.

Fig. 7. Spread of e.p.p. in another fibre. Same co-ordinates as in preceding figure.

muscle fibre should decay exponentially after the transmitter has subsided. The time constant of the decay of end-plate charge should be the same as the time constant of the muscle membrane as determined by other methods (cf. Katz, 1948). In order to measure the total displacement of charge, the spread of the e.p.p. along the fibre was plotted at various moments (Fig. 9). The area under each curve gives a relative measure of the charge on the fibre surface (or rather of the 'deficit of charge', the fibre surface having been depolarized). The area can be found accurately at short times, up to about 10 msec.; at longer times, an extrapolation is required for distances greater than 4 mm., but this introduces only a slight inaccuracy in the final points. The logarithm of the area is plotted against time in Fig. 10: the end-plate charge is seen to reach a maximum at about 1·5–2 msec. and from then on to decay exponentially with a time constant of 20·6 msec.   In another experiment, the maximum was

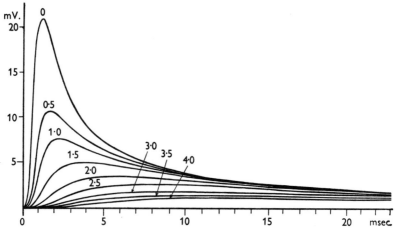

Fig. 8. Tracings of e.p.p.'s at different distances from end-plate focus. In superimposing the records, the stimulus artifact (see Fig. 5) was taken as the common point. The numbers give the distances, in mm. × 0·97, from the end-plate centre.

attained in 2–3 msec., and the charge then subsided with a time constant of 27·4 msec. These time constants are within the range of values previously found for frog muscle (see also Tables 4 and 5), and this confirms the view that, beyond the first 2 or 3 msec., the e.p.p. in curarized muscle is no longer actively maintained, and that its further time course is determined simply by the resistances and capacity of the muscle fibre.

It was pointed out to us by Mr A. L. Hodgkin that the theoretical equations describing the spread of charge along the fibre become greatly simplified if the charge has been applied *instantaneously at a point* of the fibre (see Appendix I). During the e.p.p., charge is placed on (or displaced from) points of the fibre which are usually spread out 50 to 100 μ. on either side of the centre of the nerve endings, and the displacement is nearly complete within 2 msec. These distances and times are small compared with the length and time constant of the fibre and tentatively their finite size may be disregarded, especially when analysing measurements at one or more millimetres from the end-plate focus. According to the simplified theory outlined in Appendix I, the duration T of the rising

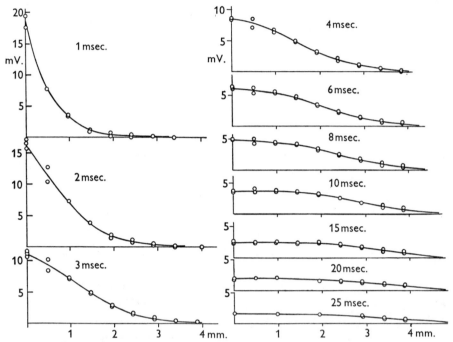

Fig. 9. Spatial distribution of e.p.p. at the indicated times after its start.

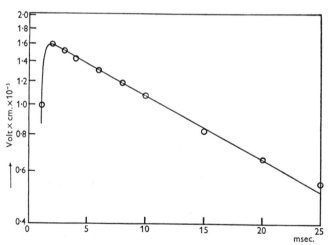

Fig. 10. The exponential decay of the end-plate charge. Ordinates: area ($\int V\,dx$) of the potential— space curves of Fig. 9, in mV. × cm., on a logarithmic scale. Abscissae: time in msec. Note: to convert ordinate readings into coulombs, multiply by $2c_m$, where c_m is membrane capacity per unit length of fibre, and the factor 2 is required because the e.p.p. spreads in both directions along the fibre.

phase of the e.p.p. at any given point, should then be related to the distance x of this point from the focus by the following equation

$$\frac{x^2}{\lambda^2} = \frac{4T^2}{\tau_m^2} + \frac{2T}{\tau_m}, \tag{1}$$

where τ_m is the time constant of the membrane and λ the length constant of the muscle fibre. These constants are related to the resistances and capacity of the fibre as follows:

$$\tau_m = R_m\, C_m,$$

where R_m is the transverse resistance and C_m the capacity of 1 cm.^{2} of membrane, and, when the fibre is immersed in a saline bath,

$$\lambda^2 = \frac{R_m}{R_i} \times \frac{\rho}{2},$$

where R_i is the specific internal resistance and ρ the radius of the fibre (for further details and nomenclature, see Hodgkin & Rushton, 1946, and Katz, 1948).

Having found τ_m, we can now use the curves of Fig. 8 and plot values of $4T^2/\tau_m^2 + 2T/\tau_m$ against x^2 (Fig. 11). According to equation (1) this should give a straight line with slope $1/\lambda^2$. The observed relation is approximately linear,

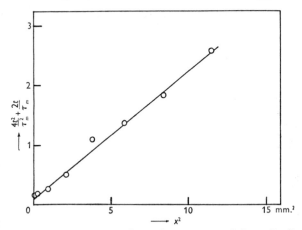

Fig. 11. Analysis of the e.p.p. in curarized muscle (see text and Appendix I). The theoretical relation is linear (slope $=1/\lambda^2$) and passes through the origin. The divergence from theory at small values of t and x is due to the fact that the rise of the e.p.p. is not instantaneous.

and λ is found to be 2·15 mm. In another experiment, the value of λ determined in the same way was 2·4 mm. This may be compared with the values of λ on p. 335, which were obtained by the 'square-pulse analysis' of the electrotonic potential: the mean value in seven fibres is 2·4 mm. (varying between 2·2 and 2·6 mm.).

To find R_m and C_m, we must make an assumption about the size and internal conductivity of the muscle fibres. The average fibre diameter in a sartorius muscle is about 75–80 μ. (Mayeda, 1890; Katz, 1948), but the fibres on the deep surface of the muscle are larger than average (Hill, 1949). Moreover, in searching for a distinct fibre which can be followed along the muscle, it is probable that one of the largest superficial fibres was chosen. We were inclined to take 100 μ. for fibre diameter and about 250 Ω.cm. for internal resistivity (cf. Bozler & Cole, 1935; Katz, 1948). The more direct experiments described on p. 335 indicate, however, that the fibre diameter was more nearly 140 μ., and this value was therefore adopted. The values calculated for R_m and C_m are 3300–4100 Ω.cm.^{2} and 6–7 μF./cm.^{2}, respectively (see Table 3). As shown in Table 5, these results

TABLE 3. Membrane constants derived from end-plate potential

Fibre	τ_m (msec.)	λ (mm.)	R_m (Ω.cm.^{2})	C_m (μF./cm.^{2})
I	20·6	2·15	3300	6
II	27·4	2·4	4100	7

are within the range of values obtained by more direct methods, and we regard the quantitative agreement as a further confirmation of our premises, namely that the e.p.p. is produced by a brief impulse of transmitter activity.

While this conclusion applies to curarized muscle, it does not hold under all conditions, and certainly not when the preparation has been treated with a cholinesterase inhibitor (see p. 337). Even in the curarized preparation, there was some variation in the time course of the e.p.p. at different end-plates (cf. Table 1) which may have arisen from variable persistence of the transmitter/end-plate reaction. Some variation, however, in the time course and spread of the e.p.p. around its focus must be expected because the spatial distribution of nerve endings varies considerably in individual muscle fibres. As Kühne (1887) has shown, the motor nerve terminals in frog muscle spread along the fibre over a distance which may vary between 30 and as much as 500 μ. The exact shape of the e.p.p. recorded at the centre of this region and the sharpness of its spatial peak must depend upon the spread of the nerve-muscle junction. If this covers a length of a few hundred microns, it will give rise to a relatively blunt peak of the e.p.p. The same effect arises, even with sharply localized junctions, if the nerve endings happen to lie on the buried side of the muscle fibre; the microelectrode cannot then be brought very close, and fine longitudinal adjustment makes little difference. In the course of locating large numbers of end-plates, considerable variations in the sharpness of localization were observed. In some cases, the position of the electrode was more critical even than shown in Fig. 6, while in other cases, a shift of 200 μ., in either direction from the centre, produced little diminution in e.p.p. size. One may surmise that this was associated with an extensive spread of the nerve endings, or their being located on the opposite side of the fibre.

Direct measurement of the membrane constants

It was desirable to determine the resistance and capacity of the muscle fibres, under similar experimental conditions, but in a more direct way than used in the preceding section. For this purpose, the rectangular pulse technique was employed as described by Hodgkin & Rushton (1946) and Katz (1948), except that intracellular electrodes were used to pass current through the membrane, and to record the resulting change of potential across it (see Methods, Fig. 4). The current was an inward directed pulse through the membrane, of about 70 msec. duration and $0 \cdot 2 \, \mu A$. intensity, which caused the membrane potential to increase by about 40 mV. The current was delivered by a rectangular pulse generator, but its shape and intensity depended upon the resistance of the microelectrode which was liable to change during the current flow. This showed itself usually in a gradual reduction of current strength, from its initial peak to a more steady level which was reached after some 10–20 msec. The current pulse was examined on a double-beam oscilloscope, and it was ascertained that a period of sufficiently steady current flow, and steady membrane potential, preceded the break of the pulse. Under these conditions, the level of the membrane potential reached at the end of the pulse, and the transient potential changes following its break, could be used to determine the relevant fibre constants.

Applying the cable theory of Hodgkin & Rushton (1946) to the present case, we find that, for a distance x between the two internal electrodes, the steady potential change V recorded at one electrode is related to the steady current I flowing through the other electrode by the following equation:

$$V = \frac{I}{2} \sqrt{(r_m r_i)} \exp \left[-x / \sqrt{(r_m / r_i)} \right], \tag{2}$$

where r_m and r_i are, respectively, the transverse resistance of the membrane times unit length and the longitudinal resistance of the fibre per unit length. The term $\frac{1}{2} \sqrt{(r_m r_i)}$ is the effective resistance between inside and outside, measured at a point far from the tendon, while $\sqrt{(r_m / r_i)}$ is the length constant λ.

Thus the values of r_m and r_i can be found from measurements with two different electrode separations. The time constant of the membrane can be determined from the time course of decay of the membrane potential, for instance by measuring the time of decline to 15 % with zero separation, or by comparing half-times at different distances (cf. Hodgkin & Rushton, 1946).

The electrodes were placed into the same muscle fibre about 10 mm. from the pelvic end. The 'polarizing' electrode was left there, while the recording electrode was moved from a position only 20–30 μ. away to a distance of $1 \cdot 6$ mm. and finally back to the original or an intermediate point. The resting potential was measured at the recording electrode, and the current was monitored in every case. The results are shown in Table 4. The values of λ, τ_m, r_m and r_i were obtained directly, while those of d, R_m and C_m are based on an assumption regarding the internal conductivity of the fibre. Its specific

TABLE 4. Membrane constants derived from 'square pulse analysis'

(Temperature 19° C. R_i is assumed to be 250 Ω.cm.)

Fibre	Resting potential (mV.)	λ (mm.)	τ_m (msec.)	$\frac{1}{2}\sqrt{(r_m r_i)}$ (Ω.)	"d" (μ.)	R_m (Ω.cm.²)	C_m (μF./cm.²)
I	89	2·3	31	210000	132	4000	8
II	91	2·3	37·5	215000	131	4100	9
III	85	2·4	29	135000	168	3400	8
IV	79	2·6	33	215000	139	4900	7
V	90	2·2	33	232000	123	3900	8
VI	89	2·2	34	193000	135	3600	9
VII	82	2·5	44	230000	132	4800	9
Mean	86	2·4	34·5	204000	137	4100	8

resistance R_i was taken as 250 Ω.cm., in accordance with earlier measurements of Bozler & Cole (1935) and Katz (1948). The fibre diameter was then calculated from

$$d = \sqrt{\left(\frac{4}{\pi} \times \frac{R_i}{r_i}\right)}, \qquad (3)$$

the mean value of d being 137 μ. This seems rather large, but it is within the known range of fibre diameters of frog's muscle (Mayeda, 1890), and it is likely that during the present experiments the largest fibres have been selected.

The values of R_m and C_m obtained in this series are listed in Table 5, together

TABLE 5. Summary of different measurements of R_m and C_m in muscle

Method and reference	Preparation	R_m (Ω.cm.²)	C_m (μF./cm.²)
External electrodes (Katz, 1948)	Small bundles and isolated fibres (75 μ.)	1500	6
	Toe muscle (45 μ.)	4000	4·5
Internal electrodes, e.p.p.	Sartorius	3700	6·5
Internal electrodes, 'square pulse'	Sartorius	4100	8

with other measurements on frog muscle. The most notable feature in this table is the large value of the membrane capacity (4·5 – 8 μF./cm.²) which exceeds that of several non-medullated nerve axons by a factor of 5.

The displacement of electric charge at an end-plate by the neuromuscular transmitter

With the use of these figures we can calculate the quantity of electric charge which is removed from the surface of a curarized muscle fibre, during the local action of a nerve impulse. This quantity is of special interest because it gives us an indication of the depolarizing power of the neuromuscular transmitter, and of the minimum number of ions which flow through the active end-plate surface. Presumably, when acetylcholine is released from the nerve endings it reacts with the end-plate so as to form a local 'sink' into which the surrounding muscle membrane discharges. But whatever the mechanism of this action, the discharge of the muscle fibre during the e.p.p. must be brought about by a transfer of ions across the end-plate membrane, and the number of ions which are transported across the end-plate surface must be large enough to provide for the observed displacement of charge.

It might be argued that, even during a subthreshold e.p.p., some regenerative reaction occurs in the surrounding muscle membrane which reinforces the local transfer of ions, quite apart from the primary action at the end-plate itself. But if such a regenerative process were at all important, it would have a noticeable effect on the time course of the e.p.p. and on the membrane constants derived from it. For example, the resistance and time constant so determined should have a larger value than when measured with the usual method of anodic polarization (p. 335). No such difference was observed, and we feel justified in assuming that the muscle membrane is discharged passively into the 'sink' at the motor end-plate.

It was shown in Fig. 10 that during the first 2 msec. of the e.p.p. the displacement of charge from the muscle membrane reaches a maximum and then declines exponentially. The maximum charge amounts to $3 \cdot 2 \times 10^{-3}$ V.cm. multiplied by the capacity per unit length of fibre. During normal impulse transmission considerably more charge is transferred across the end-plate: the results of Table 2 indicate a three- to five-fold amplification, following the withdrawal of curarine.

With a membrane capacity of 6 μF./cm.^{2} and a fibre diameter of 135 μ., the capacity of 1 cm. of fibre is $2 \cdot 45 \times 10^{-7}$ F., and the transfer of charge during the subthreshold e.p.p. is 8×10^{-10} coulombs. This corresponds to a net transport of at least 8×10^{-15} mol. of univalent cations inward, or anions outward, across the end-plate membrane. In the absence of curarine, the figure increases to $2 \text{-} 4 \times 10^{-14}$ mol. This is the *minimum* quantity of ions which the transmitter causes to flow across a single end-plate during one impulse. It is a surprisingly large amount, considering the small size of the end-plate area: it is equivalent, for instance, to the transfer of sodium across 0·8 mm.^{2} of non-medullated axon membrane during a single nerve impulse (Keynes & Lewis, 1950).

The number of ions which contribute to the production of the e.p.p. must, in fact, be larger than this estimate, as it represents only the net transfer of charge, i.e. the excess of cations over anions moving in one direction. Presumably the movement of ions is brought about by a reaction between acetylcholine and its receptors in the end-plate: it may involve a direct entry of acetylcholine ions into the muscle fibre or a permeability change leading to increased flux of other ions across the surface (cf. Fatt, 1950). It would be an important step in the study of this problem if the quantity of acetylcholine released by a nerve impulse at a single end-plate could be compared with the quantity of ions required for the production of an e.p.p.

The local discharge of the fibre surface is opposed, relatively slowly, by the flux across the membrane of potassium, chloride and other 'diffusible' ions which are responsible for the gradual return to the resting level. In the curarized muscle, the initial displacement of charge is much more rapid than subsequent leakage across the membrane, and there is very little overlap between the two phases.   A very different situation arises when the action of the transmitter is prolonged, by the use of a cholinesterase inhibitor.

The effect of prostigmine on the end-plate potential

The action of several anti-cholinesterases has been studied carefully by Eccles & MacFarlane (1949), who found that there is invariably a marked lengthening of the active phase during which the e.p.p. is built up. In Fig. 12

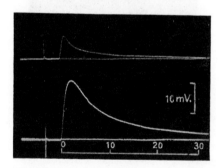

Fig. 12. Effect of prostigmine, in curarized muscle. The lower record was obtained from the same end-plate, after addition of prostigmine bromide (concentration 10^{-6}). Time, msec.

an intracellular record of this effect is shown. In a curarized muscle fibre, (3×10^{-6} D-tubocurarine chloride), an e.p.p. was observed rising to a peak of 7 mV. in 1·1 msec. and falling to one-half in another 2·1 msec. After an addition of 10^{-6} prostigmine bromide, the response at the same end-plate built up to a more rounded peak of 19 mV. in 2·1 msec., and then fell to one-half in another 5·2 msec. The effect is very similar to that previously described on whole muscle, with a moderate dose of eserine (Eccles, Katz & Kuffler, 1942) and other cholinesterase inhibitors (Eccles & MacFarlane, 1949).

It was shown by Eccles et al. (1942) that eserine produces a much more dramatic lengthening of the e.p.p. in the uncurarized muscle, though recording becomes then more complicated because of the presence of muscle spikes. We have confirmed their observation under somewhat different conditions. Nerve-muscle transmission can be blocked by lowering the external sodium concentration to one-fifth (cf. Fatt & Katz, 1950b) leaving an e.p.p. of similar shape, though usually of somewhat slower rise and fall than in the curarized muscle (see Tables 6 and 1). If prostigmine is added to the solution, a striking

TABLE 6. End-plate potential in sodium-deficient solution

(Mean values of twenty-five experiments at 20° C. Na concentration reduced to one-fifth by substitution of isotonic sucrose.)

Resting potential (mV.)	E.p.p. peak amplitude (mV.)	Time from onset to peak (msec.)	Time from onset to half-decline (msec.)
83	9–28	2·1 (1·1–2·6)	5·9 (3·2–7·8)

change occurs, shown in Fig. 13. The e.p.p. is lengthened enormously, much more than in the experiment of Fig. 12. Instead of passing through a sharp peak, the e.p.p. rises to a plateau which is maintained for some 30–40 msec., and then declines to one-half in 0·1 sec., as compared with 6 msec. (see Fig. 14).

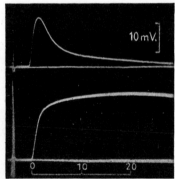

Fig. 13. Effect of prostigmine in a 'low-sodium' muscle. Upper record: E.p.p. in sodium-deficient muscle (4/5 of Na replaced by sucrose). Lower record: after addition of prostigmine bromide (10⁻⁶). Time, msec.

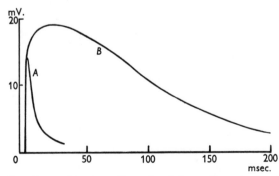

Fig. 14. Superimposed tracings of e.p.p.'s. A: low-sodium muscle. B: like A, but after adding prostigmine bromide (10⁻⁶).

There is strong evidence (see Brown, Dale & Feldberg, 1936; Eccles *et al.* 1942; Eccles & MacFarlane, 1949) that this effect is due to the protection of acetylcholine against rapid hydrolysis, and that therefore the amount of acetylcholine, initially released by the nerve impulse, continues to build up the e.p.p. and to maintain it against the simultaneous spread and leakage of charge along and across the surface membrane. The quantity of ions which passes through the end-plate in the prostigmine muscle must greatly exceed the figure given above for the curarized muscle. An estimate of the excess can be obtained by comparing the 'areas', i.e. the time-integrals, of the e.p.p.'s in the two cases: this area is about 50 times larger for the prostigmine-e.p.p. of Fig. 13, than for a 'curarine'-e.p.p. of the same initial rate of rise.

This is an important point in connexion with the alternative modes of acetylcholine action which have been suggested (Katz, 1942; Fatt, 1950). If, for instance, acetylcholine were to depolarize the end-plate by direct penetration, the quantity of ions released by a single impulse must provide not only the electric charge which is placed on the muscle fibre during the ordinary e.p.p. but the much larger quantity which is needed to maintain the e.p.p. in eserine- or prostigmine-treated muscle.

It is of interest to trace the time course of the transmitter/end-plate reaction and its changes under the influence of prostigmine. This can be done approximately by an analysis of the e.p.p. which has been previously described (Katz, 1948, p. 529). The analysis depends upon a knowledge of the time constant of the membrane, and on the assumptions (i) that the time constant is not appreciably affected by prostigmine, and (ii) that the transmitter reaction can be treated as the equivalent of an applied current pulse. There is good evidence that the first assumption holds true (Eccles *et al.* 1942) but the second is oversimplified (cf. Section B below), though not likely to lead to serious error in the present comparison. In Fig. 15 the result of such an analysis is shown for (*a*) the e.p.p. of curarized muscle, (*b*) of curarine-prostigmine-treated muscle and (*c*) of Na-deficient and prostigmine-treated muscle. The curves show, strictly speaking, the time course of three current pulses which, with a membrane time constant of 25 msec., would alter the membrane potential in a manner identical with the three observed types of e.p.p. It will be noted that, even in the presence of a cholinesterase-inhibitor, there appears to be an initial impulsive phase of transmitter action, which is followed by a long period of low-level activity. Similar phenomena have been described and discussed in detail by Eccles *et al.* (1942) and Eccles & MacFarlane (1949).

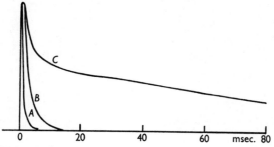

Fig. 15. 'Transmitter action' curves, obtained by analysis of e.p.p.'s. *A*: muscle treated with curarine; *B*: curarine + prostigmine; *C*: low-sodium + prostigmine. The ordinates have been scaled to the same maximum.

B. *The electric response of the normal end-plate membrane*

In the normal muscle fibre, the e.p.p. rises at a much greater rate and leads to a propagating spike and contraction. The electric response at the end-plate differs from a conducted action potential in a characteristic manner (Figs. 16–19, 21). A large e.p.p. invariably precedes the spike and forms a 'step' during the rising phase of the record. After the peak a discrete 'hump' is seen in most cases, indicating a continued action of the transmitter during the falling phase of the potential.

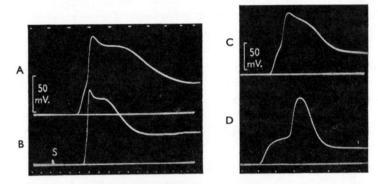

Fig. 16. End-plate responses in normal preparation. Four end-plates, showing step, spike and hump (except in D where the safety margin is low and a delayed spike without hump is seen). *S*, stimulus artifact. Time marks, msec.

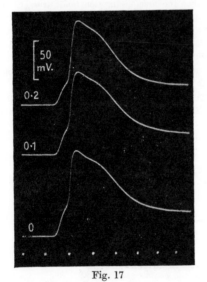

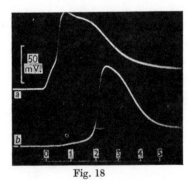

Fig. 17   Fig. 18

Fig. 17. Three records from the same muscle fibre, at distances of 0, 0·1 and 0·2 mm. from the end-plate focus. Time marks, msec.

Fig. 18. Records from the same fibre (*a*) at the end-plate and (*b*) 2·5 mm. away. Time, msec.

The usual procedure was, first, to locate a number of end-plates in a fully curarized muscle and then remove the drug by 30 min. washing in Ringer's solution (see Methods). The same results were obtained in a few cases in which the end-plates were found, by trial recordings, in normal untreated muscle (e.g. Fig. 18). This method naturally involved a considerable wastage of fibres, and was only used as a check to ascertain that the preliminary curarine-treatment had no irreversible effects.

Measurement of 'step' and 'hump'

Before trying to analyse the components of the end-plate response, it is of interest to describe and measure its characteristics. The diagram of Fig. 20 shows the points which were chosen as a convenient measure of 'start', 'step', 'peak' and 'hump'.

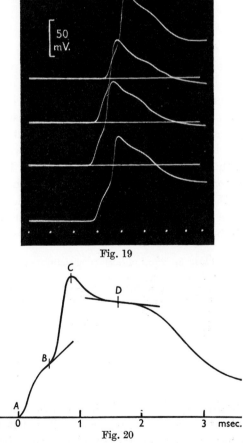

Fig. 19

Fig. 20

Fig. 19. Examples of end-plate responses in prostigmine-treated muscle fibres. Note the larger residual potential change. Time marks, msec.

Fig. 20. Diagram showing 'characteristic points' of the end-plate response.

The 'start' (point A) was taken as the point of just perceptible deflexion (about 0·3 mV., with low amplification). At the end-plate, the response rises sharply above the baseline, and this measurement was accurate within less than 0·1 msec. The 'peak' (point C) provided no difficulty, but the positions of 'step' (B) and 'hump' (D) are subject to some uncertainty. The height of the step was measured near the point of inflexion, at a level at which the spike could be seen to take off. The hump was measured at the mid-point of the flat shoulder on the falling phase. The separation between peak and hump was not always distinct (cf. Fig. 16) and the position of the hump, therefore, not always well defined. We estimate the accuracy of our measurements as being within 2–3 mV. and 0·1 msec. for the step (B), and 5–8 mV. and 0·2–0·3 msec. for the hump (D).

TABLE 7. Electric response at the normal end-plate

(Times are measured from the onset of the potential change. Active-membrane potential: p.d. across activ‹ membrane = action potential minus resting potential. Errors are the standard errors of the mean.)

Tempera-ture (° C.)	Calcium concn. (mM.)	Resting potential (mV.)	Action potential peak (mV.)	Action potential peak Time (msec.)	Active-membrane potential (mV.)	End-plate 'step' (mV.)	End-plate 'step' Time, (msec.)	End-plate 'hump (mV.)	End-plate 'hump Time (msec.
20 (16–23·5)	3·6 (1·8–9)	91±0·43	113±0·77	1·1 (0·54–2·4)	22±0·67	41±0·6 (25–54)	0·6 (0·31–1·65)	97 (80–117)	1·8 (1·3–2‹
Number of experiments	—	—	(135)	(134)	(134)	(134)	(135)	(135)	(104)	(104)‖

Results from 135 end-plates are summarized in Table 7. Most experiments were made with a solution containing 3·6 mM. calcium, i.e. twice the amount normally in Ringer. In Table 7 are included the results of twenty-five experiments in which ordinary Ringer (1·8 mM. calcium) had been used, and thirty experiments in which prostigmine bromide in a concentration of 10^{-6} had been added. These various solutions affected the measurements only in one respect, namely that the height of the initial end-plate step was less with 1·8 mM. calcium (33 mV.) than with 3·6 mM. calcium (41 mV.). The statistical significance of this difference is further shown in Table 8, in which nine 'paired' measurements on the same end-plates are summarized. Prostigmine has an important effect on the membrane potential after the spike (Fig. 19; cf. Eccles *et al.* 1942), but made no appreciable difference to the present results.

TABLE 8. Effect of calcium on end-plate step

	Calcium concn. (mM.)	Resting potential (mV.)	Step height (mV.)	No. of exps.	Step ratio and S.E. of mean
Total measurements	1·8	91	33 (26–44)	25	—
	3·6	91	41 (25–50)	71	—
Paired measurements	1·8	92	32	9⎫	1·25±
	3·6	92	39	9⎭	0·046

As with the curarine experiments (Table 1) a high degree of variability was again encountered in the size of the e.p.p. which differed at individual junctions much more than the resting or action potential of the membrane. In the present measurements, this variability showed itself, not in the level of the e.p.p. at which the muscle impulse takes off—this was relatively constant—but in the *time* needed for the e.p.p. to rise to this threshold level. The variations in the entire muscle must have been greater than is apparent from Table 7, for most of the present results have been obtained from end-plates which had been selected during the preliminary curarine treatment because their e.p.p.'s were found to be large and easy to locate. The differences in the rate of rise of the e.p.p. must mean that even under normal conditions there are large variations in the safety margin of transmission at individual junctions. Such variation has been known for a long time: it was demonstrated by Adrian & Lucas (1912) and by Bremer (1927) who showed that during fatigue or partial curarization a variable number of fibres can be made to respond by varying the interval between two nerve impulses. Another example will be shown on p. 358 below in the variable susceptibility to anodic block at different end-plates.

We did not include in Table 7 the results from a small number of fibres in which the e.p.p. failed to reach the impulse threshold. A delayed spike was then usually recorded coming from a remote junction in the same fibre (cf. Katz & Kuffler, 1941, also Fig. 28 C below). The local failure was presumably due to some abnormal condition of the muscle, but it was found side by side with end-plates at which transmission did not seem to be impaired and served further to illustrate the high degree of variability in junctional transmission.

The results of Table 7 show a wide dispersion in two other respects: (i) in the latency of the spike peak, and (ii) in the presence of a discrete hump which was clearly discernible in only some of the records. Both variations result from the variable size of the initial e.p.p.: the time to the peak includes the variable duration of the initial step, and a discrete hump could be seen only when the spike took off sufficiently early during the e.p.p. so that a residual transmitter effect, 2 msec. after the start, was not obscured by the spike peak.

In Table 2B, the responses of the same end-plates are compared (i) in fully curarized muscle and (ii) after withdrawal of curarine. The e.p.p. height was measured at a fixed interval, 0·44 msec. after the start. The results indicate that the e.p.p. in the fully curarized muscle was reduced to about one-quarter (with variations between 0·18 and 0·34). In another muscle, the same dose of curarine reduced the e.p.p.'s to about one-eighth. In general, a dose of curarine seemed to depress small e.p.p.'s more than large e.p.p.'s, and the dispersion in e.p.p. sizes, therefore, appeared to be greater in curarized than in normal muscle.

Comparison of the electric response at and off the end-plate

In Fig. 21, an experiment is illustrated in which the action potential was recorded at various distances along the same fibre. As the microelectrode moved away from the end-plate, the complex response (step-peak-hump, Fig. 21, 4–6) changed into a simple conducted spike which travelled in both directions, at a uniform velocity of about 1·4 m./sec. The initial step declined in the manner already shown for the rising phase of the curarized e.p.p., and its sharp ascent was replaced by the gradually increasing 'foot' of the conducted potential wave. The 'hump' was noticeably reduced, a few hundred microns away from the end-plate (e.g. Fig. 17), and vanished as the electrode was moved farther. The shape of the conducted spike varies somewhat from fibre to fibre, and its peak has often an 'angular' appearance as in Fig. 24 (*M*) below, but there is

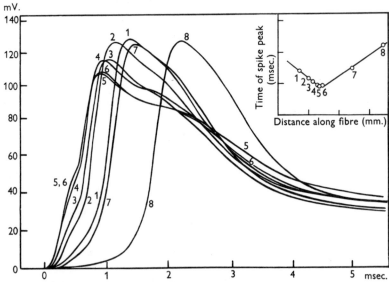

Fig. 21. The transition of electric activity from end-plate to muscle fibre. Calcium concentration, 9 mM. Temp. 17° C. The microelectrode was moved along the fibre, and records were obtained at the following positions (distance from position 1): (1) 0 mm.; (2) 0·3 mm.; (3) 0·45 mm.; (4) 0·6 mm.; (5) 0·65 mm.; (6) 0·75 mm.; (7) 1·75 mm.; (8) 2·75 mm. The resting potential was between 88 and 92 mV. during these records. Note the gradual changes in the shape of the action potential and spike latency. Inset: the time of the spike summit is plotted against distance, showing a propagation velocity of about 1·4 msec. in both directions from positions (5) and (6).

no doubt that the hump-like protrusion is a distinct feature of the end-plate response.

Fig. 21 indicates that the amplitude of the action potential increases by some 10–20 mV. as it is conducted away from the end-plate. In Table 9, the mean values of a large number of measurements, at and off the end-plate, have been listed. The resting potentials do not differ appreciably in the two situations,

TABLE 9. Active-membrane potential *on* and *off* the end-plate

(Mean values and s.e. of means.)

	I Resting potential (mV.)	II Action potential (mV.)	Active membrane potential (II − I)	No. of exps.
End-plate	91 ± 0·43	113 ± 0·77	22 ± 0·67	134
Off the end-plate	88 ± 0·6	123 ± 1	35 ± 1·1	52

Reduction of active-membrane potential at the end-plate: 13 ± 1·3 mV.

but the amplitude of the spike is considerably higher in the nerve-free portion than at the end-plate. The 'active-membrane potential', i.e. the level of the reversed p.d. during the peak, is $35 \pm 1 \cdot 1$ mV. (s.e. of mean of 52 experiments) off the end-plate and $22 \pm 0 \cdot 67$ mV. (134) at the end-plate. Thus a difference of over 10 mV. remains to be accounted for. In individual experiments the value of this difference was subject to considerable variation, but this arose to a large extent from variations in the size of the e.p.p. The peak of the action potential at the end-plate was significantly depressed only when it originated at an early moment and was followed by a discrete hump. Apparently the diminution of the active-membrane potential depended upon the persistence of intense transmitter activity at the time of the peak, and no such reduction occurred when the spike arose too late for this interaction to take place.

In order to obtain more conclusive information on the nature of the end-plate response, the initiation of a spike by the neuromuscular transmitter was compared with that by artificial electric stimulation.

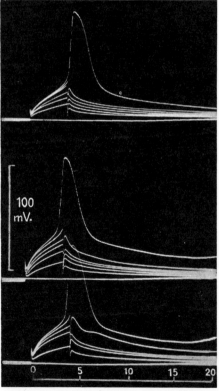

Fig. 22. Membrane potential during direct stimulation. Three different fibres, in which potential changes were recorded, near the cathode, with several subthreshold and one superthreshold current pulse. Note inflexion and local response with subthreshold current pulses. Time, msec.

The end-plate step

Two microelectrodes were placed into the same muscle fibre, less than 50 μ. apart, and one was used as a stimulating electrode by passing an outward current pulse through the membrane, while the change of the membrane potential was recorded by the other electrode. With a sufficient current strength, the membrane potential falls from its resting level, of 85–90 mV., to a point at which a spike is generated. The process is shown in Fig. 22, the time course of the curves being very similar to those previously obtained with external electrodes (Hodgkin & Rushton, 1946; Katz, 1948). The important point is that the height of the step which precedes the action potential is substantially the same as the height of the end-plate step during neuromuscular transmission. The step was measured in the same way as indicated in Fig. 20, and the results are shown in Table 10. In twenty experiments, using 3·6 mM-$CaCl_2$, the mean

TABLE 10. Comparison of initial 'step' with direct and indirect stimulation

	Direct stimulation			End-plate potential		
Calcium concn. (mM.)	Resting potential (mV.)	Step height (mV.)	No. of exps.	Resting potential (mV.)	Step height (mV.)	No. of exps.
3·6	86	39 (31–50)	20	91	41 (25–50)	71
1·8	85	36 (30–41)	7	91	33 (26–44)	25

height of the step was $39 \pm 1·2$ mV. as compared with $41 \pm 0·6$ mV. for the e.p.p., while in seven experiments with 1·8 mM-$CaCl_2$, it was 36 mV. (compared with 33 mV. for the e.p.p.). The result was the same whether the stimulus was applied at the nerve-free end of the fibre, or at the end-plate position. The level at which the spike originated seemed to be independent of the time taken to reach it: this time depended upon the current strength, and in the different records varied between 0·3 and 8 msec.

The measurement of the step height is related to the excitation threshold of the muscle fibre, that is to the critical level at which the membrane potential becomes unstable. This level can be found by using a short threshold shock (see Hodgkin, Huxley & Katz, 1949), or by breaking the current at the critical point at which the membrane potential is left 'in the balance', neither rising nor falling for a short time after the break. In practice, the current pulse was increased in small steps, and the largest potential change which just failed to flare up into a spike was taken as an indication of 'threshold' (Fig. 22). Using this method, the threshold depolarization was found to be several millivolts higher than the step, measured in the conventional way adopted above. Measurements of 'step height' and 'threshold level' are shown in Table 11, the means of eight experiments being 38 and 44 mV. respectively. These values are considerably larger than the figure of 15 mV. recently reported for the giant axon of the squid (Hodgkin *et al.* 1949), but the experimental conditions differ in two important respects: (*a*) the threshold of the squid axon was measured by uniform stimulation of a long length of fibre instead of *at one point*, and (*b*) the resting potential of the isolated squid axon is about 30 mV. less than that of

TABLE 11. 'Step' height and threshold level

(Calcium concentration 3·6 mM. in all fibres except VIII where it was 1·8 mM.)

Fibre	I Resting potential, (mV.)	II Step height, (mV.)	III Threshold level (mV.)	Difference (III – II), (mV.)
I	87	39	44	5
II	85	35	37	2
III	82	36	42	6
IV	78	31	36	5
V	81	38	47·5	9·5
VI	91	42·5	50·5	8
VII	90	46	50	4
VIII	88	38	43·5	5·5
Mean	85	38	44	6

frog muscle. If we were to define 'threshold' as a critical *membrane potential*, rather than a critical *depolarization*, the difference between the two sets of measurements would almost vanish, the 'threshold' being at about 45 mV. in either case.

It is safe to conclude from the present experiments that the height of the end-plate step is determined by the threshold of the surrounding muscle membrane, and that the threshold of this region does not differ by more than a few per cent from the threshold of other parts of the muscle fibre.

The end-plate spike

The analogy between an applied current and the neuromuscular transmitter helps us to account for the height of the initial step, but it fails to account for the further course of the end-plate response, for its reduced amplitude and the appearance of a hump on its declining phase.

It might be suggested that the size of the spike would, for some reason, be smaller at the point where it originates than after it has been conducted over a distance, and that this would account for the discrepancy of the active-membrane potentials in Table 9. It was important, therefore, to compare the active-membrane potentials for a locally initiated and a conducted spike. Two successive records were taken from the same point of a muscle fibre, in a nerve-free part: first observing the conducted spike which was elicited some distance away, either via the nerve or by a direct stimulus through another internal electrode. The second microelectrode was then inserted close to the recording point (less than 50 μ. distant) and another, direct, stimulus was applied. An example is shown in Fig. 23 where the peaks of the two action potentials are seen to differ by only 2 mV. The twitch during the first response usually produced some local damage associated with about 10% drop of the resting potential, but evidence will be presented, on p. 354 below, that this did not cause an immediate noticeable change in the active-membrane potentials, whose measurements therefore remained valid.

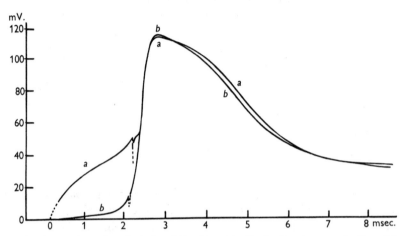

Fig. 23. Comparison of conducted and 'locally originating' spikes in a muscle fibre. The stimulating electrode was (a) 40 μ., and (b) 2 mm. from the recording electrode.

The effect of local mechanical damage can be appreciated quantitatively in the following manner. In the unstimulated fibre, the resistance across the membrane was on the average 200,000 Ω. (Table 4) and the potential difference 90 mV. Neglecting any initial leakage (cf. Nastuk & Hodgkin, 1950) a 9 mV. (10%) reduction of the resting potential implies that a small leak has sprung around the microelectrode, amounting to a shunt of 1·8 MΩ. (cf. Appendix II). During the spike, the effect of this shunt becomes much less important because the resistance across the membrane has fallen to about 20,000 Ω. (see p. 356 below); the reduction of the active-membrane potential (35 mV.) caused by a leak of 1·8 MΩ. is less than 0·5 mV.

In six experiments in which conducted and locally initiated spikes were compared, the active-membrane potential of the former was on the average 1·5 mV. less than that of the latter, an insignificant difference (s.e. of mean ± 1·3 mV.) and of opposite sign to that required.

The second possibility which had to be examined was that the features of the end-plate response might be imitated by a direct stimulus, if the applied current pulse were maintained throughout the period of electrical membrane activity. When this was done, a number of interesting changes were produced which will be described in the following section, but they bore no resemblance to the end-plate response. On the contrary, under the influence of a maintained outward current, the action potential continued to build up to a higher peak, and there was no indication of a hump during the decline. This effect of the applied current was seen invariably, whether the current was passed through the end-plate or through other regions of the fibre surface.

It might further be suggested that the characteristic features of the end-plate spike depend upon special properties of the muscle fibre at the junction, quite irrespective of release and local action of the transmitter. To decide this question, the action potential must be recorded at the end-plate when it is set up (a) by a nerve impulse (N) and (b) by a direct stimulus (M). Two successive records were obtained from the same end-plate with alternative stimulation of N and M. The sequence of the shocks was varied in different experiments. Usually, however, the direct stimulus was applied first, as it caused only one

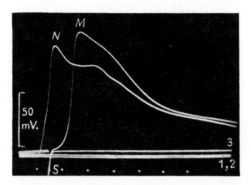

Fig. 24. Response to nerve (N) and direct (M) stimulation at the end-plate region of a muscle fibre. The direct current pulse was applied about 1·5 mm. away. S: stimulus artifact at the end of the direct pulse; 1 and 2: baselines (the lower corresponding to N the upper to M) showing a small drift of resting potential between the two stimuli, 3: electrotonic potential due to a subthreshold pulse. (The unusual notch in the N response following the hump, was due to an external spike potential of adjacent fibres.) Time marks, msec.

fibre to contract. An example is shown in Fig. 24, and for better comparison the two records have been superimposed, by displacing one along the time axis, in the tracings of Fig. 25. It is clear that the muscle spike (N) arising from an e.p.p. fails to reach the level which it attains (M) in the absence of the e.p.p. The results of fifteen similar experiments are summarized in Table 12. The

TABLE 12. Comparison of M and N spikes at the same end-plates

	M			N			Difference (M − N) of active-membrane potential (mV.)
Fibre	Resting potential (mV.)	Action potential (mV.)	Active-membrane potential (mV.)	Resting potential (mV.)	Action potential (mV.)	Active-membrane potential (mV.)	
			A. Three selected experiments				
I	88	119	31	85	101	16	15
II	90	121	31	85	97	12	19
III	90	115	25	93	103	10	15
Mean	89	118	29	87	100	13	16
			B. Fifteen experiments				
Mean	87	111	24	80	91	11	13±1·3

first part of this table contains the measurements on three fibres, in which little or no local damage occurred, and the resting potential did not change appreciably between the two records. The mean values of all measurements are shown in the second part of Table 12; they include several experiments in which a substantial

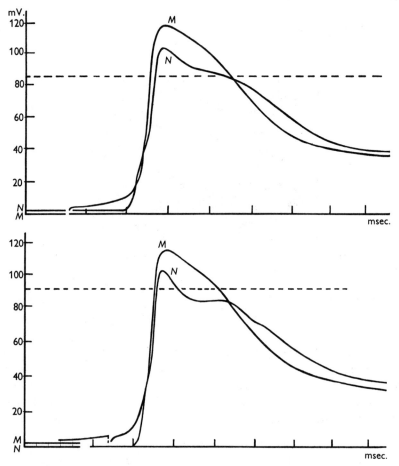

Fig. 25. Tracings of N and M responses at the end-plate region. Examples from two end-plates. Broken line: zero p.d. across membrane. A small drift of the resting potential between successive stimuli is indicated by the displacement of M and N baselines.

drop of the resting potential occurred after the first stimulus, but as pointed out above (see p. 354 for further details), the measurement of the active-membrane potential remains valid. Whether we take average values or selected experiments in Table 12, the result is equally conclusive. It shows that the reduction of the active-membrane potential must be attributed to the effect of the neuromuscular transmitter. This reduction amounts to more than 10 mV., and if we compare Table 12 with the previous results of Table 9, it appears that the differences in active-membrane potentials recorded *on* and *off* the end-plates are thus entirely accounted for.

This observation throws some light on the mode of action of the neuro-muscular transmitter. The reaction between acetylcholine and the end-plate not only fails to reach the level which is attained by the membrane action potential, but it drags the action potential down to a lower level. A simple explanation of this fact would be provided if the transmitter/end-plate reaction were to 'short-circuit' the active muscle membrane. The spike arises from a sudden and specific increase of sodium permeability, casusing the membrane potential to approach the equilibrium level of a 'sodium electrode' (Hodgkin & Katz, 1949; Nastuk & Hodgkin, 1950; Hodgkin, 1951). The e.p.p. does not appear to be produced in this way, and we assume that during the action of acetylcholine the end-plate undergoes a much more drastic change of its surface properties and becomes permeable to ions generally. We assume, in other words, that the end-plate membrane suffers a transient insulation break-down of the kind postulated by Bernstein and Höber, in contrast with the active change of the surrounding muscle membrane which is now known to depend upon a selective permeability to sodium. This 'short-circuit' hypothesis has a number of interesting consequences, some of which have been worked out in Appendix II and subjected to experimental test in the following sections.

In the first place, the hypothesis implies that under the most favourable conditions—in the absence of blocking agents and with the maximum quantity of acetylcholine being released—the e.p.p. could approach, but not exceed, simple depolarization. In order to depolarize, i.e. to provide an effective short-circuit for the resting potential, the leakage resistance across the end-plate has to be considerably less than the 200,000 Ω. across the resting muscle membrane (see Appendix II). To reduce the active-membrane potential from 35 to 22 mV., the leakage across the end-plate has to be of the same order as the reduced resistance across the active fibre surface. It will therefore be of great interest to find the value of this active-membrane resistance.

During normal impulse transmission, the required leakage of the end-plate 'sink' may also be estimated from the known rate at which the resting muscle membrane is discharged through this sink (normally 40–50 mV. in about 0·5 msec.) and the two independent estimates should be compared.

In Appendix II, the depolarizing effect of a shunt resistance suddenly placed across the muscle membrane has been calculated and the results indicate that the leakage of the active end-plate is of the order of 20,000–30,000 Ω. during normal transmission. In the following section, experiments are described which indicate that the resistance across the active fibre surface is of the same order of magnitude.

Finally, it follows from the 'short-circuit' hypothesis that the size of the e.p.p.

should be directly proportional to the resting potential. For example, if we were to raise the membrane potential to twice its normal resting level, by 'anodizing' the end-plate region, the same short-circuiting effect of the transmitter should then produce twice as large an e.p.p., and this relation should hold under all conditions, during neuromuscular block as well as in normal impulse transmission.

Resistance changes of the active fibre membrane

Measurements with alternating current have shown that the membrane impedance of nerve and muscle fibres undergoes a rapid diminution during the passage of an impulse (Cole & Curtis, 1939; Katz, 1942). Cole & Curtis concluded that the 'high-frequency conductance' (see Cole, 1949) of the axon membrane increases about 40-fold during the spike. The exact time course of this change was difficult to determine, but it is certain that the membrane conductance reaches its peak very rapidly during the rising phase of the action potential.

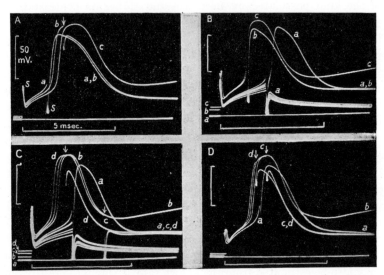

Fig. 26. The effect of an extrinsic current during the muscle spike. Examples from four muscle fibres. A: three responses, with the current (*a*) being broken at the beginning of the spike, (*b*) near its peak (marked by arrow), (*c*) being continued throughout. Note the rapid transition at the arrow, from 'current-on' to 'current-off' curve. B: (*a*) several subthreshold and one superthreshold pulse; (*b*) and (*c*), two responses with current *off* and *on*, respectively. C: showing several subthreshold and four superthreshold stimuli. With the latter, the current was broken either at the beginning (*a*), or during the spike indicated by arrows (*c*), (*d*), or maintained throughout (*b*). In B and C, note drift of resting potential (initial baseline displacement), but little or no change in active-membrane potential. D: four spikes, with the current alternatively *off*, *on*, or broken at moments marked by arrows. Note rapid change at the arrows, from current-*on* to current-*off* type of response. S: stimulus artifacts at make and break of current pulse.

It is possible to obtain an estimate of the changes of membrane resistance by passing a constant current through the fibre membrane and measuring the p.d. which the current adds (henceforth called the 'extrinsic p.d.') during and

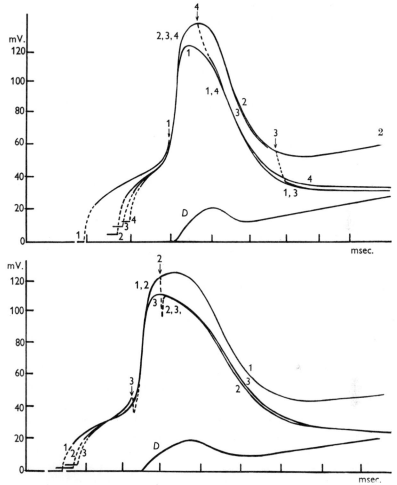

Fig. 27. Effect of extrinsic current during spike. Superimposed tracings. Examples of *on* and *off* curves from two muscle fibres. The 'extrinsic potential' built up by the current pulse during the spike is shown by curve *D* (which is obtained by subtracting the mean *off* from the *on* curve). Note: although the resting potential fell progressively, as seen by the displacement of initial baselines, the active-membrane potentials showed little change.

after the spike. The procedure was to stimulate with a second microelectrode and to break the applied current at various moments after threshold had been reached (Fig. 26). The experiment depended upon a comparison of successive spike records, with the current on or off, and it was necessary in the first instance to decide whether successive records, obtained usually with progressively falling resting potential, are strictly comparable. It has already been mentioned that a 10 or 20% drop of the resting potential, due to mechanical injury, does not necessarily invalidate the measurements of the active-membrane potential. The justification for this is shown in Fig. 27. In this figure, successive records have been superimposed, by shifting the individual spikes horizontally, until the ascending phases met, but *without* shifting them vertically. Although the resting potentials (initial baselines) differed by several millivolts from one record to the next, the action potentials remained almost exactly superimposable. If the current was maintained beyond the initial subthreshold period, there was:

(i) No noticeable change in the maximum rate of rise of the spike.

(ii) A distinct addition to, and broadening of, the peak.

(iii) An increase in the maximum rate of fall of the spike.

(iv) A later gradual redevelopment of the extrinsic potential difference.

If the current was broken at any moment during this sequence, the membrane potential returned from the 'current on' to the 'current off' curve within a fraction of a millisecond. It would appear from the results in Fig. 27 that we are justified in using the 'off'-curve as a baseline, from which the extra p.d. due to the maintained outward current can be measured. The only region in which reliable measurements could not be made was the steep ascending phase. A slight lateral displacement of the superimposed records would make a considerable difference here. It is unlikely that the applied current produces a large extra p.d. during this phase: (*a*) because the upstrokes of the super-imposed curves, as in Fig. 27, cannot be displaced from each other by more than 30 μsec. without noticeably mismatching the later parts of the curves; and (*b*) because the membrane conductance is known to reach its peak during the rising phase, and hence only a small extrinsic p.d. could be expected. It was, indeed, somewhat surprising to find that such a conspicuous potential change is produced by an applied current at the peak of the spike. Previous measurements (Kuffler, 1942*b*) indicated that no such addition occurs and that, on the contrary, the whole of the electrotonic potential collapses during the spike peak. But the discrepancy between Kuffler's and the present results is explained by the fact that we have recorded the action potential within 20–40 μ. of the cathode, while in the previous work an electrode of about 2 mm. width was used which would reduce the observed p.d. effectively to zero. It will be noted from equation 2 (see p. 334) that immediately at the cathode the p.d. produced by an applied current is proportional to $\sqrt{(r_m r_i)}$ so that, even when the membrane resistance has dropped to 1% of its resting value, one-tenth of the previous electrotonic potential should still be observed. But the length constant $\sqrt{(r_m/r_i)}$ is then also reduced to one-tenth so that, 1 or 2 mm. away, the extrinsic p.d. will be effectively abolished.

The time course of the extrinsic p.d. is indicated in Fig. 27 (D). As has been pointed out, the initial part of this curve (D) coinciding with the steep ascending phase of the spike is uncertain and depends upon the exact point at which the records have been superimposed. There is, however, no such uncertainty about the later course of the extrinsic p.d., measured during and after the peak of the spike. It has a characteristic shape with a maximum 0·5–1·0 msec. after the peak of the spike, and a minimum about 1 msec. later. This was observed in all fifteen experiments of this type, and it suggests that during the spike the muscle membrane undergoes two separate phases of increased ion permeability, one associated with the rise, the other accompanying the fall of the action potential. It will be noted that a relatively large extrinsic p.d. is built up during the slow initial phase of decline (the 'angle'), but it drops to a minimum later when the action potential falls more rapidly. This result seems to be analogous to recent observations by Weidmann (1951) on mammalian heart muscle and has an interesting bearing on the ionic theory of the impulse developed by Hodgkin & Huxley (1950; see also Hodgkin et al. 1949). According to this theory, two separate permeability changes occur during the spike: the rising phase is associated with a momentary increase of permeability to sodium ions, but this is a transient change which becomes rapidly exhausted or inactivated. It is followed after a brief delay by a phase of high potassium permeability which leads to a rapid return of the membrane potential to its original level. The present results provide evidence for two separate changes of membrane conductance, a transient increase during the ascending phase, and a second increase during the fall. The two conductance changes may well be associated with the two separate phases of sodium and potassium transfer envisaged by the theory of Hodgkin & Huxley.

In nine experiments, the strength of the outward current was measured simultaneously with the extrinsic p.d. From the ratio of the two values, an approximate estimate of the membrane resistance can be obtained. The estimate depends upon the assumption that the time constant $r_m c_m$ of the active membrane is brief compared with the time course of the extrinsic p.d. and the associated resistance change. Although this is over-simplified, it is approxi-

TABLE 13. Resistance across fibre membrane during the falling phase of the spike

(Measured at the 'dip', cf. Fig. 27, D.)

Summary of the values of $\frac{1}{2}\sqrt{(r_m r_i)}$ in nine experiments:

9000   23,000   14,000   24,000   24,000   21,000   42,000   22,000   12,000 Ω.
Mean 21,000 Ω.

mately true for the relatively slow changes after the peak of the spike, when the time constant of the membrane appears to be of the order of 0·3 msec. (compared with 30 msec. in the resting muscle). In Table 13 the ratio of extrinsic p.d./outward current is given, at the time of the 'dip', in nine experiments. The mean value is about 20,000 Ω., varying between 9,000 and 42,000 Ω. These values represent the transverse resistance $\frac{1}{2}\sqrt{(r_m r_i)}$ of the active muscle fibre, measured during the falling phase of the spike: they are about one-tenth of the resting value (Table 4) which indicates that the membrane resistance r_m, at that moment, is only about 1 % of the resting values, 40 Ω.cm.^{2} instead of 4000 Ω.cm.^{2}. During the rising phase of the spike, the resistance is presumably even lower. At the time of the spike summit, the extrinsic p.d. is of about the same size as during the 'dip', and we may tentatively regard the value of 20,000 Ω. as representing the active-membrane resistance during the peak of the spike as well as later during its falling phase.

The time constant of the active membrane is, therefore, also of the order of 1 % of the resting value, about 0·3 msec. compared with 30 msec. This is borne out by the fact that the added extrinsic p.d. disappears within a fraction of a msec. when the current is broken during the spike (Fig. 27).

We suggested that the active end-plate, in spite of its minute size, short-circuits the surrounding active fibre membrane, bringing its potential down, from 35 to 22 mV. In order to produce this effect, it is clear that the active end-plate must itself have a low resistance, of the order of 20,000 Ω. The presence of such a low-resistant sink must have an important influence on the further time course of the action potential, and it is possible to explain the appearance of the end-plate 'hump' without additional assumptions. It can be seen from Fig. 25 that the 'hump' is in reality due to a rapid fall of the active-membrane potential from its peak towards a lower level which is not far from zero, and to a delayed return from this to the resting level. The hump is probably due to a continued short-circuiting of the membrane which not only reduces the 'sodium-potential' of the active fibre membrane, but causes it to discharge quickly when the period of high sodium permeability comes to an end. Similarly, the continued leakage through the end-plate must delay the restitution of the membrane potential, and these effects are probably responsible for the characteristic 'hump' of the end-plate spike.

To summarize, the neuromuscular transmitter not only produces an e.p.p. which gives rise to a muscle spike, but it interacts with the further course of the spike by depolarizing the active membrane and holding its potential close to zero.

The relation between end-plate potential and resting membrane potential

It is possible to change the p.d. across the fibre membrane, by means of electric currents, over a fairly wide range without substantially altering the resistance or capacity of the membrane (Hodgkin & Rushton, 1946; Katz, 1948). This method helps one to distinguish between three conceivable mechanisms by which the e.p.p. may be produced. The e.p.p. might be the result of one of the following processes: (a) the transfer across the end-plate of a fixed number of ions (for example, by extrinsic current flow from the motor nerve);

(*b*) a shift of the membrane potential towards a fixed new level (determined, for instance, by a *selective* permeability change to one species of ions); (*c*) the establishment of a *non-selective* ion sink, equivalent to placing a fixed leak resistance across the membrane.

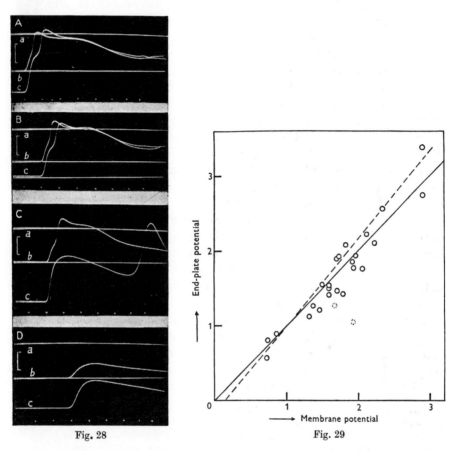

Fig. 28   Fig. 29

Fig. 28. The effect of increased ('anodic') resting potential on the size of the e.p.p. Examples from four end-plates. *a*: zero p.d. across membrane; *b*: normal resting potential; *c*: resting potential has been increased by applied inward current. At C, transmission is blocked by the inward current, while at D transmission had failed at the normal level of the resting potential. Voltage scale: 50 mV., time marks: msec. (Record A(*b*) was taken with too high electrode resistance, giving some amplitude reduction; in all other records no appreciable distortion occurred.)

Fig. 29. Relation between size of end-plate potential and initial membrane potential. Normal resting and end-plate potentials are taken as unity. Normal resting potentials were: 90 mV. mean (65–104 mV.). E.p.p's were measured at a fixed time after their start (before the spike originated or, if transmission was blocked, at the peak of the e.p.p.). The full line indicates direct proportionality; the broken line intersects the horizontal axis at the theoretical junction p.d. between Ringer and myoplasm (see text).

Process (a) would give a constant amplitude, and constant charge, of the e.p.p., independent of the initial level of the membrane potential (provided resistance and capacity of the membrane remain constant).

Process (b) would result in a variable amplitude, but approximately constant final level of the e.p.p., rather like that attained by the peak of the spike whose level is only slightly affected by changes of resting potential (Fig. 28).

Process (c) would reduce the resting potential to a constant fraction and lead to a directly proportional relation between the size of the resting membrane potential and the amplitude of the e.p.p. (see Appendix II).

The experimental procedure was to raise the resting potential to a higher level by subjecting the membrane to an inward current. The e.p.p. was observed at the normal resting potential (mean value 90 mV.) and at the increased level (varying between 118 and 235 mV.), and its size was measured at a fixed interval after the start. Examples are shown in Fig. 28, and the results of twenty-six experiments have been plotted in Fig. 29. The mean increase of resting potential in twenty-one experiments (not including the five observations discussed below) was 87·5%, the corresponding increase of e.p.p. size was 84%. There is little doubt that the size of the e.p.p. is approximately proportional to the value of the initial membrane potential, a result which is consistent with the 'short-circuit' hypothesis (c), but not with the other hypotheses stated above.

The results of these experiments were obtained at junctions with widely different safety margins. At some the e.p.p. formed so large a proportion of the resting potential that no anodic block could be produced; at others transmission was readily blocked by an inward current (cf. Katz, 1939), and a pure e.p.p. produced, and finally at some end-plates, the e.p.p. was small and transmission failed even without the application of an inward current. The proportional relation between e.p.p. and membrane potential shown in Fig. 29 was found regardless of the condition of the individual junction.

It may be argued that even when the end-plate has become completely short-circuited, a junction potential of some 14 mV. (Nastuk & Hodgkin, 1950) would remain between the outside bath and the myoplasm. On this basis, the theoretical relation should follow the broken line in Fig. 29 rather than the full, 45°, line.

In Fig. 29, the results of three measurements are included in which the resting potential had dropped below the original level, owing to local injury. Under these conditions, the theoretical relation is no longer exactly linear, but the divergence is too slight to be noticed.

Another point requires comment: not all muscle fibres were able to withstand strong 'anodization', and at times there were signs of dielectric breakdown when the membrane potential had been raised to some 200 mV. This showed itself in a rapid decline of the membrane potential while the inward current was maintained. The two measurements shown in Fig. 29 as dotted circles were made in this unstable condition and should, therefore, be disregarded.

DISCUSSION

A large part of our results is 'descriptive' and deals with the intracellular recording of potential changes at the motor end-plate. These results may be briefly discussed in relation to previous work in which similar techniques or preparations have been employed.

The values of resting and action potentials of the 'muscle fibre', as distinct from its end-plate (Table 9), agree with those reported by Ling & Gerard (1949) and Nastuk & Hodgkin (1950). At the end-plate, the resting potential is the same, but the action potential is reduced, provided excitation occurs via the nerve and the intensity of the transmitter action is high. The general features of the normal end-plate response (the 'step-peak-hump' complex) agree very well with those recently reported by Nastuk (1950).

The composite nature of the end-plate response had previously been demonstrated in an admirable way by Kuffler (1942a) who applied an external recording electrode to an isolated nerve-muscle junction. The records obtained by Kuffler differ from our results in some important respects, and these differences require an explanation. Kuffler employed a special technique of 'interface recording' which amounts in effect to the application of a microelectrode to the surface of a muscle fibre in a large volume of saline. This method had certain advantages and was well suited to Kuffler's delicate preparation, but it must be realized that under these conditions the observed potential change follows the time course of the *membrane current*, not that of the *membrane potential* (see Bishop, 1937; Lorente de Nó, 1947; Brooks & Eccles, 1947). This leads to important differences in the shape of the e.p.p. and spike, for the membrane current depends upon d^2E/dx^2, the curvature of the surface potential gradient, and may be directed inward or outward through the membrane. The 'interface' method is, in fact, a differential recording technique which is very sensitive to changes in the local potential gradient, but its results cannot be directly interpreted in terms of the membrane potential. For example, when the interface electrode was moved along the muscle fibre, the response changed very critically, and at 0·5 mm. from the end-plate, the initial e.p.p. deflexion had not only declined, but reversed its sign. This reversal means that the position of the electrode has been moved from the end-plate 'sink' where current flows *into* the fibre, to an adjacent region where the current *leaves* the fibre. At the centre of the junction, a triphasic response was recorded the first phase of which consisted of a 'pure e.p.p.' not superseded by a spike. This naturally led to the supposition that the membrane potential during the e.p.p. may attain the same level as during the spike; but with this conclusion, the present results do not agree. In our opinion, the absence of a spike component in Kuffler's experiment merely implied that the inward current through the end-plate had reached a peak during the initial

e.p.p. and begun to decline when the spike originated. To explain this behaviour, we may refer to the results of Fig. 21 and Table 9, where it is shown
that the size of the e.p.p. is *greatest*, while the size of the spike is *least* at the
centre of the junction. Hence, during the transition from e.p.p. to spike, the
electric response at the end-plate changes from the position of a spatial maximum to that of a spatial minimum, and during this process the curvature of
the potential gradient, and the membrane current, reverse. The situation may

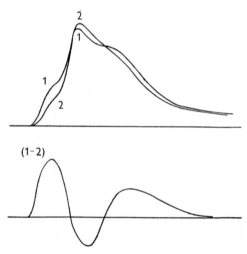

(1–2)

Fig. 30. Diagram explaining the derivation of 'interface' recording (cf. Kuffler, 1942 *a*) at the
centre of the end-plate. The upper part indicates the changes of membrane potential, (1) at the
centre of the end-plate, and (2) a small distance from (1). The lower part illustrates a 'differential'
record (1) minus (2), which resembles Kuffler's 'inter-face' recording.

be appreciated more easily by the simplified diagram in Fig. 30 in which
Kuffler's relevant record has been reconstructed as differentially recorded
between a point at, and slightly off, the centre of the junction.

To summarize, it would appear that the discrepancies between Kuffler's
and the present results can be explained by differences in recording technique,
remembering that we are concerned with changes of the membrane potential
which are not faithfully recorded with an external microelectrode.

In its quantitative aspects the present paper provides strong support for
certain views previously presented: for example, it has again been confirmed
that the transmitter action at the nerve-muscle junction is a brief impulsive
event, and that the characteristic spread and decay of the e.p.p. is largely
determined by the resistance and capacity of the resting muscle fibre.

In addition, there have been two pieces of information which invite further
comment: first, the determination of the quantity of electric charge which is
transferred across the end-plate, and secondly, the fact that the end-plate

reaction leads to a smaller potential change, but apparently a larger change of conductance (per unit area), than the normal membrane spike.

It has been pointed out that the electric charge which flows across the normal end-plate during a single impulse requires the net transfer of at least $2-4 \times 10^{-14}$ mol. of univalent cations inward or anions outward and that this quantity becomes multiplied by a factor of about 50 in the presence of a cholinesterase inhibitor. The question arises how such a large flux of ions can be maintained across the presumably minute area of the motor end-plate, and what species of ions are involved. We are not in a position to answer this question, but certain, otherwise plausible, mechanisms are eliminated by the present results. It has recently been shown by Fatt (1950) that acetylcholine ions produce a substantial depolarization of the end-plate even when the external electrolyte content has been reduced to a small fraction and when no sodium is present in the outside fluid. Fatt considered the possibility that the flux of acetylcholine cations themselves might produce the necessary inward current. This did not seem a full, or very likely, explanation, but it remained conceivable under the conditions of his experiment. In view of our present results, we feel that this hypothesis has become untenable. If acetylcholine were to depolarize the end-plate by direct penetration, it would have to be released in quantities of some $1-2 \times 10^{-12}$ mol. per junction per impulse, for enough acetylcholine ions must be made available to produce and maintain the e.p.p. in the prostigmine-treated muscle. We have no adequate information concerning the surface or the volume of the nerve endings at which acetylcholine is released, but it is difficult to believe that they are large enough to contain this amount of acetylcholine. If we take Kühne's (1887) drawings of the terminal arborizations in frog muscle, we are likely to over- rather than under-estimate the size of the nerve endings (see Couteaux, 1947). The surface area of Kühne's nerve-endings tree may be as large as 10^{-4} cm.^{2}, and its volume as much as 2×10^{-8} cm.^{3}. Even if we were to assume that the intracellular cation content of all these structures is made up entirely of acetylcholine, at a concentration of 120 mM., the amount of acetylcholine inside the nerve would be only $2 \cdot 4 \times 10^{-12}$ mol, i.e. barely enough for one or two impulses. Hence, even with such extremely favourable, though unrealistic, assumptions we are led to the absurd result that practically the whole cation store of the nerve endings would have to be exchanged during a single impulse in order to produce an e.p.p.

The only reasonable alternative appears to be that small quantities of acetylcholine alter the end-plate surface in such a way that other ions can be rapidly transferred across it, not only sodium and potassium, but probably all free anions and cations on either side of the membrane. Apparently, we must think in terms of some chemical breakdown of a local ion barrier which occurs as soon as acetylcholine combines with it, and whose extent depends upon the number of reacting molecules.

An explanation of this kind fits the facts reasonably well: it helps us to understand why a depolarization by acetylcholine can still be produced in the absence of external sodium salts, and it explains why the action potential, as well as the resting potential, is short-circuited by the e.p.p. Finally, it satisfies the requirement for a very large amplification of ionic currents which must occur at the point where an impulse is transferred from minute nerve endings to the enormously expanded surface of the muscle fibre.

Our results suggest that the action of acetylcholine 'short-circuits' the muscle fibre at the end-plate and so reduces the active-membrane potential, but this effect does not occur when the muscle fibre is stimulated directly. It appears, then, that the action potential of the muscle fibre, if started elsewhere, sweeps past the end-plate region without stimulating its neuroreceptors, for if they were made to react in the way in which they respond to a nerve impulse, the active-membrane potential would be the same in either case. It is a characteristic property of nerve or muscle membranes to respond to an electric stimulus with a regenerative electrochemical reaction. This reaction is now known to depend upon a selective increase of sodium permeability (Hodgkin & Huxley, 1950), leading to rapid entry of sodium into the fibre with a consequent lowering of its surface potential and reinforcement of the initial electrical alteration. This reaction proceeds towards an equilibrium level which is near the potential of a sodium electrode (Hodgkin & Katz, 1949; Nastuk & Hodgkin, 1950; Hodgkin et al. 1949). Our evidence indicates that the end-plate receptors do not behave in this manner: they react to acetylcholine and various other chemical substances, but apparently not to the local currents of the muscle impulse; and if the end-plate does not respond to electric stimulation, then its electrical reaction to acetylcholine cannot be regenerative in the manner of the electric excitation of the surrounding membrane. Thus, it appears that the end-plate, i.e. the neuroreceptive area of the muscle fibre, differs from the surrounding fibre surface not only in its specific sensitivity to chemical stimulants, but in its lack of sensitivity to electric currents.

APPENDIX I

The solution of the problem considered here has been kindly provided by Mr A. L. Hodgkin.

In the special case in which a charge is placed instantaneously, at time $t=0$, on a point along the fibre, at distance $x=0$, the solution of the general differential equation for the leaky capacitative cable without net current, viz.

$$-\lambda\frac{d^2V}{dx^2}+\tau_m\frac{dV}{dt}+V=0$$

takes the form

$$V=\frac{q_0}{2c_m\lambda\sqrt{(\pi t/\tau_m)}}\exp\left(\frac{-x^2\tau_m}{4\lambda^2 t}-\frac{t}{\tau_m}\right),\tag{4}$$

where q_0 is the charge initially on the membrane and c_m is the capacity of the membrane per unit length of fibre. Taking the natural logarithm of equation (4) we obtain:

$$\log_e V=\frac{-x^2\tau_m}{4\lambda^2 t}-\frac{t}{\tau_m}+\log_e\frac{q_0}{2c_m\lambda\sqrt{(\pi t/\tau_m)}}.\tag{5}$$

Since x appears only in the first term on the right of equation (5), if for any given t, $\log_e V$ is plotted against x^2, a straight line will result with slope equal to $-\tau_m/4\lambda^2 t$, from which λ can be obtained. When applied to the curves of Fig. 9, for t greater than 3 msec., this method gives values of λ between 2·35 and 2·1 mm. For the peak of the potential wave at any position x, $dV/dt=0$; so from equation (5) by differentiating and equating to zero, one finds that

$$\frac{x^2}{\lambda^2}=\frac{4t^2}{\tau_m^2}+\frac{2t}{\tau_m}.$$

This equation provides a simple means of evaluating λ. Plotting $4T^2/\tau_m^2+2T/\tau_m$ against x^2 (T is the time of peak potential at distance x) a straight line is obtained with slope equal to $1/\lambda^2$. This method was used on p. 332, with the results shown in Table 3.

APPENDIX II

The 'short-circuiting' of the end-plate during neuromuscular transmission

It is suggested that acetylcholine short-circuits the end-plate and thereby discharges the surrounding muscle membrane and gives rise to a propagated spike. The short-circuit resistance thus placed across the end-plate surface must be low enough to produce the characteristic features of the normal end-plate response, viz. (i) to depolarize the membrane at an adequate rate and (ii) to shunt the active membrane effectively and reduce its reversed p.d. At the normal nerve-muscle junction, the resting potential is about 90 mV., and the e.p.p. reduces it to one-half in about 0·5 msec. Experiments with anodic block (cf. Fig. 28) indicate that the maximum end-plate depolarization is reached at about 1·2-1·3 msec. (20° C.) and, in the absence of a muscle spike, amounts to about 70 % of the resting potential.

The resting muscle fibre can be represented by the electrical cable model shown in Fig. 31. The quantities have been computed from Table 4 ($E_0 = 90$ mV., $r_m = 100,000$ Ω.cm., $r_i = 1·6$ MΩ./cm., $c_m = 0·3$ μF./cm.). If a short-circuit

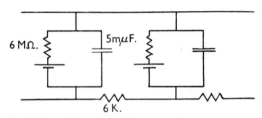

Fig. 31. Two sections of an artificial transmission line representing the passive properties of a muscle fibre. The input resistance at *one* end of the line is approximately equal to the resistance across the midpoint of a muscle fibre; the time constant is 30 msec. and the length constant is represented by thirty-two sections. The e.m.f. was replaced by a dry cell (1·58 V.).

resistance R is placed, at time $t = 0$, across the mid-point of this transmission line (neglecting 'liquid junction potentials' and assuming the line to be longer than $8\sqrt{(r_m/r_i)}$) then the potential V at this point changes with time according to the following equation which has been kindly derived for us by Dr E. J. Harris:

$$\frac{V}{E_0} = 1 - a[1 - \exp t/\tau_1 . \mathrm{erfc}\sqrt{(t/\tau_2)}] + b \, \mathrm{erf}\sqrt{(t/\tau_3)}, \tag{6}$$

where
$$\tau_1 = R_0^2 \, c_m/(r_i - R_0^2/r_m),$$
$$\tau_2 = R_0^2 \, c_m/r_i,$$
$$\tau_3 = r_m c_m,$$
$$a = r_i/(r_i - R_0^2/r_m),$$
$$b = R_0\sqrt{(r_i/r_m)}/(r_i - R_0^2/r_m),$$
$$\mathrm{erfc}\sqrt{(t/\tau_2)} = 1 - \mathrm{erf}\sqrt{(t/\tau_2)},$$
$$R_0 = 2R.$$

Using equation (6), the depolarization at $t = 0·5$ msec. has been calculated for various values of R (Table 14). Another way of finding the potential changes,

TABLE 14. Relation between short-circuit resistance and 'end-plate potential.'

R (Ω.)	'e.p.p.' at $t = 0·5$ msec. (mV.)
15,000	65
20,000	56
30,000	46
50,000	32

at various points of the line, consists in constructing an electrical model similar to that of Fig. 31 and recording the changes of potential at the desired point. A line of 100 sections was used, each having the components shown in Fig. 31. This line had the same input impedance and time constant as an average muscle fibre taken from Table 4. The 'characteristic length' (i.e. about 2·5 mm.) was represented by thirty-two sections and the resting potential was replaced by a dry cell (1·58 V.). When a series of different short-circuit resistances was placed across the end of this line, a family of curves was obtained, plotted in Fig. 32. To depolarize this model at approximately the same rate as the normal end-plate (50 % depolarization in 0·5 msec., 70 % in 1·25 msec.) a short-circuit

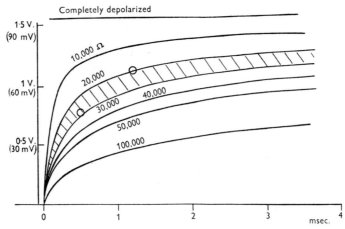

Fig. 32. Depolarization resulting from a short-circuiting of the transmission line. The two circles indicate the depolarization levels observed during the rise of the normal e.p.p. This corresponds to short-circuiting by 20,000–30,000 Ω. (shaded area). Ordinates: depolarization in volts (corresponding values for muscle fibre in brackets). Abscissae: msec.

resistance of 20,000–30,000 Ω. must be used. As the release and decay of the transmitter are gradual processes, one may assume that the resistance of the end-plate membrane falls, during the first msec., to a value rather less than 20,000 Ω. and then gradually recovers, but the average value during the rising phase of the e.p.p. appears to be about 25,000 Ω.

During normal impulse transmission we thus have, very roughly, an end-plate 'sink' with a leak resistance of the order of 25,000 Ω., in parallel with an active muscle membrane which—when *not* short-circuited by the active end-plate—produces a peak potential of 35 mV. and has a resistance of the order of 20,000 Ω. (Table 13). The presence of the end-plate sink reduces the active-membrane potential from 35 mV. to $35 \times 25,000/(25,000 + 20,000) = 19.5$ mV. This drop of 15·5 mV. may be compared with the observed reduction of 13 mV. (Tables 9 and 12) and 16 mV. (Table 12).

An e.p.p. can be imitated in even more realistic fashion by placing a transient short-circuit, e.g. a series combination of resistance and capacity across the artificial line, with the result shown in Fig. 33. It is then a simple matter to reconstruct the experiments of p. 357, where an approximately linear relation

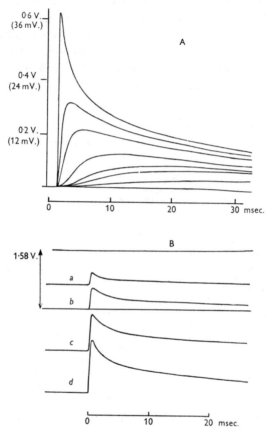

Fig. 33. A: artificial e.p.p.'s. Oscillograph tracings from various points along the artificial line, when a short-circuit of 20,000 Ω., in series with a 0·012 μF. condenser, was placed across it. The distances from the short-circuited points were, successively from above: 0 sections (corresponding to the end-plate centre); 5 sections (corresponding to about 0·4 mm. from the end-plate centre); 10 sections (0·8 mm.); 20 sections (1·6 mm.); 30 sections (2·4 mm.); 40 sections (3·2 mm.); 60 sections (4·8 mm.) Co-ordinates as in Fig. 32. B: relation between artificial e.p.p. and initial voltage level. b, 'normal' voltage and e.p.p.; a, line voltage reduced by partial short-circuit; c and d, line voltage increased by applied inward current.

between resting potential and e.p.p. was observed. As during the actual experiment, the resting potential of the model was increased by passing an inward current (through 10 MΩ.) into the line, and it was reduced by a steady shunt imitating the effect of local mechanical injury. Under these conditions, a linear relation betwen e.p.p. and resting potential was obtained over a range from 40 to 240% of the normal level.

According to the present hypothesis, an end-plate which has been depolarized by applied acetylcholine should act as a partial short-circuit to the muscle fibre, and one would expect this to shorten the time course of a superimposed e.p.p. This prediction appears to conflict with experimental observations (e.g Fillenz & Hanafin, 1947) according to which the time course of such an e.p.p. remains unchanged. During a steady depolarization, however, additional factors must be considered which the present simple hypothesis does not take into account. The resistance of the surrounding muscle membrane does not remain constant, but has been found to increase or decrease during depolarization, depending upon the extent of the potential change (Katz, 1948). A moderate depolarization leads to a prolonged 'local response', associated apparently with entry of sodium ions into the fibre. This causes the initial potential change to build up to a higher level, and locally raises the resistance and time constant of the fibre membrane (cf. Hodgkin, 1947; Katz, 1948). A similar situation apparently occurs when acetylcholine is applied, for it has recently been shown (Fatt, 1950) that in the presence of sodium ions, the depolarization around the end-plates builds up to a higher maintained level than if sodium salts have previously been withdrawn. Fatt suggested that this is due to the regenerative action of sodium ions, which tends to spread and reinforce the depolarization in the surrounding region and thus increase the steady state resistance of the membrane. Hence, during steady depolarization by acetylcholine, we may have to consider a situation in which the end-plate 'sink' itself presents a low resistance, while the resistance and time constant of the surrounding fibre membrane are raised.

SUMMARY

1. The electrical properties of the 'motor end-plates' of frog muscle have been investigated with an intracellular recording electrode.

2. The resting potential of the end-plate membrane is about 90 mV. at 20° C.; it is the same as elsewhere along the muscle fibre and is unaffected by curarine.

3. When neuromuscular transmission is blocked, a simple end-plate potential (e.p.p.) is recorded which reaches 20–30 mV. in some fibres, but varies in amplitude over a wide range at different junctions. The e.p.p. rises sharply, reaches a peak in 1–1·5 msec. and declines to half in another 2 msec. The e.p.p. spreads electrotonically along a few mm. of the muscle fibre.

4. In a curarized muscle, the displacement of electric charge from the fibre membrane reaches a maximum at about 2 msec. after the start of the e.p.p., followed by a gradual replacement. The restoration of charge follows an exponential time course, with a time constant of 20–30 msec.

5. An analysis of the distribution of charge indicates that the active phase of neuromuscular transmission is a brief, impulsive, event lasting only a few msec., and that the prolonged spread and decline of the e.p.p. are determined by the resistance and capacity of the resting muscle fibre. The values of the membrane resistance and capacity determined from the properties of the e.p.p. are 4000 Ω.cm.^{2} and 6 μF./cm.^{2} Another series of measurements, using applied inward current and an analysis of the electrotonic potential, gives 4000 Ω.cm.^{2} and 8 μF./cm.^{2} respectively.

6. The net electric charge which is transferred across a curarized end-plate during one impulse is of the order of 8×10^{-10} coulomb, corresponding to 8×10^{-15} mol. of univalent ions.

7. In normal muscle, this value becomes 3–4 times larger. After treating the muscle with a cholinesterase inhibitor, the e.p.p. becomes greatly prolonged and the total amount of charge transferred through the end-plate increases by a factor of up to 50. Under these conditions a charge, equivalent to at least 10^{-12} mol. of univalent ions, passes through the 'end-plate sink', while building up and maintaining the depolarization of the surrounding fibre membrane.

8. During normal impulse transmission, the electric response of the end-plate differs from that of other parts of the muscle fibre in three respects: (i) the response is initiated by a large e.p.p., forming an initial half-millisecond step of about 40 mV. height; (ii) the peak of the spike is *reduced*, the reversed p.d. across the active membrane being about 20 mV., as compared with 35 mV., at other points of the fibre; (iii) during its fall, the action potential passes through a 'hump', at a level of the membrane potential which is not far from zero.

9. The height of the initial step signifies the threshold level at which the potential of the muscle membrane becomes unstable: a step of the same height is seen, when an action potential is set up by passing outward current through a muscle fibre, at or off the end-plate.

10. The subsequent characteristic features of the end-plate response (reduced peak, followed by 'hump') cannot be reproduced by an extrinsic current. Moreover, they are *not* seen when an action potential, produced by *direct* stimulation, is recorded at the end-plate, the active-membrane potential being then about 15 mV. larger than during neuromuscular transmission. Hence, the local action of the transmitter depolarizes not only the resting, but also the active surface of the muscle fibre.

11. A simple hypothesis is put forward to explain the features of the end-plate response, and also certain previous observations concerning the electromotive action of acetylcholine. Assuming that acetylcholine produces a large non-selective increase of ion permeability, i.e. a short-circuit, of the end-plate, then the production of the e.p.p., the diminution of the active-membrane potential, and the hump during the falling phase can all be explained, as well as the fact that acetylcholine depolarizes the end-plate even in the absence of sodium salts (Fatt, 1950).

12. A quantitative estimate, based upon two independent sets of measurements, indicates that the end-plate membrane is converted, during normal impulse transmission, into an ion 'sink' of approximately 20,000 Ω. leak resistance.

13. The size of the e.p.p., at normal or blocked junctions, can be varied over a wide range by increasing the resting membrane potential with anodic polarization. E.p.p. and resting membrane potential are found to be approximately proportional, as would be expected from the above hypothesis.

14. During the muscle spike, the membrane resistance falls to a small fraction, approximately 1%, of its resting value. The resistance change occurs in two phases, associated respectively with the rise and fall of the action potential, and probably corresponding to the separate phases of increased sodium and potassium permeability (Hodgkin & Huxley, 1950).

We wish to thank Prof. A. V. Hill for the facilities provided in his laboratory and Mr J. L. Parkinson for his invaluable help. This work was carried out with the aid of a grant for scientific assistance made by the Medical Research Council.

REFERENCES

Adrian, E. D. & Lucas, K. (1912). *J. Physiol.* **44**, 68.
Bishop, G. H. (1937). *Arch. int. Physiol.* **45**, 273.
Bozler, E. & Cole, K. S. (1935). *J. cell. comp. Physiol.* **6**, 229.
Bremer, F. (1927). *C.R. Soc. Biol., Paris*, **97**, 1179.
Brooks, C. McC. & Eccles, J. C. (1947). *J. Neurophysiol.* **10**, 251.
Brown, G. L., Dale, H. H. & Feldberg, W. (1936). *J. Physiol.* **87**, 394.
Cole, K. S. (1949). *Arch. Sci. physiol.* **3**, 253.
Cole, K. S. & Curtis, H. J. (1939). *J. gen. Physiol.* **22**, 649.
Couteaux, R. (1947). *Rev. Canad. Biol.* **6**, 563.
Eccles, J. C. (1948). *Ann. Rev. Physiol.* **10**, 93.
Eccles, J. C., Katz, B. & Kuffler, S. W. (1941). *J. Neurophysiol.* **4**, 362.
Eccles, J. C., Katz, B. & Kuffler, S. W. (1942). *J. Neurophysiol.* **5**, 211.
Eccles, J. C. & MacFarlane, W. V. (1949). *J. Neurophysiol.* **12**, 59.
Fatt, P. (1950). *J. Physiol.* **111**, 408.
Fatt, P. & Katz, B. (1950a). *Nature, Lond.*, **166**, 597.
Fatt, P. & Katz, B. (1950b). *J. Physiol.* **111**, 46P.
Fillenz, M. & Hanafin, M. (1947). *J. Neurophysiol.* **10**, 189.
Graham, J. & Gerard, R. W. (1946). *J. cell. comp. Physiol.* **28**, 99.
Hill, A. V. (1949). *Proc. Roy. Soc.* B, **136**, 228.
Hodgkin, A. L. (1947). *J. Physiol.* **106**, 305.
Hodgkin, A. L. (1951). *Biol. Rev.* (in the Press).
Hodgkin, A. L. & Huxley, A. F. (1950). *Abstr. XVIII int. physiol. Congr.* p. 36.
Hodgkin, A. L., Huxley, A. F. & Katz, B. (1949). *Arch. Sci. physiol.* **3**, 129.
Hodgkin, A. L. & Katz, B. (1949). *J. Physiol.* **108**, 37.
Hodgkin, A. L. & Rushton, W. A. H. (1946). *Proc. Roy. Soc.* B, **133**, 444.
Hunt, C. C. & Kuffler, S. W. (1950). *Pharmacol. Rev.* **2**, 96.
Huxley, A. F. & Stämpfli, R. (1949). *J. Physiol.* **108**, 315.
Katz, B. (1939). *J. Physiol.* **95**, 286.
Katz, B. (1942). *J. Neurophysiol.* **5**, 169.
Katz, B. (1948). *Proc. Roy. Soc.* B, **135**, 506.
Katz, B. & Kuffler, S. W. (1941). *J. Neurophysiol.* **4**, 209.
Keynes, R. D. & Lewis, P. R. (1950). *Nature, Lond.*, **165**, 809.
Kuffler, S. W. (1942a). *J. Neurophysiol.* **5**, 18.
Kuffler, S. W. (1942b). *J. Neurophysiol.* **5**, 309.
Kühne, W. (1887). *Z. Biol.* **23**, 1.
Ling, G. & Gerard, R. W. (1949). *J. cell. comp. Physiol.* **34**, 383.

Lorente de Nó, R. (1947). A study of nerve physiology. *Stud. Rockefeller Inst. med. Res.* **131–132.**

Mayeda, R. (1890). *Z. Biol.* **27,** 119.

Nastuk, W. L. (1950). *Abstr. XVIII int. physiol. Congr.* p. 373.

Nastuk, W. L. & Hodgkin, A. L. (1950). *J. cell. comp. Physiol.* **35,** 39.

Rosenblueth, A. (1950). *The Transmission of Nerve Impulses at Neuro-Effector Junctions and peripheral Synapses*, p. 325. New York.

Rushton, W. A. H. (1937). *Proc. Roy. Soc.* B, **123,** 382.

Weidmann, S. (1951). *J. Physiol.* **115,** 227.

QUANTAL COMPONENTS OF THE END-PLATE POTENTIAL

By J. DEL CASTILLO AND B. KATZ

From the Department of Biophysics, University College, London

(*Received* 25 *January* 1954)

In this paper a further study is made of the spontaneous synaptic potentials in frog muscle (Fatt & Katz, 1952*a*), and their relation to the end-plate response. It has been suggested that the end-plate potential (e.p.p.) at a single nerve-muscle junction is built up statistically of small all-or-none units which are identical in size with the spontaneous 'miniature e.p.p.'s'. The latter, therefore, could be regarded as the least unit, or the 'quantum', of end-plate response. A convenient picture of how hundreds of such quanta, each capable of producing a miniature potential of 0·5–1·0 mV, can build up an e.p.p. of, say, 70–80 mV is provided by the hypothesis that separate parcels of acetyl-choline (ACh), released from discrete spots of the nerve endings, short-circuit the muscle membrane. The unit changes of membrane conductance produced at many parallel spots summate and lead to an intense depolarization of the muscle fibre.

Although this is a plausible view, there is no direct proof that the normal e.p.p. is made up in this quantal fashion. The evidence comes from experiments in which the 'quantum content' of the e.p.p. had been reduced to a small number by lowering the external calcium concentration (Fatt & Katz, 1952*a*). It was then found that the size of the end-plate response approached that of the spontaneous potential and at the same time exhibited large random fluctuations, apparently involving steps of unit size. Similar observations were made by Castillo & Engbaek (1954) on muscles treated with Mg-rich solutions. The statistical behaviour of the end-plate response under these conditions has been investigated in more detail and subjected to a quantitative analysis.

METHODS

The technique for intracellular recording of e.p.p.'s and miniature potentials has been described in earlier papers (Fatt & Katz, 1951, 1952*a*; Castillo & Katz, 1954). The m. ext. l. dig. IV of English frogs was used, immersed in an isotonic solution containing concentrations of $CaCl_2$ and $MgCl_2$ adjusted so as to reduce the response to any desired level. In most experiments prostigmine (10^{-6}, w/v) was added to increase the amplitude of the potentials (without altering their 'quantum content'). The usual procedure was to locate a suitable spot with the internal electrode and record

del Castillo, J., and B. Katz. Quantal components of the end-plate potential. *J. Physiol.* **124**: 560–573, 1954.

spontaneous potentials on moving film. Then, a large number of end-plate responses to single or pairs of nerve volleys were recorded, using a swept time-base and one or a few seconds interval between records. Finally, another series of spontaneous potentials was recorded before the micro-electrode was withdrawn from the fibre.

The amplitudes of the potentials were measured and their distribution displayed in a histogram. With low Ca and high Mg concentrations, all-or-none fluctuations are observed in successive records, with frequent total failures of e.p.p. response. Special importance was attached to the counting of 'failures' and 'successes', as their proportions provided a simple and decisive test of our hypothesis. A precaution which had to be taken was to guard against intermittent failures of response due to other causes, e.g. inadequate stimulation or nerve damage leading to block. The first source of trouble was avoided by using a strong shock, the second source could be recognized without much difficulty, because nerve block, if it occurred at all, developed in a rapidly pro-gressive manner and was unrelated to the size of the initial end-plate response.

In several muscle fibres there was evidence of a remote, second, motor nerve supply (cf. Katz & Kuffler, 1941) producing small and slow miniature potentials and e.p.p. response. These were of discrete shape and could be discarded without ambiguity, when counting responses and measuring amplitudes.

The ext. l. dig. IV contains some muscle fibres of the 'slow system' supplied by small motor axons (Kuffler & Vaughan Williams, 1953; Katz, 1949). As most experiments were made below the level of propagated spikes, the question arises whether we may not sometimes have been recording from 'slow' muscle fibres. This is unlikely because the characteristics of the response were those of the e.p.p.'s of 'twitch fibres' (sharp localization and low threshold whenever tested, high resting potential, short latency, monophasic e.p.p. response). Spontaneous discharge of miniature potentials had previously been shown to occur at end-plates of ordinary 'twitch fibres' (Fatt & Katz, 1952a).

RESULTS

When a muscle was soaked in a solution containing approximately 10 mM-$MgCl_2$, transmission became blocked and subthreshold e.p.p.'s could be recorded at individual junctions. A characteristic feature of these responses was their random fluctuation in successive records. This is illustrated in Fig. 1 where twelve responses, together with some spontaneous miniature potentials, are shown. If the response was further reduced, by increasing Mg or lowering Ca concentrations, the amplitude fluctuations became even more pronounced and were found to be of discontinuous character. In the experiment of Fig. 2, for instance, the majority of records showed no response at all. On the average only about one out of seven nerve impulses elicited an e.p.p. whose size was of the same order of magnitude as the spontaneous potentials.

This behaviour is characteristic of block by high Mg and low Ca, and very different from curare-block. With increasing doses of curarine the e.p.p., at individual junctions, is progressively reduced in size and may eventually become undetectable, but we have never found the response to be abolished, or to fluctuate, in the quantal manner shown in Fig. 2.

If one proceeds to add Mg or withdraw Ca, a practical limit is reached when the e.p.p. response becomes too infrequent to be distinguished from a spon-taneous discharge. There are no differences in amplitude which would enable one to discriminate between the two forms of activity; the distinction depends entirely on the constant latency of the response and random timing of the spontaneous discharges. In a normal frog muscle, at 20° C, the latency of the e.p.p. varies only within a fraction of a millisecond, but in the present experiments we have accepted 1–2 msec as the maximum latency fluctuation, and disallowed as 'response' any potentials which arose outside these limits. In practice, unless the frequency of spontaneous firing was high and the

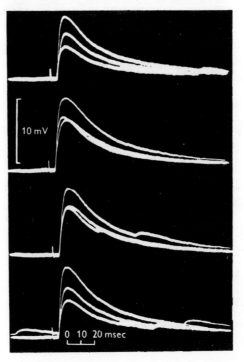

Fig. 1. Fluctuation of e.p.p. response at a single nerve-muscle junction, treated with 10 mM-Mg (Ca concentration was normal: 1·8 mM; prostigmine 10⁻⁶). Intracellular recording. In each record, three superimposed responses are seen. Note scattered spontaneous miniature potentials.

frequency of responding very low, there was little chance of confusing a spontaneous potential with an e.p.p.-response: for example, in Fig. 2 (latency of five 'accepted responses' being constant within 1 msec; spontaneous firing rate 2·2 per sec) the chances of one of the 'accepted responses' being 'spontaneous' are about 5 %, and the chances of more than one arising spontaneously are quite negligible.

Most experiments were made at an intermediate level of blocking when the proportion of failures at individual end-plates was of the order of 50 %. The remaining responses were scattered in amplitude over a wide range, as illustrated in Fig. 3. (Responses to pairs of nerve impulses are shown in this figure.) Many e.p.p.'s fall evidently within the range of sizes of the spontaneous potentials. Others are larger and probably represent multiple units of response. It is interesting that the large e.p.p.'s occasionally show a just noticeable inflexion on their rising phase (e.g. Fig. 3, record C_1) indicative of their composite nature and of imperfect synchronization of the contributing units.

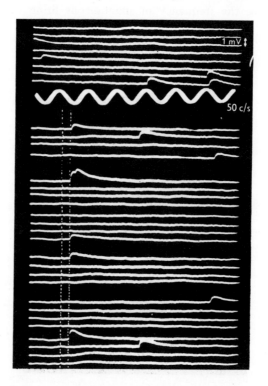

Fig. 2. This muscle was treated with reduced Ca (0·9 mM) and 14 mM-Mg concentration. The top part shows a few spontaneous potentials (traces separated by 1 mV steps). The lower part (below the 50 c/s time signal) shows responses to single nerve impulses. Stimulus artifact and response latency are indicated by a pair of dotted vertical lines. The proportion of failures was very high: there are only five responses to twenty-four impulses.

The experiments of Figs. 1–3, made at different levels of neuromuscular block, have one feature in common, namely a wide fluctuation in e.p.p. amplitudes. In Figs. 4 and 5, the distribution of amplitudes in two experiments is shown, both of spontaneous potentials and response. It is clear that these results cannot be analysed, nor even satisfactorily described, without a statistical treatment.

Suppose we have, at each nerve-muscle junction, a population of n units (cf. Fatt & Katz, 1952a, 1953) capable of responding to a nerve impulse. Suppose, further, that the average probability of responding is $\bar{p}$ (the chances p

may differ greatly for the individual constituents, but are supposed to remain constant during the experiment) then the mean number of units responding to one impulse is $m = n\bar{p}$. Under normal conditions, $\bar{p}$ may be assumed to be relatively large, that is a fairly large part of the synaptic population responds to an impulse. However, as we reduce the Ca and increase the Mg concentration, the chances of responding are diminished and we observe mostly

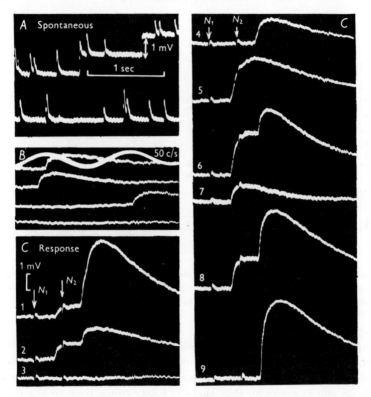

Fig. 3. Muscle was treated with a solution containing 0·45 mM-Ca and 6 mM-Mg. Intracellular recording from single junction. A and B: spontaneous miniature e.p.p.'s. C: examples of responses to paired nerve impulses. Timing of stimuli N_1 and N_2 is indicated by arrows. Failure of response to N_1 in C_4 and C_9, failure to N_2 in C_5 and C_7, double failure in C_3. 50 c/s time signal applies to B and C. A was recorded on slow time base and shows two calibration steps of 1 mV.

complete failures with an occasional response of one or two units. Under these conditions, when p is very small, the number of units x which make up the e.p.p. in a large series of observations should be distributed in the characteristic manner described by Poisson's law (their relative frequencies being given by $\exp(-m)\, m^x/x!$).

To test the applicability of Poisson's law may seem difficult, because all we can do is measure amplitudes of supposedly composite e.p.p.'s; we cannot count the components directly. The task is, however, made easier because the presence of spontaneous activity gives us an independent measure of unit size.

We can obtain the value of m, i.e. the mean number of units responding to one impulse, in two ways: first, from the relation

$$m = \frac{\text{mean amplitude of e.p.p. response}}{\text{mean amplitude of spontaneous potentials}}. \tag{1}$$

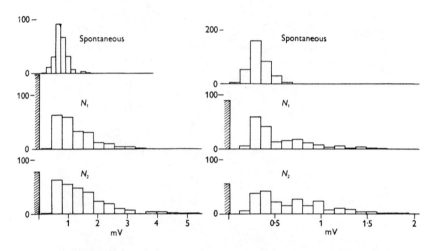

Figs. 4 and 5. Histograms from two end-plates, showing distribution of amplitudes of spontaneous miniature potentials and of the responses to pairs of nerve impulses (7 msec interval between N_1 and N_2). *Failures* are not represented as a 'class', but their number is indicated by the height of the shaded columns.

Equation (1) is a simple re-statement of our hypothesis, namely that the e.p.p. is made up of units of the same size (though not necessarily composed of the same individuals) as the spontaneous miniature potentials. Equation (1) depends on the assumption that there is linear summation of the miniature components of the e.p.p.: this is justified provided the amplitude of the e.p.p. is only a few per cent of the resting potential (cf. Fatt & Katz, 1951), but equation (1) fails to apply to larger responses.

Secondly, we can use the first term of the Poisson series $(\exp(-m)$, for $x = 0)$ which gives the proportion of failures. Hence

$$m = \log_e \frac{\text{number of nerve impulses}}{\text{number of failures of e.p.p. response}}. \tag{2}$$

Combining (1) and (2) we obtain

$$\frac{\text{mean amplitude of response}}{\text{mean amplitude of spontaneous potentials}} = \log_e \frac{\text{number of impulses}}{\text{number of e.p.p. failures}}. \tag{3}$$

Equation (3) provides a useful test of our hypothesis and depends only on measurements of mean amplitudes and counting of 'failure' and 'success' of e.p.p. response. The results of several experiments in which this test has been applied are shown in Table 1 and Fig. 6. The agreement between the two

TABLE 1. In the last two columns the validity of equation (3) is tested in ten experiments. They include four experiments in which responses to pairs of impulses have been utilized (N_1–N_2 intervals 3·5–11 msec). It will be seen that the value of m (i.e. A/B or $\log_e C/D$) is larger for N_2 than for N_1, an effect which is discussed in the following paper.

Date		Mean response (mV) (A)	Mean spont. potential (mV) (B)	No. of impulses (C)	No. of failures (D)	A/B	log_e C/D
2. vi. 51		0·495	0·875	328	188	0·57	0·56
23. i. 53, A	N_1	0·334	0·46	289	113	0·73	0·94
	N_2	0·588			76	1·28	1·33
23. i. 53, B	N_1	0·358	0·305	280	89	1·17	1·15
	N_2	0·528			56	1·73	1·61
28. i. 53	N_1	0·727	0·72	357	138	1·01	0·95
	N_2	1·14			78	1·58	1·52
4. ii. 53	N_1	0·495	0·335	319	84	1·48	1·33
	N_2	0·905			27	2·7	2·47
24. ii. 53		0·089	0·565	118	99	0·16	0·18

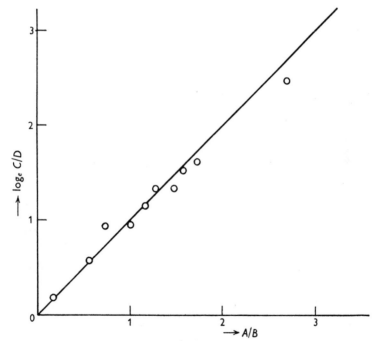

Fig. 6. The results of ten experiments summarized in Table 1 have been plotted, showing the consistency of the two methods of determining the value of m (equations (1) and (2)).

$$\text{Ordinate}: \log_e \frac{\text{number of impulses}}{\text{number of e.p.p. failures}}. \quad \text{Abscissa}: \frac{\text{mean e.p.p. response}}{\text{mean amplitude of spontaneous potentials}}$$

The line corresponds to equality of these two estimates of m.

determinations of m, corresponding to the right and left sides of equation (3), is very satisfactory and may be regarded as a strong support of our initial hypothesis.

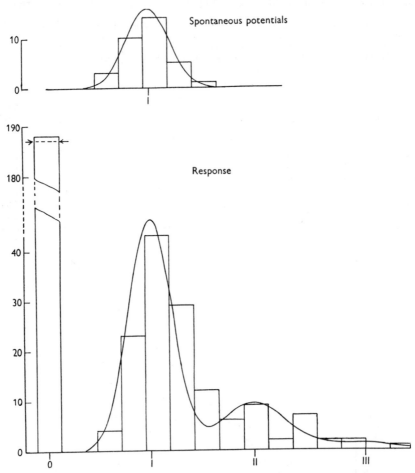

Fig. 7. Histogram showing distribution of amplitudes of spontaneous miniature potentials and end-plate responses at a Ca-deficient junction (experiment of Fatt & Katz, 1952a, pp. 119–120). In the lower part, the continuous curve has been calculated on the hypothesis that the responses are built up statistically of units whose mean size and amplitude distribution are identical with those of the spontaneous potentials (see text). Expected number of failures shown by arrows. Abscissae: scale units=mean amplitude of spontaneous potentials (0·875 mV).

The experiment of Fig. 7, the results of which were reported by Fatt & Katz (1952a), has been analysed more fully. The value of m was first determined by equation (1), and the expected numbers of the Poisson series were calculated. For $x=0$ (failure of response), there was excellent agreement between calculated and observed values, but for the terms $x > 0$ account had to be taken of the scatter of amplitudes of the 'unitary' spontaneous potentials. This was done by (a) fitting a Gaussian curve to the spontaneous potentials, and (b) using x times the mean and variance of this curve in distributing the Poisson classes. The resulting theoretical distribution of e.p.p. amplitudes is shown by the continuous curve in the lower part of Fig. 7. Although the fit with the observed histogram is not accurate, the general agreement is good considering that except for a single scaling factor (the total number of e.p.p.'s) the

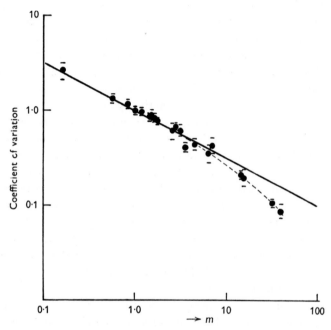

Fig. 8. Relation between coefficient of variation and mean amplitude of e.p.p. in twenty-one experiments. Logarithmic scales. Abscissa: mean e.p.p., divided by mean spontaneous potential (i.e. nominal value of m). Ordinate: standard deviation of e.p.p., divided by mean (i.e. 'coefficient of variation' of e.p.p.). E.p.p. amplitudes had been grouped for this purpose in 'unit classes' (i.e. with class centres at $n \times$ mean spontaneous potential). Bars have been placed at ± 2 s.E. of the 'coefficient of variation'. Full line shows theoretical relation for Poisson-distributions.

constants chosen in calculating the curve had been determined independently. The main discrepancies vanish if the mean size of the unit response is taken to be 7% larger than the mean spontaneous potential, a difference which is probably within limits of experimental error.

In other experiments the e.p.p. amplitudes were grouped more coarsely into classes of unit-width, and a χ^2 test was applied; also, the coefficient of variation of e.p.p. amplitudes (grouped in such unit classes) was determined and compared with the expected coefficients $m^{-0.5}$ (Fig. 8). These tests were less accurate than the preceding analysis, but the results agreed with the view that the responding units are distributed in Poisson-fashion provided the quantum content of the e.p.p. is small (< 3). When the tests were extended to larger e.p.p.'s (m exceeding 10), there was a consistent discrepancy, the observed fluctuation of e.p.p. amplitudes covering a smaller range than expected (see Figs. 8 and 9).

<h3 style="text-align:center">DISCUSSION</h3>

The most interesting evidence is that shown in Table 1 and Fig. 6 for small values of m. The agreement between the two determinations of m can hardly be fortuitous and supports the view that the spontaneous miniature potential is the least 'quantum of action' at the nerve-muscle junction, the e.p.p. being built up statistically of such quanta. Furthermore, one may conclude that at this reduced level of m, the statistical chances of any one unit responding to a single impulse are very low, and in successive records the responses represent different members of a large, mostly inactive, population.

It is tempting to speculate what the precise probability of the unit response may be. For this, it is not sufficient to know only the value of m; we also require information of the total number of available units n. Moreover, it does not follow from the results that all units have the same chance of responding; a Poisson distribution would be obtained even from a non-uniform population, provided only the probabilities of responding are small and constant for each individual member (Kendall, 1948). If the whole synaptic population consisted of, say, 500 units, and m is unity, then the average chance of any unit responding to one impulse would be 1/500, but individual probabilities may be considerably higher for some and much smaller for many other members of the population.

What happens under more normal conditions when we raise the Ca and lower the Mg concentration? The value of m becomes large and the statistical analysis unsatisfactory. It is clear, however, that the response fluctuates much less than predicted from our equations (Fig. 9). Now suppose the size of the population n remains constant, then the increase of m would be due to an increased probability p. If the population is uniform, the distribution of responses would change from a Poisson to a binomial form. Associated with this one may expect a reduction in statistical spread, for the coefficient of variation for a Poisson series is $\sqrt{(1/m)}$, while that of a binomial distribution is only $\sqrt{\left(\dfrac{1}{m}-\dfrac{1}{n}\right)}$. Closer examination, however, shows that this argument is insufficient to account for the observed divergences. We can set a lower limit to the value of n: the normal e.p.p. is about 100 times larger than a miniature potential and must be composed of an even greater number of units because unit increments of the e.p.p. would diminish at high levels of depolarization (cf. Fatt & Katz, 1951). There is also reason to believe that the normal e.p.p.

does not involve the whole population, so that $n=200$ is a conservative estimate. With $m=32$, the coefficient of variation would be $\sqrt{(\frac{1}{32}-\frac{1}{200})}=0\cdot162$, compared with $0\cdot177$ in a Poisson distribution (when m/n is very small). The observed coefficient, however, is about $0\cdot11\pm0\cdot005$, and a significant discrepancy of this kind remained for all experiments in which m was greater than 10.

There are two other factors which are more likely to provide an explanation. One factor has already been mentioned, viz. a failure of linear summation of miniature potentials, when m becomes large and the amplitude of the total e.p.p. an appreciable fraction of the resting potential. Application

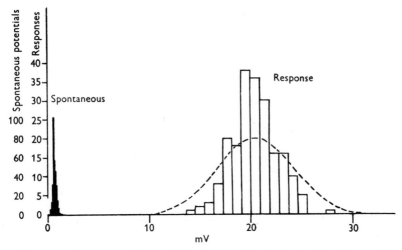

Fig. 9. Histogram from an experiment with large e.p.p. Nominal value of m (using equation (1)) is 32. Dotted curve: expected distribution of e.p.p.'s (modified Gaussian curve allowing for scattered unit size: mean $=20\cdot4$ mV), $\sigma=3\cdot7$ mV. Note large discrepancy between observed and expected distribution.

of equation (1) and of the superposition theorem may lead to serious error if the e.p.p. response exceeds a small fraction (5 %) of the resting potential. Suppose each 'transmitter unit' produces a fixed leakage conductance ΔG across the end-plate membrane, then the increment of potential ΔP which it contributes to the e.p.p. becomes less the greater the existing leakage and the lower the membrane potential (cf. Fatt & Katz, 1951). This must have an important effect on the observed coefficient of variation, because (a) the actual number m would be greater than that calculated from equation (1), and (b) the scale of the amplitude fluctuations would be reduced in proportion to ΔP. We have made only a rough estimate of this effect, but it seems that it may account for a large part, if not the whole, of the observed discrepancy.

The other factor which may be involved is that different members of the population may *not* have the same chances of success, and that for large values of m some individual units have a high probability and respond almost every time, while others have a low probability and contribute to the e.p.p. only occasionally. The presence of some units which respond regularly is bound to diminish the statistical fluctuation of the e.p.p. In general, the coefficient of variation for this case is less than that expected for a binomial distribution (see Table 2).

TABLE 2. Coefficients of variation for different distributions

(From Kendall, 1948; the coefficient of variation is expressed here as a simple fraction, instead of per cent.)

Poisson ($p \ll 1$)	Binomial (var $p = 0$)	'Non-uniform population'
$$\sqrt{\left(\frac{1}{m}\right)}$$	$$\sqrt{\left(\frac{1}{m} - \frac{1}{n}\right)}$$	$$\sqrt{\left(\frac{1}{m}\left(1 - \frac{\operatorname{var} p}{\bar{p}}\right) - \frac{1}{n}\right)}$$

n = total number of units available at a single junction.
m = mean number of units responding to one impulse.
$\bar{p} = m/n$ = average probability of response (per unit per impulse).
var p = variance of individual probabilities (p being assumed to vary among responding units, but not during successive impulses).

This last factor should not be confused with the case in which probabilities of response vary during the set of observations, e.g. if the value of m suffered a progressive change. In this case the standard deviation of the e.p.p. amplitude would become greater, not less. A small effect of this kind was present in some experiments and could be checked by dividing the observations into groups. The drift of the mean value, however, was not large enough to affect the result seriously.

CONCLUSIONS

The following picture emerges from the present study: transmission at a nerve-muscle junction takes place in all-or-none 'quanta' whose sizes are indicated by the spontaneously occurring miniature discharges. The number of quantal units responding to a nerve impulse fluctuates in a random manner and can be predicted only in statistical terms. The average 'quantum content' of the e.p.p. depends on the probability of response of the individual units, and this varies with the external Ca and Mg concentration (for a more detailed hypothesis, see Castillo & Katz, 1954). It is possible that some synaptic units respond more readily than others, but with a sufficiently high Mg and low Ca level the chances of excitation of all units are so small that a Poisson distribution is obtained.

Under more normal conditions, the e.p.p. is large and the statistical fluctuation small. While the evidence for the quantal composition of low-level e.p.p.'s ($m < 5$) seems conclusive, inferences about the normal behaviour are indirect and can only be made by extrapolating into a range in which the present statistical analysis can give no useful information. There are, however, good reasons for supposing that the normal e.p.p. is built up of a large number of units of the same kind as described here, furthermore that even the normal e.p.p. involves only a fraction of the total synaptic population, the average probability of response apparently being less than unity. This suggestion is based on the finding that the size of the e.p.p. can be increased from nil to well above the 'normal-Ringer' amplitude by raising the Ca concentration, *without* increasing the size of the spontaneous miniature e.p.p. (Fatt & Katz, 1952a, b; Castillo & Stark, 1952). If one accepts the present results as showing that the miniature e.p.p. is the basic unit of response, then the effect of Ca must be to raise the quantum content m of the e.p.p., either by increasing the size of the population n or its probability of responding $\bar{p}$. We have assumed in our argument that a change of probability, rather than population size, is involved, though the formal distinction between these two modes of action is not very profitable until more is known about the nature of the molecular reaction whose probability we are considering.

SUMMARY

1. The relation between response and spontaneous activity at a single nerve-muscle junction has been studied.

2. By increasing Mg and lowering Ca concentration, the amplitude of the e.p.p. can be reduced to that of a spontaneous 'miniature potential'. At the same time, a large random fluctuation of successive e.p.p. amplitudes is observed.

3. Statistical analysis indicates that the e.p.p. is built up of small all-or-none quanta which are identical in size and shape with the spontaneously occurring miniature potentials.

4. When the average 'quantum content' (m) of the e.p.p. is small ($m < 3$), its amplitude fluctuates in a manner predictable by Poisson's law. At higher levels ($m > 10$), deviations occur which may be due to a reduction in the 'unit-increment' of the e.p.p., or to variation in the probability of response among different synaptic units.

5. The statistical behaviour of the normal nerve-muscle junction and the influence of Ca and Mg ions are discussed.

We are indebted to Mr J. L. Parkinson for his unfailing assistance. This work was supported by a research grant made by the Nuffield Foundation.

REFERENCES

DEL CASTILLO, J. & ENGBAEK, L. (1954). The nature of the neuromuscular block produced by magnesium. *J. Physiol.* **124**, 370–384.

DEL CASTILLO, J. & KATZ, B. (1954). The effect of magnesium on the activity of motor nerve endings. *J. Physiol.* **124**, 553–559.

DEL CASTILLO, J. & STARK, L. (1952). The effect of calcium ions on the motor end-plate potential. *J. Physiol.* **116**, 507–515.

FATT, P. & KATZ, B. (1951). An analysis of the end-plate potential recorded with an intra-cellular electrode. *J. Physiol.* **115**, 320–370.

FATT, P. & KATZ, B. (1952a). Spontaneous subthreshold activity at motor nerve-endings. *J. Physiol.* **117**, 109–128.

FATT, P. & KATZ, B. (1952b). The effect of sodium ions on neuromuscular transmission. *J. Physiol.* **118**, 73–87.

FATT, P. & KATZ, B. (1953). Chemo-receptor activity at the motor end-plate. *Acta physiol. scand.* **29**, 117–125.

KATZ, B. (1949). The efferent regulation of the muscle spindle in the frog. *J. exp. Biol.* **26**, 201–217.

KATZ, B. & KUFFLER, S. W. (1941). Multiple motor innervation of the frog's sartorius muscle. *J. Neurophysiol.* **4**, 209–223.

KENDALL, M. G. (1948). *The Advanced Theory of Statistics.* 4th ed., vol. I, pp. 122 *et seq.* London: Griffin.

KUFFLER, S. W. & VAUGHAN WILLIAMS, E. M. (1953). Small-nerve junctional potentials. The distribution of small motor nerves to frog skeletal muscle, and the membrane characteristics of the fibres they innervate. *J. Physiol.* **121**, 289–317.